U. S. Dept. Agriculture Handbook No. 18   Issued August 1951

Soil Survey Manual

By
SOIL SURVEY STAFF
Bureau of Plant Industry, Soils, and
Agricultural Engineering

This is a Revision and Enlargement of U. S. Department
of Agriculture Miscellaneous Publication 274, the
Soil Survey Manual, Issued September 1937,
and Supersedes it.

Effective 1952, the Soil Survey was transferred from the former
Bureau of Plant Industry, Soils, and Agricultural Engineering to the
SOIL CONSERVATION SERVICE
Reissued in October 1962 with no change in text.

Agricultural Research Administration

UNITED STATES DEPARTMENT OF AGRICULTURE

For sale by the Superintendent of Documents, U. S. Government Printing Office
Washington 25, D. C. - Price $3.50 (Buckram)

CONTENTS

INTRODUCTION

The *Soil Survey Manual* is intended for use by soil scientists engaged in soil classification and mapping. Attention is directed primarily to problems and methods of making and interpreting detailed basic soil surveys in the United States and territories. The earlier edition,[1] published in the autumn of 1937, reflected the developments growing out of the ideas, work, and publications of hundreds of scientists since the beginning of the United States Soil Survey in 1899. Substantial progress has been made since 1937 in the soil survey itself and in related fields of soil research. Further, soil surveys are now used by more people, in more ways, and, above all, with more precision than formerly.

The increased use of soil maps and interpretations has led to increased testing of the results, both scientifically and practically. Inadequacies appeared that required correction. Continually, new knowledge about soils needs to be incorporated into the classification and into the interpretations. New research methods and new cartographic methods need to be evaluated, adapted, and used as they are appropriate to improve soil surveys and to reduce their costs.

Nearly the whole of the earlier edition of the *Manual* has had to be revised. Although some appear to be drastic, few of the revisions are out-and-out changes; most of them are modifications and elaborations to achieve the specificity and completeness required to make the final results more nearly quantitative and more useful. For example, essentially all soil mapping is now done on aerial photographs, and the discussion of the older cartographic methods has been condensed in appendices.

Some new terms have been added and a great many redefined, especially to permit increased accuracy. This process of redefining will need to go on as long as soil research continues. The discovery of new relationships and the formulation of new concepts require an expansion of language.

Many of the technical terms used in soil science are common words, taken out of the body of language and given precise and sometimes unusual meanings. A large part of them originated as folk terms among rural people. Such words as "loam," "texture," "structure," "heavy," "light," "profile," "horizon," and even "soil" may have a deceptive familiarity to the layman using the language of soil science. Similar technical words have arisen in the same way in the other languages, often with slightly different shades of meaning, not revealed in the ordinary lexicon. The meaning of coined words, like "Lithosol" and "illuviation," or of those taken bodily from other languages, like "gley" or "Chernozem," once

---

[1] Soil survey manual. U.S. Dept. Agr. Misc. Pub. 274, 136 pp., illus. 1937.

v

learned, are not so likely to be confused with other meanings as are redefined common words.

Even though newly coined words are more easily defined than the older ones are redefined, their use on soil maps and in soil survey reports intended for the general reader is limited. For some new concepts a writer has no alternative to technical terms. These he needs to define for the general reader. Commonly, however, the older more general words must be used in soil survey reports, insofar as possible, in order to capitalize on the readers' present understanding. But in the scientific work itself specific terms should be used in the sense of accurate definitions. Thus there is no escape from a certain amount of "double language."

Need of accurate definition.—Special effort has been made in this revised text of the *Manual* to define terms and to use them as specifically as possible. Since the early edition, much progress has been made toward uniformity of terminology among soil scientists. Better definitions are still needed within our own language, and especially better transliterations among the various languages. Some nearly arbitrary selection among alternatives has been necessary in the *Manual*.

A separate glossary is not included because much duplication would result and because many definitions are clearer when set within an explanatory context. Where definitions might lead to long and highly technical statements, explanations are given instead. Page numbers of the Index in bold type refer to definitions and explanations of the terms.

The relationships of the soil survey to other researches have deepened and broadened as its uses and interpretations have expanded. It has seemed that this *Manual* should be broad enough in scope to lead into the most important of these relationships, but it cannot develop them in detail. Even the field of soil classification, above the lower categories, lies mostly outside of its scope. A few references to fuller discussions are given in the text, and a suggested reference shelf is included near the end.

Since the earlier edition was prepared (during 1935–36) all phases of the work have been under study by the Soil Survey staff. Following intensive study and revision, mimeographed copies of new statements about many individual subjects treated in the *Manual* were circulated both for guidance in making soil surveys and for criticisms and suggestions. Since all the basic soil survey work in the United States is carried on cooperatively with the State land-grant colleges and universities, several scientists in those institutions have helped a great deal in criticizing statements on special subjects and the draft of this edition of the *Manual*. Besides, informal cooperation is carried on with the research organizations of several foreign countries. Scientists from these countries have given us the benefit of their valuable experiences and judgments. Several read all or parts of the draft manuscript and made valuable suggestions for its improvement.

Other modifications can be expected, especially in classification and nomenclature, as our knowledge and experience advance.

Some prospective changes are under study and are mentioned here and there in the text.

The authors have had great help from the criticisms and comments given by readers of the *Manual* published in 1937. It is hoped that readers of this revised edition will note errors and omissions and call them to the attention of the Soil Survey staff so that any subsequent edition may be improved.

Arrangement of topics.—It is assumed that most readers of the *Manual* will have had training equivalent to that of a graduate holding the Bachelor of Science degree from a curriculum in soil science like that officially recommended by the Soil Science Society of America.[2] It is expected that many readers will need to carry on collateral reading in soil classification, general soil science, geology, interpretation of aerial photography, geography, economics, and general agriculture.

The authors have further assumed that soil survey party chiefs and those wishing to prepare for such responsibilities will want to study all parts of the *Manual*. Therefore, the topics are arranged roughly in the order that problems arise in starting, carrying out, and completing a soil survey, although, of course, a party chief must have a view of all aspects to begin with, since the several phases of the work are closely interrelated. It is assumed that others who are not concerned in the whole job may find the *Manual* a helpful reference for particular items that can be located from the table of Contents or the Index.

---

[2] Soil Sci. Soc. Amer. Proc. 6: 507. 1941.

SOIL AND LANDSCAPE

First let us briefly review the working concepts of soil and of the principles of scientific method upon which this *Manual* is based. These have been formulated only after many years of trial and error. When the Soil Survey began in the United States, more than 50 years ago, there was no organized body of knowledge that we have come to know as soil science. This is not to say that nothing was known about soils. Indeed farmers had learned a great deal through experience over the centuries, and much of their knowledge had been brought together in several compilations, some as early as Roman times. With the rise of agricultural chemistry during the nineteenth century, more was learned about soils that was useful. Yet it was not until some time near the end of the century that the knowledge about soils gained from farming, from agricultural chemistry, from biology, and from geology was coordinated. Nor could it be coordinated without some unifying concept of the soil itself.

The early concepts.—With few exceptions, like Hilgard's ideas,[1] the notions of soils held by soil workers at the time the Soil Survey began were based upon assumptions stemming mainly from the ideas of the great German chemist, Liebig, as modified and perfected by agricultural chemists and plant physiologists working on samples of soil in laboratories and greenhouses and on small plots of soils in the field. The soils were rarely examined below the layer turned in regular tillage. The assumption of soil character, or working theory, which was more or less unconsciously conceived, may be briefly summarized as the balance-sheet theory of plant nutrition or the-soil-is-like-a-bank idea. Soils were considered to be more or less static storage bins for plant nutrients that could be used by plants but had to be replenished as used. Of course, the amounts of nutrients removed from soil by harvested crops and those returned in manure, lime, and fertilizers are important to an understanding of soil productivity;

---

[1] The soil scientists of today cannot help being amazed at the general neglect of E. W. Hilgard's important and pioneer work, first in Mississippi (GEOLOGY AND AGRICULTURE OF THE STATE OF MISSISSIPPI. 391 pp., Jackson, Miss. 1860.); then in the Cotton Belt as a whole (A REPORT ON COTTON PRODUCTION IN THE UNITED STATES; ALSO EMBRACING AGRICULTURAL AND PHYSIO-GEOGRAPHICAL DESCRIPTIONS OF THE SEVERAL COTTON STATES AND CALIFORNIA *in* volumes 5 and 6 of the 10th Census of the United States. Washington. 1884); and finally in California (SOILS; THEIR FORMATION, PROPERTIES, COMPOSITION, AND RELATIONS TO CLIMATE AND PLANT GROWTH IN THE HUMID AND ARID REGIONS. 593 pp., illus. New York and London. 1906.).

1

but a great deal more is needed for our understanding of soils and their management requirements. In fact, this simple balance-sheet theory, by itself, has but little prediction value.[2]

The early geologists generally accepted this notion of soil fertility. They filled the conceptual storage bin with ground rock of various sorts—granite, sandstone, calcareous till, and the like. They went further, however, and showed how the weathering processes modified this material and how the geological processes of landscape formation used it in the construction of land forms, such as glacial moraines, alluvial plains, loessial blankets, and marine terraces. Shaler's monograph on the origin and nature of soils[3] went about as far as it was possible to go with this geological concept of soils; although many details were added in Merrill's treatise.[4]

Professor Milton Whitney and his coworkers in the new soil research unit of the United States Department of Agriculture, established near the end of the nineteenth century, were impressed by the great variations among natural soils—persistent variations in no way due to the effects of agricultural use. Special emphasis was given to soil texture and to the ability of the soil to furnish plants with moisture as well as nutrients. Professor F. H. King of the University of Wisconsin was also emphasizing the physical characteristics of soils.[5]

The Soil Survey began in response to the recognized need for helping farmers locate themselves on soils responsive to management and, once located, for helping them to decide what crops and what management practices were best for the particular kinds of soil on their farms.

In early surveys, soils were conceived to be the weathering products of recognized geological formations, defined by land form and lithological composition. Many of the earlier field workers were trained in geology, because only geologists were skilled in field methods and in the scientific method of correlation appropriate to the field study of soils.

Shortly after field work began, it became obvious that many important soil characteristics were not definitely related to either broad land form or rock type. It was noted that naturally poorly drained soils have different characteristics than naturally well drained soils, and that sloping soils are unlike level ones. On broadly similar glacial till from Maine to Montana, and down to the Ohio River, markedly contrasting soils are developed in

---

[2] See KELLOGG, CHARLES E. CONFLICTING DOCTRINES ABOUT SOILS. Sci. Monthly 66: 475–487. 1948.

[3] SHALER, N. S. THE ORIGIN AND NATURE OF SOILS. U. S. Geol. Survey Ann. Rpt. 12: 213–345, illus. 1891.

[4] MERRILL, G. P. A TREATISE OF ROCKS, ROCK-WEATHERING AND SOILS. New ed., 411 pp., illus. New York and London. 1906.

[5] See for example, KING, F. H. A TEXTBOOK OF THE PHYSICS OF AGRICUL-TURE. Ed. 3, 604 pp., illus. Madison, Wis. 1910.

the various climatic and biotic zones. Yet for several years the geological view dominated in the field, and the balance-sheet theory of plant nutrition in the laboratory. Although they were taught in many classrooms until the late 1920's, neither theory actually worked well in the field as a basis for reliable predictions to farmers. As a consequence, all sorts of special little concepts were formed that broke down in contradiction when applied to a great continental area like the United States.

Broader and more useful concepts of soil were developing among some American soil scientists, especially Hilgard. The necessary data for formulating these broader concepts came in rapidly from the field work of the Soil Survey during the first decade of its operations. After Hilgard, the longest reach toward a more satisfactory concept was made by Coffey.[6]

Soil profiles and the concept of individual soils.—Meanwhile, beginning in 1870, a new concept of soil was developing in the Russian school of soil science.[7] The results of this work became generally available to Americans through the publication of Glinka's great textbook in German and especially through its translation into English by C. F. Marbut.[8] Boiled down to its essentials, soils in the Russian concept were conceived to be independent natural bodies, each with a unique morphology and resulting from a unique combination of climate, living matter, parent rock materials, relief, and time. The morphology of each soil, as expressed in its profile, reflected the combined effects of the particular set of genetic factors responsible for its development.

This was a revolutionary concept, as important to soil science as anatomy to medicine. The soil scientist did not need to depend wholly upon inferences from the geological nature of the rocks, or from climate, or from other environmental factors, considered singly or collectively; rather, he could go directly to the soil itself and see the integrated expression of all these in its morphology. This concept made it not only possible but necessary to consider all soil characteristics collectively, in terms of a complete, integrated natural body, rather than individually. In short it made a soil science possible.

[6] COFFEY, G. N. A STUDY OF THE SOILS OF THE UNITED STATES. U. S. Dept. Agr. Bur. Soils Bul. 85, 114 pp., illus. 1912.

[7] See the following references:
GEDROIZ, K. K. SOIL-ABSORBING COMPLEX AND THE ABSORBED SOIL CATIONS AS A BASIS OF GENETIC SOIL CLASSIFICATION. (Trans. by S. A. Waksman) Nossov Agr. Expt. Sta. Paper 38, 29 pp. Lenigrad. [In papers on soil reaction 1912-25.]
KELLOGG, CHARLES E. RUSSIAN CONTRIBUTIONS TO SOIL SCIENCE. Land Policy Rev. 9: 9–14. 1946.
NEUSTRUEV, S. S. GENESIS OF SOIL. Russ. Pedol. Invest. 3, Acad. Sci., 98 pp. Leningrad. 1927.

[8] GLINKA, K. D. THE GREAT SOIL GROUPS OF THE WORLD AND THEIR DEVELOPMENT. (Trans. from the German by C. F. Marbut.) 235 pp. Ann Arbor, Mich. 1917.

With the early enthusiasm for the new concept and for the rising new discipline it made possible—soil science[9]—some went so far as to suggest that the other sciences were unnecessary to soil study. Perhaps some extreme statements in this tone were made to declare a certain sense of autonomy and freedom from the older concepts of geology and agricultural chemistry rather than from thoughtful conviction. Certainly the reverse of independence from other sciences was true, for besides laying the foundation for a new science with its own principles, the new concept made the other sciences even more useful. In soil morphology, the soil scientist found a firm basis on which to classify the results of observation, of experiments, and of practical experience, and to develop principles of prediction value.

Under the intellectual leadership of C. F. Marbut[10] the new concept was further broadened and adapted. As first explained, this concept emphasized individual soil profiles—soils at points on the earth's surface—even to the subordination of external soil features and surface geology. This weakness become more clearly evident in the United States, perhaps, because of the great emphasis upon detailed soil maps for their practical prediction value. Progress was rapid because of the large body of important field data already accumulated. By 1925 a large amount of morphological and chemical work was being done on soil profiles throughout the country. The data available around 1930 were summarized and interpreted in accordance with this concept, as

---

[9] Terminology is still confused. A large amount of applied soil science, and even some fundamental soil science, is still included under agronomy in several colleges and universities in the United States. Partly to differentiate it from applied agricultural science, another large field of application is termed "soils engineering." Terms like "soils geology" and "forest soils" are also used for parts of the field of soil science. "Soil technology" has been used in the narrow sense of soil manipulation—drainage, irrigation, erosion control, tillage, and the like—and also in the broader sense of all applied soil science. Similarly, "soil conservation" is commonly used not only in the narrow sense of erosion control but also in various broader senses up to "soil management for sustained production."

In Europe generally, the word "scientist" has a somewhat more exalted connotation than in the United States. Thus individuals hesitate to call themselves "soil scientists." They prefer a single word like "pedologist." Unfortunately, in the United States, pedology has come to mean only those phases of the more general field of soil science that relate directly to soil morphology, genesis, and classification. In this sense pedology is even too narrow for the work of the Soil Survey. Further, the term "soil science" has at least some self-evident connotation to the layman. The authors see no better alternative in the United States than "soil science" for the general field—for the science that treats of soils, including their nature, properties, formation, functioning, behavior, and response to use and management. In many countries this also defines "pedology" as the term is now used in them.

[10] See the following:

MARBUT, C. F. THE CONTRIBUTION OF SOIL SURVEYS TO SOIL SCIENCE. Soc. Prom. Agr. Sci. Proc. (1920) 41: 116–142, illus. 1921.

———— A SCHEME FOR SOIL CLASSIFICATION. 1st Internatl. Cong. Soil Sci. Comm. 5, Proc. and Papers 4: 1–31, illus. 1928.

SOIL SCIENCE SOCIETY OF AMERICA. LIFE AND WORK OF C. F. MARBUT. 271 pp., illus. Columbia, Mo. 1942.

viewed by Marbut, in his great work on the soils of the United States.[11]

Marbut always emphasized strongly that soil classification should be based on soil morphology, since theories of soil genesis were both ephemeral and dynamic. He was led to emphasize this point so much—perhaps even to overemphasize it—because of the previous errors made by acceptance of the balance-sheet theory and the geological concept under which soils had been assumed to have certain characteristics without the scientists taking the trouble to examine the soils to see whether they were like they had been assumed to be. Marbut was trying to make the point abundantly clear that examinations of the actual soils were essential for developing a system of soil classification and for making soil maps of prediction value. (This still needs emphasis today. Even yet schemes of soil classification and mapping are occasionally put forward that are designed to avoid the work of profile examination!)

Extreme interpretations of Marbut's emphasis upon morphology as the basis for classification led to the suggestion that the soil classifier could neglect genetic principles and relationships. Such extremes should be avoided. A soil is not really understood until its genesis and the reasons why it varies from other soils are known. Not until the morphology and genesis of a soil are known can research to discover new and improved management systems be planned most effectively. Without such organized knowledge, purely empirical mass plot work alone must be resorted to with the hope that something will work. This is the situation now with many tropical soils. The Ground-Water Laterite soils are an example. Until their genesis is worked out, finding practical systems of soil management by empirical plot trials alone seems nearly hopeless. Fundamental soil research should be emphasized more as a basis for classification, applied research, and the invention of new techniques.

One may conceive, perhaps, of the development of an accurate system of soil classification on the basis of morphology alone; but in practice it is doubtful that completely satisfactory results can be had. Besides accurate morphology, genesis is needed to guide the work and to test the results. Neither one nor the other can be neglected. Yet in the meantime, classification of soils of obscure genesis shall need to be handled as well as possible, largely on the basis of morphology alone.

Soils as dynamic three-dimensional landscapes.—The concept of soil was gradually further broadened and extended around 1930 and the years immediately following.[12] This revision in concept was not so dramatic as the earlier one; it was more a matter of consolidation and balance. Previously the major emphasis had been on the soil profile. Soil profiles come very near to occupying

---

[11] MARBUT, C. F. SOILS OF THE UNITED STATES. *In* U. S. Dept. Agr. Atlas of American Agriculture, pt. 3, Advance Sheets No. 8, 98 pp., illus. 1935.

[12] See KELLOGG, CHARLES E. MODERN SOIL SCIENCE. Amer. Scientist 36: 517–536, illus. 1948.

single points on the earth's surface; whereas soils have shape and area, breadth and width, as well as depth. Morphological studies began to be extended from single pits to long trenches or to a series of pits over a soil area. The morphology of a soil is expressed by a range of profiles from a modal profile, not by a single profile or even by a typical one. Further, early emphasis upon genetic soil profiles had been so great as to suggest that in the absence of such genetic profiles, as in a young Alluvial soil, there was no "true" soil! A sharp distinction had been drawn between rock weathering and soil formation. Although distinction between these sets of processes is necessary, it is equally necessary to recognize that rock weathering and soil formation are sets of processes going on at one time in the same landscape. Soils are dynamic not only as soil profiles but also as landscapes.

Clarification and broadening of the concept of soil also grew out of the continuing emphasis upon detailed soil mapping and especially with the emphasis upon predictions of estimated yields for adapted crops under physically defined sets of management practices for each kind of soil shown on the maps. Many of the older descriptions of soils had not been sufficiently quantitative, and the classificational units had been too heterogeneous for making the yield predictions and management predictions needed for individual farm planning. The use of air photos, begun during the late 1920's, had greatly increased the accuracy of plotting soil boundaries. To meet the needs for farm planning, greater precision of interpretation was also required. This development of schemes for summarizing predicted yields and soil behavior under defined sets of management practices not only made the soil survey far more useful but also forced a reconsideration of the very concept of the soil itself.

Soil defined.—First of all, soil is the natural medium for the growth of land plants, whether or not it has "developed" soil horizons. Soil in this sense covers land as a continuum, except on rocky slopes, in regions of continuous cold, in very salty playas, and elsewhere that the cover of soil disappears. Soil has many forms. Its characteristics in any one place result from the combined influence of climate and living matter, acting upon the parent rock material, as conditioned by relief, over periods of time, including the effects of the cultural environment and man's use of the soil.

In studying the characteristics of soil and in predicting its potentialities for use, we cannot work with the whole continuum at once. Individual kinds of soil must be recognized. To make use of experience and of the results of research, classification becomes a necessity. It is through classification, as a tool, that we organize our knowledge and remember it, see relationships among soils and between them and their environment, and formulate principles of prediction value.

In the sense of an individual in the continuum, a soil is a dynamic three-dimensional piece of landscape that supports plants. It has a unique combination of both internal and external characteristics that have definable ranges of expression. Each individual kind of soil has a modal set of characteristics within the limits set by *our* logic. Its upper surface is the surface of the land; its lower surface is defined by the lower limits of soil-forming processes; and its sides are boundaries with other kinds of soil, where changes occur in one or more differentiating characteristics, related, in turn, to one or more of the genetic factors. Through research, the behavior of soils under defined conditions can be predicted.

Many thousands of unique kinds of soil exist in the world— as many as there are significant combinations of the genetic factors. The characteristics of each can be learned through observation and research in the field and in the laboratory. The history of a soil and its potentialities are contained in these characteristics, considered collectively. *The influence on soil behavior of any one characteristic, or of a variation in any one, depends upon the others in the combination.* (Probably more faulty predictions about soils result from failures to recognize this principle than from any other error.) A general system of soil classification comprehends all observable relevant characteristics.

Soils, then, are landscapes as well as profiles. The soil mapper has always recognized this in drawing soil boundaries. Commonly they come at the foot of an escarpment, at the margin of the swamp forest, or at some other obvious boundary among natural landscapes. The hardest soil boundaries of all to plot are those that can be located only through repeated examination of soil profiles because the controlling genetic variable is obscure. In detailed soil mapping, examinations of soil profiles are always essential to test the location of boundaries and to identify the bounded landscapes.

In the concept of soil as landscape, slope is an important soil characteristic. Soils, like other natural bodies, have shape. Formerly one wrote "soils on sloping land;" now we say simply, and more correctly, "sloping soils." Temperature is an important soil characteristic, even though it cannot be preserved in samples. The same may be said of stoniness and microrelief. A soil is a natural thing out-of-doors. Like a river or a glacier or a volcano, it cannot be brought into the laboratory. Thus, no matter how much and how valuable are the data we obtain on soil samples in the laboratory, the final synthesis into predictions can be made accurately only on the basis of all the characteristics of a soil as a landscape out-of-doors.

Since one cannot distinguish accurately under all conditions between "soil" and "not-soil," a precise general definition is impossible. The same is true of other well-understood basic words like "house," "plant," or "stone." Many thousands of individual kinds of soil have been defined. In most of these, but not all, one can decide clearly between the soil and the not-soil beneath it. Ordinarily we think of soil as including the upper part of the earth's crust that has properties different from the rock material because of the influence of the soil-forming factors. Yet the definitions of many individual soils must go further and include layers beneath that influence their behavior. Then, some soil-landscapes that support plants gradually thin to moss-covered rock and finally to bare rock with no clear separation between soil and not-soil that applies generally. Plants may be grown under glass in pots filled with samples of soil, with peat, with sand, or even with water. Under proper conditions all these media are productive of plants but some are not-soil. Plants even grow on trees; but trees are regarded as not-soil. Yet perhaps the most important quality of soil is its productivity for plants.

The following general definition of soil may serve those who need one: *Soil is the collection of natural bodies occupying portions of the earth's surface that support plants and that have properties due to the integrated effect of climate and living matter, acting upon parent material, as conditioned by relief, over periods of time.*

Scientific methods.—To understand the significance of any particular soil characteristic, or of any one genetic factor, sets of soil characteristics must be defined and compared. These sets are the units in soil classification.[13] To find the place of an unknown soil in the system of classification, or to understand the relationship of one soil to others in the system, the sets of characteristics are compared. This method of scientific correlation is the principal tool in soil classification.

Because of its universe and methods, soil science does not fit neatly with the physical sciences, the biological sciences, or the earth sciences. It is all three, but is not any one exclusively. Principles and methods from all three are used, in addition to those that are peculiar to soil science itself.

A large and growing body of fundamental scientific knowledge is the concern of soil science and of no other discipline. These facts emphasize the importance of seeing the science as a whole. No matter how much a soil scientist specializes, he must maintain a broad view of the whole field. In some sciences, like chemistry and plant physiology, for example, dependence is placed chiefly on one general scientific method—the experimental method. Unconsciously, some have assumed that the experimental method is the only method in science. Certainly it is a very useful one in soil science. With this method, the specific effects of variations in individual soil characteristics, and groups of soil characteristics, can be observed under defined conditions. The scientist then sets up experiments on plots representing an individual soil in which he can control the other variables, or at least account for their effects, besides the one under study. A large part of what has been learned about the behavior of specific kinds of soil has resulted from controlled field experiments, natural experiments, and the analyses of the records of operating units—farms, gardens, and forests.

---

[13] See section on Units of Soil Classification and Mapping.

Yet a great many matters must come under scientific study that cannot be subjected to experiment. For example, we can get at the relative influences of different climatic regimes on the genesis of unlike soils from granite, say, through the use of both the experimental method and the method of correlation. The experimental method deals with soils at small places, almost points. Through the method of correlation the sets of data from different places are compared and principles developed from them that fit the facts.

Useful results can only come out of those experimental plots that are fair samples of a defined kind of soil. To interpret the results, either for an understanding of soils or for predictions about their behavior, they must be synthesized in terms of defined soil units. This is the function of soil classification. Its stuff comes from observation and the experimental method; its working tool is the method of logical scientific correlation.

Soil classification depends upon the results from all branches of fundamental and applied soil science. On the other hand, the results from the other branches of soil science can only be synthesized for accurate application through soil classification, whether soil maps are made or not. Soil classification has been so intimately associated with soil mapping, for which it is an immediate necessity, that some individuals in other branches of soil science have not always seen that, in the long run, soil classification is just as important to their work, especially to the orderly application of their results.

In applying soil science to forestry, farming, grazing, and engineering, some means must be had for recognizing the individual units of the classification system in the field. Few people among those needing to use the principles and predictions of soil science can identify these units. Thus it is essential to have soil maps. Assuming an adequate system of soil classification, with the units consistently named and with reliable predictions, an accurate soil map makes possible the orderly application of our knowledge to specific areas—fields, farms, forests, gardens, roadways, and the like.

Soil mapping itself is an applied science or art. The quality and usefulness of the result, however, depend upon a vast background of both fundamental and applied science. They depend upon what is known generally and upon what is known specifically by the particular group of scientists doing the work. Every soil survey area presents a new challenge. It is by no means simply a matter of mapping a few dozen standard soil types and phases. Soils are not so easily standardized. The relationships between each soil and its neighbors, and between each soil and the factors of its environment, must be sought out and clarified. All likely potentialities for use must be explored and definite judgments arrived at, insofar as possible, in quantitative terms.

This places a high premium on the resourcefulness of the field scientist in making full use of all existing data and principles and in capturing the essentials in the soil-use experience laid out before him. Nor can the field scientist depend exclusively upon local sources of information. Important potentialities are suggested from experiences on similar soils elsewhere, even in other countries. Then the final results must be presented in terms of adapted crops, management practices, and land use systems, with awareness of the factors that influence such systems. In short, a modern soil survey is a difficult research undertaking requiring intense thoroughness and broad scope.

The rewards of work well done can be very satisfying, both intellectually and emotionally.[14] Certainly the complexities involved in understanding a soil and predicting its behavior are enough to tantalize the imagination of any man. Then with accurate soil maps, land users everywhere can make full use of science and technology to bring forth the great potentialities in the soil, under efficient management systems, for the sustained abundance the world so desperately needs.

---

[14] For the personal story of a soil surveyor's life in the field, see Macy H. Lapham's CRISSCROSS TRAILS: NARRATIVE OF A SOIL SURVEYOR. 246 pp., illus. Berkeley (Calif.) 1949.

CHARACTER OF SOIL MAPS AND REPORTS

A *soil map* is a map designed to show the distribution of soil types or other soil mapping units in relation to other prominent physical and cultural features of the earth's surface. The units may be shown separately or as soil associations named and defined in terms of taxonomic units. This definition is intended to exclude maps showing single soil characteristics like texture, slope, depth, color, or arbitrary combinations or two or more of these; maps showing soil qualities like fertility or erodibility; or maps showing individual soil genetic factors or combinations of them.

Maps of one or more soil features may be made directly from field observations or by selection and generalization from a soil map. On a soil map, however, combinations of all observable features relevant to the nature and behavior of the soil are comprehended as named taxonomic units—natural bodies with distinct sets of soil characteristics.

Selected interpretations of soil conditions may be shown on maps. From a soil map one may derive a series of simple interpretive maps of the same area showing, for example, the relative adaptability to alfalfa, corn, or other plants, erosion hazards under defined classes of management, drainage requirements for optimum production, irrigation potentialities, and many others. In the making of such generalizations, some soil boundaries are omitted; for example, those boundaries between soils equal in erosion hazard on the map of erosion hazard. But these particular boundaries may be important on another interpretive map, say one showing productivity classes. Thus different boundaries are omitted on different interpretive maps made from the same soil map.

Most such interpretations are ephemeral. They need to change with changes in the agricultural arts and in the cultural environment. If a basic soil map is made accurately, such interpretive maps can be revised easily from time to time as needed. But if only "judgment" maps are made on the spot, without a soil map, with any significant change in the agricultural arts or the cultural environment all the field work needs to be done over again. In planning soil surveys, this point can scarcely be overemphasized. Occasionally "short-cut" rural land surveys are made for some narrow objective, perhaps at a slightly lower cost than for a basic soil survey, only to become obsolete in a short time. Such maps cannot be repaired because vital data were ignored, facts were mixed with interpretations, boundaries between mapping units were drawn inaccurately, or because of some combination of these. Some rural areas have been mapped more than once by such short-cut surveys at a total cost approximating or even exceeding that of a basic soil survey and still there is no usable

11

map for making predictions or recommendations to farmers about adapted crops, estimated yields, and soil management practices.

A soil map by itself, without a text guide to its interpretation, cannot be useful to anyone except those soil scientists intimately acquainted with the units as named in the map legend. To all others an accompanying text, as well as the map legend, is essential. The soil survey includes both map and text. In the text, commonly called the *soil survey report*, are described the natural and cultural features of the area surveyed; the characteristics, use capabilities, management requirements, predicted average crop yields, and predicted long-time effects of management systems for each of the soil types, phases, and other mapping units; and the principal factors responsible for soil formation.

The character and form of soil surveys vary with the soil conditions, the agricultural potentialities, and the problems to be dealt with. Also, they have changed over the years with advancements in soil science and in cartographic techniques. Even more important has been the increased demand for precision in order to make effective use of the great developments in agricultural technology.

UNITS SHOWN ON THE MAPS

Identification of units.—The first step in making a soil survey is the establishment of the units of classification to be shown on the maps. Their nomenclature within the general system of classification *follows* their accurate definition, based upon observations made in the field as supplemented by data from the laboratory. The basic unit is the natural soil type—the lowest[1] unit in the natural (or genetic) system of soil classification. By "natural system" is meant the system in which all relevant features of soils are considered as unique interrelated sets of characteristics, including those important to the practical purposes that soil maps serve, but without exclusive emphasis upon any one of them.

Each soil type is unique. It is defined as a unique combination of surface features, like slope and stoniness, and of internal characteristics—the texture, structure, color, chemical composition, thickness, and other properties of the horizons that make up the soil profile to whatever depth is significant. These units are characterized by field and laboratory observations of the chemical, physical, biological, and mineralogical features of the horizons, the geological nature of the parent rock material, and the geomorphological characteristics of the landscape.

Any one soil type includes the soils that are alike in characteristics that are significant to the nature and functioning of the soil in the natural landscape. Differences in features that are not significant in the natural landscape, but which are significant to

---

[1] The soil phase as a subdivision of a soil type may be regarded, from some points of view at least, as a lower unit. But since phases are separated within soil types, series, families, and great soil groups on the basis of differences significant (as differentiating soil characteristics) only under culture and not in the natural landscape, they are not usually regarded strictly as essential parts of the natural system. (See also p. 289 *et seq.*)

the use of the soil in farming, forestry, or grazing are recognized in subdivisions within the soil type (or soil series). Commonly, differences in slope, stoniness, or degree of erosion within the soil type that are not significant in the natural landscape but which are significant to its use are shown as *soil phases*. Whereas soil types are defined within a narrow range of a whole set of characteristics, including all those of genetic or applied significance, phase distinctions within soil types are based wholly on applied considerations. Thus soil types everywhere should be defined in the same way; but phases are more narrowly defined where the agriculture is intensive and less narrowly defined where it is extensive. The guides to phase distinctions are wholly pragmatic.

In defining the classificational units, including phase distinctions, emphasis is given to the relatively permanent features that influence response to management and not to ephemeral or transitory features, like the differences in plant nutrients caused by recent fertilization, liming, or similar soil management practices. It must be recognized that the immediate productivity of areas of the same soil type, or phase, may vary because of recent management history. This is especially true of soil types that respond greatly to fertilizers. Nevertheless, there should not be significant differences in productivity for climatically adapted crops among areas of the same kind of soil, if properly mapped, *when given the same management*. In very old agricultural areas, however, practices have changed the soils fundamentally, and their classification.

Observable features and inferred qualities.—In carrying out the soil survey and in reporting the results, the observable features need to be clearly distinguished from those soil qualities that are learned only by inference.

In the completed soil survey, the features of each kind of soil are listed. Among those observed directly are slope (degree, shape, and pattern), stoniness, depth, and the color, structure, texture, and other significant features of each horizon of the soil profile. Other observations include soil temperatures, kinds of plants and their rooting habits, features caused by erosion, and so on. Many characteristics are determined partly through the use of scientific instruments. Among these are the contents of clay, organic matter, plant nutrients, exchangeable cations, and the various clay minerals in the soil horizons. The pH of each soil horizon is also determined. As needed, the degree of aggregation, permeability, kind and amount of soluble salts, and the effects of additions of water are determined. It may be emphasized again that the soil units may be grouped and interpretive maps made according to one of these observable characteristics, but such maps are not basic soil maps.

Through interpretation from observed features, the qualities of kinds of soil may be learned by inference. Soil fertility, for example, may be estimated from observable characteristics, from the results of experimental plots, and from the experiences of farmers having records on fields consisting largely of one kind of soil. Soil fertility, however, is not directly observable. It is the quality that enables the soil to provide the proper compounds, in the proper amounts and in the proper balance, for the growth of specified plants, when other factors, such as light, temperature, moisture, and the physical condition of the soil, are favorable. Thus soils may be grouped into fertility classes only by inference. The same is true of tilth—the physical condition of the soil in respect to its fitness for the growth of a specified plant. Combining both of these qualities, fertility and tilth, one arrives at the concept of productivity, defined as the capability of the soil for producing a specified plant or sequence of plants under a specified set of management practices.

Groupings of soils by inferred qualities are essential to the interpretation of a soil survey. Besides fertility, tilth, and productivity, several other qualities may be inferred from the basic soil survey if the research is carried on competently. These qualities include erodibility, irrigability, response to drainage, workability or physical condition in respect to tillage, and crop adaptability. Groupings of soils according to use capability, either in the general sense or in the special sense employed by the Soil Conservation Service in its program of assistance to farmers, are easily made from the detailed soil map and report, or can be read directly from the soil map.

Identification of boundaries.—Having established the units of classification and identified these units on the ground, boundaries are drawn among them on accurate base maps or aerial photographs. The scales to be used depend upon the uses to be made of the map and the relative intricacy of the soil pattern.

After the soil units have been defined and their relationships to the environment worked out, most soil boundaries can be located on the land surface by recognizing where changes in one or more of the genetic factors occur. That is, excavations or borings are needed chiefly to identify the profile of a soil landscape. The actual boundary can usually be drawn most accurately by careful observations of the landscape. Nonetheless, there are important exceptions where the relationships between the differentiating soil features and genetic factors are obscure. For example, the depth and thickness of an iron crust or of a horizon of carbonate accumulation, or the depth to a water table, may be variable although there is no corresponding variation in surface features. In such instances, examinations of the soil are necessary for locating boundaries as well as for identification.

Soil boundaries must be drawn accurately. Despite the large proportion of attention given to soil classification in contrast to methods of soil mapping, a large part of the poor soil maps in the world are poor mainly because of inaccurate boundaries—boundaries guessed at rather than determined. In soil survey work great emphasis must be given to honesty in research. It is more difficult to check the results of a soil mapper than to check those of a laboratory worker, and the damage from incorrect soil boundaries may be very serious to the map user.

KINDS OF SOIL MAPS

Depending upon the detail with which boundaries between the mapping units are plotted in the field, three general kinds of original soil maps are recognized: (1) Detailed, (2) reconnaissance, and (3) detailed-reconnaissance. Of these the detailed soil survey is the most useful and most important. The third, detailed-reconnaissance, is not really a separate kind but is a soil map having parts of each of the first two kinds.

Besides original soil maps made from field surveys, there are relatively small scale soil maps showing associations of the taxonomic units. *Generalized* soil maps are developed through orderly abstraction from original field surveys, either detailed or reconnaissance. *Schematic* soil maps are compiled from spot field observations of the soils and their genetic factors, and from maps of geology, climate, land form, vegetation, and relief. Generalized soil maps of representative areas guide the compilation of schematic maps and are usually included in some parts of them.

Detailed soil maps.—On a modern detailed soil map, the soil types and phases are mapped in the detail required to show all boundaries between mapping units, including areas of one unit within another, that are significant to potential use (generally to plan field management systems). The classificational units are defined narrowly enough to be homogeneous genetically and to permit making such significant differential predictions as available knowledge permits; and the boundaries between mapping units are plotted on base maps or aerial photographs from observations made throughout their course, along with such natural features as streams and lakes and such significant cultural features as ditches, roads, railways, and houses.

Specific guides on the many items are presented elsewhere in this *Manual.* The base map needs to be complete and accurate because land lines (section lines, township boundaries, and the like), roads, houses, streams, and other obvious features are needed as local reference points by map users. Great detail in soil mapping, without a detailed base, is largely wasted, since the user is usually unable to locate himself properly and read the map accurately. Accuracy of a soil map is therefore not determined primarily by general geodetic accuracy but by what might be called local accuracy—the relation of the soil boundaries to the other features that the map user can identify. For example, even though a soil boundary may be plotted within the general limits of accuracy, should it be on the wrong side of a house or road, the usefulness of the map and the user's confidence in it are greatly reduced.

The detail of boundaries required depends partly upon the prospective use of the map. If small bodies of one kind of soil occur within areas of another kind of soil and thereby significantly affect management, the small bodies of soil should be separated or indicated on the map by defined symbols, even if they are an acre or less in extent. Judgment in mapping such areas is also influenced by the relative contrast between the two kinds of soil.

Even with large map scales some taxonomic units are often so intricately interlaced with one or more others that the association of them needs to be recognized as the mapping unit. In mapping areas of complex patterns where all the soils contained in paddocks or fields are treated alike, it may be more useful to show well-defined soil complexes than to map individual taxonomic units in minute and intricate detail.

The scale of mapping depends upon the purpose to be served, the intensity of soil use, the pattern of soils, and the scale of other cartographic materials available. Commonly a scale of 4 inches equal 1 mile (1:15,840) is now used for field mapping and one of about 2 inches equal 1 mile (1:31,680) for publication. Few detailed soil surveys that meet modern standards can be made in field scales less than 1:20,000 except in comparatively uniform terrain. For planning irrigation developments and in areas of very intensive farming the field mapping scales may need to be larger, say 1:7,920 or even 1:5,000. For engineering work, like planning for highway or airport construction, the detail needed may require a field mapping scale of around 1:2,500 or even 1:1,000,

In former years many soil maps were made in the field at a scale of 1 inch equals 1 mile (1:63,360 or 1:62,500) and published at the same scale. Later, the field mapping scale was doubled to 1:31,680. After the use of aerial photographs became general, the field scale was increased again to around 1:20,000 or 1:15,840. Publication scale continued for some time at 1:63,360 or 1:62,500. Some of the detailed maps plotted in the field on aerial photographs and reduced to these scales in publication are extremely difficult to read. So the publication scale was later increased to 1:48,000 and then again to 1:31,680 or 1:24,000. These larger scales have become necessary for easy legibility, although broad geographic relations among the soils are less clearly seen with the reduced total area of land on a single map sheet. The advantage of having the detailed soil survey of a county on one single map, however, has had to be sacrificed for clear reading of detail in reference to individual fields and farms.

No general rule can be laid down for guiding the number of soil examinations required per unit area nor for the intervals between traverses, except that these can rarely be more than one-fourth mile wide and usually need to be narrower.

Reconnaissance soil maps.—On a reconnaissance soil map the boundaries between the mapping units are plotted from observations made at intervals and not necessarily throughout their whole course as on the detailed soil maps. Reconnaissance maps vary widely, from "semidetailed" soil maps that approach the specifications of a detailed soil survey to maps of soil associations made from traverses at intervals of several miles. Reconnaissance maps are usually planned for exploratory purposes—to discover and outline areas of soil suitable for more intensive development (see page 435 *et seq.*). They are particularly useful in new and relatively undeveloped regions for identifying areas of promise for settlement or more intensive use.

In some reconnaissance surveys, the classification units are less precisely defined than in detailed soil surveys. Usually the mapping scale is smaller and fewer mapping units can correspond to the taxonomic units. In older reconnaissance work, it was customary to show named soil types on the map for areas that were really undefined mixtures of that soil type with others. This was done especially where research was insufficient to develop a complete classification. It is now possible to make far better and more useful maps by using defined soil associations.

In modern reconnaissance mapping, the taxonomic units are sought out, defined, and named as in a detailed soil survey. These are then mapped in groups as geographic associations. Such an association may contain several sharply contrasting soil types and phases. Each association is defined in terms of the named taxonomic units, their relative proportion, and their pattern. The associations are named in terms of the more prominent taxonomic units.

During the progress of the work, representative sample areas of each soil association are mapped in the detail required to meet the specifications of a detailed soil survey. These areas are carefully located, and small maps showing the detail are reproduced separately in the accompanying text. The usual supplemental laboratory data and other data are assembled by taxonomic units. Predictions about adapted crops, estimated yields, management requirements, and so on are also made for these units as they are in the detailed soil survey.

Agricultural scientists and advisers can examine the sample areas and learn how to identify the individual taxonomic units within the particular soil associations that concern them.

This scheme of reconnaissance soil mapping has a wide application in new and relatively undeveloped areas. It makes possible better appraisals of regional potentialities than the older reconnaissance soil maps with poorly defined mapped units. It permits the rapid surveying of large areas where development cannot await the completion of a detailed soil survey. At the same time it gives advisory agriculturists an opportunity to make those specific recommendations that can only be made on the basis of local, narrowly defined soil types and phases.

Good reconnaissance maps can be made only if there is enough detailed mapping of representative sample areas to establish the modal definitions of the taxonomic units and their permissible ranges of variability. Specifications for individual maps will vary widely. In mountainous regions or other areas not likely to be used intensively, traverses are made at less frequent intervals than on land suitable for farming.

Many of the soil maps made in the earlier years of research in the United States, which were looked upon as detailed soil maps in terms of the techniques of that time, are regarded as reconnaissance soil maps under modern specifications. The increased detail did not come in any single year and there were wide variations in the skill and vision of individual supervisors and soil survey party chiefs.

Detailed-reconnaissance soil maps.—On a detailed-reconnaissance map some portions satisfy the specifications for detailed soil maps, whereas other portions are reconnaissance soil maps. Such maps are made of counties or other geographic units containing areas of soil used or potentially useful for agriculture and other large areas that are unsuited. The part covered by reconnaissance may be rough mountainous land, raw acid peat soils, stony desert soils, dry sandy plains or hills, or other landscapes unsuited to farming.

The boundaries between the detailed and reconnaissance types of survey on the one map may be made in one of two ways: (1) The boundaries may follow section lines or other land lines and be shown in a smaller sketch map on the margin of the soil map; (2) the legend on the map may be divided into two parts. The mapping units listed under the reconnaissance legend, and boundaries among them, are defined and mapped according to the specifications for the reconnaissance map; whereas those units listed under the detailed legend and boundaries among them and between them and the units listed under the reconnaissance legend, are mapped according to the specifications of the detailed soil map.

Where the area covered by reconnaissance is considerably larger than the area covered in detail, it may be convenient to publish the reconnaissance portion separately from the detailed mapping. The detailed maps can then be published on extra sheets at a larger scale.

Generalized soil maps.—In order to see the broad geographic relations among soils, small-scale maps are necessary to bring out the contrasts among regions. The best of these are generalized from detailed soil surveys. Such maps vary in scale and detail from soil association maps of counties at a scale of 1 inch equals 1 mile (1:63,360) to single maps of large regions showing associations dominated by one or more great soil groups.

The descriptive legends of soil association maps indicate the relative proportions and patterns of the several classificational units that compose them. If the map is included as a part of a detailed soil survey, the text that explains the individual taxonomic units on the detailed soil map can serve for both. If the soil association map is published separately, descriptions and predictions for all taxonomic units within the associations should be attached, perhaps in tabular form.

The publication of detailed soil maps at scales as large as 1:31,680 and 1:24,000 has increased the need for generalized soil association maps so that broad areas can be viewed as a whole. Since the county is a convenient unit for many kinds of agricultural work in the United States, a soil map is needed to exhibit the whole county in such a way that the various parts of it stand out according to the principal soil features and patterns that are basic to types of farming and community problems.

Since the uses of generalized soil maps are so varied, it is more difficult to write specifications for them than for detailed soil maps. For the lowest level of generalization, the one most useful in agricultural advisory programs, we may proceed on the following basis: Farms are usually made up of several soil types. It is the combination of soil types that gives the soil association its distinctive character and sets the potentialities and limitations within the farm unit. Experience on individual fields is synthesized, classified, and extended on the basis of soil types and phases as defined in the detailed soil survey. Experience with whole farm units, made up of combinations of soil types, is synthesized, classified, and extended on the basis of soil associations. Consequently, the legend and detail of a useful soil association map are planned to show the use suitabilities of these broad geographic groups of soils. Of course, boundaries between soil associations cross some farms, just as the soil type boundaries cross some fields. If large areas of a single soil type do dominate many whole farms, the soil type may be shown separately. But rarely is this possible. In recognizing very small strips of highly productive Alluvial soils, for example, it must be recalled that the Alluvial soil usually is only part of the farm and is used in association with the adjacent uplands. In such instances, it may be misleading to separate small strips of Alluvial soils as a distinct association and the upland soils as one or more others. In other words, excessive detail in the soil association map can lower its usefulness.

The development of a proper legend for such a generalized soil association map requires judgment based upon a study of both soils and farming systems in whole farm units. The form of the legend for a soil association map is influenced by cultural environment, or expected cultural environment in a new area, more than is that for a detailed soil map. It must be so influenced if the soil association map is to be most useful for indicating whole-farm and community problems and potentialities. Well-made soil association maps interpreted in the light of data from experimental plots, fields, and farms, are exceedingly valuable for classifying farms according to their basic potentialities and for guiding agricultural advisers in the geographic emphasis they should give within a county or district to various educational and demonstration programs. Soil association maps serve as an excellent basis, in fact the only satisfactory one, for suggesting the approximate locations of experimental farms, pilot-research farms, and demonstration farms[2], and for suggesting where the experience from these farms is most applicable. For the exact location and plans of such farms a detailed survey is required. Soil association maps indicate the areas where the agricultural adviser should emphasize liming, erosion control, drainage, forest planting, use of phosphatic fertilizers, expansion of pastures, and like practices or combinations of them.

Still smaller scale soil association maps of States or regions are useful in assisting the advisers in community development.[3] On these, the smallest land area to claim attention is larger than a farm, generally about the minimum size for a homogeneous agricultural community.

Schematic soil maps.—In form and appearance these resemble generalized maps of soil associations. Scales are usually small, say 1:1,000,000 or smaller, although useful ones are made at larger scales. For many areas, especially in new and undeveloped regions, it is useful to have an approximate or estimated soil map even in advance of an organized field soil survey, either reconnaissance or detailed. Such maps may be made by estimating the soil pattern. If carefully done by highly competent scientists, this is a great deal more than guessing.

First, all available data, both at spots and in map form, on the soils and the climate, vegetation, geology, and land form, are gathered and studied. In wild areas, these data may consist mainly of notes taken by scientific travelers and rough maps made from aerial photographs without proper ground control. A soil is the unique result of five interrelated factors: (1) Climate and (2) living matter, as conditioned by (3) relief, acting on (4) parent rock materials for periods of (5) time. Therefore, if reasonably good estimates can be had of all but one of these factors, the missing one may be interpreted by geographic correlation. This is the principle. If good topographic maps are available, often surprisingly good soil maps can be forecast by experienced soil scientists thoroughly familiar with the combinations of environmental factors that produce different kinds of soil.

Since the amount and reliability of available data vary greatly from place to place, schematic soil maps always need to be accompanied by a sketch map showing relative reliability.

---

[2] An *experimental farm* is one on which experiments are conducted on single enterprises without regard to the farm unit as a whole, say plot studies of fertilizers, crop varieties, and rotations, or pasture experiments with grazing animals. On a *pilot-research farm* the aim is to find the optimum combination (or combinations) of practices suited to the farm as a unit. Both the experimental and pilot-research farms are managed for research results, and decisions are made by the scientists in charge. On the *demonstration farms*, proved practices are applied mainly by concentrating advisory services to help the *operator* make the best decisions possible toward optimum farm and home development. *Predevelopment* farms, part way between pilot-research and demonstration farms, are sometimes established a few years in advance of settlement as guides to the new settlers.

[3] For an example of this use see MONTGOMERY COUNTY [Alabama] FARM PROGRAM. Agricultural Extension Office, Montgomery, Ala., 61 pp. (c. 1947.)

The interpretation and use of schematic soil maps for agricultural and engineering purposes follow the same course as for generalized maps. The soil associations need to be defined according to the taxonomic units that compose them, their proportions, and their patterns. Then the characteristics and predictions may be given for the individual taxonomic units insofar as they can be estimated; and soil potentialities and problems for community development may be given for whole soil associations. Commonly it is not possible to go further down the scale in the taxonomic classification than great soil groups, with subdivisions according to parent rock, slope, depth, and stoniness.

The compilation of a schematic soil map is often the first logical step in planning more detailed study and survey of a large undeveloped area. After compilation of the schematic soil-association map, representative sample areas may be mapped in detail. Keys and tables of predictions for the local soil types and phases *within* each soil association can be worked out. After the sample areas have been mapped in detail, the approximate schematic map first drafted can be revised. The schematic map can then be published, along with the detailed sample maps and their explanations, as a useful guide for appraising the potentialities of the various parts of the region. The published survey should include specific guides that will enable agricultural advisers to recognize local soil types and phases, for these will aid them in making specific recommendations to soil users.

Exploratory soil maps.—These maps resemble schematic soil maps except that the mapping units are identified mainly by original observations of soils within the area, even though the boundaries are largely compiled from other sources.[4]

REQUIREMENTS FOR THE SOIL SURVEY REPORT

The report, or text accompanying the soil map, is an essential part of the soil survey. Since its form and content depend upon the purposes to be served, these must be thoroughly understood in advance. The report is not an extra chore to be done after the map is made; it needs to be developed along with the mapping in the field. For a basic general-purpose soil survey, a complete statement of all essential soil characteristics and their variabilities needs to be included, regardless of the immediate practical needs to be served. The soil scientists in the field need to know as much as possible about the probable uses; but they must also not be prejudiced by these to the point of omitting significant soil characteristics because they seem relatively unimportant at the moment. Time and time again, soil surveys have been found to be very useful indeed for purposes never dreamed of by the soil survey party doing the original field work. If the essential facts were recorded, the maps could be interpreted readily for the new purpose; otherwise, the field work had to be done over again.

[4] As one example see KELLOGG, CHARLES E., and NYGARD, IVER J. EXPLORATORY STUDY OF THE PRINCIPAL SOIL GROUPS OF ALASKA. U. S. Dept. Agr. Agr. Monog. No. 7, 138 pp., illus (map). 1951: Washington, D. C.

The uses of the soil survey are expanding so much that more than one report is sometimes necessary. For the lay reader, explanation of interpretations as they relate to his immediate problems may be all that is required. This may be included in the basic report or published separately. Such statements may need to be revised from time to time with changes in the agricultural arts and in economic conditions, and issued as supplements. Then too, special reports on engineering features or other interpretations may be necessary. Ordinarily, the publication of such special reports in the United States is a responsibility of the cooperating local research institute, like the State agricultural experiment station, rather than the Federal Soil Survey.

Normally, as the work progresses, the soil survey report grows out of the descriptive soil legend. The soil descriptions are already complete when the mapping is finished. The available geological, climatic, and agricultural data are obtained in advance of the field mapping, for they are useful in developing the descriptive legend and guiding the taking of field notes.

PURPOSE OF SOIL MAPS AND REPORTS

The Soil Survey includes those researches necessary (1) to determine the important characteristics of soils, (2) to classify soils into defined types and other classificational units, (3) to establish and to plot on maps the boundaries among kinds of soil, and (4) to correlate and to predict the adaptability of soils to various crops, grasses, and trees, their behavior and productivity under different management systems, and the yields of adapted crops under defined sets of management practices.

The fundamental purpose of a soil survey, like that of any other research, is to make predictions. Although the results of soil research are being applied increasingly to engineering problems, such as the design and maintenance of highways, airports, and pipelines, applications are chiefly in the agricultural field, including forestry and grazing. It is purposeful research.

The many thousands of different kinds of soil have unlike management requirements for economic, sustained production. For centuries farm families learned as best they could through trial and error what methods worked best on their various fields. This knowledge passed on from father to son, but it could not be transferred readily to other areas, nor could the experience on other farms be applied safely.

With the development of modern science, agriculture is being made continually more efficient. Progress has been phenomenal during the 50 years since soil surveying began in the United States. Even the rate at which agricultural efficiency is being increased is itself accelerating as this *Manual* is being written. Experiments with soils, plants, and animals are being continued in many parts of the world. New farming systems are being tested in both research and practice. Fundamentally, soil classification serves as the basis for classifying, synthesizing, and reporting these results of research and experience. The more agricultural science progresses, the more important this work becomes. The investments in machinery and materials per acre of cultivated land are increasing. The planning of farm systems for optimum sustained production needs to be done far in advance of the operations for the best results made possible by modern science, with revisions from season to season. The importance of precise recommendations—differential recommendations from field to field and from farm to farm—increases. Soil maps serve as the basis for such differential recommendations.

Crop plants and soil management practices are so sensitive to the differences in soil that a soil survey adequate for this basic need is certain to serve a great many other purposes as well. In fact, no other maps of large areas of land are made in such detail and involve so many significant factors as do soil maps.

SYNTHESIS OF AGRICULTURAL DATA FOR APPLICATION TO SPECIFIC AREAS

The soil survey is an integral part of an effective agricultural research and advisory program. It is clearly impossible to carry out exhaustive and expensive researches on every field and farm. Representative samples of land must be chosen. The soil type or phase, accurately defined and named in a standard system of classification, is the only reliable basis yet found for selecting such samples. Every experimental plot is a sample of a landscape. It should be an accurate and representative sample of a kind of soil worth sampling. Thus the soil survey has an important rôle in the planning of research, especially in the selection and location of experimental fields and farms.

New discoveries from experimental work and on farms need to be extended to other areas of similar soils. For optimum use, new methods must be tested widely in farming systems. As the new discoveries are tested, the results can be classified by kinds of soil. When we know that a certain soil area is Miami silt loam, let us say, a great body of research and farm experience is available to allow us to predict its management requirements, the crops that may be grown and their yields, and the long-time effect of various management systems on its productivity.

Without the results of a large amount of correlative research and of careful farm analyses to help them, the scientists in soil survey will be unable to give good predictions. Contrariwise, it is through the soil survey that the results of a host of other researches can be precisely applied.

Through study and comparison of soil types and phases which are defined as sets of soil characteristics, of the sets of genetic factors that go with them, and of the synthesized results of farm analyses and correlative research, general principles of soil behavior are developed for various levels of soil groupings. In going to the higher categorical levels of classification, from soil type to series, to families, to great soil groups, and finally to suborders, the number and precision of the generalizations are reduced.

For detailed predictions and recommendations, the soil type, or a phase of a soil type, is the safest base because of the narrow range of characteristics. If all possible interpretations are to be given, it is the only possible base. But for some one interpretation, as response to liming or the erosion hazard, several soil types and phases can be grouped together.

It should be emphasized that soil scientists, acting strictly as soil scientists, give predictions rather than recommendations. The prediction statements and tables in a soil survey report are designed to predict the results from using the soil types or phases in various defined ways. But the alternative to be recommended for a specific operating farm depends upon the economic environment of the farm and the skill, facilities, and desires of the operator. Then too, for most soils several combinations of practices are possible.

Given an accurate soil map of a farm, alternative cropping and soil management systems for that farm may be developed from the predictions given. With competent soil survey work, with predictions about the other production factors—livestock feeding, performance of machinery, disease protection, and the like—and with adequate consideration of the economic factors, optimum farming systems can be developed.[1] Clear statements of the alternatives are necessary so that agricultural advisers and farm operators can make proper selections from among them.

Since the decisions about farming practices are made within millions and millions of individual managerial units, classification must be detailed enough to include all the significant soil characteristics—all basic land features that significantly affect soil use and management. The maps must be detailed enough to indicate areas of soils significant to a farm management system. They must show these areas accurately in relation to local reference points shown on the map that the user may recognize on the ground.

FARM PLANNING

Increasingly, the results of the soil survey and of the correlative research are applied by the farmer, often with some advice, through the development of a farm plan. Such a plan to be useful does not need to be elaborate. In addition to the use of each field, it shows field boundaries, alternative boundaries, and more or less permanent structures, such as buildings, fences, drainage and irrigation canals, terraces, waterways, and the like. The soil boundaries may be obtained from the soil map. A few of these may coincide with certain field boundaries. In fact, a major contribution of soil mapping to farm planning is the help it gives in relocating field boundaries in order to make fields more nearly uniform. A field containing one kind of soil can be handled more effectively than one containing two or more contrasting soils. The use of the several fields should be indicated tentatively as far in advance as practicable, with alternative cropping systems, so that shifts can be made with unusual weather or with significant changes in economic conditions.

A good farm plan is carried beyond the field layout and cropping system to a farm budget. Such a budget is very important as a test against the physical layout. Farm plans that have called for drastic changes have often failed unless first tested against an estimated budget. To make a budget, at least rough inventories are required of carry-over feeds, machinery, and livestock.[2] For most farms, several alternative plans, with budgets, may be calculated, any one of which will maintain and improve the soils.

[1] For a discussion of the development of optimum farming systems, see BLACK, JOHN D., et al. FARM MANAGEMENT. 1,073 pp., illus. New York. 1947.

[2] See JOHNSON, NEIL W., and BARNES, C. P. PLANNING FARM RETURNS. U. S. Dept. Agr. Yearbook 1943-47. (Science in Farming): 905-910, Washington, 1947; and also Black, J. D., et al. in the General Bibliography.

The one chosen depends upon the skill, resources, and likes of the farm family.

It is unnecessary here to go into a detailed explanation of farm planning except to point out its requirements so that those making detailed soil surveys can make sure their work will be satisfactory for the purpose. In planning, the farmer and his adviser should consider the enterprise combinations that are adapted to the farm as a whole, their economic feasibility, and the skills, resources, and desires of the farm family. No matter how listed, all phases of soil use and farming practices are interrelated. With that in mind, the following is a check list of the principal elements in the farm plan for sustained production that depend wholly or partly upon a proper interpretation of the soil conditions that are taken into account in soil classification and mapping and in the soil survey report.

1. *Major land uses.*—The plan needs to be balanced among the major land uses—crops requiring tillage, forestry, and pasture—according to the pattern of soil types on the farm and the requirements for balance among the several enterprises. Where livestock is produced, the farm needs a proper balance between pasture and feed crops. The several farm operations have to be balanced in relation to the labor supply. Provision needs to be made for the home orchard and garden where practicable.

2. *Cropping system.*—A well-planned cropping system is needed that fits the kinds of soil on the farm. Usually crops should be grown in rotations or mixed cultures. Good seed of those varieties having the greatest disease resistance, drought tolerance, yield, and quality should be used. Most soils produce best with crop rotations that include meadows having deeply rooted legumes or grass-legume mixtures.

3. *Tillage methods.*—The methods employed in tillage should be aimed to prepare seedbeds properly and on time, to make the soil receptive to water, to incorporate organic material, lime, and fertilizer deeply where necessary, and to control weeds. Where soil blowing is a hazard, the surface must be left cloddy and trashy. Many good machines are available from which selections can be made. On some soil types, the moldboard plow, or turning plow, is best; on others, it should not be used.

4. *Protection.*—Both crops and livestock should be given the necessary protection against winds, insects, and other hazards. It is often important to know whether or not the soil can be used for growing shelter belts.

5. *Water control, use, and disposal on the land.*—Every farm needs an orderly system of water use and disposal. Many farms have naturally well-drained soils and dependable rainfall. A large number do not. Excess runoff of rain water must be reduced to the minimum with protective close-growing plants, strip cropping, terracing, or in other ways, so that the water will soak into the soil for plant growth and not be lost or cause erosion. On

erodible soils where rains are intense, unless the management plan provides for runoff and erosion control, all other practices may come to nothing. Although the amount of erosion that has already taken place is significant, the important thing is to assess the hazard of erosion, whether or not much has taken place. Some soils need drainage. Low lands need protection from floodwaters. Many soils will respond to irrigation. Some of these practices require community effort, but a lot can be done by the farm family itself.

6. *Use and conservation of organic matter.*—Large and unnecessary losses of animal manure and crop residues often take place through fire, leaching, and neglect. Yet many soils respond enormously to the addition of organic matter. Part of the need for soil organic matter can be met in a cropping system itself by using a grass-legume mixture, deeply rooted legumes, green-manure crops, and cover crops.

7. *Reaction control.*—On acid soils liming is a first essential to create soil conditions favorable for the availability of the other plant nutrients and for the deeply rooted legumes. In the regions of low rainfall, provisions are required for eliminating excess salt or alkali and for preventing their accumulation under irrigation.

8. *Fertilization.*—A system of fertilization may need to be developed in the farm plan to make possible the best combination of high-yielding crops. We must always recall that fertilization may offer an excellent opportunity to expand the choice of crops that may be grown. One cannot recommend the precise amounts of fertilizer to use from the soil map alone; other aspects of the farming system already mentioned and previous use must be considered. For both lime and fertilizer recommendations, it is helpful to have the results of appropriate chemical tests in areas where reliable ones have been developed. The reader should be able to interpret from the soil map and report, however, the general fertilizer requirements and the production that may be expected from systems involving their use; but the need for phosphorus, say, on any one field will depend also on the amounts that have been used in former years and on other phases of the farm plan.

These aspects of farm planning are so clearly interrelated that decisions about one influence the others. The crop rotations, for example, depend on liming and fertilizing and the erosion hazard; the nitrogen fertilizer required depends partly on the legumes grown and the manure applied; and so on.

Farm classification can be a great aid to advisory work and to farm planning, especially where the soils, and the optimum sets of practices to go with them, are contrasting. With a detailed soil map and the pattern of farm boundaries, farms may be grouped according to amounts and kinds of soil resources into classes of farms having similar potentialities and problems. The need for this kind of farm classification is greatest in areas where the local variations among soils are greatest. In Iowa, for example, the need is less striking than in a State like Tennessee, where the local soil variations are many and great.

RURAL LAND CLASSIFICATION

The results of the soil survey are often applied through an intermediate grouping of the soil types and phases, often called "land classification." The soil units shown on the map may be grouped into classes on any one of several bases, such as (1) degree of some characteristic like texture, stoniness, slope, or acidity; (2) adaptability to some crop or group of crops; (3) productivity under certain sets of management practices; (4) erosion hazard and general management requirements for erosion control; (5) potential irrigability; and (6) response to lime, phosphate, potash, or other fertilizers. It is clearer to call groupings like these "soil groups" than to label them "land classes," in order to avoid the broad connotation of the word "land."

The data of the soil survey are often used to classify, for various purposes, specific geographically defined bodies of land, like sections, "forties," or farms, as shown in a cadastral survey. A clear distinction is needed between the classification of specific land tracts—sections, lots, or other cadastral subdivisions— perhaps more aptly referred to as land classification, and the classification of land into kinds, types, or classes irrespective of cadastral or property boundaries. In the former, distance from market, size of tract, and other relevant factors of the institutional environment can be evaluated with some accuracy; whereas distance from market or size of area are not relevant in grouping the soils, let us say, according to productivity for adapted crops, except as the general social and economic environment fix the perimeter within which the groupings need to be made. No one recommends, for example, that research be undertaken now to find the productivity of soils in Maryland for paddy rice, nor of those producing sugarcane in Hawaii for buckwheat or rye.

Multiformity of land classes.—In a sense the soil survey may be called a kind of land classification. Although it does not include all the characteristics of place, it certainly recognizes a larger proportion of the ones relevant to local land use, and more accurately, than any other survey systematically carried over large areas. But as the term "land classification" has been most commonly used, it usually refers to something far less complete and detailed than a modern soil survey.

The term "land classification" can easily become very confusing. The attributes of any area are exceedingly numerous, and their relevance varies enormously in different parts of the world; yet any one or any combination of the attributes *may* be chosen as criteria for a "land classification." The matter is even worse than that. Many "land classifications" are more or less personal interpretations of undefined combinations of attributes, economic appraisals, or use experiences, often in relationship to a shifting undefined standard. Lands have been classified using tax delinquency, condition of farm buildings, growing vegetation, intensity of use, patterns of use, and so on as criteria of use capability or other land qualities, in both meticulous detail and broad sweeps. Many of these classifications have been useful but some have been misleading indeed, partly because ephemeral standards were used in the work and especially because factors relevant and vital to the purpose of the classification were not taken into account.

The misuse of land classifications often comes about by shifting a fixed method from one soil or cultural region to another. For example, in some areas a general relationship has been found between soil quality for farming and tax delinquency, partly because of the common overassessment of unresponsive soils. In such an area, land classification based primarily on tax delinquency and whether or not land is cleared may give a workable basis for rural zoning. A similar classification fails badly, however, in an area where there is plenty of labor for clearing land, or where unresponsive soil is not overassessed. In some soil regions an exceedingly close relationship exists between native vegetation and soil groups based on the productivity of the kinds of soil for cultivated crops. Yet possibly only 100 miles away, with a slight difference in climate, the "good indicator" species push well over onto soils unsuited to farming. Since plants grow as a result of a combination of growing conditions, they cannot be taken as a certain evidence of either climate or soil. Examples of similar errors could be multiplied many times.

Land classifications based mainly on present land use are perhaps the most likely to mislead. Yet they can be very useful, too. Many institutional, economic, and historical factors, besides soil productivity, have combined to determine present use. Intensive use does not necessarily indicate highly responsive soils, adapted crops, nor optimum farming systems. Large areas of responsive soils in the world remain largely unused because of lack of transport or industry, or from the accidents of colonization; but land-use maps, especially where intensity of use can be interpreted from the maps, can be useful as a supplement to the soil map. By comparing the two maps, one may ascertain what users have found to be possible and what areas are used with less than the possible intensity. Such comparisons give a beginning point for searching out the obstacles to optimum soil use, many of which may turn out to be economic or institutional.

Another source of confusion in land classification to many has been the search for a simple, all-purpose classification of land according to its characteristics and capabilities. This the authors now regard as an impossibility, despite hopes expressed in the first edition of this *Manual* and elsewhere. If the classification is simple, relevant factors must be omitted. The number of significantly different soil series runs into the thousands for the continental United States alone. There are even more in the tropics. Then, when we add to these the necessary phase distinctions for variations within soil types, the number of kinds of soil becomes much larger. Besides soil, as defined in this *Manual*, there are climatic variations that are significant to growing plants within the environment even of some soil types. All sorts of variations in vegetation may be expected. Thus the classification cannot be simple except for an easily defined, narrow, single purpose. As already explained, it is generally far cheaper to make a basic soil survey from which a great many simple groupings, or "land classifications," may be derived by interpretation, than to concentrate on one narrow immediate objective at a time in separate surveys.

Nor can there be an all-purpose classification or grouping. A grouping made primarily to indicate erosion hazard and for planning erosion control will not serve adequately as a grouping for tax assessment, for example. It will fail one purpose or the other. Even with an accurate, highly detailed soil survey in hand, an up-to-date timber cruise may be needed for some kinds of land classification, or perhaps a detailed map of field patterns and land use. For still other purposes, additional research to establish costs for drainage, irrigation, or land clearing is required. To go ahead and get all these data, along with the detailed soil survey, on the chance that they may be needed some day, would increase the cost beyond reason.

Groupings by use capabilities can be made from a good soil survey with adequate correlative research; but such groupings are bound to be transitory and will need to be changed with changes in the agricultural arts, especially in new or undeveloped areas.

Some confusion between soil maps and land classification has resulted from assumptions of 25 years and more ago that soils were defined in terms of soil profile alone. (Regrettably, some in the Soil Survey staff once made this error, too.) Actually, as already explained, landscapes are classified and mapped in soil surveys, not simply soil profiles. Some who accepted the early definition of a soil type as a profile, and who realized that any mapped area had actually a range of profiles, attempted to get around the difficulty by conceiving "land types" or "natural land types" as mapping units defined in terms of soil profile, slope, stoniness, depth (including truncation by erosion), and the like. Such a definition of "land type" is not necessarily different than the present concept of "soil type." But some went further too, and included, under the same name, other mapping units now recognized as soil phases or soil complexes. This led to great confusion, especially in the absence of nomenclature and definitions to differentiate kinds or groupings of "land types." As nearly as one can make out, these "natural land types" can be placed in soil classification as (1) soil types, as now defined in terms of all soil characteristics, including slope, stoniness, and depth, as well as soil profile; (2) phases of soil types; and (3) associations (or complexes) of soil series, soil types, or phases. By using defined units in soil classification, one may go ahead, with orderly abstraction, to the higher taxonomic groups and to soil associations for generalized maps.

Clearly it is best to use soil classification and nomenclature throughout.[3] Then the results of research and experience can be utilized at all levels of generalization. It is difficult to see the need for the "natural land type." Assuming that "land types" could be somehow standardized and research results related to them, they still remain an inadequate basis for genetic classification. For this, we must fall back on soil classification. Future progress in taxonomic land classification seems to lie primarily along the line of improving our soil classification and of including better definitions of the categories, the individual units within the categories, and the geographic associations of taxonomic units. There appears to be no other reliable basis for a scientific classification. Conceivably, one might develop a nongenetic system, based wholly upon morphology, but the prospects are dim.

Classification of social units of land.—The very term "land" itself connotes use. The broad use classes include: (1) Cropping, (2) grazing, (3) forestry, (4) recreation, (5) mining, (6) urban, (7) public services (highways, railroads, airports, electric power lines, cemeteries, and so on), (8) wildlife preservation, and (9) protection (land managed to protect water supplies or other lands). Some of these are often combined, as for example, forestry, protection, recreation, and wildlife preservation. Besides, some land is essentially not capable of producing materials or services of value and may be called *wasteland*. One might add still another class as *idle land*—land capable of producing but not now being used.

The soil survey is concerned primarily with the first three use classes—cropping, grazing, and forestry—but also has a great deal to contribute to management plans for the others. Some kinds of soil can be used only in certain of these general use classes. That is, some are not useful for cropping but may be used for forestry or grazing. Other kinds of soil can be used in any of the ways listed, except perhaps for mining. Thus, often the same kind of soil has a different set of capabilities within these several broad use classes. Generally, of course, people tend to use the soils for the most intensive use for which they are economically capable. But there are many exceptions. Usually soils unsuitable for farming are used for forestry, recreational parks, and the like; but in a densely populated community on highly productive soils, some of those productive for crops may need to be used for wood lots, parks, and public services.

In the classification of specific tracts of land—farms, ranches, forests, pastures, or gardens—according to potential productivity, say for tax assessment, or of prospective tracts according to irrigability, assumptions of the use class must be made. The determination of the use class of a particular tract is partly a matter of the potential productivity of the kind of soil, and partly a matter of its geographic position and size in relationship to other kinds of soil, to existing or proposed roads, canals, wells, and markets, and to other land tracts.

[3] Except for miscellaneous land types as defined later.

For example, one cannot assign a soil area to use for crops unless the area is large enough for an economic unit. Thus, in regions of soil dominantly suited only to grazing or forestry, small areas of soils well suited to crops must be assigned to the other dominant use, except as they may be located strategically at a ranch or forest headquarters. Soils suitable for grazing cannot be so used, at least with full intensity, in the absence of a water supply. On the other hand, a small area of soil suited only to grazing or forestry, but surrounded by a large area of soil well suited for crops, may be little more than wasteland if no economical management plan can be developed for it.

Although distance from market does not directly affect the classification of taxonomic soil groups or land classes, it may greatly affect the classification of social land units or tracts. As a simple example, we might imagine a large area of Chestnut soils, well suited to the usual range of crops, extending out from a railway station. For the first 5 or 6 miles potatoes may be grown in the rotation. At greater distances from the market, wheat may dominate, first primarily for direct sale and, at greater distances, with increasing amounts used for stock feed. Finally, a place is reached where essentially all the crops, both forage and grain, are marketed through livestock. From an analysis of production and marketing costs a schedule may be prepared showing the percentage reduction in the basic rating of the units because of this distance factor. Then too, the distance must be corrected according to transport facilities: Poor roads must count more than good roads. The relationship between the effective distance and the rating factor is a second order differential equation, not a linear one, since the differences in costs of marketing per acre of cropland between, say, 5 and 6 miles are much greater than those between, say, 35 and 36 miles because of the difference in use.[4] Somewhat similar schedules are needed for land units with intermittent water supply.

The contrast between simple taxonomic land classification and the classification of specific land tracts may be illustrated in a system designed for classifying land according to irrigability. As a first step, a detailed soil classification and map is made for the area. For purposes of planning the layout of the project, the soils are grouped according to their arability under irrigation, without regard to location within the area. Such a soil grouping, or "land classification," and map predict what would be the result of irrigation for every part of the area. Then questions need to be raised about the accessibility of specific tracts of arable soils to roads and canals and about the combination of various soil areas into economic farm units. Some areas of soils cannot be irrigated economically, of course, because of their unresponsiveness or likelihood of deterioration, regardless of location; some other soil areas are highly suitable except where isolated in small

---

[4] Such an equation and its development is explained in A METHOD OF RURAL LAND CLASSIFICATION by Charles E. Kellogg and J. K. Ableiter. U. S. Dept. Agr. Tech. Bul. 469, 30 pp., illus. 1935.

tracts that cannot be reached economically or fitted into a farm unit; and areas of other kinds of soil are called irrigable if water can be supplied conveniently, but nonirrigable if water charges are high.

Thus, two quite different maps of the same area, both accurate, might be called "land classification according to irrigability." The first one represents the distribution of taxonomic groups and might better be called, perhaps, "a grouping of soils according to arability under irrigation." The second map, made on the basis of the first one with consideration of the additional factors of location, is a classification of geographically defined areas and should be called, perhaps, "a classification of land according to irrigability." This second map follows an accurate development of the first one from a detailed soil survey. Besides serving this immediate purpose of developing the land classification according to irrigability, the detailed soil survey is used for developing individual cropping and soil-management systems optimum for the specific kinds of soil that were grouped into the more general classes.

The classification of specific geographically located areas of land ordinarily must take account of those characteristics of place that influence decisions among the land-use classes and the decisions about relative intensity of use within the classes. In classifying land for tax assessment, for example, the soil units— types and phases—are first rated according to their productivity under alternative systems of management, within each use class, on a taxonomic basis. Secondly, the use classes of the geographic land tracts—sections, forties, or farms—are determined. Many tracts have mixtures of the use classes, say both cropping and grazing. Thirdly, ratings of the taxonomic groups within the use classes for each geographic land tract are adjusted according to distance from market, water supply, and so on, as these influence potential production.

This brief discussion has dealt only with a few principles and examples, but it is hoped that readers may test old schemes of "land classification" and new ones certain to be proposed. Further discussion would scarcely be appropriate in this *Manual*. No general guides for "land classification" exist, partly because of the wide variety of activities included by at least someone under this term.

LAND APPRAISAL

Rural land appraisals for determining the value of land as mortgage collateral or for tax assessment might be regarded as special kinds of land classification. Social land units, mainly farms, are evaluated in terms of potential production within the institutional and legal environment.

Tax assessment.—Some of the essentials of a method of land classification for tax assessment have been outlined as an example under the heading Multiformity of Land Classes (p. 28). For accurate work, a basic detailed soil survey is required, partly because of the need for indicating the relevant factors in relation to farm boundaries, and partly because adjustments will need to be made from time to time as conditions change.

If the basic soil factors are recorded, as in a basic soil survey, reinterpretations and regroupings in the light of changed conditions can be made easily and in an orderly fashion. But if they are not and only judgments of soil productivity, or of soil groups based on such judgments, are recorded, each revision will require a complete resurvey. For example, let us think of a modern detailed soil survey that indicates 150 or so separate kinds of soil for some area, like a county. These units may be grouped into 5 or 10 productivity classes, or into any other number of classes, according to the accuracy required and the availability of precise data for evaluating differences in responses to management. If, however, *only* these classes are mapped, the survey is soon out of date. If the soil types and phases are accurately mapped, the groupings can be readjusted and revisions made in the appraisal of specific tracts without additional mapping.

Besides the basic soil resource, the appraisal may need to take account of farm improvements—buildings, fences, and the like—according to the State laws governing appraisal. In some States improvements are not taxed; in most they are. If these improvements are appraised in terms of replacement value, absurd results may be had, say where previous owners have constructed buildings far larger and more elaborate than the farm unit requires. Often the laws require that land must be appraised according to its productivity in the most intensive possible use, say for crops, even though it is actually used for extensive grazing or forestry. In the various States special statutes may permit present use to carry some weight. Laws vary widely in the degree to which potential use of farm land for urban or suburban residences must be weighted in assessment. Presumably the ideal in assessment is to make appraisals, according to potential productivity, that differentiate fairly among all the properties. Everyone realizes that excessively high taxes are unfair. A great deal of land that has reverted to the State because of nonpayment of taxes would have remained in private hands had the assessments been reasonably based upon the productivity in such uses as forestry and grazing, instead of on a presumed productivity for farming. But very low taxes are also unfair. Speculators may be allowed to hold undeveloped or only partially developed land needed for settlement at little or no cost—land which they hope to sell or use later at great profit.

Before a proper job of soil groupings and alternative ratings for the various use groups can be developed, and especially before attempts are made to appraise social units, a study needs to be made of both common laws and statute laws that influence assessment. Then appropriate schedules can be developed and adjusted ratings of the taxonomic groups made, in terms of the combinations of present characteristics that need to be dealt with, for each property within the area. Nearly every area presents special problems.

Appraisal for loans.—An accurate detailed soil map with ratings of the individual soil types and phases according to crop potentialities, estimated yields, and long-time effects of the alternative management systems furnishes the best basis for estimating the productivity of a farm and its basic long-time value. It is, of course, helpful to have also records of the individual farm business.

The appraisal of a farm cannot be based, however, upon the soil alone. The distance from market and other characteristics of place must be considered as they affect the kinds of uses for the farm and the productivity of the farm unit. Buildings, fences, and other improvements need to be evaluated in relation to the potential use of the farm unit, as well as water supply, noxious weeds, and the like.

Besides the basic value of the land and its improvements in relation to potential use, the loan appraiser can scarcely escape taking account of the prospective manager of the farm and his skill in relationship to its potentialities.

SETTLEMENT OF NEW LANDS

For centuries land settlement was on a trial-and-error basis. Those fortunate enough to find responsive soil in an area large enough for effective community development, and able to adapt their practices to kinds of soil new to them, were successful. Many thousands of settlers were not so fortunate; their work and efforts came to little or nothing, and their most productive years were wasted.

Through the use of soil surveys these wastes can be largely avoided, at least those due to improper soil and lack of advanced knowledge of what soil management practices to follow. Some exceptions must be allowed for little known kinds of soils never before used by civilized man equipped with the tools and services of modern industry. But the number of these is really small outside the tropics.

It must be emphasized, however, that the soil survey of a new or undeveloped area needs to be correlated with soil conditions in known areas. The necessary predictions of crop adaptability, yields, and management requirements will need to be based, in new areas, upon research results and farm experience gained from similar soils elsewhere, although perhaps not identical ones.

In planning a community, the soil map is useful in locating roads, schools, and other public services in order to keep costs at a minimum and provide orderly settlement as compactly as possible. Helter-skelter settlement with individual settlers far from one another, even though on responsive soils, raises serious social problems and results in high costs for medical facilities, transport, and schools.

In a new area, usually the best procedure is to make a reconnaissance or schematic soil association map (as defined earlier) from existing data and scattered observations in order to identify the most promising places for settlement. This map serves for broad planning of highways and other public services. Then detailed soil surveys should follow in the various parts of the area according to priority of development, considering soil character and other relevant factors. Beyond these considerations, the use of the soil survey for settlement is not unlike its use in settled areas.

GUIDANCE OF PROSPECTIVE FARM BUYERS

The modern soil map and report furnish the prospective farm purchaser with more relevant information upon which to make a decision than does any other single publication. This point is important, and those writing soil survey reports need to bear it in mind. A part of the use of the soil survey for this purpose parallels its use for land appraisal for loans, already briefly outlined. In addition, it gives a picture of the surrounding land and the potentialities of community development. The soil map and report help a prospective buyer select the area in which he wants to buy before he gets down to considering a particular farm. The report explains the farming systems followed by other farmers, the crops grown, the market facilities, and so on. In short, the soil survey report and map should give the prospective buyer a clear picture of the principal potentialities and problems.

After reading from the soil map the kinds of soil on a farm he may be considering, the prospective buyer can consult the tables of yield predictions and management requirements and develop a tentative farm plan with budget estimates of expenses and income. For accuracy, these need to be adjusted to other soil differences due to past management. Where practicable, he should compare these estimates with other budgets from similar farms as another check.

No matter how accurate the soil map or complete the supporting data, purchasers should be advised to visit a farm before making a final decision. Factors that are important to an individual family defy accurate description in writing and figures.

LAND-USE PLANNING

Most land users have some sort of plan to guide their operations. Some farmers have only a simple plan of the crop pattern for the following year; others have carefully prepared plans in writing, with a map, for several years in advance—plans that are revised with the seasons. As science and technology are used more and more for optimum sustained production, individual farm planning becomes increasingly important. This kind of planning is usually called "farm planning," since it deals mainly with decisions made within farm boundaries.

The term "rural land use planning" on the other hand, is commonly used for policies and programs that influence the use of lands in a whole community or area containing many individual farms or other units of operation. Examples include the planning of irrigation or drainage districts, rural transport systems, electric power distribution lines, flood-control structures, large dams, public land acquisition, rural zoning, and the like.

Many county plans or goals have been made by farm leaders and agricultural advisers jointly. These vary widely in detail and scope.[5] For the best development of these plans or programs, a detailed soil survey and carefully generalized soil association map are most helpful. Because the soil survey for individual farm planning needs to be detailed, it is difficult to obtain a view of the soil resources in the whole community and in the contrasting parts of counties except with a soil-association map generalized from it.

For many planning purposes, it is helpful to the users to have the boundaries of soil associations as an overlay on the detailed soil map and also separately on a smaller scale map showing the roads, say on a scale of about 1 or ½ inch equals 1 mile. As has already been pointed out, the experience gained from pilot-research farms, demonstration farms, and from the analysis of other farms can be synthesized by soil associations in order to guide advisory programs and other public programs designed to eliminate handicaps for economic sustained production.

The planning of irrigation.—An especially detailed soil map is required in planning irrigation. This map is often a difficult one to make because soil characteristics need to be considered in relation to a very different environment than the natural one. Deep layers that contain soluble salts or that are impervious to water, which may have little or no influence on the soil under desert or semiarid conditions, may be very important to its behavior under irrigation. Soils that are well drained naturally may become swamped with extra water. The soil survey must predict such conditions and whether or not they may be overcome and, if so, by what methods.

Here, too, generalized maps, based upon the detailed ones, are needed for planning the transport and water facilities in the area as a whole and for arriving at a final map of irrigability as explained previously in the discussion of land classification.

The planning of drainage.—In principle, planning of drainage is similar to the planning of irrigation. Here also, soil characteristics of little influence in the natural state become very important when the soil is drained. Many expensive drainage projects have failed because the soils were unproductive after drainage. In some instances, the soils were very sandy, and after a brief period

---

[5] A large number of these have been developed. This is not the place to review this work in detail. A recent example, among a great many, is the one already cited—MONTGOMERY COUNTY [Alabama] FARM PROGRAM (c. 1947). A pioneer rural plan was published by Lee Roy A. Schoenmann as LAND INVENTORY FOR RURAL PLANNING IN ALGER COUNTY, MICHIGAN (Mich. Acad. Sci., Arts, and Letters 16: 329–361, illus. 1932) based upon the SOIL SURVEY OF ALGER COUNTY (U. S. Dept. Agr., 1934). Other examples include: LAND USE CLASSIFICATION IN MIDLAND COUNTY, MICHIGAN, LAND-USE PLANNING REPORT (Bur. Agr. Econ., U. S. Dept. Agr. and Mich. State Col. 1940); and AGRICULTURAL PLANNING, VALLEY COUNTY, MONTANA. (Bur. Agr. Econ., U. S. Dept. Agr., and Mont. State Col. 1941. [Processed.]).

of cultivation the organic matter disappeared and the soils became too loose and too dry in summer for crop growth. Others had organic soils so acid that enormous quantities of lime were required for raising the pH to that level necessary for crop plants. Such additions of lime, besides being costly, often worsen the problem of other nutrient deficiencies through unbalance.

Drainage of peat lands raises problems requiring the special attention of soil survey parties. After drainage, organic soils often shrink and settle unevenly. For this reason tile drainage frequently fails. The tiles may get out of position. In detailed soil surveys where drainage of such lands is proposed, through soundings and study of the deep materials, it is possible to predict such settling and recommend measures by which difficulties may be avoided. Often it is necessary to arrange for keeping the water table nearly constant through combined drainage and subirrigation, even using the same canals.

Public land acquisition.—Land purchase, as for blocking out National or State forests or grazing districts or for the development of public parks, needs to be planned in relation to the use capabilities of the whole area affected by the purchase units. The detailed soil survey is an essential basis for appraising individual parcels, and, if supplemented with a generalized map of soil associations, for planning the project boundaries. Such purchases can have pronounced influences on community development and, with proper planning, can reduce scattered settlement and otherwise assist the objectives of rural zoning.

The planning of large dams for water storage.—The effects of alternative locations and heights of the structures upon land use needs to be taken into account. By carefully plotting alternative pool lines on the detailed soil map, accurate comparisons can be made. Thus it may be found that one alternative may cover with water much more soil productive for crops than another. Then, after the pool line has been established, plans can be developed with a detailed soil map for the economic use of all partially flooded farm units, through reorganization, in order to keep the "taking line" (the line below which land is purchased) as near the pool line as possible and thus hold the area of unused land or public land around the pool to a minimum. In the margins of some pools, areas of highly productive soil are flooded only occasionally. Such areas may be used for crops to good advantage a large part of the time if attached to an economic farm unit. With a detailed soil survey, such planning can be done in an orderly way.

Planning measures for flood reduction.—Often planning for flood reduction involves the study of the soil conditions of a whole watershed in order to estimate infiltration rates, runoff, and the effects of land management and structures on runoff and erosion. Costs and benefits of alternative plans should be calculated. A detailed soil survey, supplemented by a generalized soil-association map, furnishes a very large part of the basic data for such planning. A full set of predictions and yield estimates under alternative systems of management for each mapping unit is essential for accurate results.

Rural zoning.—Ordinances are often developed by county governments to promote orderly use of the land.[6] Roads, schools, and other social services for scattered farms in areas generally unsuited to farming are very costly for other taxpayers. Such isolated settlers often increase the fire hazard in forests. By blocking out areas suited mainly to forestry, grazing, or recreational use, in which settlement for farming is not permitted, roads and schools may be provided for the community more efficiently. Accurate soil maps, along with interpretations made according to use capability, furnish a sound basis for developing such ordinances.

These few brief examples are only intended to give the reader an idea of the kinds of use to which soil surveys are often put in rural land-use planning. All such uses cannot be specifically anticipated in advance; but when a soil survey is undertaken in any area, supervisors should be fully aware of any such possible uses. Even though a rural zoning ordinance does not yet exist, for example, if it is clearly needed to solve serious problems of local government management, the soil survey work should be done in anticipation of its use for that purpose.

ASSESSING POTENTIALITIES FOR SPECIAL CROPS

The economical production, use, and marketing of many special crops depends upon having more than the minimum volume of production needed to support canneries, freezing units, or other special processing and marketing facilities. When a new enterprise of this sort is undertaken in a community, a large area, often split among many different farms, must be developed at once, along with the factory and marketing facilities. Special interpretations of the soil mapping units may be made for the crop, and interpretive maps prepared from the soil map showing classes of soils according to their use capabilities for the particular crop. Such maps serve as a sound basis for assessing the potentialities for the enterprise in a community and for indicating the particular farmers that may cooperate.

FOREST MANAGEMENT

Foresters are becoming increasingly aware of the importance of an understanding of soils and their relation to growth, stand composition, and other factors affecting optimum forest management. Even the incidence of certain forest diseases, like little-leaf of shortleaf pine for example, is related to groups of soils. The soil survey makes possible the synthesis of results from research and from experience and the orderly application of the available

---

[6] See the following: ELY, R. T., and WEHRWEIN, G. S. LAND ECONOMICS. 512 pp., illus. New York. 1940; and WEHRWEIN, G. S. THE ADMINISTRATION OF RURAL ZONING. Jour. Land and Pub. Util. Econ. 19: 264–291. 1943.

knowledge, in forest management in much the same way as in farm management.

ENGINEERING USES

Soil surveys are being used increasingly in engineering work, especially in highway and airport planning and construction and for predicting trafficability of heavy vehicles. The basic facts about soils needed to predict their behavior in fields include most of those needed to predict their behavior as subgrades or foundation materials. The several soil properties have different relevancies for the two interpretations—agricultural and engineering—but the same basic classification serves both.

Detailed soil maps are helpful first of all in planning locations for structures and for predicting the problems of construction and maintenance to be dealt with. Especially in the absence of detailed geological surveys, they are useful in locating such materials as sand, gravel, clay, and suitable "topsoil" for dressing banks and other areas to be planted.

For detailed highway and airport planning, a highly detailed original survey is usually needed on a scale of about 1:1,200, using the same basic soil classification as that described in this *Manual*, with such refinements as may be required, especially for indicating the physical properties of deep strata. After engineering tests on soil horizons have been made and classified by soil type, each type can be characterized and its behavior subsequently predicted without extensive testing. Classification by tests alone, unrelated to genetic soil types, gives little that can be used as a basis for prediction at a new or proposed site without additional time-consuming and costly testing.

Since the interpretation of soil classification and soil maps for engineering purposes is a highly specialized field in itself, the reader is referred to a special manual on the subject,[7] and to a summary of soil surveys in the United States as they pertain to engineering uses.[8]

OTHER USES

Soil surveys, besides their many widely recognized uses, also serve a host of others to which some attention must be given. For many areas they are the most complete base map and are so used in the absence of up-to-date topographic or planimetric maps. This fact, and the fact that detailed soil maps, detailed topographic maps, and detailed geological maps are often used to supplement one another, emphasizes the need for geodetic accuracy, standard scales in publication, standard symbols, and correct naming of features.

Soil maps have been used to locate and design pipelines. They are helpful in locating radio stations. With interpretation, they

---

[7] MICHIGAN STATE HIGHWAY DEPARTMENT. FIELD MANUAL OF SOIL ENGINEERING. Rev. ed., 304 pp., illus. Lansing. 1946.

[8] OLMSTEAD, F. R., HICKS, L. D., and BODMAN, G. B. ENGINEERING USE OF AGRICULTURAL SOIL MAPS. Highway Res. Bd. Bul. No. 22, 128 pp., illus. 1949.

can be used as maps of surface geology. They are useful in studying land form and geomorphological processes. With study of sample areas, they can be used to construct maps of the original vegetation and to predict successions of plant cover.

The hazards of nutritional deficiencies among plants and even among animals may be anticipated from soil maps where the relationships of deficiencies to soil types have been identified through correlative research at sample sites. In recent years, important relationships have been worked out between many soil types (and soil groups) and deficiences of such trace elements as copper, boron, manganese, molybdenum, iron, cobalt, and zinc, as well as of phosphorus, potassium, calcium, nitrogen, magnesium and sulfur. By no means all important soil types have been characterized, especially for the trace elements, and much more research is needed. As already explained, recommendations for an individual field depend partly on previous and current management as well as on soil type; yet the area where these deficiencies are likely, and the general practices to be followed, can be interpreted from a proper soil map.[9]

With generalized and schematic soil association maps, broadly defined agricultural potentialities and problems that relate to the soil or soil use can be seen regionally, nationally, or even on a world-wide basis of comparison.

INTERNATIONAL COORDINATION

Since all places in the world having the same combination of soil genetic factors have the same kind of soil, knowledge gained through research and experience in one place is relevant to all like places. Contrariwise, good practices for sustained production on one kind of soil may be wasteful or even ruinous on a different kind.

The need for close correlation between those engaged in soil surveying and other researches is obvious if proper definitions and predictions are to be developed for soil types and if full and accurate use is to be made of other research results. This is true internationally as well as nationally. To make optimum use of agricultural science in any country, it is essential to have a consistent world-wide scheme of soil definition and nomenclature. That is, the results of competently managed research on a well-defined Latosol, Podzol, or Chernozem are useful in all countries having soils like the ones investigated, regardless of where the work is done.

Much work has been done in this field of soil geography. More is needed. The unrealized opportunities for improving the planning of agricultural research and for increasing its effectiveness to all are very great. Fortunately, as this *Manual* is being prepared, greatly increased emphasis is being given to soil classification and mapping in many countries and to the exchange of soil scientists and of information about soils.

---

[9] See Ignatieff, as cited in the General Bibliography.

PREPARATION FOR FIELD WORK

Before going to the field for survey work, plans are made and the essential materials and equipment assembled.

WORK PLAN

Most soil survey work in the United States is conducted as an integral part of the soil research programs of the United States Department of Agriculture and the State agricultural experiment stations. Besides, other State and Federal research, service, and educational agencies cooperate in projects of special interest to them by furnishing personnel or materials.

Many technical details and the services of several kinds of specialists are involved in a soil survey. Besides the soil scientists in field and laboratory, at least some assistance, often a great deal, must be had from geologists, plant scientists, and others. Skilled photogrammetrists, cartographers, draftsmen, and editors are essential to the work. Several agencies are usually involved as participants or as interested users of the results.

A clear understanding of the work to be done and the rôle of each participant needs to be had at the start. The general specifications, plan, and assignment of professional workers are set forth in a *Soil Survey Work Plan*, drawn up by the supervisory scientist, with the help of those responsible for cartography and laboratory services, and agreeable to the sponsoring agencies. Above all, a qualified scientist needs to be selected for *party chief*. Upon him, more than upon any other individual, depends the thoroughness of the research and the quality of the final soil map and report.

The essential items of the *Soil Survey Work Plan* are:

1. Name, location, size, and boundaries of survey area. (Include sketch map for areas other than whole counties.)
2. A paragraph describing the principal physical features of the area.
3. The names of initiating and cooperating agencies.
4. Reasons for the survey, together with any special uses to be made of it.
5. Type of survey (detailed, detailed-reconnaissance, reconnaissance of soil associations) and features to be mapped, including any special features not included in the standards for a basic soil survey.
6. Field and publication scales for the maps.[1]
7. An annotated list of previous surveys of soil, relief, geology, or vegetation.[1]
8. Equipment and transport needed and agencies responsible for supplying.
9. Names of proposed workers (and agency of each) for soil survey party, including party chief.
10. Kind, scale, quality, source, and availability of base map materials and the primary control in the area.[1]
11. Scale and other features of map to be published and method of construction from field sheets.[1]
12. Plans for preparation and publication of report.

13. Date for initiating field work, location of first field headquarters, and estimated date for completion of field work.
14. Plans for supplementary laboratory work and scientists responsible for it.[2]
15. Estimated costs by contributing agencies:
    (a) Field mapping by man-days, including salaries, travel, and equipment.
    (b) Supplemental research and summaries for soil ratings and soil survey report.
    (c) Supplemental laboratory work.
    (d) Map preparation and editing.[1]
    (e) Publication.[1]

[1] Developed jointly with Cartographic Section.
[2] Developed jointly with laboratories of cooperating agencies.

ASSEMBLY OF CARTOGRAPHIC DATA

The use of good cartographic base material is essential for a successful soil survey. On it depends the accuracy of plotting the soil boundaries and symbols, the rate of progress, the methods and costs of map construction, and the quality of the published map. Since all these items directly affect the cost and accuracy of soil maps, supervisory scientists need to give the assembly of cartographic materials first priority once an area is selected for survey.

Even the order in which areas are taken up for soil survey should be guided by a study and analysis of available cartographic data. That is, no area should be selected for survey in advance of aerial photography or equally good base material unless the most compelling reasons exist for doing so; and areas having good topographic base maps made with the aid of aerial photographs should be given preference.

Preliminary study and analysis.—Before its selection for use in the field, cartographic material needs to be studied in relation to all operations in both the field and the cartographic office, considering accuracy, economy, any special needs of a cooperating agency, and efficiency of use by the field party and by the cartographers. All available cartographic material is considered. Some may be helpful even though it is not used directly as the principal base.

If new aerial photography is under contract, usually a soil survey should be postponed until the photographs are released. The availability of new topographic maps, still in manuscript form and not yet generally available, should influence the selection of a specific area. Although uncontrolled aerial mosaics may appear useful at first glance, in the final analysis they may be more expensive than individual aerial photographs because of poor quality, lack of stereoscopic coverage, and inaccuracies. Topographic maps made with high standards of accuracy may have to be discarded because of insufficient detail and small scale. The efficient use of aerial photographs may be limited in some areas by insufficient control for constructing an accurate base map.

Without such an analysis, an area may be selected for which so little good material is yet available that costs for field work or map preparation, or both, may be very high; or a poor combination of materials may be selected from among those available. Such failures in initial planning lead to inaccurate soil boundaries, excessive costs, and substandard published maps. Plans for the survey are worked out jointly by soil scientists and cartographers, so that all costs—for field work, map compilation, and publication—are taken into account. A minor change in field operations, for example, may have a large influence on later costs.

Locating material.—So many agencies obtain aerial photography, prepare aerial mosaics and planimetric and topographic maps, and establish control that the field scientists cannot be expected to know all that is available or about to become available. Although some agencies release map information periodically, these reports do not cover many activities in planning and operational stages. Since most Federal mapping agencies and many commercial firms maintain offices in the Washington area, the Cartographic Section of the Division of Soil Survey maintains liaison with nearly all map-making groups. It is a regular function of the cartographic office to maintain records of all available materials and of work in progress and to seek materials from all agencies for any new survey area. In this way, it is possible to obtain complete information on the status of aerial photography, mapping, and control activities for any area in the United States.

Selection of scale.—Many factors need to be weighed together to determine the best scale to use for a soil survey.

The purpose of the map needs first consideration. Since most detailed soil maps are designed to carry the data needed in planning efficient farming systems, the map must have large enough scale to indicate areas of significance in farming, either by boundaries or by defined symbols. This does not mean that the scale needs to be large enough so that field boundaries, terraces, ditches, and farm buildings can be plotted directly on the soil map. Most farm plans should be drawn on enlarged aerial photographs or other large sheets so that details important only to the specific farm may be written on them. Soil maps on such large scales would be too unwieldly to file and use. The scale of the soil map needs only to be great enough to permit accurate plotting and recording of the significant data.

If the survey is reconnaissance—with a generalized or schematic map of soil association and only samples of each association in detail—the scale can be much smaller.

Generally, the scale of mapping increases with the intricacy and complexity of the soil pattern and especially with intensity of soil use or potential use. The patterns of soil types and phases are very complex in areas of Ground-Water Podzols and Half Bogs or of Lithosols and Alpine Meadow soils, for example, but the low potentialities for use argue against the practicality of highly detailed mapping except in sample areas to define the mapping complexes or associations. Where small areas of soil must be enclosed with boundaries, the scale needs to be large enough to show them without exaggeration and to permit placing clear symbols in them. If field sheets have a large proportion of the symbols outside of the areas they represent and keyed into them with an arrow, the scale is too small, excessive detail is being mapped, the symbols are too long, or there is some combination of these evidences of poor planning.

The scale should be no larger than necessary to show the details required for the objective of the survey. A large increase in scale increases the number of separate sheets to deal with, the amount of joining of sheets, and costs for compilation and reproduction.

The scale of manuscript maps made in the field or generalized from highly detailed field sheets needs to be reasonably close to the publication scale. Except in special surveys, where the field sheets indicate data not to be published, and photographed copies of them serve the special purpose, the field scale should rarely be more than twice the publication scale. Otherwise the published map is likely to be too complex for easy reading or data on the field sheets must be omitted. The selection of only part of the data from the field sheets increases compilation costs and the chances for error. Some poor soil maps have been made at great cost by publishing at 1 inch to the mile (1:63,360) work done in the field at 4 inches to the mile (1:15,840). If a field scale of around 1:7,920 is clearly needed and the map is to be published at 1:31,680, a manuscript map (besides the field sheets) ordinarily is required at some scale above 1:15,840.

In the United States most detailed basic soil maps are now made with field scales between 1:15,000 and 1:20,000 and published at 1:24,000 and 1:31,680. Yet, very detailed surveys, say in irrigated areas or other intensive areas of complex soils, may be made at field scales as large as 1:5,000. For detailed highway and airport planning, soil maps are often required at scales as low as 1:1,000, but those rarely need to be reproduced in large editions. Scales for soil association maps made in reconnaissance surveys may run from 1:20,000 to 1:500,000, depending on the purpose.

Except for detailed-reconnaissance surveys, uniform scale should be used throughout an area. Mappers using base material of varying scale are likely to map the soils in varying detail also. A lack of uniformity in the kinds and sizes of soil areas shown greatly reduces the usefulness of the soil map, since it presents a distorted picture of the soil pattern. Such distortion can be seen on a few published soil maps for which field sheets of unlike scales had been assembled to a uniform scale.

Much cartographic base material is flexible enough to permit reproduction at a number of scales for field use. Many aerial negatives have a scale of 3.168 inches equal 1 mile (1:20,000). Prints of excellent quality and detail can be had at scales from 2 inches equal 1 mile (1:31,680) to 8 inches equal 1 mile (1:7,920). Of course, aerial film may be at various scales; yet reduction and enlargements are usually satisfactory within one-half to three times the original scale. Aerial mosaics or planimetric and topographic maps can be considerably enlarged or reduced to appropriate scales for field mapping.

The cartographic laboratory of the Division of Soil Survey is equipped to prepare enlargements and reductions of aerial photographs, aerial mosaics, planimetric maps, and topographic maps as may be required in cooperative soil surveys.

Since it is usually possible to obtain the base material at a proper and uniform scale, it is important to decide on a definite scale for the soil survey in the planning stage, and to make the original requests for material at that scale. This is far more economical than attempting changes in scale after the base material is received. Such changes may require recopying and cause avoidable delays.

Factors determining type of material selected.—Frequently two or more kinds of cartographic material suitable as bases for soil mapping may be available. An area may be wholly or partly covered by two or more types of aerial photographs, aerial mosaics, planimetric maps, or topographic maps. The choice of materials depends upon their relative advantages for the whole job, including map compilation and reproduction as well as field use. The base material selected must be adequate for the whole job, not for just one activity alone.

Uncontrolled aerial mosaics, for example, may appear advantageous for field use, yet they may be wholly unsatisfactory for constructing the final map because of inaccuracies. Obsolete or substandard maps present similar problems. Such maps often require so many revisions that their value is offset by time-consuming corrections in both field and office. Work plans calling for the use of such materials, made without analyses of the whole process, have led to high costs in relation to the accuracy of the published map.

Available materials of possible use may include aerial photographs, of single or multiple lens, aerial mosaics of varying accuracy, photo maps, planimetric maps, or topographic maps. If no suitable base maps or aerial photographs are available, and the survey must be made, the field scientist may need to make a map with the plane table or, in wild heavily wooded country, with the compass. (See pp. 455 to 463.) Where two or more types of base material must be used, careful evaluation should be made to obtain uniformity in accuracy, planimetric detail, and scale. Other uses of the survey besides publication influence the selection. If, for example, a detailed classification of land tracts is to be made, as in irrigation planning or in assessment, a different base may be better and cheaper than that employed for the usual basic soil survey. Time is sometimes an important element in selection. Material readily available may be used even though better material will be available at some later date. If differences in quality are great, the survey schedule should be altered if possible.

Generally, the best base materials for detailed soil surveys, in order of preference, are single-lens aerial photographs, controlled aerial mosaics, transformed multiple-lens aerial photographs, standard-accuracy topographic quadrangles, standard-accuracy planimetric maps, and original plane-table maps. It is best of all to have both good aerial photographs and accurate topographic maps.

Relatively large-scale reconnaissance surveys are best made on controlled aerial mosaics or standard-accuracy topographic or planimetric maps. Small-scale reconnaissance surveys are made on many types of general maps having good accuracy and planimetric detail or on aerial photo indexes.

Since a complete soil survey is expensive, proper selection of the base material can have a great influence on efficiency. Frequently mistakes in planning are caused by overemphasizing the cost of the base material. Where aerial photography is available, costs for pictures rarely exceed 1 to 2 percent of the cost of the entire field work. Even original aerial photography would seldom exceed 5 to 10 percent of the total. Yet the base material frequently means the difference between an excellent soil map and a poor one. Costs of base material need to be weighed against its use in all operations—field mapping, map preparation, and publication. The use of low-cost materials may give apparent savings for the field sheets, but result in doubling the costs of map preparation and reproduction. Since conditions vary widely from place to place, no hard-and-fast rule can be given for selecting base material. Each area must be studied as an individual problem.

Procedure for obtaining base material.—After the work plan has been developed and the base material decided upon, it is furnished through Cartographic Section or, by arrangement with them, directly from other sources. Plans should be made as far in advance as possible, since many agencies have small staffs available for supplying photographic prints and other materials and some delays are inevitable.

KINDS OF BASE MATERIALS

The characteristics, advantages, and disadvantages of the principal kinds of base material used in soil mapping are outlined in the following paragraphs.

Aerial photographs.—Nearly all detailed soil mapping is now done on aerial photographs. Improvements in them and in their use and interpretation are being made continually.

Types.—Oblique and vertical pictures may be regarded as two basic types of aerial photography. Multiple-lens photography is a combination of the two. Single-lens vertical photographs are best for soil mapping, although oblique and multiple-lens photographs can be used. Thus emphasis in this *Manual* is given to single-lens vertical photographs flown to the specifications of the United States Department of Agriculture.

Stereoscopic and alternate coverage.—Specifications of the United States Department of Agriculture for aerial photography require the overlap in line of flight to be about 60 percent; whereas the overlap between adjacent flight lines averages around 30 percent. This overlap, with which all ground images appear on two or more photographs, permits stereoscopic vision of any ground object within the area. Such photography is said to have *stereoscopic coverage;* and adjoining photographs are called *stereoscopic pairs.*

If every other photograph in a continuous stereoscopic series is removed, the remaining series is called *alternate coverage,* and adjoining photographs, *alternate pairs.* Alternate pairs of photographs overlap only about 20 percent—too little to permit stereoscopic study of the entire area. Such alternate coverage is inadequate for constructing base maps by photogrammetric methods based upon stereoscopic coverage.

Contacts and enlargement.—Aerial photography is exposed on film or glass negatives at a predetermined scale and fixed negative size. The scale of the photograph depends on the height of the aircraft and the focal length of the camera. The size of the negative varies with the aerial camera.

The scale of aerial photography depends on the purpose of the photographs. Most of the aerial photography for the United States Department of Agriculture is flown with an 8.25-inch focal length aerial camera at altitudes of about 15,000 feet. The resulting scale is approximately 3.168 inches equal 1 mile, or 1:20,000. Such negatives give satisfactory reductions and enlargements within a scale range of about 1:7,500 to 1:32,000. Most needs for soil mapping can be met within this range of scale.

Aerial photographs made directly from the original negatives are called *contact prints.* These have the same scale as the negatives. In contact printing no rectification of errors or scale changes can be made, although poorly exposed negatives can be improved. Contact prints are the most economical to make. When properly processed they are best in quality.

Aerial photographs may be readily enlarged or reduced; this is one of their great advantages as a base for soil mapping. The process requires projection of light through the negative and precise adjustments for scale. It is therefore slower and more expensive than contact printing. Some detail is lost in the preparation of enlargements, but with skillful operators using modern processing equipment and the original negatives the loss is negligible.

Enlarging has certain advantages. With adequate ground control, all prints in an area can be brought to a nearly uniform scale. Prints having excess tilt, causing displacement of objects and scale changes, can be rectified to minimize the errors. Pictures for areas having photography at two or more contact scales can be brought to a common scale. Such operations require more time than simple enlarging; and for scale-ratioing or rectification, adequate ground control is essential. Nonetheless, later savings may more than offset the cost of bringing pictures to a common scale.

Satisfactory enlargements from average film should not be expected at scales requiring more than a 2½-diameter enlargement from the contact negative. The photograph becomes grainy and much detail is lost.

Photographs flown for the United States Department of Agriculture are usually made with aerial cameras having a negative size of either 7 by 9 inches or 9 by 9 inches. Enlargements, of course, increase the size of the photograph as well as the scale. The following shows how the size of sheets, in inches, varies with enlargement:

Contact prints (Scale 1:20,000 3.168 in. = 1 mile) Inches	Enlargements (Scale 1:15,840 4.00 in. = 1 mile) Inches	Enlargements (Scale 1:7,920 8.00 in. = 1 mile) Inches
7 by 9	11 by 14	22 by 27
9 by 9	14 by 14	27 by 28

Photo indexes.—Photographic indexes are available for most of the photography available in the United States Department of Agriculture, and in other government agencies as well. These are prepared by fastening the individual photographs of an area together. The images are matched and the photographs overlapped so that all marginal data are visible. The assembly is then photographed at a smaller scale, often in several sheets for convenient handling. Most indexes available in the United States Department of Agriculture are on sheets about 20 inches by 24 inches and have a scale of around 1 inch to the mile (1:63,360). Four to five index sheets cover an average county.

Photo indexes are useful for determining the number and location of individual photographs within an area. Since the low cost of the indexes is easily made up in the time saved, they should always be obtained when available. They are also useful for schematic mapping.

Advantages and disadvantages.—The greatest single advantage of aerial photography in soil surveying is the wealth of ground detail shown. Physical and cultural features that it would be impractical to show on base maps are represented in infinite detail on the aerial photograph. Field boundaries, isolated trees, small clumps of bushes, rock outcrops, buildings, and plant cover all assist the soil scientist in orientation and in plotting his data. Photographs increase both the speed and accuracy of his work. Streams, lakes, and swamps that are difficult to plot accurately by ground methods become control on the photographs.

Because large areas can be photographed rapidly, field scientists may be supplied with highly detailed base material in a short time. Compared to other methods of obtaining original bases with comparable detail, aerial photography is by far the most rapid and economical method. Isolated areas, difficult to map by ground methods, are no handicap to the photographic aircraft, provided suitable landing fields are within operating distances. Aerial pictures are especially helpful to the soil scientist faced with the problem of making accurate soil surveys in wild areas proposed for agricultural development.

Stereoscopic vision, or the ability to see depth, is another advantage of aerial photographs in soil mapping. With photographs having overlap adequate to permit stereoscopic study, the soil scientist has before him a relief model of the area, complete with all of its intricate cultural and physical detail. Such a model affords an opportunity for study of the area in advance of field work. His traverses can be laid out most effectively. The study of plant cover, relief, drainage patterns, and other details helps greatly in planning the field work. Streams, swamps, and other features may be tentatively drawn in advance.

Adequate base maps having the necessary detail to carry the soil survey data can be constructed economically and within a reasonable time from aerial photographs, provided that the photography is of good quality, that the ground control is adequate, that modern photogrammetric facilities are available, and that qualified photogrammetrists supervise the work.

Despite these advantages, aerial photography has some disadvantages and limitations in soil surveying. Photographs are inferior to good topographic or planimetric maps in the following ways: (1) Elevations are not shown; (2) the photographs lack a precisely uniform scale throughout the area because of variations in ground elevations and altitudes of the photographic aircraft; (3) the soil scientist is forced to handle more sheets than when using large maps, resulting in more matching, joining, and filing; (4) differences of scale between adjoining photographs create some minor difficulties in matching and transferring soil boundaries from one photograph to another; (5) distances and directions cannot be so accurately measured because of distortions due to tilt, displacement, and other inherent errors; and (6) although far more detail is shown than on standard maps, it is not always so legible and more skill is required to interpret it. Many details on aerial photographs, such as field boundaries, fence rows, wooded areas, and crops are ephemeral and change more rapidly than the selected features shown on a standard map. For this reason old photographs may be more difficult to use than good maps made from them about the same date as they were taken. Yet these limitations are small in relation to the advantages.

Procedure for obtaining.—Approximately 90 percent of the United States has been photographed during the past 15 years. The major portion of this photography is suitable for soil mapping. Much of it is old and difficult to use because of changes in vegetation and cultural detail. Areas are being continually reflown, however, as changes justify.

Once the survey area is selected the order for photographs should be placed as soon as possible. Such requests should give the exact boundaries of the proposed survey, the scale of photography needed, whether stereoscopic or alternate coverage is to be used, and the date the survey is to commence. Any special requirements, such as weight of paper or finish, should be added also. Aerial film held by other Federal agencies is normally available on loan to the Cartographic Section for the preparation of reproductions. Because of limited facilities, however, it is necessary to have some photographic prints prepared by the agency having the original film. As prints from much of the aerial film are in great demand, it often takes a long time to get prints or enlargements.

In estimating the time required to obtain original aerial photography, time must be allowed for preparing specifications, awarding contracts, photographing the area, and inspection and acceptance of the work. Perhaps the most uncertain factor is weather. The frequency of suitable days for photographic flying varies in different parts of this country and in different seasons. In places aerial photography taken at some seasons is better than that taken in others. For example, the best photography in the southeastern part of the United States is had during the winter months, when the vegetation least obscures the ground.

Costs.—The cost of original aerial photography varies greatly, depending on the local weather conditions, availability of airfields, and so on. That flown to specifications of the United States Department of Agriculture has varied considerably in different contracts from year to year. During the 10-year period 1939-49, yearly average costs varied from $1.93 per square mile in 1939 to $4.06 in 1945. Costs in 1949 average $2.71 per square mile, or less than one-half cent per acre.

Reproductions from original film are furnished from other agencies at rates based on costs of labor and materials. Within the United States Department of Agriculture unit costs in 1950 for reproduction were as follows:

Quantity:	Contact prints (1:20,000) Each	Enlargement (1:15,840) Each
1 to 5	$0.80	$1.55
6 to 100	.50	1.00
Over 100	.45	.90
County coverage	.40	.80

Where original aerial photography is available the cost of contact prints in stereoscopic coverage for a county is about 26 cents per square mile. For stereoscopic coverage with 1:15,840 enlargements the cost per square mile is 52 cents. These costs are a minor fraction of the total for a basic soil survey.

Aerial mosaics.—Aerial mosiacs are made by assembling and matching individual aerial photographs to form a continuous photographic image of an area. A few photographs may be used to cover a small area, or hundreds of them may be assembled for a large one. Several methods of assembly may be used, and the results vary widely in accuracy and usefulness.

Types.—The two general types of aerial mosaics are the uncontrolled and the controlled. The uncontrolled mosaic is made simply by matching like images on adjoining photographs without the use of ground control. No corrections are made for scale, tilt, or displacement. Since the photographs are matched by picture images only, without geographic control of their position, an uncontrolled mosaic is not suitable for accurate mapping and is difficult to use in map construction. In making a controlled mosaic, the photographs are adjusted to ground control; distances and directions are measurable; and the individual photographs are brought to correct scale and corrected for tilt and displacement. Each photograph is matched and adjusted so that image points on the photograph fall in their true geographic positions on the map grid. Since a controlled mosaic closely approaches the accuracy of a good planimetric map, the soil scientist can use it as a base in soil surveying.

Between the inaccurate, uncontrolled mosaic, on the one hand, and the accurate, controlled one, on the other, are a wide variety of semicontrolled mosaics for which different forms of ground control are used. Thus mosaics vary greatly and must be carefully checked for adequacy before use in detailed soil mapping.

Advantages and disadvantages.—An aerial mosaic has the advantage of covering a large area in one photograph. Thus fewer sheets need be matched. Mosaics can be made to cover a specific area, like a township, a small watershed, or a drainage basin. Where controlled mosaics are available, their accuracy over that of the individual photographs is also an advantage to the soil scientist in plotting soil boundaries and in transferring them to adjoining sheets.

In reproducing sheets for field use from a mosaic, a small margin of overlap can be retained, or the sheets can be reproduced to match without overlap. This is an advantage, since the soil scientist frequently has difficulty in matching adjoining aerial photographs that have wide margins of overlap.

A major disadvantage of aerial mosaics in soil surveying, as compared to overlapping photographs, is that mosaics themselves cannot be used for stereoscopic study of the area. The great value of such advance study of an area has already been emphasized.

As with planimetric and topographic maps, the accuracy of mosaics cannot always be assessed by their appearance. They must be field checked. Extreme difficulty may be had in the field with a mosaic that appears in the office to be of top quality. Even though an uncontrolled or semicontrolled mosaic may be usable in the field, it may be impossible to construct an accurate map for publication except at great additional expense. Thus the whole job should be considered when planning the use of an aerial mosaic.

Preparation.—The Cartographic Section of the Division of Soil Survey is equipped to prepare a limited number of controlled aerial mosaics suitable for soil mapping in areas with adequate ground control already established. The normal procedure is as follows: Obtain all ground control in the area, plot it, lay out the projection, and construct a radial plot; obtain the original aerial film; restitute all prints to fit the controlled grid, using care in the processing to insure a uniform tone and quality; trim the photographs, apply the adhesive, and adjust and assemble the prints on the mosaic board; prepare the necessary sheet borders, titles, and footnotes; make copy negatives of the complete mosaic; and reproduce the number of copies required.

Procedure for obtaining.—Where it is best to use controlled mosaics for a soil survey, the request for such work should be made well in advance. Facilities are not available for preparing mosaics for all soil surveys, nor should mosaics be recommended unless they will expedite field work, use of field sheets by co-operating agencies, and map publication.

Costs.—The cost of aerial mosaics for a soil survey is naturally higher than for the individual pictures used; yet in some areas the use of a good controlled mosaic may reduce the total cost of the survey. Part of the costs may be charged to the normal cost of the map preparation. Obtaining control data, preparing the control plot, and making the necessary sheet layouts are a normal part of the map preparation in many areas. The aerial prints have to be supplied to the field party anyway; therefore only the operations of assembling, adjusting, and reproducing the mosaic are added costs.

The cost of mosaics is generally less than that of preparing a planimetric map for the soil survey and higher than that for individual aerial photographs.

Photomaps.—The photomap is a form of aerial mosaic. Unlike the conventional mosaic, physical and cultural features are shown as they are on a planimetric map, and the sheets are laid out uniformly on a definite projection, as is done with standard topographic or planimetric maps. Photomaps are usually reproduced in large quantities by offset lithography or some similar process. Frequently, the planimetry is shown in color. Color emphasizes and gives greater legibility to planimetric detail, for it contrasts with the black-and-white photographic background.

Types.—No fixed standards have been established for photomaps. Although good accuracy may be generally assumed, because of the expense of constructing and reproducing a photomap, the soil scientist should test the accuracy of a photomap before using it in the field.

Photomaps are usually published in sheets in minutes of latitude and longitude depending on the scale; but in sectionized parts of the United States, the sheets may be laid out to cover one or more townships.

Photomaps vary widely, depending on scale and purpose. Some are published with only grid lines and appropriate titles and foot-notes; others show the usual planimetric features—roads, drainage, buildings, railroads, power lines, and the like—sharply defined with appropriate standard symbols, and with place names for the prominent features. On printed copies of some photomaps the planimetric detail is indicated by overprints in color—drainage in blue, cultural features in black, and special features in other appropriate colors. Such photomaps are sometimes called *planisaics*. A few photomaps include topography or terrain form lines, with the contours or form lines printed in brown, as on standard topographic quadrangles. These are called *toposaics*. Photomaps with contours to show exact topography can usually be assumed to be well constructed and accurate. Where approximate form lines of the terrain are shown instead, the photomap is probably made to less precise standards.

Three general types of photomaps can be roughly defined as follows: (1) Those reproduced in small editions by photography rather than lithography, in which the photographic background appears like it would in the aerial photograph, with lines and symbols in black or white lines on this background; (2) those printed in large editions by offset lithography in black and white, with planimetric line work overrun in black on a photographic halftone background made with a fine dot screen; and (3) those reproduced by offset lithography in two or more colors, with the photographic background shown by halftone screens in black or grey and the planimetry, contours, or other special features overrun in appropriate contrasting colors.

Advantages and disadvantages.—Since the photomap is an advanced stage of the aerial mosaic, it has many of the same characteristics, advantages, and disadvantages. The delineation of cultural and drainage features is a major advantage over the conventional controlled mosaic, since it eliminates or reduces the possibility of errors in interpretation of planimetric detail and the resulting errors in soil boundaries that may occur when mosaics are used. The soil surveyor normally spends less time classifying and delineating such detail with a recent photomap than with an aerial mosaic.

Normally, the photomap can be relied upon to be more precise than the conventional mosaic. Photomaps sufficiently precise to meet the standards for published soil maps can be used readily in the map assembly.

The disadvantages of the photomap are similar to those of the controlled mosaic. Photomaps cannot be used for stereoscopic study of an area. This is a handicap, but not so great a one as that encountered with the conventional mosaic, on which physical and cultural details are not delineated.

Because of methods used in producing them in large numbers, photomaps frequently lack the photographic detail found on photographic copies of a mosaic. Unless exceptionally fine screens are used in the offset lithography, the photographic detail reproduced is not of high quality.

Procedure for obtaining.—Photomaps prepared by other organizations, like other base materials, are obtained through the Cartographic Section. Full information on the accuracy of photomaps needs to be had before their use is recommended. It is not practical to prepare photomaps for use in soil surveying alone.

Accurate identification of drainage and cultural features **require** field editing.

From time to time, however, photomaps may be produced for publishing a soil map. A controlled mosaic can be constructed in advance of field mapping and used by the soil scientist as a base for mapping. The surveyor classifies the cultural and drainage features on the mosaic while making the soil survey. By using the original mosaic as a base, and preparing color separations for drainage, culture, and soils, the Cartographic Section can prepare the soil map as a photomap.

Cost.—A photomap costs more than a conventional controlled mosaic, because costs for field editing, drafting the cultural and drainage features, and making lithographic reproductions must be added. The cost of a soil map as a photomap should be comparable to that for the conventional soil map, provided color tints for soils were omitted from the photomap.

Topographic maps of standard accuracy.—A topographic map presents both horizontal and vertical positions of the physical features of a land area on a flat plane at definite scales. Published maps usually show such cultural features as roads, railroads, and buildings in black; drainage features in blue; and contour lines in brown. Some also show additional features, such as vegetation, in overprints of green or other colors.

Most topographic maps published by the United States Geological Survey and other Federal maps meeting these requirements carry marginal notes indicating compliance with the National standards of map accuracy. The standards for horizontal accuracy of maps published at scales larger than 1:20,000 prescribe that not more than 10 percent of the tested points shall be in error by more than one-thirtieth of an inch. On maps published at scales smaller than 1:20,000, the error shall not be more than one-fiftieth of an inch. These limits of accuracy apply only to positions of well-defined points, like roads, monuments, large structures, and railroads, which are readily visible and which can be plotted at the scale of the map within one-hundredth of an inch. Standards for vertical accuracy require that not more than 10 percent of the tested elevations be in error by more than one-half of the contour interval.

Types.—Because of the prescribed standards of accuracy, topographic maps vary little, even though published by different agencies. Some differences may be noted in format, scales, boundaries of latitude and longitude, and classification and presentation of planimetric detail—differences due primarily to needs for meeting specific requirements.

Standard topographic maps are published in quadrangles bounded by parallels of latitude and meridians of longitude. Generally, topographic quadrangles are 30 minutes, 15 minutes, 7½ minutes, or 3¾ minutes of latitude and longitude. Scales vary with topography and contour interval. The most usual publication scales are 1:24,000, 1:31,680, 1:48,000, 1:62,500, and 1:63,360.

Maps of smaller scale are useful to the soil scientist only for reconnaissance mapping. Few topographic maps are published at scales larger than 1:24,000.

Advantages and disadvantages.—The reliable accuracy of standard topographic maps gives them definite advantages in measuring distances and directions. The topographic pattern is very helpful to an understanding of soils and in the study of drainage, irrigation, and erosion cycles. The planimetric detail on the maps relieves the soil surveyor of a part of this task when mapping soils.

As a base for detailed soil mapping, the topographic quadrangle lacks the ground detail—field boundaries, isolated trees and bushes, fences, and similar features—that are shown on a good aerial photograph or mosaic. The small scale of many topographic quadrangles and the lack of coverage for large areas are further disadvantages. Drainage patterns on the standard topographic quadrangle are not shown in the detail needed for soil maps. Some old topographic maps are not accurate and need a great many revisions. The topographic maps of recent years, made from aerial photographs, are much more accurate.

In planning the use of topographic quadrangles in the preparation of soil maps for publication it must be recalled that a great deal more is involved than simply transferring soil boundaries to the quadrangles. Their use may or may not reduce costs, depending on the project.

Where recent, large-scale topographic quadrangles cover all, or a large part, of a soil survey area they are very useful in publishing the soil map. The use of such accurate quadrangles eliminates the necessity of constructing a base, which is especially helpful in areas with much culture. Then too, in densely wooded areas an accurate topographic map shows more points for location than an air photo. Such quadrangles serve only as a manuscript base, however, even after they are assembled into sheets of the size needed for the soil map. It is still necessary to transfer the soil data to this manuscript and prepare glass negatives or nonphotographic metal-mounted blue-line manuscript maps[1] for the color separations that show culture, soils, and drainage. These color separations are then drafted or engraved, new lettering layouts are prepared, and the printed lettering is applied to the color separations. Plates for the soil separation tints are then made and the various tints blocked out. Composite proofs are prepared and edited. The complete color separations are then copied, lithographic plates made, and the lithographic copies printed.

With old topographic quadrangles, made to less precise standards and requiring much revision, it may cost more to prepare the soil map than to make a new base from aerial photographs. The difficulties of transferring soil boundaries and symbols from the aerial photographs and adjusting them to fit old

---

[1] See Notes on Map Compilation and Reproduction, Appendix III.

quadrangles, and of revising the planimetry, more than offset the saving made by using them.

Only recent large-scale topographic quadrangles covering most of the survey area are recommended for use as a base. It is best of all if both aerial photographs and recent topographic maps made from aerial photographs are available.

Procedure for obtaining.—Standard topographic maps are published mainly by the Topographic Branch of the United States Geological Survey, the United States Coast and Geodetic Survey, and the Army Map Service of the Corps of Engineers.

The Cartographic Section of the Division of Soil Survey receives new lists and new topographic quadrangles as they are published and can supply available topographic maps needed for soil surveys. In addition, the Cartographic Section can supply information about areas in progress, expected dates of completion, and details concerning the topographic mapping program. Frequently preliminary proofs or copies of manuscript material may be obtained in advance of publication, where the need is urgent. When aerial photographs are supplied for a soil survey the Cartographic Section normally forwards all available standard topographic quadrangles as well, since such maps are helpful as reference for place names and for soil study, even though not used as the mapping base.

Costs.—The topographic quadrangle of standard accuracy is expensive to construct and publish. It serves many useful purposes, besides serving as a planimetric base for soil maps.

Planimetric maps of standard accuracy.—A planimetric map presents the horizontal position of the physical features of an area on a flat plane at definite scales. Unlike the topographic maps, no vertical distances are indicated. Otherwise, they are usually published in a form like topographic maps. Although no generally accepted precise standards for planimetric maps have been established, many mapping agencies have established standards that approach or equal those for topographic maps. Only such accurate planimetric maps are used for soil mapping.

Types.—Although standards for planimetric maps vary more than those for topographic maps, they are usually published in quadrangles similar to topographic maps and at approximately the same scales. Some differences result from variations in the map needs of the agencies preparing them. As a base for soil mapping, these differences are minor, compared to accuracy.

Advantages and disadvantages.—Planimetric maps have some of the same advantages of topographic maps as a base for soil surveying. A major exception is the omission of topography so valuable for soil study and interpretation. Then too, accuracy is less certain. Where accuracy is equal to that of good topographic maps, planimetric maps are helpful, even though the soil mapping is done on aerial photographs.

Procedure for obtaining.—As with standard topographic maps, the Cartographic Section receives copies of published planimetric quadrangles and can obtain them when needed. Where available, they are normally supplied with the aerial photographs for reference.

Cost.—Although cheaper than topographic maps, accurate planimetric maps cost more than the conventional controlled mosaics for comparable areas.

Other types of maps.—Many other types of maps are published by public and private agencies. These range from the small-scale road maps distributed by oil companies to the large-scale detailed maps used in city planning. Most of these are designed, constructed, and reproduced to meet a special purpose. Certain details on such maps are usually emphasized to meet special requirements by exaggerating certain items and subordinating others. The small-scale road map is a typical example. On such a map the highways, highway numbers, towns, cities, points of interest, and mileage distances are prominently shown, while drainage, railroads, pipelines, power lines, and public land lines are omitted or subordinated.

Aeronautical charts are special-purpose maps designed and constructed specifically for air navigation. The scale is small so that large areas may be shown on a single sheet. Ground features prominent from the air are emphasized in bold and simple symbols. Other features of equal importance on the ground but less noticeable from the air are subdued or omitted entirely. Elevations are shown in gradient tints, permitting the navigator to determine quickly the necessary flight altitude over a given area. Navigation data are shown in bright overprints.

The plats prepared from public land surveys are another form of special-purpose map, designed to present the data of the survey. The scale is large, and plats usually include a survey unit, such as a township. Courses and distances, subdivisions of sections, acreage figures, and other data from the survey are shown. Cultural and drainage features are reduced to a minimum and are accurate only on the survey lines.

Special-purpose maps of the kinds described in preceding paragraphs have little or no value as bases for detailed soil surveys. Such maps are very useful, however, for reference.

For broad reconnaissance soil surveys special maps may be useful as bases. Aeronautical charts, for example, are useful for rapid small-scale surveys of large areas. They have sufficient detail for orientation, accuracy is good at the small scale, and the generalized relief facilitates soil mapping.

The Cartographic Section can supply field parties with many special maps, including aeronautical charts, geologic maps, forest maps, coast and harbor charts, conservation survey maps, Census Bureau maps, Post Office maps, and highway maps.

EQUIPMENT

Requirements for equipment vary so widely from area to area that only those of general use are discussed here. Other sections of the *Manual* mention items for special needs. Plane tables, and accessories for them, and compasses are dealt with in the Appendices.

SPECIAL EQUIPMENT FOR AERIAL PHOTOGRAPHS

The materials used to delineate culture, soil boundaries, and symbols on aerial photographs and mosaics should be selected for ease of use, including correction, neatness, clarity, and permanence. These materials are now sufficiently standard that they may be readily obtained from commercial suppliers.

Pencils.—Despite a wide range in personal preference for types and hardness of pencils, the basic requirements are the same. The pencil marks need to be sharp, clear, and legible, but made without scratching or cutting the photographic emulsion. Pencils should be soft enough to leave a legible line yet not soft enough to smear with ordinary handling of the pictures. Too soft a pencil leaves a coarse heavy line that smears a dirty residue over the surface of the photograph and conceals other data. A very hard pencil scratches or indents the photographic emulsion, makes inking difficult, and requires such hard erasures for making corrections that the photographic emulsion may be broken.

Variations in the surface of the aerial photograph and in atmospheric conditions partly govern the choice of pencils. On hard and glossy photographs it is necessary to use a soft pencil for the line work to adhere. On the softer matte finishes, a harder pencil is better. A softer pencil is used during damp weather or in humid climates than is used during dry weather or in the desert.

Depending on conditions just mentioned, standard drafting pencils of good quality ranging from H to 4H are used in dry regions, and HB to 3B for moist regions or during periods of damp weather.

Inks.—Inks should be bright-colored, of opaque density, free-flowing, waterproof, rapid-drying, and of the kinds that photograph well.

Where the inking is done directly on the aerial photograph, a standard waterproof drafting ink should be used. If the inking is done on an acetate or plastic overlay, rather than directly on the aerial photography, special inks are used that adhere well to these media and that are easy to handle. These are called acetone inks and they etch the plastic slightly. Such special inks are too difficult to remove for use directly on photographs; in their removal the photographic emulsion is frequently damaged and brown stains are left. Standard waterproof drafting inks may be used on acetate or plastic overlays if sealer coatings are applied over the ink work immediately to prevent rubbing off or chipping. Such plastic sealer coatings can be applied with a soft cloth, brush, or spray. They dry rapidly, are transparent, and can be marked on with pencil or ink. Only a light coat of sealer should be applied. In preparing some kinds of contact prints from the original sheets, the sealer sticks to the rollers if too much has been used.

Only those colored inks are used that permit good photographic copies of the field sheets. Many colors do not photograph well unless copied through filters. Such filters may bring out any one color by subduing another. The use of filters also increases the time required for copying. Generally, black, red, and brown photograph well. The photographic qualities of blue, green, and yellow are normally poor but may be increased by mixing small amounts of the more photographic colors with them.

Mixed colors, as for example, black mixed with blue, should contrast on the field sheets and yet permit satisfactory copying. If a line is to appear in blue on a field sheet yet contain enough black to permit good photo copies, only a little black ink should be mixed in the blue.

Transparent overlays.—A number of transparent materials suitable for overlays on aerial photographs or mosaics are on the market. These fall into two general classes: (1) Plastics and (2) acetates. Both can be obtained in a variety of thicknesses and finishes.

Overlay materials should have dimensional stability. If one without dimensional stability is selected, difficulties are had in maintaining registry between the overlay and the photograph and in matching one overlay with another.

The most useful materials for overlays range from 0.005 to 0.080 inch in thickness. Enough thickness is needed to give stiffness and to avoid curling, yet not so much that sheets are bulky and difficult to handle.

The best overlays are transparent, with a grained surface. These have maximum transparency and their surface is suitable for both pencil and ink work. India ink can be used on ungrained acetate or plastic if soiling with perspiration or other oily substances is avoided. A sealer needs to be applied immediately afterward.

A transparent dimensionally stable material, with matte finish on one side and about 0.008 inch thick, is entirely satisfactory.

Types of photo paper.—In ordering aerial photographs and mosaics it is sometimes helpful for the soil scientist to specify the type and finish of paper on which the photographs are to be printed. Of the many kinds, some are satisfactory and others unsatisfactory for soil mapping.

Most photographic papers are available in three thicknesses or weights, as light, single, and double. Lightweight papers are too thin and flexible for most soil mapping. They tend to curl and lack dimensional stability. Where copies of field photographs thin enough to use over a light table in transferring data from one sheet to another are wanted, the lightweight papers are satisfactory. An extra thin paper is made that is especially good for this purpose.

Single-weight paper is somewhat thicker than the lightweight papers and is commonly used for printing aerial photographs to be used only in offices. Even this weight is too light for satisfactory field use where photographs are handled a great deal and exposed to variable weather conditions.

Double-weight paper is approximately twice the thickness of single-weight. It is stiff and does not curl, has a reasonable degree of dimensional stability, and is best for photographs that are to be used in the field for soil mapping.

Photographic finishes are classed broadly as glossy, semimatte, and matte. The surface of a glossy photograph is too slick and polished to accept pencil or ink well, and cannot be used conveniently. Semimatte and matte finishes take pencil and ink well, and these finishes are used on photographs on which survey data are to be plotted.

Waterproof papers are advantageous on some soil surveys. They can be processed somewhat faster than the conventional photographic paper and, if properly processed, their dimensional stability is somewhat better. For soil surveys in warm humid regions the waterproof paper has the advantage of absorbing less moisture.

Pens.—Pens should have points ranging from medium-fine to fine. Pens with stiff firm points are much preferred to those having soft flexible nibs. Unless used by an expert, pens with highly flexible nibs spread, and lines are either too heavy or too light. Such points soon lose their spring if abused and need to be discarded. The stiffer, coarser pen lasts longer and permits more uniform and consistent line work.

Erasers.—For cleaning soft pencil lines from aerial photographs art gum is usually satisfactory. Hard pencil lines can be removed with a soft pliable eraser. Ink lines not removable with a soft pliable eraser can be taken off by first dampening with alcohol or water and then erasing. Care must be taken not to let the photographic emulsion become wet enough to break or tear with erasing. Coarse or abrasive erasers should not be used on photographs. The emulsion becomes so scratched and broken that reinking is difficult or impossible.

The sketchmaster.—The sketchmaster is a small instrument used to reflect the image of the aerial photograph to a manuscript map. The photograph is mounted parallel to the manuscript map on a tripod-supported frame. The operator looks down through a half-silvered mirror at the front of the instrument and sees the image of the photograph superimposed on the manuscript map (fig. 1). He can adjust the length of the three legs to correct for tilt and difference in scale. The sketchmaster can be used for sketching at scales ranging from one-half to twice that of the photograph.

Simplicity, compactness, and portability make the sketchmaster an excellent instrument for use in field offices to transfer planimetric and soil data from the field sheets to a manuscript map. It

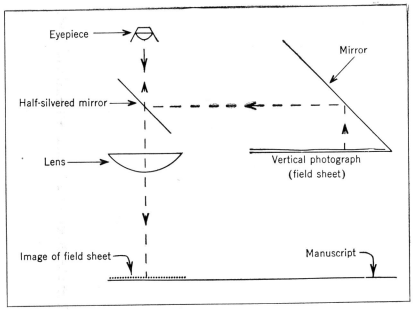

FIGURE 1.—Diagram showing the principles employed in a common type of sketchmaster used for transferring map data from a photograph to a manuscript map.

may be used for overlays and other field sheets as well as for aerial photographs.

Sketchmasters may be vertical or oblique. The vertical sketchmaster is used with vertical aerial photographs and the oblique is used with oblique aerial photographs. Since the vertical aerial photograph is used mainly in soil mapping, only the vertical sketchmaster concerns us here. The same general techniques are used with overlays of vertical aerial photographs or plane-table sheets.

In working with the sketchmaster, a framework of control is first indicated on the manuscript map, and into this framework planimetric detail is transferred from the photograph. This framework assists the operator to orient his instrument and thus to transfer the map data to their correct position on the manuscript. The framework may consist of photogrammetric stations, or culture and drainage, along with established section lines or other land lines.

If the manuscript map is a standard topographic or planimetric map, only soil boundaries and symbols, and revisions in culture and drainage need to be transferred.

An operator uses a sketchmaster about as follows:

(1) After inspecting the aerial photograph to make certain that the detail is clearly delineated, it is inserted in the frame so that it is perfectly flat and all detail is shown.

(2) The instrument is placed on the manuscript map. Looking through the eyepiece, the operator orients the instrument so that the image reflected from the instrument is near the correct position on the manuscript.

(3) Among the lenses furnished with the instrument one is selected that removes practically all the parallax at the scale to be used. With a low rig, for example, a large numbered lens is used. If a point on the manuscript moves in a direction opposite to that of the eye of the operator, a smaller numbered lens should be selected.

(4) The instrument is adjusted for scale by lowering or raising the frame on all three legs. The final leg adjustment is made with the screw feet. Correction for any tilt in the photograph may be made by adjusting the length of one or two legs.

(5) The detail on the manuscript should coincide with the detail reflected to it from the aerial photograph.

(6) The detail on the aerial photograph is now ready to be transferred to its correct position on the map manuscript. The eye is shifted slightly to bring individual controls into exact register as the detail in their vicinity is being traced. When tracing a stream, for example, the operator holds to the control on or near it. If there is no control on a feature, a skilled operator can properly orient nearby points in order to locate boundaries correctly. Transferring can be extended out to the edges of the vertical photographs.

Good light is required. The mirrors should not be touched with the hands since the salt in perspiration decomposes the chemical coating of the mirror and spoils it.

SOIL-SAMPLING TOOLS

The soil scientist's most important tool is the humble spade, supplemented by the pick and the soil auger. For exposing soil profiles for morphological examinations, as in the initial work of preparing a mapping legend, for sampling, or for photographing, the spade is used almost entirely. For the more frequent routine examinations of soils in mapping, the spade is generally but not always superior to the auger. For example, where the chief differentiating characteristic between two soil types or phases is the depth to a deep underlying stratum of clay or is the color of the substratum, a soil auger may be better than the spade, both faster and more convenient. Perhaps the worst feature of the auger is its destruction of soil structure, so important in classification and identification. In dry, stony soils, the auger is difficult to use; nor can the spade alone be used rapidly; and the pick becomes the most useful tool. Whenever practical, the spade should be given preference over the soil auger, especially in excavating the upper part of the soil—the solum. Where the soil auger is used frequently in identifying soils, some exposed profiles of the soil types should also be examined in order to check the results.

Spades and picks.—For use in collecting samples, especially after the preliminary excavation has been made, the flat square-pointed spade (fig. 2, *A*) is most convenient. The best generally useful spade, however, for ordinary use in mapping, is a modified post hole spade (fig. 2, *B* and *C*). The sharp corners of the post hole spade are removed for best results. The common tiling spade tapers somewhat too much at the end, although it is a useful tool for some soils and generally superior to the post hole spade for

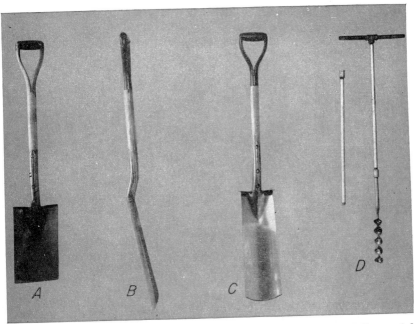

FIGURE 2.—Soil-sampling tools: *A*, Square-pointed spade, especially useful in collecting samples; *B*, side view, and *C*, front view of post hole spade, the most generally useful sampling tool; and *D*, soil auger with extension.

gravelly soils. Where deep holes are required, as in examining irrigated Alluvial soils, the long-handled irrigator's shovel is useful. It may be necessary to supplement this shovel with a heavy crowbar to penetrate dry cemented and compact layers.

The pick should always be at hand, especially for making holes in hard, dry, stony, or gravelly soils. In some soils a small trench pick will serve satisfactorily, but commonly a heavier pick with a long handle is better. One prong should be sharply pointed and the other made as a chisel. A heavy chisel-pointed bar is useful for penetrating strongly cemented or indurated hardpans.

A geologist's hammer, or small hand pick, one end of which can be used as a hammer, is also useful in examining rocks and the soil in cuts along roadsides. For moist soils and those containing many woody roots, a chisel-pointed hammer is better; whereas for dry soils a sharp-pointed hammer is better.

Augers.—The screw, or worm, type of soil auger (fig. 2, *C*) consists essentially of a 1¼- or 1½-inch wood auger, from which the cutting side flanges and tip have been removed, welded to a steel rod or iron pipe with a crosspiece at the top for a handle. The worm part should be about 7 inches long, with the distances between flanges about the same as the diameter, 1¼ to 1½ inches. If the distance between flanges is narrower, it is difficult to remove the soil with the thumb. For ordinary use augers are 40 to 60 inches long, with provisions for adding extra lengths for deep boring. An auger for continual use is made solidly throughout, and another extension auger is used for deep borings. In clay soils an auger with a 1-inch bit may be more convenient than the larger one. It is convenient to have a scale marked on the shaft of the auger from the tip.

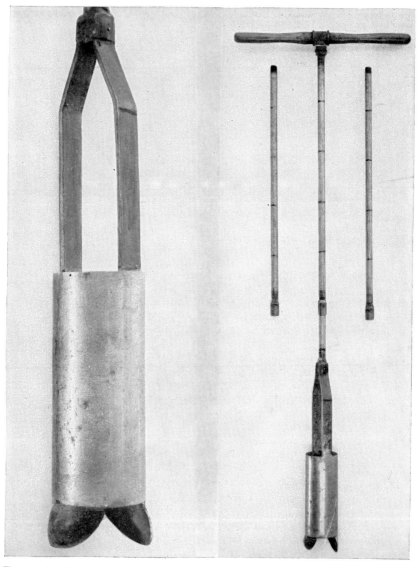

FIGURE 3.—Core type of soil auger: Left, a close view of the bit; right, a view of the whole auger, with extensions, marked at 6-inch intervals.

Generally, the core, or post hole, type of soil auger shown in figure 3 is better than the older screw type. The core type is especially favored in dry regions, and the screw type in wet ones. The core type gives a larger and less modified sample. It works well in loose dry sand and in compact soils. The cylinder is about 2 to 4 inches in diameter, commonly 3½ inches. The cutting blades are so constructed that the soil is loosened and forced into the cylinder of the auger as it is rotated and pushed into the soil. Each filling of the cylinder corresponds to a penetration of 3 to 5 inches. Although both ends of the cylinder are open, the soil becomes packed enough to stay in it while the auger is removed. If the cylinder is only partly filled, or if the soil is very dry and sandy, it may need to be tamped with a stick thrust through the upper end of the cylinder before it will stay in the auger when pulled out of the hole. Small cylinders are best for very sandy soils. A few taps of the cylinder on the ground or on a board usually loosens the soil for removal.

The core-type auger disturbs the soil, but less so than the screw-type auger. A better view of soil structure, porosity, consistence, and color can be had with the core auger, but even so, excavations are necessary for proper morphological studies. The core-type auger is not well suited to use in wet clay soils. Generally, with soils that are naturally moist for much of the year, the screw-type auger is faster.

Although soil augers are simple in design and somewhat crude in appearance, considerable skill is required to use them effectively in making dependable observations of the soil profile.

Peat sampler.—Examinations of deep deposits of peat are made with a special sampler. Although several devices are used, the one most common in the United States is the Davis peat sampler or some modification of it, as shown in figure 4. The instrument consists of 10 or more sections of steel rods, each 2 or 4 feet long, and a cylinder of brass or duraluminum, approximately 14 inches long with an inside diameter of three-fourths inch. The cylinder is provided with a plunger, cone-shaped at the lower end, and with a spring catch near the upper end. The sampler is pressed into the peat until the desired depth is reached for taking a sample; then the spring catch allows withdrawal of the plunger from its enclosing cylinder. With the plunger withdrawn and locked in that position, the cylinder may be filled with a solid core of the organic material by a further downward movement. The cylinder protects the sample completely from any contamination and does not destroy its structure when the instrument is removed.

Beginning at the surface, samples of peat are taken consecutively at intervals of 6 inches or 1 foot. The lengths of steel rods used allow an easy estimation of the depth of each sample. For very deep deposits, extra 2- or 4-foot rods are used. Each rod is threaded at one end to screw into a small coupling on the reverse end of another rod. For light work, the rods may be screwed and unscrewed with pliers; for heavy work in deep deposits, small pipe wrenches are used.

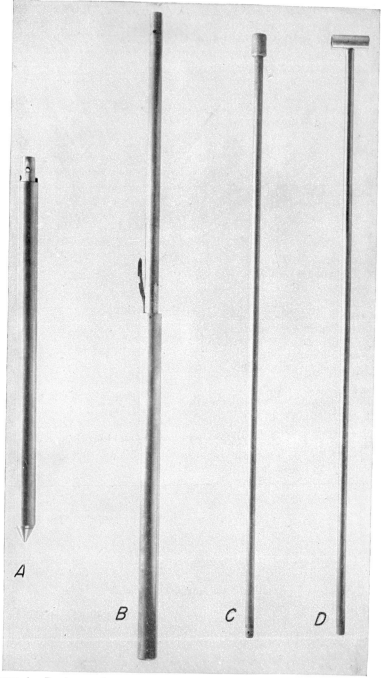

FIGURE 4.—Peat sampler: *A*, The head closed, ready for pushing into the peat; *B*, the head extended, as just prior to taking a sample; *C*, one 2-foot extension rod; and *D*, the top extension rod.

Other sampling tools.—Power augers, mounted on the rear of a truck or on a trailer, some custom made and others obtainable from manufacturers, are used in some soil surveys, either for special studies or for cutting through cemented or very compact dry soils. Some of these are of the core type, either similar to the hand core auger already described or so constructed as to obtain an undisturbed core of a complete soil profile.[2] Others are of the screw type. Further experience is needed with power augers. A custom-built one in use is shown in figure 5.

FIGURE 5.—Custom-built power soil auger: *A*, Mounted on a pick-up truck in position to operate; *B*, in position for transport; and *C*, close view of bit.

Another tool used little in routine soil mapping but of use in collecting soil samples is the King soil tube, or a modification of it, which consists of a long, narrow tube that can be driven into the soil. It is used primarily in collecting soil samples for moisture and bulk-density (or volume-weight) determinations. A short, wide tube is used for collecting samples from soil horizons for bulk-density determination. An angled cold chisel is convenient for cutting out blocks of compact or cemented soil. An ordinary

[2] For a description of a power auger see KELLEY, O. J., HARDMAN, J. A., JENNINGS, D. S. A SOIL-SAMPLING MACHINE FOR OBTAINING TWO-, THREE-, AND FOUR-INCH DIAMETER CORES OF UNDISTURBED SOIL TO A DEPTH OF SIX FEET. Soil Sci. Soc. Amer. Proc. 12: 85–87., illus. 1947.

trowel is used for sampling thin horizons and for filling sample sacks. A special trowel for this purpose consists essentially of an ordinary curved garden trowel with about one-half of the blade cut away (longitudinally) and sharpened. A straight-bladed steel fern trowel is also a good tool. A handy tool for examining soil profiles is a small steel pick of the type used by French workmen in laying slate roofs. The head of this tool has a broad-bladed chisel on one prong and a small hammer on the other. Finally, every soil morphologist needs a strong knife.

FIELD TESTING APPARATUS

Several suitable field kits for pH determinations are available. Where soils are very low or very high in pH, are highly organic, or are salty, an electrical field kit is better than the simpler colorimetric ones. Carbonates may be tested for with 10-percent hydrochloric acid solution in a small dropping bottle.

The sections on Soil Reaction and Estimation and Mapping of Salts and Alkali in the Soil should be read and appropriate apparatus obtained as required.

Besides these tests, manganese dioxide may be tested for by using a 10-percent solution of hydrogen peroxide in a dropping bottle. This is not a test for total manganese, and effervescence is not necessarily correlated with toxic concentrations. The peroxide test is useful in the field as a partial indicator of boundaries among some lateritic and latosolic soils.

No kits for chemical "quick tests" for available or soluble plant nutrients in soils are recommended. In some areas, particular ones may be useful if well standardized by field plot tests.

PLOTTING AND ASSEMBLY OF FIELD DATA

The plotting and assembly of field data are discussed early in the *Manual* because of their importance to preparation for field work, but some points may not be clear until later chapters dealing more specifically with soil classification and mapping units are studied.

AERIAL PHOTOGRAPHS IN SOIL SURVEYS

Characteristics of aerial photographs

The kinds of aerial photographs have already been described. First of all, an aerial photograph is not a map but a perspective view of a portion of the earth's surface. Like all perspectives, it does not present a true scale, and precise measurements of distances and directions cannot be made on it. In addition to the distortions of a perspective, there are those created by tilt, differences in elevation, and inherent errors of photography. Yet in contrast to maps made by ground methods, aerial photographs show more ground detail, permit a three-dimension view of the features, and afford an economical method for obtaining base material rapidly for large or inaccessible areas. From them, accurate planimetric and topographic maps can be made. For most soil mapping, there is no better medium than the aerial photograph.

Oblique photographs are taken with cameras (often hand held) pointed down at an angle such that the longitudinal axis of the camera forms an angle of less than 90° with the ground. They are classified as (1) *high oblique*, which show the horizon, and (2) *low oblique*, which do not show the horizon. The high oblique shows a large area of the terrain in panorama, whereas the low oblique shows only a small area of the ground. Although obliques serve many purposes and are useful in reconnaissance surveys as an aid to the identification of boundaries, they are not readily converted to maps and are not so satisfactory for soil mapping as vertical pictures.

Vertical photographs are taken with fixed-level cameras pointed straight down from the aircraft so that the longitudinal axis of the camera is perpendicular to the horizontal plane of the ground. Three broadly defined types are (1) the continuous-strip photograph, (2) the multiple-lens, and (3) the single-lens.

The strip photograph is a continuous-strip exposure. Strip photographs may be taken from low altitudes at high speeds by synchronizing film motion with the ground speed of the aircraft. In this way good pictures can be taken with poor light. Strip photographs so taken have little use in soil mapping because of their large scale and small coverage.

Multiple-lens photographs combine vertical and oblique camera angles. The cameras usually have three, five, or nine lenses. One lens takes a vertical view, and the others obliques. With a transforming printer, the obliques are transformed to the plane of the vertical picture to produce a composite vertical photograph composed of the center vertical picture and the transformed obliques. The multiple-lens camera is widely used where rapid and economical coverage of large areas at small scale is needed. Although the pictures are occasionally used in soil mapping, they are not recommended if single-lens pictures are available. The usually small scale, necessity for transforming prints, and difficulties of map construction make them less satisfactory than single-lens pictures. Multiple-lens photographs are also obtained through the use of multiple cameras, arranged and mounted to make vertical and oblique exposures. The tri-metrogon photograph is an example.

71

Single-lens photographs, which are taken in a series of independent overlapping exposures, are recommended for soil mapping. They have convenient size for field use and map construction, permit stereoscopic study, give excellent detail of ground features and also have satisfactory ranges of scale.

In discussing the use of aerial photographs in this *Manual*, single-lens vertical aerial photographs, made to the specifications of the Department of Agriculture, are assumed unless otherwise stated. Where it is necessary to use other types of photographs or single-lens photographs of lower standards, the Cartographic Section of the Division of Soil Survey will advise the soil scientists about methods to use and their specific weaknesses. Excessive tilt, insufficient overlap, and other deficiencies may make it impossible to use the pictures stereoscopically or to construct accurate maps from them.

Flight lines and overlap.—Most aerial photography in this country is flown north and south. Flight lines are as near straight and parallel as possible; they should not deviate from the true direction by more than 5 degrees. Flight lines are usually continuous across the area, with the first and last photograph on each flight line falling entirely outside the area boundary.

In line of flight, consecutive photographs should overlap an average of 60 percent, with no overlap less than 55 percent nor more than 65 percent. Overlap in line of flight is referred to as *endlap*. The overlap between adjacent flight lines, or *sidelap*, should average 30 percent, with none less than 15 percent nor more than 45 percent. (See figure 6.)

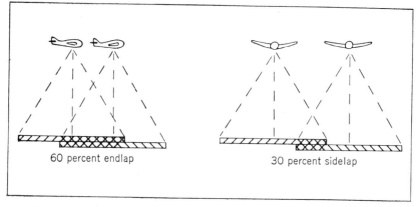

FIGURE 6.—Diagrams showing overlap in single-lens photographs.

Adequate overlap is essential for stereoscopic study in the field and for the photogrammetric processes used in map construction. Where alternate photographs—every other photograph in line of flight—are used, the overlap of standard pictures averages only 20 percent.

Full stereoscopic coverage should be obtained for soil mapping, even though the soil boundaries are plotted only on alternate photographs.

Scale.—The scale of aerial photographs is not always accurate nor uniform like that of a good map. The scale varies between photographs because of varying altitudes of the aircraft, differences in ground elevations, or tilt of the camera. The sketch in figure 7 shows that a photograph taken at camera station *A* will not be the same scale as a photograph taken at station *B* because the aircraft is at different altitudes at the times of exposures. Thus, the 20-acre field *C* will not measure the same as the 20-acre field *D* because of the elevation differences within the photograph.

The scale given for photographs is the approximate average scale computed from the mean altitude of the entire area flown, from that of a

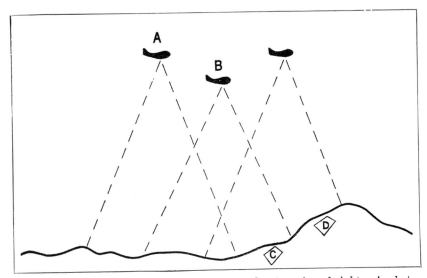

FIGURE 7.—Sketch showing differences in scale at various heights. A photograph taken at station *A* will have a different scale from one taken at station *B*. Patterns of the two 20-acre fields at *D* and *C* have different dimensions on the photographs.

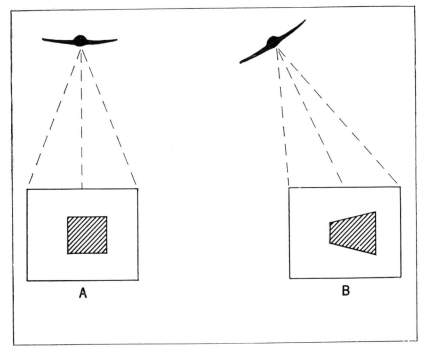

FIGURE 8.—Sketches showing distortion of a square in an aerial photograph because of tilt: *A*, normal; *B*, with tilt.

FIGURE 9.—Air photographs for the same area: Upper, normal; lower, with tilt.

fraction of the area, or from a specified datum plane. Photographs flown for the United States Department of Agriculture do not deviate more than 5 percent from the average scale. Most of this aerial photography has a scale of 1:20,000 (3.168 inches to 1 mile) from which satisfactory enlargements or reductions can be made.

Tilt.—When the plane of the camera is not level the resulting photograph is tilted. The greater the tilt, the more the objects in the photograph are distorted in shape and size. Figure 8 illustrates such distortions in the shape and scale of a square field. Figure 9 shows aerial photos for the same area, normal and with tilt. Excessive tilt may sometimes be detected by comparing images in overlapping photographs. In standard photography used by the United States Department of Agriculture tilt does not exceed 5°, nor average more than 2° in a 10-mile flight line, nor average more than 1° for an entire area.

Crab and drift.—To maintain a true flight line in the presence of side or quartering winds, it is frequently necessary that the photographic aircraft fly at an angle to the flight line. The camera is rotated to compensate for the angle of flight. Failure to do so results in *crabbed* photographs as illustrated in figure 10,A. *Drift*, a special form of crab, results when exposures oriented to the flight line continue to be made even though the aircraft has drifted from the flight line. Edges of successive photos are parallel but sidestepped, as sketched in figure 10,B. Standard specifications do not permit crab to exceed 10° from the true flight line in any two or more pictures.

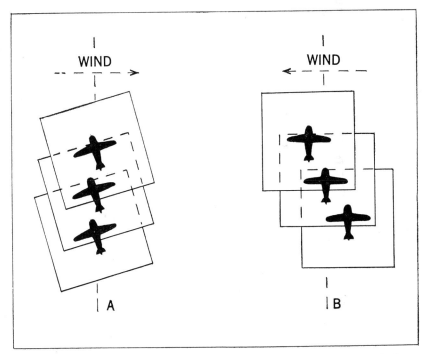

FIGURE 10.—Sketches showing irregularities in aerial photographs: *A*, from crabbing; *B*, from drift.

Displacement.—If a vertical photograph is in a plane parallel with a section of flat ground, the relationships between images in the photograph and objects on the ground are similar. If the ground objects are not all in the same horizontal plane, however, the photographs do not present objects in correct relationship to one another. This difference is called *displacement*, illustrated in figure 11. It can be seen that displacement is inward, toward the center of the photograph, for objects below the datum plane; and outward, from the center, for those above the datum plane. An object appearing at the center of an untilted photograph is not displaced, regardless of relief. Displacement and tilt are so interrelated that the layman finds it is impossible to differentiate between them. The vertical datum plane is considered only when heights of objects or differences in elevation are to be measured, as in the construction of a topographic map.

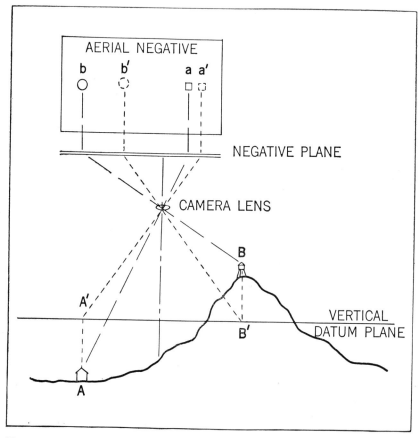

FIGURE 11.—Sketch illustrating displacement in aerial photographs. Note building *A* in the valley and watertower *B* on the hill. A vertical line through the building intersects the datum plane at *A'*. Since the building is below the datum plane, it will appear at point *a* on the aerial negative rather than at its true ground position *a'*. Similarly, the watertower, above the datum plane, will appear at *b* rather than at its true position *b'*.

Inherent errors.—Inherent errors arise from the physical limitations of materials and instruments used in taking and preparing aerial photographs and are more or less common to all photographic processing. They result from improper grinding or other imperfections in lenses, curvature of the lens field, inefficient shutters, and expansion and contraction of photographic film and papers. These errors are reduced to the minimum in modern aerial photography where only precision mapping cameras, excellent laboratory equipment, and special aero film and paper are used.

Code numbers.—Aerial photographs are marked when taken and processed to permit indexing and rapid selection. Although organizations indicate different information in various ways on their aerial photographs, the following are usually shown: (1) Date of flight, (2) time of day, (3) owner of film, (4) scale of negative, (5) project or area, (6) film roll number, and (7) exposure number. Some also show altitude, focal length of camera, type of camera, and the like.

Each aerial photograph made for the United States Department of Agriculture bears a code letter designating the project or area and individual numbers to designate the roll of film and exposure. These are in the northeast corner for north-south flights and in the northwest corner for east-west flights. The code number for the area is limited to three letters; the roll of film is indicated by number, beginning with one and continuing unbroken; and numbers indicate the exposures, beginning with one for each roll of film and continuing unbroken. For example, in the designation ABC–46–122, ABC indicates the county or area, 46 the roll of film in that county or area, and 122 the exposure in that roll. In the adjacent corner are numbers for the month, day, and year the exposure was made. On the first and last exposure in each roll of film appears the abbreviation for the organization owning the film, the approximate scale of the negatives, and the time of day the exposures were made. The organization abbreviation and approximate scale precede the usual area symbol, as BPI–1:20,000–ABC–46–122. In the adjacent corner, immediately following the date, the time of day is placed, as 6–15–48—11:30.

Photo indexes.—Aerial photographic indexes are prepared for large areas. Without an index the user of photographs is seriously handicapped in selecting the photograph for a specific area or in locating adjacent photographs in adjoining flights. Photo indexes are prepared by laying the overlapping photographs so that the index numbers of each print are visible. Standard specifications usually require the index to be in sheets 20 by 24 inches at an approximate scale of 1:63,360. The soil survey party should have the photo index of the area to expedite the location of individual photographs.

Stereoscopic vision

Although individual aerial photographs are flat in appearance, overlapping pairs can be viewed under a stereoscope and the topography of the ground becomes apparent: hills and valleys appear, buildings and trees stand up, and the slight depressions of drainage can be seen. Thus viewed, the aerial photograph looks like a detailed relief model. The soil scientist can study the ground before going into the field. Drainage and trails that are obscure on the flat photographs can be outlined in advance. Travel routes can be selected. Stereoscopic study of the pictures, both before and after the mapping, helps him to see the relations between kinds of soil and land forms.

Theory of stereovision.—In normal vision, the observer sees objects in three dimensions, namely length, width, and depth. The ability to see depth depends on sight with two eyes, each at an equal distance from the object but viewing it from a different position, or angle. Each eye registers a slightly different image. These images are fused or combined by the optic nerves and brain to give depth perception or a third dimensional view of the object. The distance between the eyes is so short that the angle and difference becomes so small at great distances that it is difficult to register depth perception.

When viewing two overlapping aerial photographs under the stereoscope, one sees the same ground area from widely separated positions. The right eye is viewing the area in one photograph, the left eye the same area in another photograph. The effect is the same as if a person were viewing the area with one eye located at one camera position and the other eye at the next camera position. The brain so fuses the images that one sees the relief in the photograph, or the third dimension.

The average person with normal vision should have little difficulty with stereoscopic study of aerial photographs. Occasionally a person with apparently normal vision is unable to use the stereoscope. This may be expected of older persons whose eye muscles are not flexible. Some feel eyestrain when first using the stereoscope.

Stereoscopic vision requires some practice. At first it may be difficult to adjust the photographs and fuse the images; yet after practice this can be done rapidly with little or no eyestrain.

Types of stereoscopes.—Stereoscopes are constructed on two basic principles. Those most commonly used in the study of aerial photographs are (1) the mirror type, which utilizes the principle of reflection, and (2) the lens type, which makes use of the principle of refraction. A third type, less commonly used, is the prism stereoscope. In this type prisms serve as reflectors, much as mirrors do in the mirror stereoscope. Designs of all types vary widely.

The mirror stereoscope has four mirrors fastened in a frame and arranged to transmit the photographic image to the eye by reflection (fig. 12). Since these stereoscopes are usually large and bulky, they are not easily portable and are used mainly for office work where plenty of table space is available. Some mirror stereoscopes are designed to fold up and fit in a small case that can be carried in a large pocket. Even these are too bulky to carry in the field while mapping.

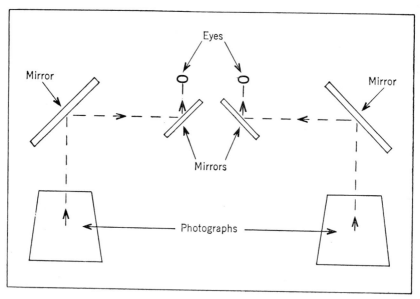

FIGURE 12.—Sketch showing the essentials of the design of a mirror stereoscope.

The mirror stereoscope gives an image nearly free of distortion. It has a wide field of vision—wide enough for one to view an entire photograph. The wide separation of the mirrors allows the photographs to be viewed without overlapping, which makes adjustment and fusion of the picture simple. Many instruments have a horizontal adjustment which allows them to be placed at various distances from the eyepiece. With this adjustment, larger scale photographs can be viewed than with the conventional lens-type stereoscope. Owing to the great optical distance between the eye and the photograph, the fused image appears to be reduced.

This is a disadvantage in studying fine detail, especially on small scale photographs. The disadvantage may be overcome by fitting the stereoscope with magnifying lens, but this increases the size and cost of the instrument.

The mirror stereoscope is especially good for the office study of aerial photographs. It is simple for the beginner to use and requires little practice.

Lens stereoscopes have two magnifying lenses mounted in a frame and supported on a stand so that the photographs are viewed directly through the lenses, or eyepieces. The lenses are ground so that the lines of sight are bent outward (fig. 13). These instruments are usually small, compact, and light. Many are designed for field use and fold into a small unit that can be carried easily by the soil mapper in the field. Most use, however, is in the field headquarters.

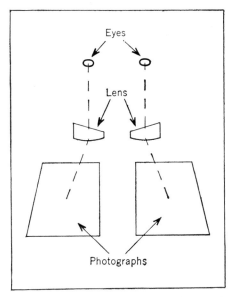

FIGURE 13.—Sketch showing the essentials of the design of a lens stereoscope. The thin edges of the lenses are inside.

The lens stereoscope gives a distorted image. It has a small field of vision, and only part of the photograph can be viewed at one time. The close spacing of the lenses, combined with direct vision, makes it necessary to place the photographs very close together or even to overlap them. Thus adjustment of the photographs and fusion of the images are somewhat difficult. For the same reason, large-scale photographs cannot be viewed satisfactorily except at the margins. Despite these disadvantages, the lens stereoscope is a useful tool for the soil scientist.

The lens stereoscope magnifies, which is a definite advantage, especially when studying minute detail or very small-scale aerial photographs. It emphasizes the relief, which is helpful in viewing nearly flat terrain.

The lens stereoscope is helpful for the field study of aerial photographs where the scale is small enough to permit its ready use. Appropriate models are light, compact, and relatively cheap.

Care of stereoscopes.—Stereoscopes are generally of rugged construction and will withstand a reasonable amount of hard use; but they are optical instruments and should be treated accordingly. "First-surface" mirrors are used in stereoscopes. In these the silver is applied to the front of the glass and not to the back. The silver coating is highly susceptible to scratching and corrosion and should not be touched. All first-surface mirrors should be protected with a soft cloth or chamois covering when not in use.

A first-surface mirror may be cleaned with soft clean cotton and alcohol. The cotton needs to be free from any grit that might scratch the silvered surface. The silvered surface is wiped gently with just enough pressure to remove the dirt. Fingerprints should be cleaned off immediately, since their residues corrode the mirror.

The lens type of stereoscope should be cleaned and cared for like a pair of glasses. Stereoscopic lenses are usually ground with one side thinner than the other in order to reflect the light rays outward. Such lens must be placed in the frame with the thick edge outward and the thin edge inward.

Use of the stereoscope.—To use the stereoscope in studying aerial photographs one must first acquire the knack of adjusting the photographs and accustoming the eyes to stereoscopic vision. This ability may be acquired in different ways.

One of the simplest methods is to place a small cross on two separate sheets of paper. With each sheet of paper under the lens, or mirror, of the stereoscope, one may look directly through the eyepieces of the stereoscope and focus the eyes on the crosses. Unless the crosses by chance are fused, one sees two crosses. After the eyes are focussed, one sheet is held firmly and the other moved slowly. The crosses move either nearer or farther from each other. The sheets are slowly shifted until the two crosses coincide and appear as one. During the operation, the eyes are not shifted nor the focus changed.

Once the crosses coincide, the sheet is moved until the image separates into two crosses again; then again the sheets are shifted until the crosses appear as one image. This practice is continued until "fusing" can be done rapidly. When the crosses are fused, the approximate location of the sheets with reference to the lens or mirrors is noted. The sheets are removed and then replaced to try focussing the eyes and fusing the crosses rapidly. When the operation can be performed quickly and accurately, one is ready to attempt stereoscopic vision with two aerial photographs.

To start, one may select two stereo-pairs of terrain with moderate relief and a distinct pattern of ground features. The photographs should be of equal tone and scale. The center of the photograph—its optical center—is located at the intersection of lines drawn between collimation marks, usually appearing as small lines at the center of each margin, and marked with a cross. The picture centers are transferred to the overlap area in each adjoining picture, and the two crosses on each picture connected with a line. The photographs are placed under the stereoscope with the overlapping detail approximately in coincidence and the lines on the photographs parallel to the eye base. The shadows should fall toward the observer and both photographs need to be well and uniformly illuminated.

The photographs are shifted horizontally and adjusted until the crosses and connecting lines are fused. Then the relief can be seen. One of the photographs should be shifted until fusion is lost, and later recovered. With practice, images may be fused rapidly. As skill develops, the observer fuses the images by observing the physical features and less by watching the crosses and connecting lines.

After skill in these exercises has been obtained, it is time to try two photographs without the centers marked and connected. Two such pictures are placed under the stereoscope with the index finger of each hand just under the same selected physical feature in the overlap area on each photograph. The eyes are focussed and the pictures shifted until the fingers approximately coincide. The fingers are moved away and the images slightly separated. Then they are adjusted until they again coincide. This practice needs to be continued with other stereo-pairs. Once the knack of placing the photographs and adjusting them until they fuse has been acquired, the operator is ready to use the stereoscope in the study of aerial photographs.

Lenses need to be focussed properly. Many stereoscopes have an adjustment for varying the spacing of the eyepieces, so that they can be separated to the correct interpupillary distance of the observer's eyes.

Generally, on aerial photographs man-made features appear in geometric patterns—with straight lines, sharp angles, and circles.

Natural features, generally, have irregular and curved lines, as in twisting streams, curving shore lines, and the like.

For interpretation of size one needs to know the approximate scale of the photograph. A round image may represent a silo on a large-scale print, and one of the same size, a large gas storage tank on a small-scale print. Size is sensed by comparison among the ground objects.

The tone, or shade, in which various features appear on an aerial photograph is due mainly to the amount of reflected light. The amount of reflected light depends upon the texture of the surface of the object and the angle at which the light is reflected. An object that reflects a large amount of light appears in a light tone on the photograph. If little light is reflected, the object appears dark.

Because of differences in the angle of reflected light, the tone of an object may be different on two consecutive photographs, especially if the surface is smooth and a good reflector of light. Thus, in one photograph, with the light rays reflected from the water to the camera, a water area appears light; in an adjoining photograph, with the angle of reflection away from the camera, the same body of water appears dark. Most natural features, however, reflect light in all directions and appear in intermediate tones, for some of the reflected light finds its way to the camera lens.

For stereoscopic study, the light should be good and each photograph should be equally illuminated, but without glare. Where possible, the observer should face the source of the light. Of course, these lighting conditions cannot always be arranged in the field.

The photographs are placed under the stereoscope in such a way that the one taken to the left of the overlap area is viewed by the left eye, and the one to the right of the overlap by the right eye. If the position of the photographs is reversed, and the left eye views the right photo and the right the left, the image of relief appears in reverse. In such an arrangement, points of low elevation appear high, and points of high elevation low. This is commonly called a pseudoscopic image.

Photographic characteristics.—Certain characteristics of aerial photographs are the basis of stereoscopic interpretation. The most important ones are the shape and size of features, the tone in which the features appear on the photographs, and the shadows cast by the features.

The shape of features is important in the interpretation of ground detail from aerial photographs. The observer needs to study the shape of ground objects as they appear on the vertical photographs in comparison with how the same features look on the ground. Frequently the tone of objects appears darker or lighter in photographs than their contrasting ground colors would suggest.

Shadows on aerial photographs often reveal the size, shape, and identity of objects. The shadows suggest the heights of objects, which are not revealed by the horizontal dimensions alone. A one-story building, for example, may look like a five-story one in the picture except for the shadow. But shadows can be deceptive. If the ground under the object slopes abruptly, the shadow may be distorted. The height of the sun at the time of exposure also affects the length of the shadow. Yet many objects with little width, like fences, flagpoles, and chimneys, are difficult to identify except by their shadows.

Interpretation.—Most field scientists become proficient in photo interpretation by using the photographs in the field where opportunities are continually offered to compare ground features with their photographic images. Study of the photographs of the area to be covered a day or so in advance can be helpful. The accuracy of interpretations is checked by observations of the ground detail. Images that are unidentifiable in the office can be identified in the field. With such practice, the soil scientist can rapidly train himself in aerial interpretation. It must always be recalled, however, that accurate photo interpretation depends on familiarity with ground conditions. Ability to interpret pictures accurately in one area is not necessarily followed by similar accuracy in another area with different conditions.

The time of day and season of the year in which photographs are taken influence interpretation. In order to have good light, most photography is taken under ideal weather conditions and during the middle part of the day. The length of shadows naturally depends upon the height of the sun. Shadows on photographs taken in summer are shorter than those on photographs taken in winter. Similarly, shadows appear much longer on photographs taken a few hours before or after noon than on those taken at noon.

Features appear differently on aerial photographs in the different seasons. Cultivated fields vary from season to season. In wet seasons, streams appear large and many small ponds may be visible. In the dry season, the same area may have no ponds and the streams may be dry beds. During summer, deciduous forests present a mass of treetops that obscure the ground detail. In winter, pictures of the same area show a confusion of tree trunks, emphasized by shadows, and trails, small drains, and other ground detail are clear. Snow on the ground obscures much of the detail. The experienced photo interpreter takes all of these factors into consideration when studying the photographs.

A few of the characteristics of some major features as they appear in aerial photographs may be helpful in acquiring skill in photo interpretation. With experience, the soil scientist can broaden his information.

Streams.—Streams are usually identified by their irregular widths and winding courses, frequently emphasized by the growth of brush and trees along the banks. In heavily wooded areas, small streams are difficult to detect. Water in stream beds is suggested by dark or light lines, depending on the angle of the reflected light. Dry stream beds are easily recognized in the open and usually appear in light tones.

Bodies of water.—Ponds and lakes appear lighter or darker than the adjoining shore, depending on the reflected light. Furthermore, they are flat. The shore lines are sharply defined and appear as irregular outlines. One end of a large lake in a photograph may appear light and the other end dark.

Marshes.—Swamps and marshes have a blurred appearance. Many display very winding channels, or small bodies of open water. Very wet areas or those partially covered with water usually appear darker than the surrounding ground.

Forests and brush.—Wooded areas appear as dark masses with irregular outlines. The intensity of tone for deciduous cover varies with the season. In summer the tone is very dark; in winter it is lighter. Coniferous forests appear dark in tone, regardless of the season. Brush areas have a dark tone in summer and a lighter one in winter, but shadows are lacking. Stereoscopic inspection suggests the height.

Cultivated areas.—Cultivated fields are readily identified by their contrasting tones and their boundaries. Many field edges are well defined by fences, hedges, trails, or roads. Terraces, contour strips, and other patterns show clearly.

Some crops can be identified by planting patterns and tone or shade. Fields with heavy standing crops or grass appear dark. Fields from which crops have been harvested recently appear lighter. During harvest of crops such as hay, wheat, and corn, fields acquire a distinctive pattern. Shocks appear as dark-colored, regularly spaced dots against a lighter background. Because of the rough surface and damp soil, freshly plowed fields are usually very dark. The pattern of plowing is frequently visible on the photograph. Orchards, vineyards, and similar plantings are readily identified by their distinctive spacing.

Roads, trails, and paths.—Roads usually appear as light lines. Cement concrete roads have well-defined edges and appear light except for streaks of oil drop in the center of each lane. Bituminous concrete or other black-surfaced roads may seem dark. Most improved roads are identified by long straight stretches, gentle curves, and regular width. Unimproved roads are more irregular, have sharper curves, and vary in width.

Trails meander and often follow the contour. Paths are even more indistinct and irregular. If used a great deal, paths and trails appear as light streaks.

The appearance of roads, trails, and paths changes with the season because of shadows cast by trees and partial covering by overhanging vegetation.

Railroads.—Railroads appear much like roads on the photographs but are usually darker and narrower. They have long straight stretches and smoother curves than roads. The roadbed material affects the tone appearance of the railroad. Large cuts and fills, water tanks, spur lines, and stations are distinct along the right-of-way.

Buildings.—Buildings are readily identified on aerial photographs. Their size is suggested by their relation to the scale of the photograph; and comparative heights can be estimated from the shadows. Isolated buildings often have roads or trails leading to them. Individual buildings in groups may be indistinct because of the collective shadows.

Land form.—With practice, land form may be suggested from the photographs. In fact, land forms may be clearer in aerial photographs than on any map or from the ground. As a start, the soil scientist may consult some of the standard texts on this subject.[1]

USING THE AERIAL PHOTOGRAPH

Techniques of using aerial photographs in soil mapping differ from those of using maps because measurements of courses and distances are less precise. Even though the vertical aerial photograph looks like a map, it is not an accurate plan of the ground surface.

Stereoscopic interpretation and delineation.—To begin with, the soil survey party should study the photographs of the survey area. Each mapper needs to be familiar with the film-roll and picture numbers, the sequence of flight lines, and direction of flights. Study of the photo index will also serve to give a view of the whole area and of the conditions to be met during the survey. Such study can be helped by laying out photographs for parts of the area on a table top as a sort of rough unassembled mosaic.

Once the survey is under way, it is helpful to study the photographs with the stereoscope before going into the field. Preliminary interpretations of features can be made and the scientist can familiarize himself with the ground conditions.

It is frequently helpful to delineate in advance certain ground features. Drainage can be accurately plotted on the photograph. The plotting of drainage features in heavily wooded areas is especially helpful to field orientation. Trails and obscure paths can be marked for reference. Possible places where streams may be crossed and routes through rough terrain can be tentatively selected. Buildings that might otherwise be overlooked can be marked for checking in the field. Such features as gullies, areas of eroded soil, pasture or idle land, and forests can be tentatively outlined and the time of scientists in the field thereby conserved. Delineations should be made in pencil, to be inked after confirmation in the field. Rivers, lakes, and other prominent water fea-

---

[1] See, for example, SMITH, H. T. U. AERIAL PHOTOGRAPHS AND THEIR APPLICATIONS. 372 pp., illus. New York. 1943.

tures can usually be inked in advance. Clearly defined stream courses can be inked as dashed lines, and after field inspection the dashes can be closed, or dots inserted, to indicate either perennial or intermittent streams.

Match lines and matching.—A *match line* is an arbitrary line drawn in the overlap area of a photograph to serve as a boundary for the mapping on the photograph and is to be matched by a similar boundary drawn through identical points on the adjoining photograph.

When stereoscopic pairs of photographs are used in mapping soils, the match lines should be placed to limit the plotting of data to the central parts of the pictures where distortion is least. If alternate photographs are used, match lines must be placed near the outer limits of the photographs in the narrow margin of overlap. Necessarily, a match line so placed includes the least accurate outer edge of the photograph. Thus using alternate pictures may increase the difficulty of plotting soil boundaries accurately, of matching soil boundaries from one sheet to another, and of transferring soil data to the base map, and decrease the accuracy of area measurements.

Match lines can be placed on photographs either with or without the stereoscope. In the stereoscopic method, a line is placed approximately midway in the overlap area of a photograph. This photograph and its adjoining mate are placed under the stereoscope, the images fused, and the match line transferred to the adjoining picture. This process is continued through the line of flight and between adjoining flights.

In placing a match line without the stereoscope, two distinguishable features are selected along the outer edge of the area to be mapped on the photograph and connected by a straight line. The same features are identified on the adjoining photograph and connected. The process is continued throughout the area.

If it is helpful in soil mapping, the match lines may follow some prominent ground feature, like a road, railroad, or river, even though it is irregular or curving. In sectionized areas, match lines may coincide with the land lines.

The colors of match lines should contrast with those of other lines. Green ink is frequently used for match lines.

Although the placing of match lines requires time, they are a necessity for good mapping. They avoid mapping of duplicate areas on adjoining photographs, facilitate the transfer of soil boundaries from one photo to another, and simplify the cartographic transfer of soil data from the aerial photograph to the base map.

Soil boundaries and other mapping should be broken sharply and precisely at the match line when inked. Soil symbols should be kept within the match line if possible.

The matching of the mapping on one photograph with that on another can be done in several ways. The mapped photograph and an adjoining unmapped photograph can be placed under the stereoscope and the images fused. The mapping along the match line of the completed photograph can then be transferred stereo-scopically to the adjoining unmapped photograph, although this is not good practice. It is better to join sheets *after* mapping as a check on the uniformity of the work being done by individual members of a soil survey party.

If adjoining photographs are at the same scale, a strip of trans-parent paper or plastic can be placed along the match line of a mapped photograph. The marginal mapping is marked on the transparent strip. This strip is then placed along the match line of another mapped photo for checking or of an unmapped photo for transfer of the soil boundaries to the match line.

Another method, which is particularly useful when adjoining photographs vary in scale, is to transfer boundaries by reference to photographic images. Along the match line one observes the relationship of the soil boundaries to such features as isolated trees, clumps of bushes, field corners, and the like. The same features are located along the match line of the adjoining photo-graph and the boundaries checked or transferred to their same position of relationship to that feature. Difficulty is had if dis-tinguishable ground objects are few.

One could scarcely overemphasize the need for care in match-ing the mapping on one photograph with that on others, both for joining of lines and for checking of the classification. Roads and streams need to be continuous from one photo to another. Special care is needed at the corners where four photographs come to-gether. Without a systematic method, it is easy to make errors that will make later interpretations of the mapping difficult or doubtful.

A record should be maintained of the matching of adjoining photographs. This is especially useful where a number of soil scientists are working in the survey area. A transparent overlay over the photo index makes a good means of keeping such a record. As the photographs are matched, the overlay can be marked. Some place the letters N, S, E, and W on each sheet and cross them out as the sheet is joined on the north, south, east, and west.

Inking on the photograph.—After completing the survey on a photograph in pencil, with boundaries matched to previously completed and adjoining photographs, the field sheet should be inked. For clarity and checking, it is helpful to ink the three major classes of features in contrasting colors that have good photo-graphic qualities. For example, roads, railroads, buildings, and other cultural features may be in red, drainage features in blue-black, soil boundaries and symbols in black, and section lines and numbers in red or green to avoid confusion with roads.

Each group of features can be inked in a separate operation. Culture can be inked first in red, for example, and the classifi-cation of roads and other features checked. Drainage can then be inked in a blue-black and inspected to see that individual drains are properly joined, matched, and classified. Soil boundaries can be later inked in black. When inking the soil boundaries, it is best to close each individual area as one proceeds, or to ink the soil boundaries up to some specific line, like a road or field boundary. As a soil area is closed, the symbol should be placed as near the center as practicable. If the soil area is long or irregular, additional symbols should be added for easy reading of the mapping, but no more. Soil symbols should be placed to be read from the same direction throughout the survey and should be approximately parallel. Where soil areas are so small that the symbol must be placed outside the area, it must carry a pointer to the area to which it applies. Place names are usually the last to be inked. These can be in black or in the same color as the feature to which they apply. By leaving them to the last, they can be placed where they will not obscure soil symbols and other detail. Place names need to be arranged in ways that leave no question about which features they designate. Names of railroads, rivers, and other features that continue across a number of photos need not be repeated on each one—only enough for clarity. Care should be used in the placing of stream names so that no confusion arises as to which branch of a stream a name applies.

The inking of the major features on a soil map separately, and in contrasting colors, permits the checking of each group of features individually. This usually results in fewer mistakes. The colors also facilitate the interpretation of the original field sheet by other users. If all plotted data are inked in one color, the field sheets appear congested and it is harder to check and to interpret them.

Inking on overlays.—Inking on overlays is done in the same way as inking on photographs. Opaque inks should be used, as overlays are frequently reproduced by direct printing methods. If standard waterproof drawing inks are used on plastic overlays, they should be coated lightly with a plastic spray to seal in the ink and prevent chipping.

Orientation of the aerial photograph.—One of the advantages of the aerial photograph is the rapidity with which it may be oriented in relation to the local detail and the unusual ease with which the soil scientist can locate his position on the photograph. Normally in field use, the photograph is oriented by locating features on the ground having images readily identifiable on the photograph.

In relatively flat areas with scanty detail, orientation is more difficult. In some places it is helpful to mount the photograph on a plane table set up over an identifiable point. The photograph may be oriented toward a second identifiable point with the plane table oriented by its compass. Then short traverses may be run in the area. Since variations of scale within the photograph make some difficulty, it is necessary to tie the traverse to all identifiable landmarks along the route. Long unbroken lines of traverse are rarely necessary. Nearby rather than distant features should be used for orientation because of scale variations within the photograph.

Heavily wooded areas present problems in both orientation and location. These can sometimes be overcome by running short traverses into the wooded area from the identifiable features on the outskirts of the area. Stereoscopic delineation of drainage features on the aerial photograph before going into the field often helps a great deal, and stereoscopic study of the relief while in the field contributes to orientation and location in wooded areas, especially in hilly districts.

Sometimes it is necessary to carry the orientation forward from one photograph to another. This is done by overlapping the photographs. The photo centers are first marked by drawing intersecting lines from the tick marks on the sides of the photographs and transferring the center of the rear photograph to the forward photograph and that of the forward photo to the rear one. The photographs may then be laid over each other so that the centers are superimposed in the overlap area. With a compass, a magnetic north line may be placed on a photograph that has been properly oriented by identifiable features. Then the north line is transferred to adjacent overlapping photographs either by association of identifiable features or stereoscopically, and the second photograph is oriented by using the compass.

The aerial photograph may be oriented with respect to true or magnetic north when it is used with a detailed map of the area. Two matching and identifiable points should be selected on both the photograph and the map, preferably along a line near the center of the photograph. The compass bearing of the line through the points on the map can be measured with a protractor and the photograph oriented accordingly. When the orientation is made with a compass, the points selected should be easily identifiable on the ground. Unless the land is too heavily wooded, a plane table with compass is better than a hand compass.

Shadows on the aerial photographs serve to give rough compass orientation provided one knows the time of the year and day at which the photograph was taken.

Plotting soil boundaries.—Plotting of soil boundaries is largely a matter of keeping oneself properly located with relation to the detail of the photograph and drawing the soil boundaries in relation to the identifiable images on both the photograph and the ground. Keeping himself accurately located on the picture is the first requirement of the soil mapper. Soil boundaries are plotted in relationship to easily identified landmarks, such as field boundaries, streams, buildings, edges of forests, isolated trees, roads, and similar features. With abundant detail, compass orientation and measurement of distances are not necessary and the soil scientist is not tied to a traverse. He is free to move about and examine the soil types as necessary. As measurements are not necessary, the difference in scale within the photograph or between photographs are of little or no significance.

New features that need to be mapped and that have been established since the photos were taken should be located by survey *resecting*: intersecting lines, as nearly as possible at right angles to each other, from identifiable positions, locate a new position. Measured distances from identifiable features will give the location of such features. Usually the intersection of two measured distances will be accurate enough for this purpose.[2]

When one has become thoroughly familiar with the soils of the area and their relationships to the features of the landscape, many soil boundaries may be visible on the photographs. These boundaries can be plotted on the photographs and verified as the survey progresses.

On photographs of heavily wooded areas or others with few identifiable features, it may be necessary to measure directions and distances in order to plot the soil boundaries accurately. This is best accomplished by using the photograph on the plane table. If the photograph is oriented by the compass and its scale is known, measurements of directions and distances are largely a matter of correcting for distortion. Every attempt should be made to tie to identifiable images as often as possible and to use the local scale for that portion of the photograph when measuring distances.

Corrections.—Corrections on aerial photographs need to be made carefully. If the photographic emulsion is broken or scratched, ink will run and smear so that symbols and lines will not be legible. Corrections of ink lines should be made with a soft eraser or with cotton and alcohol. If a photograph is so damaged that it cannot be reinked legibly, it is best to superimpose a thin sheet of transparent plastic over the area and reink the data on this. The plastic overlay should be securely fastened to the photograph.

HORIZONTAL CONTROL FOR AERIAL PHOTOGRAPHS

To transfer the soil boundaries and symbols from an aerial photograph to a compilation base, a planimetric map of good quality is required. In areas having no adequate map, it is necessary to construct a base from the aerial photographs.

The scale of the map, its accuracy, and orientation and placement on the earth's surface depend on horizontal ground control. This control is the framework of a map and comparable to the foundation and steel frame of a large building. After completion, the frame is hidden from view.

A horizontal ground-control station is a precise point on the earth's surface, the position of which has been accurately determined by field survey methods in relation to certain parallels of latitude and meridians of longitude. Many such stations are scattered throughout the United States. These have been and are being established by the United States Coast and Geodetic Survey, the United States Geological Survey, the Corps of Engineers of the United States Army, the Lake Survey, the Mississippi River Commission, and, to a limited extent, by private mapping and engineering firms. The positions and descriptions of these stations are readily available from the records of the establishing agency.

---

[2] See also Appendix I. Map Preparation with the Plane Table.

Distribution and extent.—Soil survey parties are not equipped to establish ground control and depend upon and use the control already established by other agencies. Using these control stations as a base, the Cartographic Section of the Division of Soil Survey establishes photogrammetric control points between widely spaced ground points by a process commonly known as radial triangulation. These photogrammetric control points (also called supplemental control) are then used on the map base for the proper orientation and placing of each aerial photograph in order that all culture, drainage, and soil boundaries may be shown in their true positions on the soil map.

The density of established horizontal ground controls in the United States varies from 2 to 3 miles between stations in highly developed areas to 75 miles in some of the Western States. It is general practice for the Cartographic Section to utilize all established horizontal ground-control stations immediately adjacent to an area that is being mapped, because they add to the accuracy and simplify the preparation of the soil map.

With the radial triangulation method, the distribution of ground-control stations ideal for accuracy is one in approximately every 16 square miles of area, plus points in the near vicinity of all map corners, and points in every 3 to 5 photographs along the boundaries of the area. Unfortunately, these conditions seldom exist. Either too few points have been established or they are not distributed proportionately. Thus, in most survey areas it is necessary to use each control station. Where sufficient ground control is lacking within the area, it is necessary to use control stations up to 5 miles beyond its border. Aerial photographs are needed for the station and for the intervening area. Established ground control is so sparse in some mapping areas that it is necessary to use surveys of railroads, highways, and utility companies and the General Land Office. These, of course, provide a lower degree of accuracy than proper control stations.

Description of control stations.—Horizontal ground-control stations fall into three general classes: (1) Monuments, (2) landmarks, and (3) road and fence intersections.

The first is most important. Monuments are permanently established by geodetic triangulation and traverse with a high degree of accuracy. The exact point located is marked by a concrete block, galvanized pipe, or cut stone with a bronze station marker imbedded in the top. Some of the older stations are marked by triangles or crosses cut into stone monuments or on natural rock outcrops. Many of these have bronze markers cemented in drill holes in the rock. Most of these stations are described at length so that they may be readily recovered. The descriptions include distances and directions from two or three towns, a route description to the station site from some town, ownership of the property on which the station is located, distances from nearby objects to the station, and angles and distances to reference, witness, and azimuth marks.

935034°—51——7

Landmarks used as ground-control stations include church spires, smokestacks, water towers, air beacons, lighthouses, flagstaffs, and sharp mountain peaks. Their positions are obtained through triangulation and they usually have a high order of accuracy. Short descriptions are available, including date of their location.

Third, and of a lower order of accuracy, are such ground points as the intersections of the center lines of roads, intersections of the projections of fence lines with the center lines of roads, railroad intersections, road and railroad crossings, and intersections of roads or railroads with section lines. These stations are obtained along the route of a transit traverse, and their position and a short description are available from the establishing agency. They are of relatively lower accuracy than others because they are not marked in any way on the ground and the recovery of the precise point established by the traverse is problematical.

Methods of locating and identifying stations.—With the initiation of a soil survey in an area, the Cartographic Section of the Division of Soil Survey obtains positions and descriptions of all established ground-control stations that exist in and adjacent to the area. The stations are then plotted on some type of existing map, and aerial photographs are obtained that will completely cover not only the area of the soil map, but also adjacent ground-control stations that need to be used for control purposes. Attempts are made in the Cartographic Section to identify each control station on a photograph. This is a very exacting task because the basic construction of the compilation depends on *all* points being identified precisely. A large percentage of points are identified in the office with certainty. Those in doubt or which cannot be identified are then referred to the soil scientist for recovery and identification in the field.

The exactness and care required of the soil scientist in the recovery and identification of ground control on aerial photographs cannot be overemphasized. The misidentification of a control station on an aerial photograph, if not detected in the radial assembly of the photographs or in the compilation, will cause distortion in the scale of the base and displacement of all planimetry and soil boundaries in the area governed by the station. Even when the misidentification is found, the station cannot be used, which weakens the accuracy of the radial triangulation or of the secondary control points. The field party should use every care possible when requested to recover and identify ground-control stations on photographs.

In requesting the information, the cartographers furnish the party chief with the photograph covering the general area of the station and with the approximate location of the station indicated on the face of the photograph by a red triangle made with a grease crayon. A copy of the description of the station is attached to the photograph

The landmark or intersection class of station is not usually described at length because it is easily recovered. Perhaps the major factor in recovery and identification is for the soil scientist to be positive of the identical point described in the original control survey. Some intersection stations such as water tanks, church steeples, and airway beacons are moved, and consequently their new location on the ground would not be represented by the old survey position. The date of the survey in the description of each such station enables the soil scientist to find out from local residents whether or not the station has been moved since the control survey established its position. After the soil scientist is positive of the recovery of the station, he identifies it on the photograph furnished him for that purpose. A small penciled circle, preferably in red crayon, about one-fourth inch in diameter, should be drawn around the station on the face of the photograph. On the reverse side, a slightly larger concentric circle should be placed directly opposite the first one and the name of the station written nearby in medium-hard black pencil. Ink should not be used on the face of the photographs used for control identification. It is not necessary for the soil scientist to locate the point on the photograph by pricking it; the exact location will be determined later in the office with the aid of a stereoscope and pricked with a fine needle. If the field man judges that the cartographer will have difficulty in pricking the point stereoscopically, he should include a sketch on the back of the photograph showing the ground detail immediately around the station.

Monumented stations present more of a problem in field identification than either of the two previous types, because many cannot be accurately identified on the photograph even with the aid of a stereoscope. The monumented stations fall into three classes: First are those stations that may be accurately pricked with a fine needle when viewed through a stereoscope or magnifying glass. The surveyor should circle the pricked point on the back of the photograph with a medium-hard pencil, write the name of the station, and, if necessary for clarity, make a small sketch of the ground and objects immediately adjacent to the station. He may give a short note on the accuracy of the identification.

Second are those stations that cannot be identified directly because they are located either in open areas nearly free of detail or in sparsely wooded areas. With these, the field scientist should obtain measurements from identifiable objects, such as roads, fences, buildings, and small trees in the vicinity of the station. These *tie points* should be as nearly at right angles to each other from the station as possible, for this will provide the most accurate position of the station when it is plotted on the photograph. Three tie points are sufficient and they may be as much as four or five hundred feet from the station. The surveyor should be cautious in his selection of tie points, for fences and buildings may be moved or rebuilt, roads may be changed, and small trees may have grown since the photographs were taken. Usually the soil scientist can tell whether or not a tie point existed at the time the photographs were taken by referring to the date in the upper left-hand corner. The tie points should then be pricked with a needle, and a small red crayon circle placed around each. On the back of the photograph, opposite the area of the tie points, a sketch should be made, in black pencil, showing the general positions of the tie points, the station, other pertinent detail, and the measured distances from the station to each tie point. The name of the station should be written and a north arrow for direction included. Although the sketch does not need to be drawn to scale, it should be carefully done, because from it the Cartographic Section will identify the true position of the station.

Third are monumented stations established in heavily wooded areas where no tie points are available and the station cannot be identified directly. With these, the soil scientist is limited to recovering the station on the ground from the description furnished him and by making a careful study of the area on the photographs with a stereoscope. When he is satisfied that his identification is the best he can do, he should prick the location, circle it on the front and back of the photograph, and otherwise handle like the first group.

The designating characters stamped into the bronze station markers should agree with the description of the station. The United States Coast and Geodetic Survey generally places two or three reference markers in the near vicinity of the station. These markers are stamped with an arrow pointing toward the station, and the station itself is stamped with a triangle. Along some traverses, monumented stations are set in pairs, usually over 500 feet apart, and the soil scientist should take care that he does not identify the wrong station.

In the examination of photographs in the field for control purposes, a stereoscope should be used whenever possible. If one is not available, then a magnifying glass should be used for pricking all points.

USE OF AERIAL MOSAICS AND PHOTOMAPS

Aerial mosaics and photomaps are generally used in soil surveying much like individual aerial photographs, except they cannot be used for purposes requiring stereoscopic vision. If the mosaic or photomap is uncontrolled, its use will parallel that of the photographs. If it is well controlled, it can be used much like a well-constructed planimetric map. Since mosaics and photomaps cannot be studied stereoscopically, more care is needed to locate accurately drains and other features in densely shadowed areas, and thereby avoid errors in plotting soil boundaries. Isolated buildings and trails may be overlooked or inaccurately identified.

A set of stereoscopic photographs may be used, however, along with a mosaic. These can be retained in the field office, studied before going into the field, and the necessary interpretations and delineations made. These interpretations can be transferred to the mosaic before taking it into the field. In transferring any changes in cultural features to the mosaic, one must be sure to note them in a bright contrasting color and be certain that they are placed on the set of sheets that carries the plotting of soil data.

Matching on controlled mosaics and photomaps is much simpler than on individual photographs. Mosaics and photomaps are usually constructed to be reproduced in quadrangles or similar sheet forms. These sheets are usually bounded by latitude and longitude lines and will fit together with no overlap. Their outer grid line serves as a matching boundary, and the detail can be matched by abutting the adjoining sheets. If the mosaic or photomap has an overlap area, it is usually very narrow, and grid lines that can be used for matching will usually appear on the inward side of the overlap area.

Since mosaics and photomap sheets normally cover a larger area than individual aerial photographs, fewer sheets are required to cover the survey area. This greatly reduces the number of match lines between sheets and the time required to transfer and to match boundaries.

Inking on mosaics and photomaps is done like it is on photographs. Overlays over a photomap or mosaic are handled like overlays over the individual aerial photographs. Since mosaic and photomap sheets are large, overlay material must possess good dimensional stability.

The use of poor, uncontrolled mosaics can frequently lead to serious difficulties in field mapping and later construction of the map—difficulties that may result in a poor map and increased cost.

USE OF TOPOGRAPHIC AND PLANIMETRIC MAPS

When using topographic and planimetric maps obtained from reliable sources and constructed by precise methods, one can assume that the cultural and physical details have been properly plotted and classified, that place names are correct, that projections and grids are accurately laid out, and that the map conforms generally to high accuracy standards.

Although more accurate than aerial photography, topographic and planimetric maps lack the minute ground detail appearing on photographs that is so helpful in soil mapping. Also such maps are commonly on too small a scale for field mapping. As topographic and planimetric maps are bounded by grid lines and are so precisely constructed that adjoining sheets match, there is little or no difficulty in joining them.

Inking on the topographic or planimetric map is done with a good grade of waterproof drawing ink. As cultural and drainage features are already printed on the map, inking involves only the soil boundaries, symbols, and changes in features. Such changes are plotted by plane-table methods and inked on the maps in a bright contrasting color such as red or carmine. Old features that have been abandoned or no longer exist are crossed out in red ink. It is helpful if these corrections and changes are made on the set of maps on which the soil data are plotted.

If the mapping is very detailed, a separate set of maps may need to be used for changes. All changes should be noted on one set of maps, either on those bearing the soil data or a separate set, but not part on each.

Where topographic or planimetric maps of high accuracy standards and sufficiently large scale exist, they are valuable as a base for soil mapping. Even though the soil mapping is done on aerial photographs, for reasons already explained, topographic maps are extremely valuable in the field work. In some instances, the field work is done on the photograph and transferred to the topographic or planimetric map with a sketchmaster.

THE FIELD LEGEND OF SYMBOLS[2]

The field legend accompanying the field sheets must include a list of all symbols other than the standard ones shown on plates 1 to 5. Occasionally, it will be necessary to add a conventional sign for some feature that is not included with the standard symbols. Any added symbols should be submitted in legend form, together with detailed definitions. Recommendations about publication of such symbols should be made, together with a statement of need and importance. Enough standard symbols are provided for in plates accompanying this *Manual* to take care of nearly all situations.

The legend includes both the symbols used to designate the individual mapping units and those used for any special soil, land, or water conditions, such as rock outcrop, gravel pit, or intermittent stream. The field name for each mapping unit is listed, along with the appropriate symbol. Where fractional symbols are used, it must be recalled that each combination is a separate, individual symbol to be named in the legend.

Standard symbols for phases of stoniness, rock outcrop, eroded soil, soil blowing, and the like need to be repeated in each legend, with definitions giving the acres that one symbol represents.

The party chief needs to check his field legends with the field sheets continually during the survey, and especially at the end of it, to be certain that the legend is complete and consistent. Failures to do so lead to unreasonable costs in map construction and to errors in correlation and in the final publication.

DETAIL OF FIELD MAPPING IN RELATION TO PUBLICATION SCALE

To show the detail significant to farm planning and to the application of agricultural science to farms, it is necessary to map soils at relatively large scales. Nearly all detailed soil surveys are now mapped on aerial photographs at scales of 1:20,000 (3.168 inches to 1 mile) and 1:15,840 (4 inches to 1 mile). Some highly detailed surveys are made at even larger scales, say as large as 1:7,920 (8 inches to 1 mile).

---

[2] The making of soil legends is discussed in the section on The Soil Mapping Legend.

Reconnaissance soil surveys are mapped at relatively smaller scales, although field mapping is frequently at 1 inch or even 2 inches to the mile (1:63,360 to 1:31,680) in order to use topographic maps or aerial photographs. (See section on Reconnaissance Soil Mapping.)

Since several copies of the field sheets may be reproduced photographically, it is usually impractical to publish all of the detail mapped in a very detailed soil survey. The scale of mapping may need to be 1:7,920 (8 inches to the mile) to meet a complex agricultural problem. If the soil map of an average-sized county in the United States—about 980 square miles—were published at 8 inches to 1 mile, it would require a map about 21 feet by 21 feet or about 180 quadrangle sheets, each 17 by 22 inches. Such a map would be costly, bulky, and difficult to use.

It is sometimes necessary to consolidate or even delete some of the soil separations for practical publication of the map, especially if the original survey includes transitory features or minor subdivisions of soil phases. The problems of excessive detail in classification and symbolization are discussed in several parts of the *Manual*. Faulty soil classification, with uncontrolled legends, is the biggest single cause.[4]

Where transitory features, such as present land use, need to be mapped or subdivisions of phases are to be mapped but not shown on the published map, secondary sheets may be used to advantage. The mapping of excessive or unnecessary detail on the master map should always be avoided. If the published map is to be much smaller in scale than the field sheets, its cost may be greatly increased unconsciously by the mappers. Without realizing how costs may mount, some field men are inclined to say: "Well, it doesn't matter if we use separate symbols for two or more similar soils, we can always tell the cartographers to combine them." It is the responsibility of the soil scientist to map only the detail relevant to the purposes for which the survey is made. Detail beyond this clutters and complicates the field sheet, slows down the field work, and increases the cost of map preparation and publication.

Any lack of clarity caused by excessive detail increases costs and reduces accuracy. Careful judgment must be used in showing detail. Symbols need to be within the delineated areas and large enough for legibility; cultural and drainage features, civil boundaries, place names, and like information that makes the field sheet usable must be legible and of appropriate size. Symbols for mapping units need to be as short as possible so that they may be placed inside the areas and still be legible. Arbitrarily "standardized" legends with long fractional symbols are poor. Such symbols take up too much space on the map. Illegible field sheets are useless.

In figures 14 and 15 the same map is shown at several scales: (Figure 14 shows a map at 4 inches to 1 mile (1:15,840). The

---

[4] See sections on The Soil Mapping Legend, Units of Soil Classification and Mapping, and Plotting Soil Boundaries in the Field.

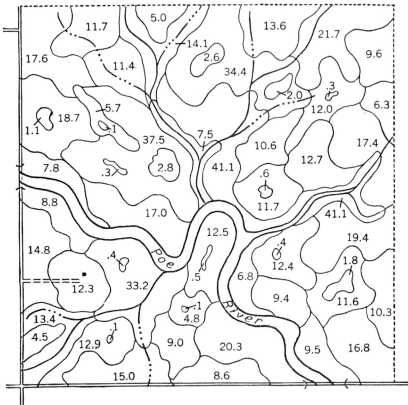

FIGURE 14.—Map at scale of 4 inches equal 1 mile. The number within an individual area gives the acreage of the area. (Compare with fig. 15.)

same map is shown in figure 15 at *A,* 3 inches to 1 mile (1:21,120); *B,* 2 inches to 1 mile (1:31,680); and *C,* 1 inch to 1 mile (1:63,360). The extent to which the detail mapped at 8 inches to 1 mile can be legibly published at smaller scales is apparent.

Combining small areas for publication.—When the detail on the field sheet is too intricate to show at the publication scale, small areas must be consolidated. When consolidations are made, the areas must be properly marked with symbols to show the disposition of the areas for which classification is being changed.

One method used to consolidate the detail to meet the requirements of the publication scale is to transfer all detail, except soil symbols, to the manuscript map and then, with reference to the field sheets, combine or omit the areas too small for publication. This method has the major disadvantage of taking a great deal of time in transferring delineations that will later be eliminated from the map. A better method is to combine the areas on the field sheets before map construction is undertaken. This combin-

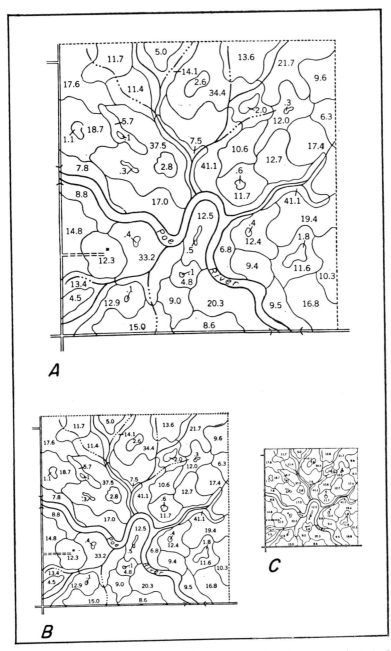

Figure 15.—Copies of the same soil map at different scales: *A*, 3 inches equal 1 mile; *B*, 2 inches equal 1 mile; and *C*, 1 inch equals 1 mile. The number within an individual area gives the acreage of the area. (Compare with fig. 14.)

ing requires ability to visualize the mapped detail at its publication scale and to follow definite rules about which areas must be combined or omitted. A helpful guide is a sheet of transparent acetate on which are outlined areas of minimum size for the scale of publication. This can be placed over the field sheet and shifted here and there to determine whether or not areas are too small for publication.

Table 1 gives a general idea of the smallest sized areas, at various field mapping scales, that may be shown at different publication scales. In this, only isolated or scattered areas are considered. If a large part of the total area were mapped in this maximum detail, it would be impossible to show it at the scales indicated.

TABLE 1.—*Minimum size of areas that can be shown on published maps of various scales from field sheets at different scales*

FIELD SURVEY SCALE OF 8 INCHES TO 1 MILE (1:7,920)

Ground area		Size on field sheet (inches)	Possible publication scale (inches to 1 mile)
Acres	Feet		
0.45	100 x 200...	0.15 x 0.30	4
0.86	150 x 250...	0.22 x 0.38	3
1.35	200 x 300...	0.30 x 0.45	2

FIELD SURVEY SCALE OF 4 INCHES TO 1 MILE (1:15,840)

0.45	100 x 200...	0.075 x 0.15	3
1.35	200 x 300...	0.15 x 0.23	2
3.44	300 x 500...	0.23 x 0.38	1

FIELD SURVEY SCALE OF 3.168 INCHES TO 1 MILE (1:20,000)

0.86	150 x 250...	0.09 x 0.15	2.5
1.33	200 x 300...	0.12 x 0.18	2
3.44	300 x 500...	0.18 x 0.30	1

If it is not feasible to combine small areas directly on the original field sheets, this can be done on reproductions of the sheets or on a transparent acetate overlay. Only the necessary symbols and soil boundaries are copied. If no need exists to keep the field sheets as they were originally mapped, the combinations may be made directly on them. Where made directly on the aerial photographs or copies of them, combinations should be indicated in a bright color that contrasts with the background of the photograph.

Especially where the soil scientist has difficulty in visualizing the field sheet at publication scale, it may be reproduced to the approximate scale for publication, and he can then make the consolidations on the small-scale reproductions. This method is costly.

All such schemes are expensive makeshifts. If the survey is properly planned in relation to both field and publication scale, they should be unnecessary. Office consolidations are never completely satisfactory. If complexes must be shown, their boundaries should be drawn in the field.

If unpublishable detail is to be mapped—and it is often neces-sary to do so—plans for handling it should be made at the start of the survey. Such detail may be shown (1) on the master map with special colors, provided this does not obscure or confuse the boundaries, planimetry, and symbols to be used on the pub-lished map; (2) secondary sheets may be used for the material not to be published; or (3) two manuscript maps may be drawn as the field work progresses, one showing all details and one showing only the material to be published. Commonly this last is the most economical alternative. Small areas of strikingly con-trasting conditions may be shown by conventional signs.

Where much selection is required from the field sheets, arrange-ments should be made to have this work done by a skilled soil scientist familiar with the area, preferably the party chief, and the estimated cost should be included in the *Soil Survey Work Plan*. (See p. 43.)

INSPECTION OF FIELD WORK

Each field party is visited several times during the progress of the survey by the soil correlator in charge. He inspects the field work and consults with the party chief. Besides examination and revision of soil classification in the descriptive legend, the field maps themselves are checked in the field for legibility and accuracy of soil identification and placement of soil boundaries.

Special attention is given to legibility of soil symbols and place names, closure of soil boundaries, accuracy of classification and symbolization of cultural and drainage features, systematic plac-ing of match lines, accurate matching of sheets, neatness of line work, and other items that influence the accuracy of the field work and the ease with which it can be used in map construction.

Party chiefs should continually check and advise the members of the party in order to insure neat and accurate inking of the field data. New employees especially need help until they are acquainted with the standards required in soil surveys. They should not be left to their own devices.

FINISHED FIELD SHEETS

The finished field sheet is the final product upon which the work and reputation of the scientist depends. It should be accu-rate, neat, and legible. It serves many other users and must be easily and accurately interpreted.

CONVENTIONAL SIGNS

The various mapping agencies of the Federal Government have developed and agreed upon standard symbols for most ground features. These standards are generally accepted for soil maps and should be used when practical.

Some special maps require symbols not normally found in the standard series. Such special symbols may be necessary because of the scale of the map or the data to be emphasized, but none should be used that may be confused with the standard ones.

In soil mapping, few such additional conventional signs are necessary.

For published soil maps the standard conventional signs are used almost exclusively. Such symbols are placed on the map according to rigid specifications as to weight of lines, sizes and spacing of dots and dashes, and the size and style of lettering. In field mapping, the standard symbols should be used, although exactness of line work is not so important.

Although some conventional signs used in the field mapping of soils do not conform to the general standards, it is still necessary that they be standardized. In the broad program of soil mapping throughout the country, standardization of as many techniques and methods as possible increases efficiency.

The cultural and natural features, other than kinds of soil, plotted in soil surveys throughout the United States are sufficiently similar to make the standardization of conventional signs practical. With a set of standard symbols, soil scientists do not need to learn new ones for each survey. By using the same symbols over and over, mappers develop skill in making them neatly and rapidly. The use of a standard set of conventional signs for natural and cultural features greatly facilitates the work of the cartographer. Obviously, the symbols for the thousands of different kinds of soil cannot be standardized.

To insure standardization at a range sufficiently wide to cover most features besides soils, a series of standard symbols for use by soil scientists are shown in plates 1 to 5. These standards include some alternatives. One set corresponds to those used on the finished soil map and closely approximates the symbols adopted generally by Federal mapping agencies. The other group represents a simplified form of the same symbols. This simplified set of symbols is solely for the convenience of the soil scientist in inking field sheets. It eliminates such symbols as double-line roads and substitutes a single line in color, and simplifies the spacing and dots for other signs. This simplified set of signs may not be appropriate in cooperative surveys if another organization plans to use the field sheets as base maps.

Signs and symbols are shown in the plates and are discussed under major classes as follows:

Works and structures

Roads.—On field sheets, roads are indicated according to the following distinctions:

1. First-class or good public motor roads are shown by solid lines. These include those public roads that may be used for automobiles at medium speeds and for hauling the greater part of the year and include all Federal, State, county, or other public roads in condition for such travel, all main or through roads in passable condition in sparsely settled sections, and all city streets and park drives open to the public.

2. Second-class or poor public motor roads and all private roads, regardless of condition, are indicated by dashed lines. Secondary roads include those public roads which, through disuse or neglect, are either impassable for automobile travel and for hauling or cannot be traveled without risk to an automobile, except at low speeds. Public roads that are passable for wagons but are not good for motor use are classed as poor motor roads.

Public roads are shown by solid or dashed lines, according to their condition; whereas private roads are shown by the dashed symbol, irrespective of condition. Public roads are those built or maintained by a public highway agency. Private roads include neighborhood roads in rural districts (except those of sufficient length and importance to be regarded as through routes, as defined above), lanes and stub roads to farms, country houses, or institutions, cemetery drives, and race tracks, and roads built or maintained by private or neighborhood funds.

Wagon roads winding through timber and other unimproved roads used principally in farm operations ordinarily are not shown on the published map. In sparsely settled country, however, such unimproved roads are shown if they offer to the public the only access to important places or to a large area of country. Occasionally, in unsettled areas, pack trails impassable to wagons or motorcars may offer the only opening to a region and should appear on the final map. It is convenient to indicate all traverses on the field sheets, but roads or trails that are not to appear on the published map should not be inked.

The class of road should be shown on the field sheets with the appropriate symbol rather than by figures. It is not convenient to indicate with figures precisely where one class of road ends and another begins, and the surveyor is apt to omit figures in a few places. In highly detailed surveys, especially where the soil map is used as a basis for detailed land classification, the class of primary roads must be subdivided according to the type of surfacing. All-weather roads may be shown with one line heavier than the other, and other primary roads by the conventional symbol. By appropriate modification, different symbols may be used for graveled roads and for paved roads where this distinction is necessary.

Buildings in general.—The map shows such permanent buildings as dwellings, public buildings, shops, factories, and other industrial establishments. Uninhabited dwellings, whether farmhouses or miners' and lumbermen's cabins, are shown only where they are important landmarks in sections of sparse culture. The conventional black square is used for all buildings except those exceeding the size of the symbol when their dimensions are plotted to scale. Houses should not be shown right next to roads unless the distance that separates them from the edge of the right of way is so small that it cannot be plotted to scale. Symbols for dwelling houses should be inked square and of uniform size on the field sheets. They are best made by outlining in ink an open square with sharp corners, and afterward filling in with ink. If houses are shown too small, it becomes difficult to make the symbols square, and, unless these are inked square and sharp, their identification as symbols for houses becomes uncertain. If it is important to distinguish houses from summer or winter cottages, the latter may be shown by leaving the square open. These symbols are used on published soil maps only where recreational land use is especially important and their use is specified in the work plan for the survey, otherwise the ordinary house symbol is used.

House blocks.—In towns of 2,500 population and under, individual houses, churches, schools, stores, factories, warehouses, and similar buildings are shown, except in business districts where buildings are constructed wall to wall and are shown as single block symbols.

In cities with population over 2,500, only prominent landmark buildings, like schools, churches, universities, colleges, and city halls are shown. Schools and churches are shown by the conventional symbol, and other buildings should be named. No other individual buildings are indicated within the city limits.

Churches and schoolhouses.—A church is distinguished by a cross, and a schoolhouse by a pennant attached to the house symbol at right angles to the roadway. A building used as both a school and a church bears the school symbol.

Railroads.—Railroads, whether operated by steam, electricity, gasoline, or other motive power, including all railroad lines listed in the Office Guide of the Railways, are shown by the broad-spaced symbol representing a railroad of any kind.

Electric trolley lines in urban areas or beyond city limits are shown by the standard railroad symbol and are designated by operating name and type, such as "Philadelphia Rapid Transit (electric)."

Double tracks, railroad yards, spur tracks, and switches are shown so far as the scale allows. Adjacent parallel tracks of two railroads are shown by staggered tie symbols and both lines are named. Adjacent tracks of one line are shown by extending the tie symbols across both tracks.

Railroads or electric trolley lines within a roadway are shown by fine cross lines having the same spacing as those on the corresponding line outside of the road. In such instances it is necessary to use the double-line road symbol on the field sheet instead of the usual single line.

In railroad yards with parallel spur tracks, only as many tracks should be inked as can be engraved legibly at publication scale, as too many tracks make difficult inking, illegible field sheets, and impracticable engraving. Where switches and sidings occur alongside single tracks, both the main track and the side tracks are inked in finer lines than the main track elsewhere; these fine lines are inked first and the extension of the main track inked afterward in a heavier line, in order to make clear copy.

Crossings at grade are shown by continuous railroad and road symbols; at grade separations, crossings are indicated by a break in the symbol for the lower crossing. A railroad crossing over a road is shown by a broken road symbol, and a road crossing over a railroad by a broken railroad symbol. (The words "overhead" or "underpass" should not be used.)

Railroad-station buildings.—A railroad-station building is shown like other buildings, except that its symbol is carried conventionally across the track to indicate the location of a train stop if this is not clear from the culture. The conventional station symbol is not drawn across the track where there is no station building; and its use is generally confined to small villages.

Bridges.—Symbols are used to show bridges across streams more than 300 feet wide, other bridges if named, and bridges in sparsely settled sections wherever the existence of a bridge is vital to the use of the road. Bridge ends are not shown for viaducts over railroads, railroad yards, roads, or streams. Names of large viaducts are given, however.

Drawbridges on roads and railroads are shown by separate symbols. Ordinary bridges and trestles on railroads are omitted. Wherever its presence would reduce the legibility of the map, the bridge symbol also is omitted.

The footbridge symbol is rarely used—only where the bridge is isolated and an important way into a large area.

Ferries.—Ferries are shown by symbol wherever the stream is wide enough to allow; where it is too narrow, the word "Ferry" is written. Names of ferries are placed on the map.

Fords.—The symbol for a road ford is similar to that used to represent a private road. The names of important fords appear on the map.

Trails.—The mapping of trails depends on their relative importance. In mountain and desert regions and in heavily wooded areas, especially where sparsely settled and where traveling is done largely along trails, important trails should be mapped and named. In the more densely populated districts where railroads and roads are plentiful, only trails such as those leading up mountains or through unimproved areas otherwise not readily accessible are shown. A mere "way through" not regularly traveled does not constitute a trail.

Steamboat routes.—Steamboat routes on lakes and rivers, over which regular public service is maintained by ferries or passenger boats, are indicated by fine dashed lines and the words "Steamboat route."

Canals and ditches.—Canals, whether for navigation, irrigation, or drainage, are shown by a double-line symbol if their actual width can be indicated at the scale employed, otherwise by a single blue line. Abandoned trunk canals constituting prominent topographic features are indicated by the long-dash symbol.

In the mapping of irrigation ditches, both mains and important laterals are shown. The mains are so designated. Canals and ditches are inked in blue.

Canal locks.—The lock symbol should point up current. The symbol for canal locks is inked only insofar as it can be engraved legibly at the publication scale, and the upper and lower gates are inked separately only where both gates can be shown legibly.

Aqueducts, water and oil pipes.—Only the principal aqueducts and pipelines are shown.

Power-transmission lines.—The alignment of high-voltage (100,000 volts or more) trunk power-transmission lines should be obtained in the course of the field survey and shown on the field sheets. Sections of power-transmission lines within corporate limits and lateral distribution systems should be omitted. Trunk lines are usually built on private right-of-ways and, in most parts of the country, are placed on steel towers. Power lines should be inked in red. They are not shown in sections of heavy culture.

Tunnels.—Tunnels of all kinds, whether for railroads or canals, are shown by tunnel symbols. The route of the tunnel is indicated by broken lines. Railroad or road tunnels are inked in black, aqueduct tunnels in blue.

Dams.—Permanent dams in streams, lakes, or reservoirs are indicated by a heavy line. Where a road follows the top of the dam, the road is shown in its correct place, and the road line on the upstream side is thickened to represent the dam. The dam should be inked to its mapped length and labelled "dam." The important ones are named.

Reservoirs.—The shore line used to represent a reservoir should correspond to the normal full state of the reservoir that is controlled by the dam. Artificial reservoirs surrounded by dams on all sides are not enclosed by the dam symbol, but are outlined in blue, like lakes and ponds. Small reservoirs are further emphasized by a blue water lining.

Levees.—Levees are shown on United States Geological Survey topographic quadrangles by hachures or contours printed in brown, and when these sheets are used as a base map, this symbol is used. The symbol to be used on other sheets is shown on plate 2 and should be inked in black.

Wharves, and so on.—Wharves, docks, jetties, breakwaters, and similar structures should be indicated by firm sharp lines and shown in such detail as the scale of mapping allows. These structures are inked in black, in outline only, as plotted to scale in the field. A narrow wharf or pier, however, is represented conventionally by a double line about the width of a narrow road. Jetties and breakwaters are inked in single heavy black lines.

Lighthouses, and so on.—All lighthouses and lightships are located on the map and shown by their respective symbols.

Lifesaving stations.—Lifesaving stations in general are shown by the house symbol, followed by the letters LSS; but lifesaving stations of the Coast Guard are shown by the same symbol followed by the letters CG.

Cemeteries.—Cemeteries are shown with their actual outlines; the name is inserted if the cemetery is a well-known landmark and if there is space; otherwise a cross is placed within the outline, or the letters CEM alongside it. Private cemeteries that are too small to plot to scale may be shown conventionally by a small square enclosing a cross, but they are omitted unless they constitute landmarks in a thinly settled country.

Airports and landing fields.—Boundaries of airports and landing fields are indicated, including those of municipal, commercial, and private airports; Federal intermediate landing fields; marked auxiliary landing fields; army airfields; and naval air stations. The symbol used for the boundary is that shown for a cemetery or small park on plate 5. The name is added, or the word "airfield."

Mines and quarries.—Mines and quarries are indicated by the pick-and-hammer symbol, together with the word "coal," "limestone," "granite," or other as appropriate. In sparsely settled sections with little culture, isolated mines, quarries, and even prospects (sawbuck cross) that constitute landmarks and are widely known are shown, together with their names.

Gravel pits are shown by the pick-and-shovel symbol. Large ones are outlined and indicated by either the symbol or by the words "gravel pit."

Oil and gas wells.—Producing oil and gas wells are indicated by a special symbol. Where such wells are so numerous as to be practically indistinguishable, only the approximate outline of the field (by dashed lines) is shown.

Furnaces and smelters.—No additional conventional sign other than that for a house is used to represent furnaces, and in many areas it is not practicable to name them. In sparsely settled sections, however, the furnaces may be the most important landmarks, and they may have well-recognized names which cling to the localities even after the practical disappearance of the furnaces themselves. In such areas, it is helpful to give the names, even though nothing remains but a ruined stack. The same rule applies to smelters, except that those shown on the map should be restricted to smelters in active or prospective operation.

Coke ovens.—Only coke ovens connected with mines in operation are shown on the maps.

Drainage

Tidal shore lines.—On soil maps the line of mean high tide ordinarily is taken as the shore line. The shore line bordering mangrove swamps, however, may be lower than mean high tide. In determining the margin of mean high water, the highest (semimonthly) tides are excluded and an average taken of the usual high tides as generally marked by the limits of vegetation. The charts of the United States Coast and Geodetic Surveys are frequently useful in checking the position of shore lines.

Shore lines of all waters should be inked in a firm continuous blue line and not broken for wharves, piers, and similar structures that may be built over the water. Such structures are inked in black. Sea and retaining walls that are simply artificially constructed parts of the shore lines are inked in blue.

Marshes in general.—Where large areas of fresh-water and salt-water marshes are recognized as soil types or soil phases no special symbol is used. Large areas designated as a land type may carry the special symbol or not, depending upon whether it will improve the readability of the map. Small areas are shown by their respective symbols, defined as to the acres represented by each one. Only small detached areas of marsh similar to adjacent larger bodies of marsh carry these symbols. Other wet spots are shown by the wet-spot symbol, q.v. Most marshes on low coasts are traversed by a network of tidal channels. Unlike the rills in mud flats, these channels are fairly permanent in location, and those that exist at mean high tide are mapped individually insofar as the scale allows.

Submerged marsh.—Marshlands that are partly submerged for many months each year are differentiated from ordinary marshes. Small areas are represented by inking grass tufts in blue (no horizontal lines between symbols) on the water surface.

River shore lines.—The mapping of broad braided rivers offers a perplexing problem, because these rivers are subject to periodic fluctuations and changes in width. As a general rule the width shown corresponds to the normal stage, defined as that water level remaining nearly stationary for the greater part of the year. This excludes stages of relatively short duration resulting from floods, whether periodical or out of season, and low-water stages. Generally, the normal stage exists for about 9 to 11 months for most streams in the relatively humid sections. If any stage of water other than the normal has been mapped by other government agencies, instructions should be sought as to the availability and best use of such cartographic material.

In areas where the flow of rivers, though active for brief periods, dwindles or ceases altogether for many months, the normal or prevailing stage is very low. Thus, rivers like the Platte and much of the Missouri are normally braided and are represented as such on the map. Where the streams have wide bottoms of unstabilized sediments, the land is shown as sand or riverwash and the principal channels are indicated as intermittent or perennial streams, double line or single line as may be required. Other bodies of land within the normal flood plain, having trees or other stabilizing vegetation, or cropland, are shown as soil types or phases. Rock outcrops are shown appropriately as such. Except in brief periods, many rivers in desert areas are no more than broad sandy washes, and they are shown by strips of sanding.

Natural lakes.—The shore line of a natural lake or pond is that corresponding to the normal stage of water. It is not necessarily the exact shore line found at the time of the survey, for the survey may have been made during a period of flood or extreme drought. An effort should be made to ascertain the shore line of the normal stage, as usually marked by a line of permanent land vegetation. The shore line used to represent a large lake subject to a gradual rise or fall over long periods is that line found at the date of survey. This date should be indicated on the water surface in ink.

Artificial lakes.—The shore line of an artificial lake is the line that represents the margin of the water surface at the full normal stage of the lake, as controlled by the dam.

Island shore lines.—The shore line of an island is that corresponding to the stage of water used for determining the adjoining mainland shore line. Islands exposed only at a stage of water below that accepted for the mainland shore line should not be mapped.

Drainage classification.—Field sheets need to indicate clearly and accurately all perennial and intermittent streams. On detailed soil surveys the pattern should be complete, partly because this pattern helps greatly in reading the soil map, especially where detailed topographic maps are unavailable. With soil types and phases well defined in terms of classes of soil slope and with the detailed drainage pattern, the length, shape, and direction of slopes are suggested to the experienced map reader.

In practice, it is well to indicate the drainage by dashed pencil lines on the photographs in advance by stereoscopic study. The lines must be confirmed and classified in the field.

Perennial streams are ordinarily inked as solid lines, but dashed lines are sometimes used instead. Since much advanced use is made of photographic copies of soil survey field sheets, the mapper should attempt to make it possible to distinguish streams from soil boundaries by form as well as color. Where a great deal of such advanced use is anticipated, perennial streams should be inked in long dashed lines with a few arrows, not enough to clutter the map, but enough to indicate the direction of the stream and help to distinguish it from adjacent soil boundaries.

Intermittent streams are classified on detailed soil surveys. Those crossable with agricultural machinery are shown with one dot between dashes, and those uncrossable are shown with two dots between dashes. Unclassified intermittent streams, as on reconnaissance soil surveys, are shown with three dots between dashes.

Perennial streams.—A perennial stream is one that flows throughout most of the year except in years of extreme drought. It is represented on the field sheet by a solid blue line or a blue line with long dashes, as just explained. It is important that the perennial character of streams thus shown be reasonably well established, especially in semiarid and arid regions where the water in these streams is vitally important to the use of the soil. In dry regions, streams having perennial water holes in their beds, even though water is not flowing everywhere on the surface during dry periods, are shown as perennial streams on the soil map. In some instances, local inquiry is necessary to supplement field observations.

Wide streams are shown by two lines drawn to scale. The double line should be used only when the actual width of the stream can be represented to scale without exaggeration. Narrower streams are shown by solid blue or dashed lines, increasing in width with the size of the stream. Stream lines taper toward the source, but should remain deep and strong to the very head.

Intermittent streams.—An intermittent stream is one that is dry for a large part of each year, ordinarily for more than 3 months. In arid and semiarid regions, intermittent streams are not reliable sources of water for stock, in contrast to perennial streams. The general standard symbol for unclassified intermittent streams is a dashed line with three dots between each pair of dashes. This symbol is ordinarily used for all intermittent streams in reconnaissance soil surveys. In detailed soil surveys, however, it is important to distinguish clearly between streams that are crossable with the usual agricultural machinery in the area and those that are not crossable. Thus, it is necessary in soil mapping to make a slight departure from the standard symbol.

Those intermittent streams that can be crossed with agricultural machinery are shown with the conventional dashes and one dot between them. Those intermittent streams that cannot be crossed with the ordinary farm machinery are shown by dashes with two dots between each pair of dashes. *Thus a detailed soil map should have no three-dot, or unclassified, intermittent streams.*

All clearly observable and mappable intermittent drainage should be shown and classified on detailed soil maps, even though a little of it may have to be omitted on published maps. (This should not be interpreted to mean that all insignificant rills and shallow gullies are shown individually.) The complete drainage system has an important relationship to the pattern of soil types and phases and assists greatly in reading and interpreting the soil map. Aggraded flats and valley floors without well-defined stream channels or scars are properly shown as miscellaneous land types or as strips of sand.

Disappearing streams.—Some streams, especially in areas underlain by limestone, disappear abruptly into caverns and may continue their courses for long distances through subterranean channels. The points of disappearance and reappearance should be located accurately, but only the surface drainage is shown.

Springs.—Only large and important springs are shown on the soil map in well-watered areas. In arid and semiarid regions, springs should be located with great care because of their vital importance to soil use. These springs usually have names that should appear on the soil map. Intermittent springs or those having salty or otherwise undrinkable water should be so designated on the map or in supplemental notes. Walled-in springs are shown like wells, by blue circles; but a spring that is a source of a stream is shown by a blue circle from which the outlet stream is plotted. The symbol for a spring needs to be made very clearly to be read distinctly.

Wells and water tanks.—As with springs, the importance of wells and water tanks depends upon their relative importance to soil use in the area. In arid and semiarid regions, both wells and tanks are shown. Artesian wells are so designated. They may or may not be flowing at the surface. In regions of few wells, all should be shown; but in thickly settled areas with many nonflowing artesian wells their presence may be explained in the report without showing them individually on the map.

Intermittent and dry lakes.—Shallow lakes and ponds that are dry for many months of each year are characteristic of arid and semiarid regions. Some of these are shown on the field sheets as specific kinds of soil. Other dry salt lakes and old playas, although not intermittent in the usual sense, are so closely akin to intermittent lakes in appearance and formation that they are shown by the same symbol. Those of large size and importance should also be described in supplemental notes.

Relief

Important mountain ranges, plateaus, bluffs, basins, valleys, and gulches are indicated on the map, generally, by the position of their names as well as by the soil conditions. Bluffs, cuts, depressions, fills, mine dumps, and narrow steep ridges are shown either by the standard symbols or by means of other conventions described in the text.

Depressions.—Natural depressions or sinks, like those common in limestone areas, are indicated on the field sheets by hachures, or by the standard symbols.

Mine dumps.—The symbol is used when mine dumps are not extensive enough to justify the inclusion of a miscellaneous land type in the mapping legend.

Boundaries, marks, and monuments

Boundaries, marks, and monuments to be shown on soil maps are indicated by the standard symbols or by other conventions described in the text.

Civil boundaries.—All civil boundaries, whether National, State, county, district, civil township, reservation (including National or State parks, forests, monuments, and bird and game preserves, and Indian, military, or lighthouse reservations), land grants, corporations (city, town, or borough), parks, and cemeteries, are shown on the map by their respective symbols.

Since these boundaries cannot be identified from aerial photographs in the office, the field scientist needs to plot them. Boundary monuments and other definite evidences of civil boundaries should be plotted, since they help in map compilation.

Necessary descriptions, survey notes, and plats of important boundary lines should be consulted. Data on National or State reservation boundaries can be obtained from headquarters prior to the beginning of the field work. Data on minor civil subdivisions can be obtained locally while the survey is in progress. Many boundaries are obscured or obliterated by natural causes or artificial works; some were indifferently marked when established; and others have lost some or all of their marks. Information from local settlers may prove of value and save time and effort in the search for obliterated lines. The word of a resident cannot be taken as authoritative, but merely as supplementing information from official sources.

Even though established land lines, as section lines, may have been placed incorrectly on the original survey, they are accepted as the *de facto* lines to be shown on the maps according to their actual position on the ground. Although some of the old Government Land Office plats may show sections to be regular, they may be irregular and must be shown on the finished map as nearly as possible according to the actual location of section corners on the ground.

Some civil boundaries are defined by statute to follow natural boundaries, such as streams or divides between drainage basins. Boundaries following large rivers should be given special attention, for they may be variously defined, as at the middle of the stream, its main current, or one of the banks. United States Geological Survey Bulletin 689 may be consulted for State boundaries. Although the field mapper is to identify the boundary line on the ground and then plot it on the map, ground conditions are sometimes found to be uncertain or lines indefinite or unmarked; for example, they may lie in streams that have shifting channels or banks difficult to determine. Again the line may not have been accepted by those living on both sides of it or by the proper county or State authorities; its location may be in dispute or even under litigation in court. The location of the State boundary line, therefore, should be subject to special attention.

The following general principles may be helpful: (1) A line marked on the ground and once accepted by competent authority is the real boundary, regardless of a statute (apparently) to the contrary. (2) Where the description of a particular bank or point in a stream is indefinite in wording or difficult of application, past practices or rulings must be sought. (3) Early Supreme Court decisions have ruled that a boundary moves with a gradually shifting channel or bank, but does not follow sudden shifts or cut-offs, and these rulings have generally been followed in recent decisions. (4) If a statute defines a boundary line as coincident with some channel or other part of a river, the location of the river itself at the time the statute became effective should govern, unless there has been a gradual change in the position of the river, as just indicated. If it is necessary to know the generally accepted location of a river at some past time, say at the time a law was enacted that made the river a State boundary, refer to General Land Office plats that were made at about the time in question. Supreme Court rulings must govern if they have been made, but few decisions that affect the details needed on soil maps have been handed down by the Court.

Civil boundaries should be verified before inking, as a precaution against errors in the interpretation of penciled field copy. Where civil boundaries of different classes coincide for a distance, the symbol of the major subdivision takes precedence, except in instances where greater clarity will be attained by another procedure. Where it is obvious that a civil boundary follows a stream or road for a short distance, the boundary symbol may be omitted to avoid confusion. In some places, however, clearness may be increased by placing the boundary symbol (in red) immediately alongside the stream or road.

County subdivision.—Only such county subdivisions are shown on soil maps as appear reasonably permanent in character and location. Those subject to frequent changes at county elections are excluded.

In general, counties are divided into small units. These bear different designations in different States, or even different designations within different counties of the same State. In the States organized from the public domain and surveyed under the public-land system, one or more of the so-called congressional townships has usually been taken as the unit of organization. In New England, and in other parts of the country affected by New England migration, are found town units, in which are vested many of the powers that in the South and in the newly settled West pertain to the county. Some counties in Maine, New Hampshire, and Vermont, in addition to the towns and cities—the only regular subdivisions—have partly organized or unorganized territory laid off by these States as plantations, gores, grants, purchases, locations, and islands.

The following summary, taken from census reports, gives the names of the primary divisions of the county, or its equivalent, in the several States and Territories:

Alabama	Election precincts.
Alaska	Recorders districts.
Arizona	Election precincts.
Arkansas	Townships.
California	Judicial townships.
Colorado	Election precincts.
Connecticut	Representative districts.
Florida	Election precincts.
Georgia	Militia districts.
Hawaii	Election districts.
Idaho	Election precincts.
Illinois	Townships and election precincts.
Indiana	Townships.
Iowa	Townships.
Kansas	Townships.
Kentucky	Magisterial districts.
Louisiana	Police jury wards.
Maine	Towns and cities.
Maryland	Election districts.
Massachusetts	Towns and cities.
Michigan	Townships.
Minnesota	Civil townships, townships, and ranges.
Mississippi	Beats.
Missouri	Townships.

Montana	School districts, townships, and election precincts.
Nebraska	Townships and election precincts.
Nevada	Townships and election precincts.
New Hampshire	Towns and cities.
New Jersey	Townships.
New Mexico	Election precincts.
New York	Towns and cities.
North Carolina	Townships.
North Dakota	Civil townships, election precincts, school townships, and school districts.
Ohio	Townships.
Oklahoma	Townships.
Oregon	Election precincts.
Pennsylvania	Townships, cities, and boroughs.
Puerto Rico	Barrios.
Rhode Island	Towns and cities.
South Carolina	Townships.
South Dakota	Civil townships, election precincts, school townships, and school districts.
Tennessee	Civil districts.
Texas	Commissioners' precincts and justices' precincts.
Utah	Election precincts.
Vermont	Towns and cities.
Virginia	Magisterial districts.
Washington	Election precincts.
West Virginia	Magisterial districts.
Wisconsin	Towns.
Wyoming	Election districts and election precincts.

Public-land lines.—In the so-called public-land States, all lands that have at any time been subdivided or "sectionized" by the General Land Office must be shown on finished soil maps by indicating such township and section lines as have been run and have been approved by the Land Office and are not under suspension. Theoretically, all corners are marked on the ground, but in practice many are difficult or even impossible to find.[5]

In well-settled parts of the country, where land lines often become property lines and sections are generally marked by roads and fences, the construction of a public-land survey net is comparatively simple. But in unsettled country or in settled areas where the roads or fences seldom conform to section lines, it is necessary to find on the ground and to locate on the map enough section corners to enable the cartographer to construct a land net built up from the Land Office plats and notes and tied to the located section corners. In some instances the old Land Office surveys are inaccurate, and the plats in no way conform to the actual section corners on the ground; therefore as many corners as possible should be located.

For map compilation it is not essential to ink the section lines on aerial photographs if they can be accurately drawn in the office from the pattern of roads and fences and from located section corners plotted on the pictures. Many users of the photographic copies of the field sheets, however, desire the lines drawn for their convenience, and the section numbers placed at the centers of the sections in figures distinctly larger than those used as soil symbols. Township and range numbers are placed on the outer edges of the sheet.

In order to avoid confusion with other cultural features, public-land survey lines are inked on the field sheets with a fine line in black or, preferably, in red or green, except where roads or canals are coincident with them. Township and range lines are made heavier. Only those township and section lines and parts thereof that have been surveyed and approved by the General Land Office, are not under suspension, and are indicated on the land plats by solid lines, should be inked on the maps. The fractional distances for section lines less than a mile are usually found

---

[5] For a description of the public-land survey system, see Beaman, W. M. TOPOGRAPHIC MAPPING. U. S. Geol. Survey Bul. 788: 161–378, illus. 1928.

on the land plats, and where accurate plats are available, such distances afford a means for plotting fractional land lines. Land lines broken at water surfaces on account of shore meanders should be broken as shown on the plats. Meander lines are not plotted or inked, and section lines are not drawn across meandered streams or lakes or across meander land.[6]

Search for public-land corners.—The time warranted in search for obscure corners is determined by the probable regularity or irregularity of the net and the proximity of corners already found. The less local information there is at hand, the greater the necessity for pioneer hunting for the needed land ties. In districts with few evidences of section lines, diligent search needs to be made on the ground for enough corners to prepare an accurate grid, because many users of soil maps locate themselves in relation to the public-land lines.

In a region where there are few roads on section lines, assistance in finding corners may be had by using an oversheet of tracing paper or cloth, upon which has been laid out to field scale either a single typical township or an entire land net covering the area to be mapped, built up in advance from the Land Office plats and notes. Such a tracing, placed in position over a field sheet as soon as the first land corner has been plotted, indicates graphically the *theoretical* location of other corners; and as more corners are found, the further placements of the tracing become more serviceable as a guide.

The field mapper should be familiar with the system of rectangular land surveys and the intricacies peculiar to it. Acquaintance with the standard monuments used for the several classes of land corners, their marks, and their bearing trees, as well as knowledge of the manner in which blazes on trees become overgrown with bark, will prove most useful both in searching for corners and in determining their authenticity where this is in doubt. Public-land corners that have been found in the course of field work are inked in red with the symbol for found-land corners. The map compiler is better served by having the location of the corners plotted than by the drawing of the lines themselves.

Township and range numbers.—Township and range numbers are placed along the margin of the map opposite the middle of each township, with the township numbers along the right and left and the range numbers along the upper and lower margins.

Triangulation stations and transit-traverse stations.—The triangulation stations and transit-traverse stations which have been tied to a traverse are indicated accurately on the field sheets in red ink with the open triangle and dot symbol. They are shown on aerial photographs as already explained in the discussion of horizontal control for aerial photographs.

Level bench marks.—Level bench marks are not to be shown on the field sheets, as their positions have not been determined geodetically. Field mappers need to distinguish triangulation stations, transit-traverse stations, and level bench marks one from another. Figures 16 and 17 show the standard markings of tablets used by the United States Coast and Geodetic Survey and the United States Geological Survey, respectively.

SPECIAL SYMBOLS

Several special symbols for soil maps are shown in plates 6 and 7. Most of these are for areas of soil phases or miscellaneous land types that are too small to enclose with boundaries and are yet large enough to influence soil use and management significantly. Definitions for these land types and phases are given in appropriate sections of the *Manual*.

---

[6] Meander land is unsurveyed land, usually between a former lake and shore or stream border at the time of cadastral survey and the present shore or border, commonly at a lower elevation.

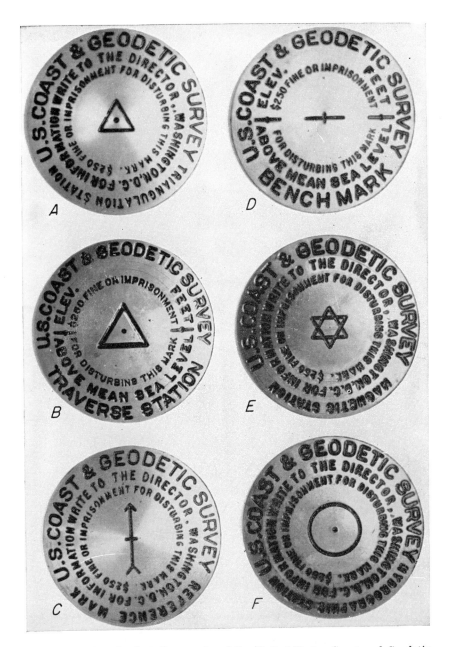

FIGURE 16.—Standard station marks of the United States Coast and Geodetic Survey: *A*, Triangulation station mark; *B*, traverse station mark; *C*, reference mark; *D*, bench mark; *E*, magnetic station mark; and *F*, hydrographic station mark. (Courtesy of Coast and Geodetic Survey.)

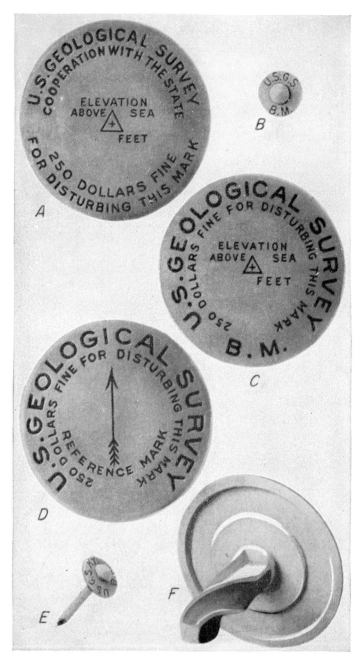

FIGURE 17.—USGS station marks: *A*, Triangulation or transit-traverse (marked "TTR" and numbered). *C*, Level bench mark, which may be later used as transit-traverse station, marked "TTR" and numbered. *D*, Reference tablet for triangulation, with arrow to station. *B* and *E*, Copper temporary level bench marks. *F*, Reverse side of *A*, *C*, or *D*. (Courtesy of USGS.)

Symbols for small areas need to be defined in terms of the acres represented by one symbol. Each area definition varies from map to map, depending on scale, intensity of land use, and purpose of the soil map. Names of symbols and the features they identify are as follows:

Name of symbol:	*Feature*
Rock outcrop	Small area of exposed bedrock.
Stoniness	For a small area of a stony phase: (a) stony, and (b) very stony.
Gravel	Small area of a gravelly type.
Chert fragments	Small area of a cherty type.
Clay spot	An exposure of clay.
Clay butte	A small clay butte—remnant of an old surface—like the miniature clay buttes in the Badlands.
Gumbo or scabby spot	Small area of Solonetz or of truncated solodized-Solonetz.
Sand spot	Small area of very sandy material.
Lava flow	Small or large area of nearly barren lava. (Reconnaissance legend only.)
Made land	Small area of fill, and the like.
Blow out	Small area of soil deeply truncated by wind.
Moderate wind erosion	(See section on The Soil Phase.)
Severe wind erosion	Do.
Wind hummocks	Small area with hummocks of wind-drifted soil.
Overblown soil	(See section on The Soil Phase.)
Moderate sheet erosion	Do.
Severe sheet erosion	Do.
Moderate gully erosion	Do.
Severe gully erosion	Do.
Moderate sheet and gully erosion	Do.
Gully	For use where individual gullies are shown to scale. (See section on Accelerated Soil Erosion.)
Uneroded spot	For small area of an uneroded soil in a larger area of eroded soil.
Kitchen midden	Old refuse dump of prehistoric people where too small to enclose with a boundary.
Wet spot	An area of soil too small to enclose within a boundary that is imperfectly to very poorly drained and is at least one drainage class lower than the area within which it is placed.
Areas of salt- and alkali-affected soil:	
Saline spot	An area of saline soil too small to enclose within a boundary.
Strongly affected	(See section on Estimation and Mapping of Salts and Alkali in the Soil.)
Moderately affected	Do.
Slightly affected	Do.
Free of toxic effect	Do.
Location of sample and reference number	Dot and reference number.

PLACE NAMES

Accurately determining the place names of cultural and physical features is very important to the soil survey because they help the user to locate himself. Names should be selected to identify all prominent features adequately. In areas where such features are sparse, it is important to name the less prominent features so that sufficient place names are given for orientation. In an isolated rural area, for example, a country store or some similar feature that would normally be unimportant, should be named. But names that contribute nothing to the use of the map and to the reader's location should be omitted.

Place names to be shown.—Names of the following features should be shown on field sheets:

Cities, towns, villages, and other settlements.
Rural post offices and railroad stations.
Country schoolhouses.
Country churches.
Experiment stations and substations.
Isolated ranches and resorts that are important landmarks in sparsely settled districts.
Important public institutions, like universities, colleges, and State hospitals.
Railroads (steam or electric). Besides the name of the railroad, it is helpful to give the name of the branch, line, or division, for complete identification.
United States highways (use number).
Bridges, ferries, and fords.
Through trails.
Principal steamboat routes on large lakes and rivers.
Large canals, ditches, and aqueducts.
Tunnels, dams, lakes, reservoirs, and large public works.
Lighthouses, lightships, and lifesaving stations.
Large parks and cemeteries, if the scale will allow.
Airports and landing fields.
Isolated mines, quarries, prospects, and oil wells.
Isolated furnaces and smelters.
Civil divisions.
Reservations.
Hydrographic features.
Prominent features of relief.
Springs, wells, and tanks, especially in arid sections where these features are of vital importance.

Determining correct names.—The soil scientist uses the best maps available in an area for guidance on place names. The place names on maps published at the National map standards have been carefully checked and edited and can be assumed to be correct. Less precise maps are also useful in determining the place names for some features. Such names should be checked or confirmed while in the area.

Where no maps are available for reference, or where the larger scale of the soil map requires the naming of features that do not appear on previously published maps, the soil scientist must use care in determining the names of the features and their correct spellings. Information may be obtained from local residents. It is best to consult more than one such source of information. If such discussions result in differences in place names, courthouse records may be checked. Local engineers and land surveyors are fre-quently a good source of reliable information. Questionable names are noted and submitted for decision to the Board of Geographic Names.

Lists of place names.—A complete list of the place names used throughout the survey is unnecessary. An annotated list of doubt-ful names is needed. The important point is that names appear on the field sheets in proper relation to the features they designate. Proper interpretation of stream names can be confusing unless the names are properly placed.

LETTERING

Neatness and legibility of lettering is perhaps more important on soil maps than on most other kinds of maps, because large numbers of many kinds of soil areas and many physical and cultural features are shown and because so much use is made of photographic copies of the field sheets. So many soil symbols and place names are used that the detail becomes confusing unless the lettering is neat, legible, and well placed. Each soil scientist must learn the art of freehand lettering.

The soil scientist should use a natural, simple style of lettering that can be done rapidly, and use it consistently (pl. 8). "Fancy" or "artistic" styles should be avoided. Among the many styles, the single stroke, either slant or vertical, best meets the requirements of soil scientists. It most nearly approaches the strokes ordinarily used in writing, adapts itself to small space, can be condensed or expanded without affecting the legibility, is easy to do, and can be made rapidly.

Figure 18 shows the single-stroke slanted letter in capitals, lower case, and numerals and suggestions for the order of strokes. In the illustration, the directions of the strokes are indicated by arrows and the sequence by numbers. Both slant and vertical letters are formed in the same manner. It is well to form the habit of following the directions and sequences of strokes as suggested in the illustration.

Skill comes with practice. The pen should be held as in writing and the strokes made with an even, steady motion. Slant or vertical lines are made with a downward stroke, and horizontal lines with a stroke from left to right. The slant of the letters should be uniform. A fine-point stiff pen is best; crowquills are too flexible. As waterproof ink dries rapidly, the pen point should be frequently wiped with a cloth or chamois.

Letters should be well formed and properly spaced. Properly made letters are of different widths. *W*, for example, occupies more space than *I* or *J*. In lettering symbols and names, this should be taken into account and the letters spaced to give neat-ness and proper position. With practice, one acquires the knack of spacing letters and judging the amount of space a specific word or symbol will occupy.

Aligning letter symbols and words approximately horizontal and parallel adds greatly to the legibility of the finished field

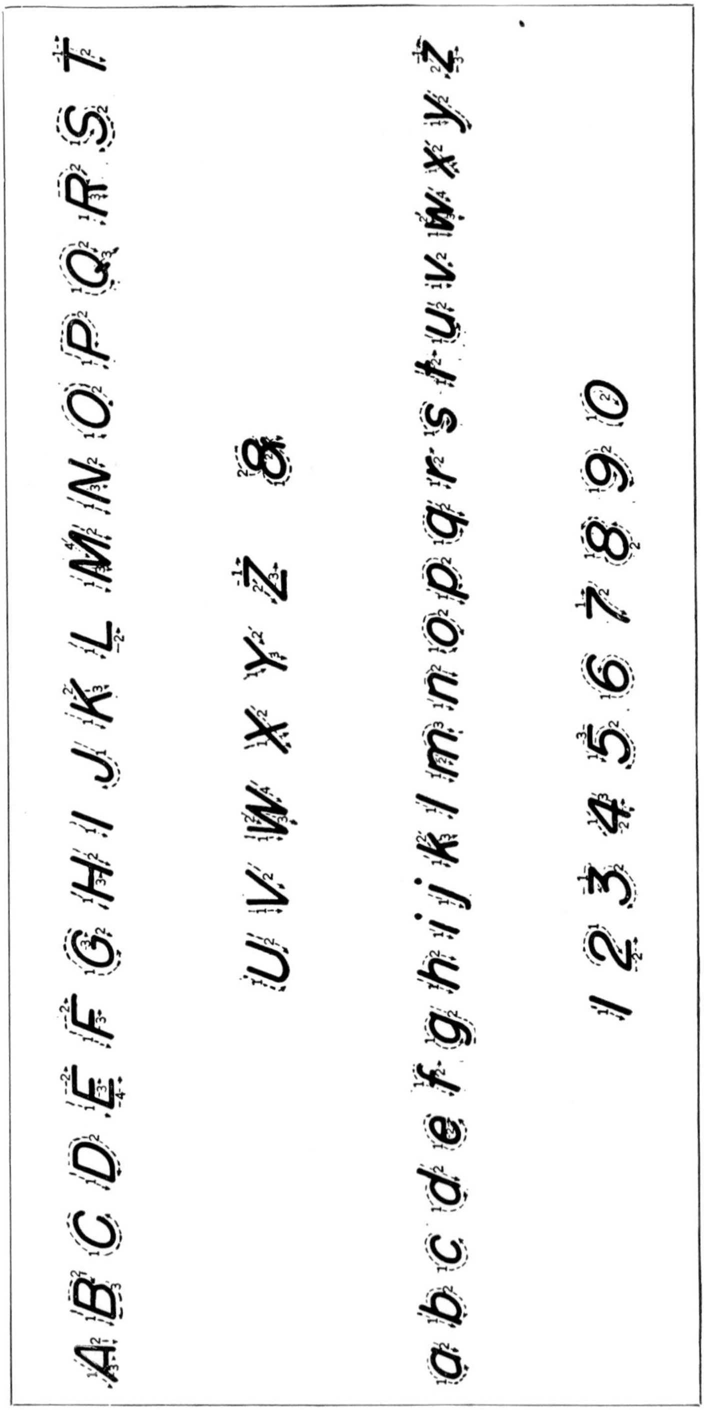

FIGURE 18.—Suggested order and direction of strokes in freehand lettering on field sheets.

sheet. Other things being equal, names of natural features are oriented with the features, and names of cultural features are horizontal.

Soil symbols should be placed as near the center of the delineated area as possible. Where soil areas are large and irregular, more than one soil symbol, placed to permit easy identification of the area, is helpful. When an area is so narrow that the symbol cannot be placed in a horizontal position, it should be placed in the area at an angle or vertically. Symbols are placed outside of their specific areas, with an arrow indicating the area, only when absolutely necessary.

It is standard mapping practice to use slant or vertical capitals, or capitals and lower case letters, to designate specific classes of physical or cultural features. In soil mapping, it is helpful to conform to these standards within the limitations of single-stroke letters. Standards for soil survey field sheets are as follows:

Features	*Lettering*
Civil divisions and cities over 2,500 population	Vertical, capitals.
Towns and villages under 2,500 population	Vertical, capitals and lower case letters.
Large water features, double-line rivers, large lakes and reservoirs	Slant, capitals.
Small water features, small streams, branches, creeks, lakes, ponds	Slant, capitals and lower case letters.
Large physical features, mountain ridges, valleys	Vertical, capitals.
Small physical features, hills, knobs, gaps	Vertical, capitals and lower case letters.
Cultural features, railways, power lines, bridges, airports, universities, cemeteries	Slant, capitals.
Soil symbols	Slant or vertical, capitals or lower case letters and numerals, as standardized for the survey.

CHECKING FIELD SHEETS

In order to meet modern requirements, most soil mapping demands that a great amount of detail be shown on the aerial photograph. Intricate patterns of boundaries among soil types and phases need to be accurate. Besides, the drainage and cultural features must be indicated clearly.

The soil scientist must recall that regardless of his knowledge of soils or his ability to classify and locate soil areas on the ground, the success of his work depends on its legibility. The results of his researches must be readily understood by others. Some omissions and errors are inevitable, of course, but a successful party chief keeps them to a very low minimum.

It is essential that all data be carefully reviewed and checked and properly matched from one field sheet to another. In order to do this accurately, it is well for the soil scientist to know where and in what form such oversights most frequently occur. With such knowledge, he can concentrate his inspection and checking on the most common causes.

Common errors.—From inspection of a great many field sheets, the following are found to be the most common mistakes, in order of their frequency:

1. Incorrect matching between aerial photographs.
2. Failures to close soil boundaries.
3. Areas without soil symbols, or with questionable ones not named in the legend.
4. Incorrect interpretation of cultural and drainage features.
5. Incorrect place names.

Differences in matching between aerial photographs occur perhaps most frequently at corners where more than two photographs abut. The most common failures are illustrated in figure 19. Aerial photographs overlap, have differences of scale in adjoining

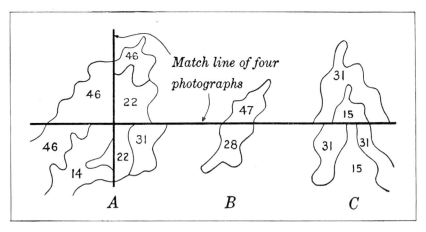

FIGURE 19.—Examples of failures to match aerial photographs: *A,* Corners fail to match; *B,* boundaries match, but not symbols; *C,* symbols match, but not boundaries.

pictures, and vary in light and dark tones; therefore, unless a systematic method is used, mistakes may frequently occur when inking the penciled field sheets. A few suggestions on avoiding such mistakes may be helpful.

1. Match lines should be placed on all photographs before mapping.
2. Match lines should be straight for long distances if possible, or follow sharply defined features, such as prominent roads or rivers. A stereoscope is useful in placing match lines on aerial photographs.
3. The matching boundaries should be transferred by relation to physical features that can be identified on the photograph rather than by scale. Some feature may be selected closely approximating the boundary line on the completed sheet and located on the adjoining sheet to continue the boundary. This can be done rapidly and accurately with the stereoscope.
4. Insofar as practicable, in order to avoid the distortion along the margins, only the center of the aerial photograph should be used for mapping.
5. Some cartographic difficulties in joining sheets may be avoided by transferring soil boundaries and symbols from the mapped sheets

to the adjoining new ones, but often this is bad practice. By studying the differences in mapping of individual members of the party at such margins, the party chief has a good check on the consistency of the mapping. In fact, many good party chiefs avoid giving individuals blocks of photographs for this very reason. By having match lines near roads, differences can be most conveniently adjusted. This scheme perhaps leads to some more work in joining but the ultimate objective of developing an accurate and consistent soil map is more nearly attained.

Omission of adequate boundaries to close all classified areas is a common error. Some typical examples of failures to close soil boundaries, thus leaving uncertainty of classification, are shown in figure 20.

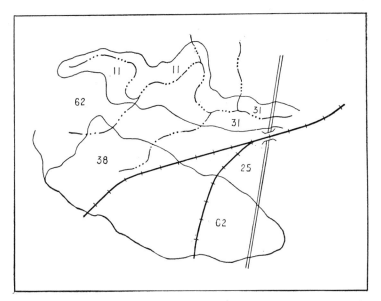

FIGURE 20.—The omission of soil boundaries causes serious errors.

To avoid such errors in closing boundaries, it is best to ink, individually, the drainage and culture first. Then the delineated soil areas are inked; each area is completely closed and its soil symbol placed before proceeding to the next one.

Areas without symbols, or with questionable or incorrect ones, occur in various forms. An area may be closed without a soil symbol; symbols may appear on the field sheet that do not appear in the accompanying legend or are unnamed; and illegible symbols may result from careless lettering or poorly made corrections. Listing each new symbol as soon as it is used, eliminates the appearance of symbols on field sheets that do not appear in the legend. When any new symbol appears to be required and is used temporarily, it should immediately be taken up with the chief of party for approval. If disapproved, the temporary symbol should be replaced before inking. This applies to *combinations* of letters and numbers used to indicate individual soil areas, not simply to the individual letters and figures in such combinations.

Practice and care in lettering, judgment in placing symbols, and careful erasures and reinking of corrections will reduce illegibility to the minimum. A carelessly made 91 may be read as 11, 71, or 77. Corrections should not be made by marking over the old symbol.

Incorrect interpretation of drainage or cultural features can seriously reduce the accuracy of soil maps. In figure 21, the

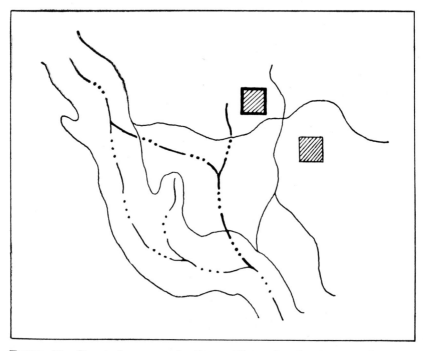

FIGURE 21.—Due to heavy woods, the positions of a fire tower and stream, light shade, were misinterpreted in contrast to their true positions, heavy shade. Consequently other drainage and soil boundaries are seriously in error.

locations of a stream and fire tower were misinterpreted due to heavy timber and the dark tone of the aerial photograph. Heavy lines indicate the true position of these features, light lines their mapped position. Because the soil boundaries were located in relationship to these two outstanding features, the result is incorrect soil classification of the area; and the necessary adjustment will affect the soil boundaries of adjoining areas. Had a careful study of the aerial photograph been made with a stereoscope, this error would not have occurred. Such instances can be greatly reduced by careful observation in the field, a study and understanding of photographic interpretation by the sur-

WORKS AND STRUCTURES

		PUBLISHED MAP	FIELD SHEET
Roads	Good motor		
	Poor motor or private		
Trails	Good pack or foot		
Railroads	Single track		
	Double track		
	Narrow gage		R.R.
	In road or street		
	Abandoned		
Railroad crossing Grade - RR above - RR beneath			
Tunnel (railroad or road)			
Bridges	General symbol		
	Drawbridges		
	Foot		-F.B.-
Ferries.		FERRY	FERRY
Fords	Road		
	Trail		
Dam			DAM
Canal or ditch			
Canal abandoned			
Flume			
Canal lock (point upstream)			
Aqueduct			Aqueduct / Aqueduct
Aqueduct tunnel			
Water pipeline			

543298 O—60—8a

WORKS AND STRUCTURES - CONTINUED

		PUBLISHED MAP	FIELD SHEET
Power-transmission line			
Buildings in general			
Summer or winter cottage			
Railroad station of any kind			
Church			
Schoolhouse			
Creamery			
Windmill			
Sawmill			
Cotton gin			
Forest fire or lookout station			
Cemetery			
Fort			
Gravel pit	Small		
	Large	GRAVEL PIT	GRAVEL PIT
Mine or quarry	Small		Show kind, limestone, coal, or other
	Large	QUARRY	QUARRY
Prospect		X	X
Shaft			
Mine tunnel	Opening		
	Showing direction		
Oil or gas wells			
Oil or gas pipeline			
Oil or gas storage tanks			
Levee			
Airway beacon			
Lighthouse			
Coke ovens			
Breakwater, wharf, dock, jetty			

DRAINAGE

	PUBLISHED MAP	FIELD SHEET
Perennial streams		
Preliminary, prior to field classification		
Intermittent streams:		
Crossable with farm machinery		
Not crossable with farm machinery		
Not classified		
Falls and rapids		
Probable drainage, unsurveyed		
Lake or pond in general		WATER
Intermittent lake or pond		INT.
Spring		
Wells or water tanks		
Artesian wells		
Wet spot		
Swamp or marsh (small isolated areas)		
Marsh (large grass or timbered areas)		
Tidal marsh (salt or fresh water)		
Submerged marsh		

RELIEF

	PUBLISHED MAP	FIELD SHEET
Escarpment, other than bedrock		
Bedrock escarpment		
Prominent hills or mountain peaks		
Sink holes and depressions: *Easy to cultivate across*	◇	◇
Difficult or impossible to cultivate across	⊖	⊖
Containing water most of the time	⊖	⊖
Sand wash (riverwash)		
Mine dump		
Sand dunes (dune land)		

BOUNDARIES, MARKS, AND MONUMENTS

	PUBLISHED MAP	FIELD SHEET
National, State, or Province line	▬▬ ▬ ▬ ▬▬	*(Red or green)*
County line	▬ ▬ ▬	*(Red or green)*
Civil township, district, precinct, or barrio	▬ ▬ ▬ ▬	*(Red or green)*
Reservation line	▬ · ▬ · ▬	*(Red or green)*
Land-grant line	▬ ·· ▬ ·· ▬	*(Red or green)*
City, village, or borough	▬ · ▬ · ▬ · ▬	*(Red or green)*
Cemetery; small park, etc.	·········	*(Red or green)*
Township line	▬▬▬▬	*(Red or green)*
Section line	··················	*(Red or green)*
Township and section corners, recovered	—+—— ⋮—⋮	—○— ⋯○⋯
Boundary monument	▬▬□▬ ▬ ▬	▬▬□▬ ▬ ▬
Triangulation point or primary-traverse station	△	△
Permanent bench mark (and elevation)	BM × 1232	B.M. 1232 ×
Supplementary bench mark (and elevation)	× 1232	× 1232
Any located station or object *(with explanatory note)*	⊙	⊙
Location of major soil samples (not published)		Ⓢ

SPECIAL SYMBOLS

	PUBLISHED MAP	FIELD SHEET
Rock outcrop	v	v
Stoniness — Stony	◖	◇
Stoniness — Very stony	ⓑ	ⓑ
Gravel	∴	∴
Chert fragments	◁	▾
Clay spot	✖	✳
Clay butte	⩔	⩔
Gumbo or scabby spot (truncated solodized Solonetz)	∅	∅
Sand spot	∷	∷
Lava flow	⟨⟨⟨⟨	⟨⟨⟨⟨
Made land	≋	≋
Blowout	‿	‿
Moderate wind erosion	⤳	⤳
Severe wind erosion	≙	≙
Wind hummocks	⩕	◖
Overblown soil	⌒	∩
Kitchen midden	#	#

SPECIAL SYMBOLS – CONTINUED

	PUBLISHED MAP	FIELD SHEET

Areas of soluble salts or alkali:

	PUBLISHED MAP	FIELD SHEET
Strongly affected	A	A
Moderately affected	M	M
Slightly affected	S	S
Free of toxic effect	F	F
Location of sample and reference number	• 26	• 26
Saline spot	+	+
Uneroded spot	U	U
Moderate sheet erosion	S	S
Severe sheet erosion	SS	SS
Moderate gully erosion	G	G
Severe gully erosion	GG	GG
Moderate sheet and gully erosion	SG	SG
Gully: *Not crossable with farm machinery*		
Crossable with farm machinery		

STYLES OF LETTERING FOR FIELD SHEETS

ABCDEFGHIJKLMNOPQRSTUVWXYZ&

abcdefghijklmnopqrstuvwxyz

1 2 3 4 5 6 7 8 9 0

Freehand vertical lettering to be used for cities, towns, churches, schools, ranches, state or county names, reservations, section numbers, land grants, and civil divisions. Also for hills, mountains, plateaus, valleys, peninsulas, islands, and other natural land features.

ABCDEFGHIJKLMNOPQRSTUVWXYZ&

abcdefghijklmnopqrstuvwxyz

1 2 3 4 5 6 7 8 9 0

Freehand slant lettering to be used for public works such as railroads, canals, U. S. highways, tunnels, bridges, dams, institutions, mines, camps, ditches, pipelines, wells, and for all hydrographic features such as oceans, bays, gulfs, lakes, ponds, rivers, streams, springs, falls, marshes, and glaciers.

SAMPLE FIELD SHEETS ON AERIAL PHOTOGRAPHS

The three following two-part plates illustrate the use of aerial photographs as a base for original soil maps, or field sheets. Numbers 9, *A;* 10, *A;* and 11, *A* are aerial photographs of widely contrasting landscapes; 9, *B;* 10, *B;* and 11, *B* are the same photographs with the original soil maps on them as drawn in the field. These plates illustrate the application of several principles discussed in different parts of the *Manual,* including inking of various symbols in red and black and match lines in green. It will be seen that some soil boundaries coincide with marks of pattern boundaries on the photographs and that others do not. Notice, also, the variation in number of reference points that the mapper walking over the terrain has for location. All soil units shown on the original soil maps were, of course, identified by observations on the ground, including soil profile examinations.

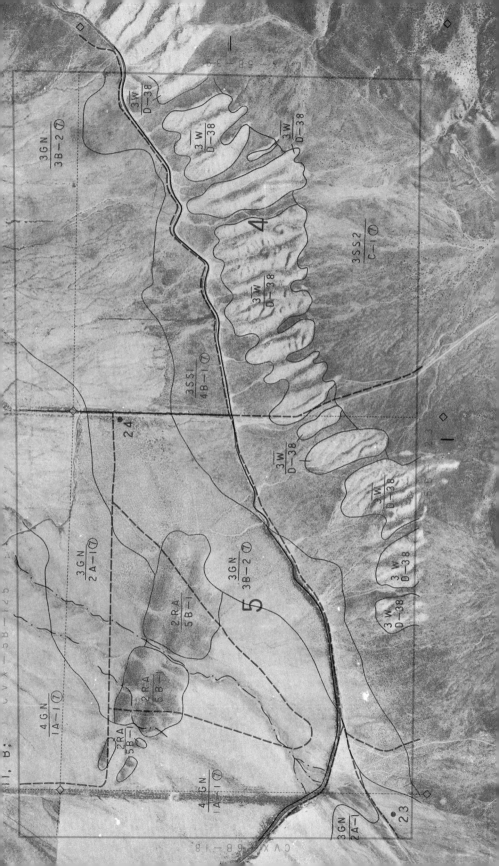

LEGEND FOR PLATE 9, *A* AND *B*

A sample photograph and field sheet in a characteristic general farming area of the eastern Middle West—Bartholomew County, Ind. The scale is about 1 : 20,000. The zonal soils belong in the Gray-Brown Podzolic group. Besides types and phases of these, there are types in the Humic-Gley and Alluvial soil groups. Only parts of the pattern of light-and-dark in the fields correspond to boundaries between Gray-Brown Podzolic and Humic-Gley soils. The soils have developed from Pleistocene valley-train materials, partly overlain by more recent alluvium and some wind-blown fines. The relief is nearly level to gently undulating. On the whole, drainage is good. Some of the boundaries separate soil-slope phases. The soils are used for general mixed farming in units of medium size. Corn and soybeans are prominent on the Alluvial soils. Here many local reference points—houses, isolated trees, field lines, road corners, and wood-lot boundaries—help the mapper to keep himself located. Yet it will be noted that the boundaries of the low-lying Alluvial soils (all those numbers ending with 73, 74, or 76) do not coincide with those of the woodland along the streams. A low sand dune in the northwestern part of the map does not show clearly in the photograph (area 605 on the map).

LEGEND FOR PLATE 10, *A* AND *B*

Sample photograph and field sheet in a mixed forested and farming area in Franklin County, N. Y. The scale is about 1 : 20,000. The land is undulating to gently sloping. The zonal soils are Podzols, but the dominant soils in this area are imperfectly and poorly drained Gray Hydromorphic and Humic-Gley soils. The large wooded area includes poorly and very poorly drained soils from sandy material of marine origin and some small spots of well-drained soils. The open farm land is used mainly in long leys; only about 10 percent is plowed annually. The soils are developed on late Wisconsin drift of low relief. The photograph was taken in September at a time when the soils were moist and color contrasts among them were at a minimum. It will be noted that few reference points for location guide the mapper in the wooded area. Within it, the individual soil types and phases make such an intricate pattern that they are included in a defined complex as the mapping unit. Even the land-use boundaries cannot be drawn from the photograph alone in the cleared places. Although very useful to the soil mapper as a base, this photograph is an example of one from which little about the soil can be interpreted correctly in the office.

LEGEND FOR PLATE 11, *A* AND *B*

A sample photograph and field sheet in a semiarid, treeless region of Sierozem soils, Utah County, Utah. The scale is approximately 1 : 16,000. A large irregular area of sloping eroded soil, developed from an old terrace remnant of Lake Bonneville, stands out distinctly as a light pattern in the lower right-hand corner of the photograph. A gently sloping, shallow, gravelly soil shows plainly as a dark pattern in the upper left-hand part. Elsewhere, patterns on the photograph fail to give reliable clues to the soil boundaries, and they must be "dug for."

veyor, and the effective use of the stereoscope. If the drainage pattern is penciled on the aerial photograph before commencing mapping by using the stereoscope, it will serve the surveyor continually as a means of orientation in heavily wooded or rough terrain.

Figure 22 shows how the location of place names is sometimes confused.

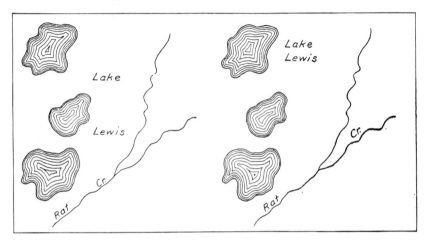

FIGURE 22.—Location of place names: Left, confusing; right, correct.

Transmittal letters.—Since the field and office work necessary to complete and to publish a soil survey continues over a considerable period and field sheets need to be shipped from one office to another, it is important that a complete record be made of all material transmitted. Even though it takes some time to check and to list large numbers of aerial photographs and other field sheets, it must be done. Shipments need to include a transmittal letter that itemizes the material. Such lists may be attached to the transmittal letter, with copies in each package.

The code, roll, and individual picture numbers should be given for aerial photographs; topographic quadrangles should be listed by name; and plane-table sheets should be assigned a number. Other maps or mosaics should be listed by name or assigned a number for identification. Supplementary material, such as photographic indexes and legends, should also be itemized.

Upon receipt of such material in any office, it should be immediately checked against the transmittal lists and receipt acknowledged. Any discrepancies need to be traced at once so that missing materials can be located.

Special instructions.—All the base-map material transmitted should be accompanied by an index map showing the location of the individual sheets and their relation one to another. Photographic indexes are ideal for aerial photographs. If photographic indexes are unavailable, a suitable one can be made by plotting the approximate center of the flight lines on a suitable base map and placing the photo numbers along the flight line in relation to the center of the pictures.

For topographic quadrangles or other base maps, an adequate index can be laid out on a small-scale map of the area. Such indexes should be marked with the name of the quadrangle or some identifying number or letter.

Overlay material, whether used with aerial photographs or other base material, is marked in the same manner as the base material. When overlays are transmitted with the base material, a specific statement that such overlays are included is needed. If corrections and additions are made on a separate set of maps, these maps are named or numbered like the sheets bearing the soil data and plainly marked and referred to as "correction sheets."

To help in locating specific sheets and in checking the material, separate items should be in order. Aerial photographs are kept in sequence by code symbol, roll number, and print number. Other base material is arranged by either name or number.

Marginal data.—Each field sheet should bear the name of the area or county, the State, the date of the survey, and the name of the soil scientist, or names, if more than one is responsible for the mapping on that particular sheet. Names of others who inked or checked the plotted data should be indicated. The scale of the field sheets should be shown. Commonly the full notes can be put only on the back of the sheet. Where they can be put on the front, they should be, so they will then appear on photographic copies of the field sheets. At least the date and the initials of the mapper should be placed on the front where they will not obscure the photograph numbers.

For use in the marginal lettering of the published map, the full name of the cooperating State agency, the name of its head or director, and the name of the soil scientist in charge of the State soil survey should be furnished. The names of both Federal and State soil scientists participating significantly in the survey are needed.

[For more detail on base map preparation see: SWANSON, L. W. TOPO-GRAPHIC MANUAL PART II.   U. S. Coast and Geod. Sur. Spec. Pub. 249, 570 pp., illus. 1949.]

EXAMINATION AND DESCRIPTION OF SOILS IN THE FIELD

Two essential elements of a soil survey require intensive field research: (1) Complete descriptions of the mapping units and (2) the location and plotting of soil boundaries. We shall review generally the problem of developing a complete mapping legend before discussing in detail the many individual items that enter into descriptions of soil units—the descriptions that serve as a fundamental basis for soil identification, classification, and interpretation.

Following the decision to make a soil survey of an area, a work plan should be prepared that sets forth the scale of mapping, the general methods to be used, the names of the scientists in the party and its organization, administrative arrangements for transportation, materials, and laboratory service, and the like, together with full descriptions of the uses to be made of the field results, insofar as they can be anticipated, and of all available maps, soil data, and aerial photographs. Where two or more research organizations are cooperating in the soil survey, their relationships need to be defined. (See pp. 43 to 48.)

A descriptive legend, as complete as possible, including *all* soil separations and *all* symbols that are to appear on the soil map, except for the standard symbols given in plates 1 to 5, should be prepared and made available to each member of the field party before any plotting of soil boundaries is undertaken. The first duty of the party chief in a new area is the preparation of such a legend, with at least skeleton descriptions of the mapping units. As the work progresses, especially in a new and undeveloped region, this legend needs to be revised from time to time.

On entering the area to be surveyed, the party chief should scout it thoroughly to get a general picture of the soils, geology, vegetation, and agriculture. Wherever possible this should be done in company with the regional supervisory scientist and the representatives of interested State and local agencies. Frequently, however, it is necessary for the party chief to undertake this work on his own responsibility. He should, of course, obtain the help of any competent and interested soil scientists available.

It is helpful for the party chief to reach the area in advance of his assistants so that he may familiarize himself with the soils, collect the preliminary data, prepare a preliminary field legend, and plan the work program. Toward this end, he must first have clearly in mind the objectives of the soil survey. His problem will be to determine how the soil mapping units and other features may be defined and shown on the map, clearly and definitely, without oversimplification on the one hand and without excessive detail on the other. First, the party chief must

123

determine the mapping units and symbols to be shown. Next, these units must be examined carefully at several places and clearly described. It is desirable that all soil units be examined and described in advance of any mapping. Where this is impractical, all the principal soil units may be defined, together with the subordinate ones in part of the area, leaving the others to be determined later as work progresses.

Where a new soil survey area lies adjacent to areas already mapped, representative examples of soil types already established and described should be examined in them. Full use should be made of any soil maps and reports available within the same general region or for like soil regions in other parts of the country. Usually, the party chief will find it extremely helpful to establish a small working library of soil reports and books or bulletins describing the geology, vegetation, and agriculture of the area.

CLASSIFICATION IN FIELD LEGEND

The setting up of a legend for a detailed soil survey requires first of all the identification and definition of the individual taxonomic units—soil series, soil types, and soil phases. These are sets of soil characteristics that are determined from the examination of sample areas. No soil type or phase can be *identified* on just two or three features alone, although one may be *separated* from a similar soil type or phase on the basis of one of two differences only.[1] Many fail to appreciate this distinction. In our minds we comprehend soils by comparison. Until we compare the soils of widely different climatic and biologic zones, we often fail to appreciate how very many characteristics most of the soils in a local area may have in common.

In a detailed soil survey enough taxonomic units—sets of soil characteristics—must be established and defined to permit the clear recognition and identification of every significant area of each soil in the project. The characteristics in each set are not precisely fixed; some range from the norm, or central standard, of the unit is allowed. In establishing these permissible ranges, no characteristic can be allowed so great a range that the fundamental nature of the unit, as a soil landscape, differs significantly from place to place in morphology, genesis, or behavior under use. Nor should the range in any characteristic be fixed narrower than its significance to the unit as a whole. In the present state of soil science, at least, it is impossible to lay down general quantitative rules about individual characteristics, because the influence of any one characteristic, or of a change in any one, depends upon the others in the set. That is, with one profile combination of clay minerals, exchangeable bases, texture, and structure and with a given land form, slope ranges within the set should be held narrowly, say between $\frac{1}{2}$ and 2 percent of slope. With

---

[1] A soil phase may be separated from the typical soil type or another phase of the same soil type on the basis of a difference in a single feature, such as slope; but a phase in one soil type is separated from a phase in another soil type on the basis of a set of characteristics.

other combinations of characteristics, the slope range may be 3 to 7 percent, 3 to 10 percent, 30 to 50 percent, or any one of a great variety. Small differences in clay content are critical in some sets of characteristics and not in others. The same may be said for any characteristics of soil horizons or array of soil horizons within the profile. Arbitrary combinations of "single-factors" are bound to lead to absurd results.

In defining soil units we must rely on experience and judgment in selecting allowable ranges for any set of soil characteristics. The practical purpose of the soil map must be served, and morphologically unlike soils must be separated.

The individual soil units need to be sufficiently homogeneous to permit making those differential predictions about their behavior and use that the principles and data of soil science permit us to make. We should go further toward narrower ranges in characteristics *only where sound scientific evidence shows that such differential predictions can be expected after further research.* Whatever classification is established in the field, the party chief should continually test it against the results of other research and against the experience of land users. Unnecessary separations reduce the value of his map.

As methods of measuring soil characteristics are refined, and with experience in the field, the soil scientist can establish and recognize continually narrower ranges in soil characteristics. We must guard against establishing narrower ranges just because our methods permit it. It is nearly as bad an error to split up soil types or phases into units not significantly different from one another as it is to include two significantly different units, inadvertently, within one. Furthermore, it is important that the boundaries between the units come at the place of greatest significance in terms of the sets of soil characteristics as a whole. As a simple illustration, we may think of stoniness: Let us say that areas of one soil type are similar in all differentiating characteristics except stoniness and that the range in stoniness extends from a low degree, where the soil can be cultivated, to a high degree, where it cannot be cultivated. In defining phases, or subdivisions, of this soil type, the main point of separation should be that critical place above which the land cannot be cultivated and below which it can be cultivated. On another soil type, this same separation may be neither significant nor necessary because other soil characteristics make it unsuitable for cultivation, regardless of stoniness. It would be as great an error to define stoniness narrowly in the second example as it would to omit the subdivision in the first.

Unreasonably detailed soil classifications, where they occur, commonly result because the soil correlator, the party chief, or both, have failed to face the job of classification. Many experience a real temptation to avoid the mental effort required. A common way of evading the problem of classification is that of setting up arbitrary classes of selected soil characteristics, such as texture, structure, color, and the like, along with arbitrary depths, classes of slope, accelerated erosion, and stoniness, and then letting combinations of these fall where they may. The soil scientist can shrug his shoulders and say: "We have recognized the facts." But the job of the scientist is not only one of gathering facts. He should gather the *relevant* facts and present them in ways whereby they may be readily interpreted. That is the purpose of classification. The details of soil analysis and morphology go into the notebook, not on the map. Between the detailed descriptions and the map lies the problem of soil classification.

Under a scheme devised to avoid classification, if class intervals are selected that will show significant differences in soil characteristics where the allowable range in these characteristics is narrowest, the intervals selected will certainly be much narrower than significant for places where the allowable range of characteristics is wider. The final result is an enormous number of arbitrarily defined separate units (really undefined as soils and even sometimes identified only by local numerical symbols without names that tie them into a standard system of soil classification!), the large majority of which are not really significantly different from one or more other units. In the application of such a scheme, despite the large number of separations—perhaps 2,000 where a proper system of classification would require only 150—some of them will still be too heterogeneous for making practical predictions, either because the arbitrary class intervals for some soil characteristics were not narrow enough in a few instances, or because of exclusion from consideration of characteristics relevant in only a part of the soil units. Such a scheme leads inevitably to poor soil mapping. For one thing, soil boundaries can be plotted accurately only if they come at a *significant* place in the landscape. Besides that, if soil mappers have a large number of boundaries to draw, they are less likely to get any of them accurately placed than they are if they have a smaller number of really significant boundaries.

As explained in detail in subsequent chapters, each separate observed characteristic of a soil horizon—as color, structure, texture, and pH—should be described in notes with standard terms for class intervals. Insofar as possible, standard terms should be used for inferred qualities, even though such qualities cannot be combined arbitrarily into meaningful soil types and other classificational units. The reader will note that some class intervals have slightly flexible ranges so they may be accommodated to specific sets of soil characteristics. Occasionally, class intervals for single characteristics need to be subdivided; often two or more need to be combined.

The normal soil.—First the classifier needs to study the relationships between the soil profiles in his area and the various combinations of environmental factors—slope, parent material, land form, vegetation, climate, and the like. He learns these relationships by comparison. As a general standard of comparison he should, if possible, define the *normal* soil (or soils). In the sense used here, a normal soil is one having a profile in equilibrium or nearly in equilibrium with its environment, developed under good but not excessive drainage from parent material of mixed mineralogical, physical, and chemical composition, and expressing the full effects of the forces of climate and living matter.[2] The typical representatives of the zonal great soil groups are normal soils. If the survey area lies within one principal climatic and physiographic region, one normal soil may serve as a standard for the whole area; otherwise each distinct region within the area will need to be considered separately.

The normal (or zonal) soil may not be the most productive nor the most extensive. Indeed, examples of zonal soils are not always found within the survey area. All the soils may be young, as in an active flood plain, or wet, as in swamps, or extremely limy, or very hilly, or because of some other combination of characteristics, development of a zonal soil has not occurred. In such a soil survey area all of the soils are members of intrazonal and azonal groups. Yet even in such areas, it is helpful to study similar climatic regions and to visualize what the zonal soil would be, if the appropriate landscape were present.

Frequently, several soil types in one area may all occupy normal positions but vary from one another in significant ways. That is, several soil types may satisfy all the requirements defining normal soils and belong to the same zonal great soil group, yet be developed from different mixtures of parent materials the natures of which are significantly reflected in the respective soils. In such a situation one may define the normal soil—the estimated normal soil—by orderly abstraction from the characteristics of those in the group.

A working concept of the normal soil, even in a survey area lacking one, can be a helpful standard for orderly study and arrangement of the other soils and for understanding their morphology and genesis.

Selection of sample areas.—The locating of sample areas should be directed toward one basic aim—to establish a standard for each unit against which other soil units can be compared. It must be emphasized that phases of soil types can be accurately defined and established only in relation to the defined standards for the soil types. The descriptions of some soils also take account of the effects of such processes as the silting of sandy soils being irrigated with muddy waters or flooded with water from glacier-fed streams, or the erosion of sloping hillsides, or the heavy fertilization of soils naturally low in nutrients, or the effects of long grass leys on podzolic soils. Still, the description should be objective and the conditions observed should be clearly apart from predictions of change that are expected to result from processes going forward.

Examinations of soil profiles may be made from road cuts during mapping, but detailed examinations for type descriptions

[2] Of course, it may be said that every soil is "normal" in the sense that it reflects its own history.

(and especially for important soil samples) should not be made in such places unless the road cuts are unusually fresh. Exposure of the soil in a road cut to freezing-and-thawing and to wetting-and-drying leads to great changes in soil structure. Layers of dust may accumulate on the soil along roadsides. In woodland areas the much greater light intensity along the roads favors the growth of grasses and other herbaceous plants that change the character of the upper soil horizons. At times dust from road-surfacing material is highly calcareous and changes the pH of upper layers of podzolic soils, after which other changes follow.

Having selected a representative place for a type description, an excavation is made extending through the solum and into the parent material. It is necessary that the excavation have at least one smooth vertical wall that is wide enough to show the entire profile clearly. It is important that this wall be as uniformly illuminated as possible and that the excavation be large enough to allow an examination of the soil in full depth. With Ground-Water Podzol, Tundra, solodized-Solonetz, self-swallowing soils, and other soils having well developed microrelief, it is helpful to have a trench dug in order that an accurate description can be made throughout both swale and mound.

Mapping units.—After establishment of the taxonomic units, the mapping units are defined. In a detailed soil survey most but not all of the taxonomic units—soil types and phases of soil types —are also mapping units. Even when plotting soil boundaries on aerial photographs of large scale, say 1:20,000 or 1:10,000, the pattern of some taxonomic units may be too intricate to be shown accurately and clearly. These intricate areas need to be combined into a soil association or soil complex[3] and shown as one mapping unit, defined in terms of the taxonomic units making it up (which are, in turn, defined as are any other taxonomic units), their proportions, and their pattern. Usually such areas bear a compound name derived from the names of the individual members of the complex. Solidized-Solonetz and associated soils must often be shown together in complexes. Ground-Water Podzols, Half Bogs, Bogs, and sandy Podzols are also often shown together in complexes on detailed maps.

A complex may consist of two phases of a single soil type that are taxonomically distinct but not mappable as separate units; it may consist of two or more soil types in the same series, or of two or more types in different families, great soil groups, or orders.

No definite rules can be laid down for deciding exactly what level of intricacy in soil pattern should be selected for the change from the mapping of each unit separately to the mapping of defined complexes. The uses of the map and the character and pat-

---

[3] The term "complex" is used in detailed soil mapping for those soil associations or parts of soil associations that are shown together because of necessity for clear cartographic presentation. The individual members of all soil associations are shown separately in detailed soil mapping where it is cartographically feasible to do so. (See section on Units of Soil Classification and Mapping.)

tern of the soils need to be taken into account. If the contrast in response to management among the soils is very great, every effort short of confusing cartography should be made to separate them. In some instances this means separating soil areas of only one-half acre or even less on very detailed maps where soil use is intensive. If the soils are similar in many characteristics, or if they are all unresponsive to management anyway, defined complexes should be used where appreciable savings in time can be made without reducing the prediction value of the map. If the soils in an intricate complex must be treated alike in fields, mapping of the individual components may not contribute anything to the prediction value of the map, and the highly intricate pattern may confuse the ordinary user.

The use of complexes does not relieve the scientist of the necessity of accurately describing the profiles of all their components. Data from the laboratory can be used only to characterize individual taxonomic units in the complex. This is also true of carefully planned experimental plots. Data on use experience by fields, however, can be used only to characterize the complex as a whole. Yield estimates and management requirements are needed for the defined complex as a whole.

Exceedingly intricate soil maps are less serviceable to most users than those where complexes are used as mapping units rather than the individual taxonomic units. On the other hand, where complexes are used without careful definitions of the individual taxonomic units and of their proportions and patterns, the maps cannot meet the requirements of a detailed soil survey. Complexes should be used sparingly on detailed soil maps for potentially arable soils.

Most reconnaissance soil surveys are far more useful if the individual taxonomic units are defined exactly as in a detailed soil survey and then combined into defined soil associations or soil complexes for mapping than if more broadly defined taxonomic units, with undefined inclusions, are used as mapping units.

Yet even on detailed soil maps of large scale, mapping units named in terms of a single taxonomic unit are bound to include small portions of other taxonomic units and of intergrades with other taxonomic units—say up to 15 percent.

DESCRIPTION OF SOIL UNITS

The value of soil descriptions depends upon the representativeness of the site selected, their objectivity, their completeness, and their clarity. Since making soil surveys is a very large activity, necessarily involving a great many scientists, the need of standard terminology can scarcely be overemphasized. Soil descriptions by different individuals within the same soil survey party, in different parts of the country, and even in different countries, need to be compared and correlated so that relationships may be established. The field descriptions are used by the regional supervisory scientists, the laboratory scientists, and others. Furthermore, a field party chief may need to turn over his notes and maps to a successor before the project is completed.

Great efforts toward standardization of terminology have been made in recent years. Improvements have been truly remarkable, partly because of the large amount of earlier work already done and partly because of the recognized need. These changes are among the most important ones reflected in this *Manual* over the earlier edition. Standardization can, however, be carried too far. Soils are anything but simple. Our terminology must be broad enough and flexible enough to permit accurate descriptions of all relevant features in all significant detail. We must find a reasonable position between extreme orthodoxy, on the one hand, and the sloppy or irresponsible use of terms on the other. Blind following of standard terminology may lead the soil scientist to overlook important features or to ignore fine but significant distinctions in special sets of soil characteristics.

Despite the improvements made, there is much farther to go in improving terminology. Responsible soil scientists are not in complete agreement on some of the terms used in this *Manual*. Some nearly arbitrary selection has been necessary. With further study and more refined measurements, some definitions will doubtless be changed. Furthermore, individual scientists may wish to use supplementary terms and classes. This should be done by all means where judgment indicates a real need. Usually, however, it is possible to define soils within the framework of terminology suggested in this *Manual*, so that the results can be understood by all.

Before taking up the details of each item in subsequent sections of the *Manual* it may be well to glance briefly at the principal items included in a proper soil description.

THE TAXONOMIC SOIL UNIT

Having established the normal soil as a standard set of characteristics for comparison, each unique local unit, resulting from a unique set of genetic factors, is defined. All the definitions should fit together, with no overlaps or gaps. These are the basic units of classification—soil types and phases of soil types.

Since the soil of the earth is a continuum, the units often merge into one another with gradual changes in characteristics through transitional belts several yards or more wide. Although divisions between units may have to be arbitrary, several characteristics usually change together. The outer limits of the definition of any one unit are bound to coincide with the outer limits of one or more other units. Thus, at the margins between two different soil units, the soils are more like one another than the soil near the margin of each is like the standard for that unit. Some field workers become disturbed over this obvious fact, especially where the transitional belts are broad. They may attempt to set up a new unit for the transition between the two. Often, however, this results in vagueness and overlapping, with two boundaries to define and recognize instead of one, each of which is as difficult as the first.

Each soil unit is a particular kind of landscape. It is defined by its land form and profile, and ranges in each. An individual soil profile occupies a very small place, essentially a point. Thus a soil area has an almost infinite number of profiles. Just as no two white pine trees are entirely identical, neither are any two soil profiles; but all trees called white pine have certain differentiating characteristics in common, as do all the soil profiles included in one named soil type. Each soil unit must be examined and described at several points in order to establish the modal profile and the allowable range in profiles. With experience and skill the soil scientist learns to associate soil profiles with the corresponding land form and can choose the proper places for the most useful examinations. The number of examinations required to establish a unit cannot be fixed. With a little preliminary examination in road cuts or with soil augers,[4] a skillful scientist may be able to prepare a good description from three major profiles, but usually more are required. As the work progresses, these descriptions need to be tested again and again in other areas of the unit. The final soil description is that of a three-dimensional soil-landscape.

In the field notes, observations must be clearly separated from conclusions and speculations. The condition of growing crops is an observable fact, but statements about soil productivity are inferred. The scientist may observe that the soil material is nearly uniform silt loam, rich in silt, low in clay and sand, and without coarse fragments. These are observable facts, whereas the interpretation that the soil is formed from loess is an inference from these and other observable facts. In making observations the soil scientist is guided by principles of genesis, by known relationships between soils and other features of the landscape, and by principles of soil management. These principles are helpful in making decisions about the significance of observable features.

This is not to suggest that speculation about the genesis and use capability of the soil are out of place. Quite the reverse. Such speculations are to be encouraged, but they should be clearly separated from observations. The descriptions of morphology, vegetation, land form, and geology should be as objective as possible. Any experienced soil scientist can testify to the great value of complete, objective original field notes. One can scarcely overemphasize their great usefulness. Many exceedingly important interpretations and relationships have been discovered after the descriptions were prepared—when they were being studied with other descriptions or with data from the laboratory—relationships that were not in the minds of the field men when the observations were being made and recorded. Above all, the features of the soil or landscape should not be left to memory alone.

---

[4] The auger, of course, should not be used for major profile studies, nor should road cuts unless they are fresh,

Many soil scientists have difficulty in describing the obvious. Without the exercise of care, the soil scientist may return from a survey area or exploratory trip with complete notes and good photographs of the uncommon soils, crops, and farms but without clear objective descriptions of the common ones. Unless an adequate description of the norm is available, all notes taken lose accuracy and significance.

Whenever practical, basic and detailed studies should be made of virgin soils. Only in these can the upper layers be properly defined. Yet, some companion descriptions of cultivated soils are needed, because many soils change a great deal with cultivation in ways quite apart from deterioration due to erosion, loss of structure, or depletion of organic matter and nutrients. Podzols, for example, may have a thick organic mat, often destroyed in burning and clearing, that is a definite part of the natural profile and essential to an understanding of its genesis. The natural surface horizons of many soils have exceedingly low bulk-densities, which increase greatly after a few years of cultivation. To illustrate, good examples of Subarctic Brown Forest soils may have surface organic layers (A_{00} and A_0) 3 to 6 inches thick over a solum some 19 inches thick. After normal clearing and cultivation the whole solum may be 15 inches thick, due to normal losses of organic matter and increases in bulk density, without any soil removal by erosion or blowing. To make comparisons, one needs a clear concept of the standard cultivated soil as well as of the virgin soil.

Every reasonable attempt should be made to locate undisturbed virgin areas in order to describe and sample the very upper layers. Even though these are always mixed in cultivation, they are very important to an understanding of soil genesis. In them occur the most active biological processes that influence soil genesis in a natural landscape. Thus, the uppermost 1 or 2 inches of the solum may provide exceedingly important clues to genetic processes. Furthermore, forest fires or grazing may alter the surface of podzolic soils considerably. Fence rows are also to be avoided, since they often have an unusual flora and commonly have received accumulations of organic and mineral dust from adjacent fields. It is not at all uncommon for the A_1 horizons of podzolic soils to be thickened from 2 or 3 inches to 6 or 7 inches in old fence rows under grass.

The search for virgin examples of a soil unit should not, however, become an obsession that leads the scientist to something far different from the modal soil. In many survey areas it will not be possible to find good examples, especially of the productive soils, in virgin sites. It is far better to develop a cultivated standard from several good examples than to use an unrepresentative virgin one. Wherever possible the management history of these sites should be described. In many countries no good examples of the productive soils exist except in cultivated fields, orchards, or pastures. Even in our own country, virgin areas of Prairie and Chernozem soils are exceedingly scarce. Some of those that can be found may have something unusual about them that makes them suspect for use as standards. Where cultivated standards are used, every reasonable attempt needs to be taken to establish a norm for both management history and for the soil itself.

Perhaps this point deserves emphasis. Some soil scientists have what amounts to an obsession for basing soil classification on virgin soils, even to the neglect of cultivated soils, especially of those that have been markedly altered by long agricultural use. In long-cultivated landscapes, some man-made or anthropic soils are sufficiently different from the original virgin soil to require separate series designation for proper classification and interpretation, either to understand the genesis of the soils or to predict their crop adaptabilities and management requirements.[5] For such soils, the definitions must be sought in the cultivated fields. Sometimes virgin counterparts may be found for comparison and sometimes not.

By grouping all items needed in a soil description in the same way, soils can be compared easily, and several descriptions of the same soil type may be abstracted into one that is standard for the type. A suggested grouping is that given in the seven numbered paragraphs following.[6]

1. Land form, relief, and drainage.—First of all, a description is needed of the relief—the gradient, length, and shape of slopes, and their pattern. This can be usefully supplemented by brief descriptions of the kind of land form—dissected terrace, active flood plain, esker, drumlin, old plain of coalescing fans, and the like. Since these terms are primarily the responsibility of physical geologists and geomorphologists, their definitions and use should be followed. Where soil scientists need supplementary terms for finer distinctions, these should be consistent with the major definitions.

Relief and drainage need to be mentioned separately. Although runoff (or external soil drainage) is closely related to slope, internal drainage depends upon the permeability of the soil and of the material beneath it. Thus a permeable soil may be well-drained on a gentle slope, whereas a slowly permeable soil may be imperfectly or even poorly drained on the same slope. Relationships between slope and permeability cannot be defined broadly for all soils in terms of drainage. One must also take into account the character of the soil itself in assigning to it a drainage class. The climate influences drainage relationships. In a cool climate with nearly continuous rainfall, poorly drained soils may be found on steep slopes.

Where differences in elevation are significant these should be recorded, either from the topographic survey, if the map is available, or by approximate measurement with a barometer. Evidence of flooding or of recent showers of volcanic ash need to be

---

[5] For some excellent examples see EDELMAN, C. H. THE SOILS OF THE NETHERLANDS. 177 pp., illus. (Maps). Amsterdam. 1950.

[6] Only brief statements are given here of items discussed in full later.

noted. Where significant, the exposure of the site to wind or sun needs to be observed. Near the boundary between plant associations, a difference in wind or exposure may determine the association. Where moisture is limiting, north-facing slopes contrast sharply with south-facing slopes in both vegetation and soil. In northern Europe, east-west sand ridges often have Podzols on the north slopes and Brown Forest soils on the south slopes. In dry regions of the northern hemisphere south slopes may have Sierozem soils or even Lithosols, and the north slopes, Brown or Chestnut soils.

2. **Parent material.**—The first requirement is a clear description of the parent material itself—its texture, structure, color, consistence, and any other significant features, including depth and stratification. Its approximate mineralogical composition should be given insofar as it can be determined in the field. Often supplementary laboratory determinations are needed. Suggestions should be added regarding the rock source of the material, such as granite, basalt, sandstone, limestone, and so on, or mixtures of several kinds of rock. The manner in which parent materials originated should be suggested: weathering of rocks in place, wind-deposited material, glacial till, mud flow, local alluvium, general alluvium, and so on. Many terms that relate to mode of origin, such as glacial till, loess, and alluvium, are too general for soil descriptions although they are useful as supplements. Important suggestions about probable or possible differences between the substratum (as C horizon) and the original material from which the solum itself has been developed may be helpful.

3. **The soil profile.**—After the excavation has been made for the study of the soil profile, the major horizons should be located first. If these can be given letter designations, as A, B, C, and their subdivisions, well and good. Often this is not possible without some laboratory study. Generally, however, it is best to make an estimate of the letter designation and indicate uncertainties with a question mark. Where great uncertainty exists, the horizons may simply be numbered from the surface on down to the parent material.

With the horizon boundaries located, the depth and thickness of each are recorded, together with the character of the boundaries between them. The zero point for measurement is usually the top of the A_1 horizon. After measurement, each horizon is described with special attention to the following items:

Color: The color names and mathematical (Munsell) notations are taken from the standard color charts. Where the soil is streaked or mottled with contrasting colors, or where the outsides of aggregates are unlike the interiors, the principal colors are noted separately. Any relevant notes on moisture conditions may be added. Colors of moist soil are usually given in soil descriptions. In addition the authors recommend that the colors of air-dry samples be noted, especially for comparing soils in widely different locations.

Texture: Soil class is observed in the field by feeling the soil with the fingers. In former years the many disparities existing between soil class as determined in the field and by the old standard triangle were ignored. Recently these have been adjusted and the correspondence is now fairly close. In all cases of doubt, special samples should be forwarded to the laboratory for immediate attention so that the soil survey party may have a uniform basis for soil class determination.

Structure: Soil structure needs careful attention, partly because of its importance to soil productivity, soil permeability, and root growth, and partly because of its great significance in soil genesis. This latter fact emphasizes the importance of the upper layer of virgin soils, even though they may be destroyed in tillage.

Porosity.

Consistence.

Reaction and effervescence: Several useful kits are available for making these determinations.

Concretions and other special formations.

Organic matter and roots.

Chemical and mineralogical composition: Kinds and amounts of clay minerals, exchangeable bases, plant nutrients, and the like can be obtained only from laboratory examinations of samples representative of each genetic horizon. Where uncertainty exists about the uniformity of any particular horizon, it may be subdivided arbitrarily and samples taken from the several subdivisions.

4. Stoniness.—Where stones are present, notes on their number and size and their distribution in the profile are essential in evaluating the use capabilities of the soil, and in correctly establishing phases for stoniness within soil types.

5. Erosion or truncation.—Most sloping soils have at least some erosion. In areas of recent uplift, gullies and other evidences of erosion may be conspicuous natural features of the landscape. Mainly, however, severe erosion has followed changes in plant cover that have permitted greatly accelerated erosion over that normal for the type. Such features are noted and their relationship to use and the other factors of the environment suggested. It is exceedingly important to differentiate between natural erosion, however severe, and accelerated erosion. Notes on the accelerated erosion, where it exists, should be accompanied with the best possible estimate of the previous use history of the soil.

Notes on erosion, and especially on its effects, are needed for two somewhat different purposes: (1) To estimate the erosion hazard of the soil unit under different uses and management systems, and (2) to provide a basis for establishing proper classes of eroded soils and finally eroded soil phases within the soil type. Eroded soil phases need to be defined for each soil type in such a way that the definitions can be related to differential land-use predictions.

Besides truncation, the effects that erosion or soil blowing have in covering soils need to be noted.

6. Vegetation.—The principal plants are noted, both dominant and associate, and comments made about the cover generally. For example, it may be observed that a soil has a second-growth cover after cutting or fire, is revegetating after overgrazing, is now severely overgrazed, is in virgin hardwood forests, or the like.

7. Land use.—The principal crops and their condition, and the type of farming, are noted. Detailed studies of yield and soil management practices are made separately, not as a part of individual soil profile studies.

NOTEBOOKS

The soil scientist takes a great many notes in the field accurately and rapidly. So many notes are needed that methods should be systematic and simple. If the scientist sets up an over-elaborate system, he may find it too much trouble. He must provide for soil descriptions at major sites of soil examination, for observations made between sites and during mapping, for photographs, for interviews with farmers and others, and for his usual travel records. In a survey area it is usually best to keep these classes of notes, and perhaps others, in separate books.

Individual preferences vary so much that no attempt has been made to standardize the size and format of notebooks. It is important that standard terms and symbols be used and that notebooks be legible so that other men may use them, as when one party chief or soil correlator is replaced by another.

Some prefer large notebooks with pages about 8 by 10 inches. These are easy to write in and have plenty of space for sketches as well as writing. Where working out of a car, these are best for detailed soil profile descriptions. So much equipment is needed anyway that their extra bulk is insignificant.

Some prefer smaller notebooks, 3 to 5 inches wide and 5 to 8 inches long, that may be carried in the pocket, especially for notes made while mapping. The more neatly a man writes, the smaller the notebook he can use satisfactorily.

Loose-leaf notebooks have the great advantage that individual descriptions may be filed together. Many prefer them, with standard forms similar to those illustrated on page 138. Although some use bound notebooks, for the greatest number of soil scientists, loose-leaf notebooks are probably best for soil descriptions. With notebooks having six or more rings, the loss of individual sheets is rare.[7]

Some sort of form is helpful in making soil descriptions, especially for beginners. With a definite outline, important items are less likely to be omitted. Just one omission may seriously reduce the value of a description, even spoil it altogether; and a great many items need to be noted. This is not to say that good notes cannot be taken without forms. Some prefer blank pages with finely ruled lines. It is easier to accommodate the description to the peculiarities of the soil. Important features may be described at length without trying to squeeze them into a form. Some who use plain notebooks paste or write a checklist of the items on the inside cover to aid their memories.

The important thing is that each soil scientist train himself to keep complete, accurate, standard notes. Perhaps his biggest job is to learn to note the commonplace—the common soils, vegetation, crops, farms, and farming practices. Most of us are inclined to accept these, unconsciously, as "norms." Since the mind comprehends by comparison, unless we train ourselves, we shall only note and photograph departures from the norms. Then, when we attempt to develop a descriptive legend or report, our notes will be inadequate. First we must describe the normal—our bench marks.

SUGGESTED OUTLINE FOR NOTEBOOK PAGE

A uniform system for describing soils can be helped with special notebooks that provide places for all the principal items that need to be noted. By using conventional abbreviations for the defined classes of the various features, as outlined in specific sections of this *Manual,* it is possible to get descriptions into a small space. Outline pages for such notebooks are shown in figure 23. It is most convenient to have these outlines printed on opposite sides of the same sheet for a loose-leaf notebook. The individual sheets may be removed and filed under the soil names. These sheets can be as small as $3\frac{3}{4}$ by $6\frac{3}{4}$ inches and punched along one of the long margins for use in a ring-binder pocket notebook; or they may be placed in a bound notebook. A similar outline can be used for a larger page, say about $7\frac{1}{2}$ by $9\frac{1}{2}$ inches, with an additional column in which to make a sketch of the profile and more space for remarks and discussion. A great advantage of using such a scheme lies partly in the use of standard

---

[7] When working intensively within an area, for soil descriptions, some prefer loose leaves or sheets of large size (8 by $10\frac{1}{2}$ inches), held in a tatum holder or clip board. These can be filed by taxonomic units and conveniently summarized. Sheets held in a metal tatum holder are easy to write on and the metal gives good protection. Losses of notes may be held to the very minimum, since sheets can be removed and filed at the field headquarters each evening. For study in large areas, some prefer small bound notebooks, partly to avoid the danger of losing sheets and partly to reduce the equipment to be carried on planes and trains. Dangers of loss, through losing the whole notebook, are increased, however.

Soil type		Date	Stop No.	
Classification		Area		
Location			Elev.	
N. veg. (or crop)		Climate		
Parent material				
Physiography				
Relief	Slope		Erosion	
Drainage	Gr. water		Permeability	
Moisture	Salt or alkali			
Stoniness	Root distrib.			
Remarks				

Soil type

File No.

A

Hori-zon	Depth	Thick-ness	Bound-ary	Color Check. D(ry) or M(oist)	Tex-ture	Struc-ture	Con-sistence	Reac-tion	Spec. Feat.
				D M					
				D M					
				D M					
				D M					
				D M					
				D M					
				D M					
				D M					
				D M					
				D M					
				D M					

B

FIGURE 23.—Outline for standard notebook pages for soil descriptions: A, front side of sheet; B, reverse side of sheet.

notations, which makes it possible to abstract several descriptions of the same taxonomic unit into a general one for the unit as a whole.

For the outline shown in figure 23, *A* and *B*, the following abbreviations and notations are suggested. They are also useful as a check list when using a plain notebook.

Horizon: Use the standard horizon nomenclature. (See pp. 173 to 188.)

Depth: In inches or centimeters from the top of A_1, or surface mineral horizon, except for the surface of peat or muck in Bogs and Half Bogs. (See p. 185.)

Thickness: Average thickness and range, as 6(4–8).

Boundary[1]: Horizon boundaries are described as to distinctness: Abrupt—a; clear—c; gradual—g; diffuse—d; and according to topography: Smooth—s; wavy—w; irregular—i; broken—b. An abrupt, irregular boundary is ai.

Color: Soil colors are indicated by using the appropriate Munsell notation, such as 5YR 5/3. The spaces in the suggested notebook page under color are left open, except for checking whether dry or moist, in order to accommodate the small space to the need of the descriptions of individual horizons. If the soil mass is one solid color, only one notation is required. If the outsides of aggregates differ significantly from their interiors, both colors are needed. The description of mottled soil horizons needs to include the color of the matrix and the color, or colors, of the principal mottles plus a description of the pattern of mottling.

Mottling: A description of the mottling in soil horizons requires a notation of the colors and of the pattern. Colors can be given in terms of the Munsell notation or in their linguistic equivalents, since exact measurement is neither possible nor necessary. The pattern may be noted as follows:

Abundance:		Contrast:	
few	f	faint	f
common	c	distinct	d
many	m	prominent	p
Size:			
fine	1		
medium	2		
coarse	3		

Thus a medium-gray soil horizon mottled with yellow and reddish brown could be noted as: 10YR 5/1, c3d, 10YR 7/6 and 5YR 4/4 (or) 10YR 5/1, c3d, yellow and reddish brown.

Texture: The following notations are suggested:

gravel	g	loam	l
very coarse sand	vcos	gravelly loam	gl
coarse sand	cos	stony loam	stl
sand	s	silt	si
fine sand	fs	silt loam	sil
very fine sand	vfs	clay loam	cl
loamy coarse sand	lcos	silty clay loam	sicl
loamy sand	ls	sandy clay loam	scl
loamy fine sand	lfs	stony clay loam	stcl
sandy loam	sl	silty clay	sic
fine sandy loam	fsl	clay	c
very fine sandy loam	vfsl		
gravelly sandy loam	gsl		

Structure: The terms used follow the outline given on page 228.

Size or class:

very fine[2]	vf
fine	f
medium	m
coarse	c
very coarse	vc

Grade or distinctness:

structureless	0
weak[4]	1
moderate	2
strong	3

Form or type:

platy	pl
prismatic	pr
columnar	cpr
blocky[3]	bk
angular blocky	abk
subangular blocky	sbk
granular	gr
crumb	cr
single grain	sg
massive	m

Thus, the structure of the B horizon of a solodized-Solonetz may be c3cpr; that of the A_1 of a Gray-Brown Podzolic, m1cr; and that of the B_2 of a Reddish Chestnut, m2abk. Horizons having a mixed structure require two notations. The B_1 of a Red-Yellow Podzolic may be f1sbk or m2sbk.

Consistence: The notation of consistence varies with moisture content. (See pp. 231 to 234.)

Wet soil:

nonsticky	wso
slightly sticky	wss
sticky	ws
very sticky	wvs
nonplastic	wpo
slightly plastic	wps
plastic	wp
very plastic	wvp

Moist soil:

loose	ml
very friable	mvfr
friable	mfr
firm	mfi
very firm	mvfi
extremely firm	mefi

Dry soil:

loose	dl
soft	ds
slightly hard	dsh
hard	dh
very hard	dvh
extremely hard	deh

Cementation:

weakly cemented	cw
strongly cemented	cs
indurated	ci

Reaction: Use pH figures.

Indicate effervescence with HCl as:

slight	e
strong	es
violent	ev

Special features:

Concretions, for example, as:

lime	conca
iron	consir
siliceous	consi
Krotovinas	k

Other special features may be included under *"Remarks."*

Soil type: Name, as Memphis silt loam, plus field mapping number, if any.

Classification: Especially great soil group, if known.

Native vegetation (or crop): Such as: oak-hickory; short grass; wheat; apple orchard.

Climate: Such as: humid temperate; warm semiarid.

Parent material: Such as: residuum from basalt; mixed silty alluvium; calcareous clay loam till.

Physiography: Such as: high terrace, till plain; alluvial fan; mountain foot slope. Add names of formations, where known.

---

[1] In an outline, the lower boundary of a horizon is noted.
[2] Read "thin" and "thick" for platy instead of "fine" and "coarse."
[3] Unrecommended synonyms for subangular blocky are subangular nut and nuciform.
[4] "Very weak" and "very strong" may be noted as v1 and v3, respectively.

Relief: Give letter designation or name of soil slope class and indicate concave or convex, single or complex slopes. (See p. 161.)

Slope: Give approximate gradient of soil slope.

Erosion: Use appropriate class name and number. (See p. 261 *et seq.*)

Drainage: Use appropriate class name for soil drainage. (See p. 170 *et seq.*)

Ground water: Give depth to ground water or indicate "deep."

Permeability: Use appropriate class name. (See p. 168.)

Moisture: Indicate present soil moisture as (1) wet; (2) moist; (3) moderately dry; (4) dry.

Salt or alkali: Indicate concentration of either or both as slight, moderate, or strong.

Stoniness: Use appropriate class name and number. (See p. 217.)

Root distribution: Indicate depth of penetration as "deep" or to a certain depth or horizon; and abundance as "abundant," "plentiful," or "few."

Remarks: Include additional detail on listed items or include additional items, such as relative content of organic matter, evidence of worms, insects, or rodents, special mottling, and stone lines.

PHOTOGRAPHS[8]

Good photographs of profiles of the representative soil types, of characteristic landscapes, both natural and cultural, of evidences of soil processes, and of important practices, crops, and structures related to soil use and development are especially helpful. Such photographs are needed in published reports to supplement descriptions and recommendations and to give the reader a more direct "feeling" of the soils, landscapes, and agriculture. Many published soil surveys contain too few photographs of the soil and landscapes for the clearest presentation of the results of the research.

Besides their use in publications, photographs are a useful part of the record. Especially in a reconnaissance or exploratory soil survey where time is limited, photographs become an essential part of the field notes. Often one can take a picture more quickly than he can describe a landscape accurately.

Although both black-and-white photographs and color transparencies have their place, the greater need is for the former, especially since they can be reproduced easily and used as illustrations. The color transparencies, however, serve better in a record, especially for soil profiles[9].

The suggestions that follow are intended as general guides to soil survey party chiefs and others taking photographs for use primarily in soil survey reports and monographs presenting the results of the field work. During the progress of a soil survey, nearly ideal conditions of lighting may be selected; whereas on exploratory surveys many photographs need to be taken when the observer happens to be on the spot, regardless of weather, season, and time of day. Scientists vary individually in their flair for photography but with care and attention to a few simple

---

[8] The use of photographs, drawings, and maps as illustrations in published reports and monographs is dealt with in the section on The Soil Survey Report.

[9] The Committee on the Exchange of Soil Pictures and Soil Profiles of the Soil Science Society of America issues detailed suggestions from time to time for making color transparencies.

principles, most can get useful black-and-white pictures under good conditions. Sometimes professional photographers may be available, but only a few have enough appreciation of soils to compose photographs that bring out the important relationships.

General requirements.—Some of the important requirements of black-and-white pictures for publication are as follows:

(1) Photographs must be clear and distinct if they are to be most useful. This means that the subject should be well lighted and in sharp focus. Every photograph loses some part of its sharpness in reproduction; consequently publication of a photograph may reduce rather than enhance the value of an otherwise good text unless the original is clear and has adequate contrast.

(2) Field notes for each photograph should include the date, the location, and a description with soil names. These notes can be transferred to a permanent record after the film is developed. Unless an orderly system of numbering, describing, and filing is used, time, film, and equipment are essentially wasted.

(3) Emphasis should be given the most important soils, crops, and farms, and especially the normal soil. As with the making of complete notes, most soil scientists need to train themselves to photograph the commonplace. Unconsciously, one tends to accept the norm and to describe and to photograph the outstanding departures from it, forgetting to record the norm itself. Unless he plans his photographs carefully, the beginner may finish his survey with photographs of all the unusual things but with none of the dominant soils and farms. Partly, too, this is because buttes, gullies, beaches, and the like, are easier to photograph than common undulating landscapes. The beginner is more tempted to photograph an outstanding set of farm buildings or a settler's makeshift cabin than the ordinary farm layout.

(4) A useful photograph brings out one or more important points about the characteristics of the soil, its important relationships to other soils, land form, vegetation, or geology, or its use and management. No matter how clear they are, simple "views", unrelated to the soil descriptions or soil maps, should be discarded. When a photograph is used to present an idea of a soil management practice or the yield of a specific crop, for example, it should be tied down to an actual soil mapping unit, described in the text, and to defined management practices. Many pictures can serve two or more purposes at once; for example, a photograph may show a sprinkler irrigation system, a type of terrace, or a special crop adapted to several soil types, and also its use on a particular soil type. Relief and land-use pattern may be shown in one photograph. Yet one should avoid getting too much in one photograph, lest all the points become obscure. This is especially true of a broad or distant landscape view. These rarely reproduce successfully unless they are simple and unusually clear. It is generally best to make just one point in a photograph and make it clearly.

(5) A great many pictures taken for soil survey reports are too small in scale—the photographer was much too far from the

center of interest. One should be as near the soil profile, the growing crop, the farmstead, or any other center of interest as good composition makes possible.

(6) Good composition is essential for a first-class photograph. Where convenient and other factors are considered, the center of interest should be a little off center, preferably a little to the left and a little below the actual center of the photograph. Unsightly telegraph poles, fence posts, commercial signs, and other things irrelevant to the story of the photograph should be avoided, especially in the foreground. Often the observer is concentrating so intensely on the soil or other feature while exposing the film that he fails to see things that ruin the picture. Good pictures, both published and unpublished, are useful for many years. Automobiles, women's apparel, men's hats, or other items that drastically change style and "date" the photograph should be avoided since they distract the reader from the main story.

(7) Many photographs need some sort of reference scale to give a correct idea of dimensions. For close-ups, a rule of natural wood or plain white with black figures is better than a pick, shovel, watch, or the like.

(8) A great many pictures are poorly illuminated and "flat." Black-and-white pictures taken with the sun directly back of the camera are rarely good. Many taken at high-noon in summer, "when the bushes have their shadows tucked beneath them," lack enough contrast. Usually the sun should be at an angle to the subject in order to get good contrast. Photographs to show microrelief, for example, need to be taken nearly crosswise to the sun in early morning or late afternoon. For color transparencies these contrasts of light and shadow are less important than is adequate light.

(9) Generally better pictures can be taken from a tripod than without one. The composition can be better planned, the lens can be more conveniently shaded, and the aperture can be reduced to permit greater depth of focus. Use of a tripod is especially important when the light is poor. A tripod will also permit more critical focussing, which is of special importance in making pictures of soil profiles.

(10) All parts of a picture important to its story should be in sharp focus. This seems obvious indeed but it deserves special emphasis. Most of the pictures needed in soil survey notes or publications are more effective if they have the maximum depth of focus obtainable. Most can, therefore, be made more satisfactorily with a small aperture and a long exposure in order to have the greatest possible part of the view in focus. Small openings are generally better for landscapes and for soil profiles but cannot be used with rapidly moving objects. Relatively few of the photographs needed in soil survey reports, however, must include moving objects.

Soil profiles.—Soil profiles are not easily photographed. It is especially difficult to get clear black-and-white pictures that bring out the significant contrasts in structure and color among the soil horizons. Yet only those that do bring out these contrasts are useful. Some general points to observe in taking pictures of soil profiles are the following:

(1) A representative site needs to be chosen. Usually it will be necessary to prepare a soil profile in a road cut because of the difficulty of making a pit large enough to have adequate lighting of all the horizons. The photographer must avoid the temptation of taking photographs where they may be made easily in cuts where the soils are not really representative.

(2) After a vertical cut has been made with a spade, the profile needs to be cleaned and dressed to bring out the structure and other features without interference of loose roots. Beginning at the top, fragments of the soil may be broken off with a large knife or fork to eliminate spade marks. Dust and small fragments may be blown away with a small tire pump. Brooms are also used but may leave streaks. It may be helpful to moisten the whole profile or parts of it with a hand sprayer for uniformity of moisture content and comparability of contrast. Moist soils are somewhat darker than dry ones and often the colors are more intense. If the whole profile is dry, it may be useful to moisten one-half, vertically, to show the contrast between the dry and moist soil.

(3) For scale, a 60-inch rule of unvarnished and unpainted wood, $1\frac{1}{2}$-inches wide, and $\frac{1}{2}$-inch thick, with large clear black figures at 1-foot intervals, is satisfactory. White rules with black figures have also been used successfully. Large ticks or half-lines can indicate the 6-inch intervals and small ticks the 2-inch intervals. Such a rule may be made in two or three sections held together by dowels or hinges. An ordinary folding bricklayer's 6-foot rule with clear figures can be used for very large scale pictures. The zero point of the ruler should always be exactly at the top of the A_1 horizon. The unused part of the ruler can be buried at the lower end of the profile.

Good scales not only help the reading of the individual picture but also make it possible to bring several pictures to a common scale by differential enlargement.

(4) For black-and-white pictures some prefer indirect lighting to avoid shadows. Others prefer to have the sun shining directly on the profile. Strong sunlight may give unnatural results because of shadows from the structural aggregates, pebbles, and root ends.

For color transparencies direct sunlight and bright sky are preferred by some, although good results may be had with indirect lighting if it is strong. Good lighting is so important that adequate color transparencies of soil profiles usually can be made only during the middle of the day from late spring to early autumn in most parts of the United States.

(5) Photographs of soil profiles are rarely good unless the camera is close to the profile, say within 4 to 8 feet, or at the very most, 12 feet. This means careful focussing for which a tripod is usually necessary in order to use the small opening required for

good depth of focus. Most people can get the best results by setting the shutter time and opening according to an exposure meter.

(6) With a good example of a soil profile properly dressed, it is safest to make three or four exposures at somewhat different combinations of opening and shutter time. When duplicate black-and-white photographs are taken, the camera should be moved slightly between exposures or the arrangement of the scale changed to make it easy to match the prints with the proper negatives later.

PARENT MATERIALS OF SOILS

Parent material refers to the unconsolidated mass from which the solum develops. It includes the C horizon and other materials above the C from which the solum developed. The unconsolidated material directly beneath the solum is called C, or parent material, only if the evidence suggests that at least a part of the solum is developed from material of the same kind. The term *"parent rock"* is used for rock from which the parent material was formed by weathering. In many soils there is little or no weathered material—no C horizon—between the solum and the parent rock; in other words, soil formation has kept pace with weathering. The upper part of the solum may be developed from one kind of material and the lower part from another. In many soils the solum is underlain with an unconsolidated nonconforming geological stratum that is not parent material; yet such geological strata are recognized and described insofar as they have an influence on the genesis or behavior of the soil. Such strata are designated as D layers.

We may conceive of weathering and soil formation as different sets of processes even though the sets have many individual processes in common and more often than not go on together.[1] Yet a nearly convincing case may be made for considering both together as soil formation, beginning with parent rock as the independent variable in the set of five genetic factors instead of parent material as here defined.

Generally, the parent materials of soils can be grouped into four classes: (1) Those formed in place through the disintegration and decomposition of hard country rocks, (2) those formed in place from soft or unconsolidated country rocks, (3) those that have been transported from the place of their origin and redeposited either before they became subject to important modification by soil-building forces or during such processes of modification, and (4) organic deposits.

The classification and nomenclature of rocks and of geological formations fall in the field of geology and will not be dealt with in this *Manual*. Geological materials need to be defined in accordance with the accepted standards and nomenclature of recognized authorities in the field. Each soil survey party chief should use as references the best textbooks,[2] handbooks, and monographs on

---

[1] See discussion of soil profile and of solum in the section on Identification and Nomenclature of Soil Horizons.

[2] The following are examples:

CLARKE, F. W. THE DATA OF GEOCHEMISTRY. Ed. 5, U. S. Geol. Survey Bul. 770, 841 pp. 1924.

LONGWELL, C. R., KNOPF, A., FLINT, R. F. SCHUCHERT, C., and DUNBAR, C. O. OUTLINES OF GEOLOGY. Ed. 2, 381 + 291 pp., illus. New York. 1941.

FLINT, R. F. GLACIAL GEOLOGY AND THE PLEISTOCENE EPOCH. 589 pp., illus. New York. 1947.

geology that apply to the area within which he is working.[3] Besides lithological composition, the accepted authoritative names of the geological formations should be given where that can be done with reasonable accuracy. As soil research progresses, an increasing number of correlations are being found between particular geological formations and the mineral nutrient content of parent materials and soils. Certain terrace materials and deposits of volcanic ash that are different in age or source, for example, but otherwise indistinguishable, may vary widely in their contents of cobalt. Wide variations in the phosphorus content of two otherwise similar soils may reflect differences in the phosphorus content of two similar limestones that can be distinguished in the field only by specific fossils.

The principal broad subdivisions of the four classes of parent materials are suggested in the following paragraphs. The authors are mindful that in relation to soil formation the lithological composition often takes precedent over mode of formation of the rocks. That is, soils from basalt and limestone are likely to be more closely related than those from basalt and quartz diorite, for example.

MATERIALS PRODUCED BY THE WEATHERING OF HARD ROCKS IN PLACE

Materials produced by weathering of hard rocks in place are distinguished according to the nature of the original rocks and the character of the weathered material itself. We must always recall that quite different parent materials may be produced from similar or even identical rocks under different weathering regimes. As with the horizons of the solum, the texture, color, consistence, and other characteristics of the material are described. As much useful information about the mineralogical composition, hardness, and structure of the parent rock itself should be added as can be obtained.

Somewhere around three-quarters of the land area of the world is underlain by hard or soft sedimentary rocks, and perhaps one-quarter by igneous and metamorphic rocks.

Igneous rocks.—These rocks are formed by the solidification of molten materials that originated within the earth. Characteristic kinds that weather to important soil material are granite, syenite, basalt, andesite, diabase, and rhyolite.

Sedimentary rocks.—These include those rocks formed from the consolidation of sediments laid down in previous geological ages. The principal broad groups of hard sedimentary rocks are limestone, sandstone, siltstone, shale, and conglomerate. There are many varieties of these broad classes of sedimentary rocks, and many intermediate types between them, such as calcareous sandstone, arenaceous limestone, and so on. Many soils are developed

---

[3] Many maps of rock formations refer primarily to the hard rocks and not to the surface mantle of unconsolidated material, which may or may not be residual from the rocks shown on the maps.

from their weathering products and from those of interbedded sedimentary rocks.

Metamorphic rocks.—These have resulted from profound alteration of igneous and sedimentary rocks through heat and pressure applied to them. General classes important as sources of weathered parent material for soils are gneiss, schist, slate, marble, quartzite, and phyllite.

MATERIALS PRODUCED FROM SOFT ROCKS

Another group of materials, those produced from soft rocks, falls more or less intermediate between the group of mineral parent materials derived from hard rocks through residual weathering and the group derived from materials that have been transported.

Ash, cinders, and other volcanic ejecta may be regarded as unconsolidated igneous rocks; but they have been moved from their place of origin and usually they are immediately more or less reworked by wind and water.

Also included with the soft rocks are the unconsolidated equivalents of the sedimentary rocks already listed: marl, sand, silt, clay, and gravel. Usually such formations are described most appropriately within the categories that follow, but semi-indurated rocks are found that are intermediate in hardness and consolidation between those clearly recognized as hard rocks and those that are essentially unconsolidated. Chalk, for example, is one of these. It may be defined as an earthy limestone with a hardness less than 2.

Caliche is a very broad term for secondary calcareous material in layers near the surface. As the term is used, caliche may be soft and clearly recognized as the C_{ca} horizon of the soil; or it may exist in hard thick beds beneath the solum or exposed at the surface, especially in warm-temperate and warm regions of relatively low rainfall. The hardened form is also called *croûte calcaire*.

In this intermediate class are deposits of diatomaceous earth formed from the siliceous remains of primitive plants called diatoms.

TRANSPORTED MATERIALS

Taking the world as a whole, perhaps the most important group of parent materials is the very broad one made up of materials that have been moved from the place of their origin and redeposited during the weathering processes or during some phase of those processes, and which consist of or are weathered from unconsolidated formations. The principal groups of these materials are usually named according to the main force responsible for their transport and redeposition. In most places sufficient evidence can be had to make a clear determination; elsewhere the precise origin is doubtful.

In soil morphology and classification, it is exceedingly important that the characteristics of the material itself be observed and described. It is not enough simply to identify the parent material as alluvium, loess, or glacial till. Such names are used to supplement the descriptions of the material; and if doubt or uncertainty exists as to the correctness of the name, this fact is mentioned. For example, it is often impossible to be sure whether certain silty deposits are alluvium, loess, or the result of residual weathering in place. Certain mud flows are indistinguishable from glacial till. Some sandy glacial till is nearly identical to sandy outwash. Such hard-to-make distinctions are of little importance.

MATERIALS MOVED AND REDEPOSITED BY WATER

Alluvium.—The most important of the materials moved and redeposited by water is alluvium. It consists of sediments deposited by streams. It may occur in terraces well above present streams or in the normally flooded bottoms of existing streams. Remnants of very old stream terraces may be found in dissected country far from any present stream. Along many old established streams are a whole series of alluvial deposits in terraces—young ones in the immediate flood plain, up step by step, to the very old ones. Then too, recent alluvium often covers older terraces.

Generally, the alluvium may be divided into two main groups according to origin: (1) Local alluvium, like that at the base of slopes and along small streams flowing out of tiny drainage basins of nearly homogeneous rock and soil material, and (2) general alluvium of mixed origin, as that along major stream courses.

Colluvium.—The distinction between alluvium and colluvium is somewhat difficult and arbitrary. Some authorities hold that colluvium is strictly the material moved primarily under the influence of gravity, only imperfectly sorted, if sorted at all; and they include under alluvium all materials moved primarily by water. Generally, however, colluvium is used for the poorly sorted material near the base of strong slopes that has been moved by gravity, frost action, soil creep, and local wash. In the midwestern parts of the United States, for example, the established local usage by many soil scientists is to use the term "colluvium" for that part of the local alluvium at the base of slopes that has been moved into place through creep and local wash.

Lacustrine deposits.—These deposits consist of materials that have settled out of the quiet water of lakes. Those laid down in fresh-water lakes associated with glacial action are commonly included as a subgroup under glacial drift. Yet besides these there are other lake deposits, including those of Pleistocene times, unassociated with the continental glaciers. Some old lake basins in the western part of the United States are commonly called *playas* and may be more or less salty, depending on the climate and drainage.

Marine sediments.—These sediments have been reworked by the sea and later exposed either naturally or through the construction of dikes and drainage canals. They vary widely in lithological and mechanical composition. Some resemble lacustrine deposits.

Beach deposits.—These deposits, low ridges of sorted material, often gravelly, cobbly, or stony, mark the shore lines at old levels of the sea or lakes. Those formed on the beaches of glacial lakes are usually included with glacial drift, which is defined in another group.

MATERIALS REMOVED AND REDEPOSITED BY WIND

The wind-blown materials are generally divided into two classes, mainly in accordance with texture. Those that are mainly silty are called *loess,* and those that are primarily sand are called eolian *sands,* commonly but not always in *dunes.*[4]

It has been exceedingly difficult, both for geologists and soil scientists, to define loess precisely. Typically, deposits of loess are very silty but contain significant amounts of clay and fine sand. Usually, but not always, the material is calcareous. Most loess deposits are pale brown to brown, although gray and red colors are common. The thick deposits are generally massive, with some gross vertical cracking. The walls of road cuts in thick loess stand nearly vertical for years. Other silty deposits derived in other ways, however, have some or all of these characteristics. Then too, some wind-blown silt has been leached and strongly weathered so that it is acid and rich in clay. On the other hand, young deposits of wind-blown silty very fine sand, called loess, are exceedingly low in clay.

Characteristically, sand dunes, especially in humid regions, consist of sand, especially fine or medium sand, that is very rich in quartz and low in clay-forming minerals. Yet, nearly all transitions may be observed between the silty wind-blown materials called loess and the very sandy material in characteristic sand dunes. Especially in deserts and semideserts, the sand dunes may contain large amounts of calcium carbonate and of clay-forming minerals that would decompose to clay in a more humid environment. Examples may even be found of sand dunes, using sand in its purely textural sense, that consist almost wholly of calcium carbonate or of gypsum.

During periods of drought, and in deserts, local wind movements may pile up soil material of mixed texture or even materials very rich in clay. Piles of such material have even been called "soil dunes" or "clay dunes." It is better, however, to use an expression such as "wind-deposited materials" for local accumulations of materials of mixed textures moved by the wind than it is to identify them as loess or dunes.

MATERIALS MOVED AND REDEPOSITED BY GLACIAL PROCESSES

Several classes of materials moved and redeposited by glacial processes are as follows:

Glacial drift.—Glacial drift consists of all the material picked up, mixed, disintegrated, transported, and deposited through the action of glacial ice or of water resulting primarily from the

---

[4] Locally, loess is sometimes called "loam" regardless of actual texture. Relatively uniform wind-laid deposits of sand are sometimes called "cover sand."

melting of glaciers. In many places the glacial drift is covered with loess. Deep mantles of loess are usually easily recognized, but very thin mantles are so altered by soil-building forces as to be scarcely differentiated from modified drift.

Till or glacial till.—This includes that part of the glacial drift deposited directly by the ice with little or no transportation by water. It is generally an unstratified, unconsolidated, heterogeneous mixture of clay, silt, sand, gravel, and sometimes boulders. Till may be found in ground moraines, terminal moraines, medial moraines, and lateral moraines. It is often important to differentiate between the tills of the several glacial epochs. Often they underlie one another and may be separated by other deposits or old weathered surfaces.[5] Many deposits of glacial till were later washed by lakes, but without important additions. The upper part of such wave-cut till is uncommonly rich in coarse fragments as a result of the wave action in glacial lakes. *Drumlins* are long cigar-shaped low hills of glacial till, with a smooth sky line and with their long axes lying parallel to the line of movement of the ice.

Till varies widely in texture, chemical composition, and the degree of weathering subsequent to its deposition. Most till is slightly, moderately, or highly calcareous; but an important part of it is noncalcareous because no calcite- or dolomite-bearing rocks were contributed to the material or because of subsequent leaching and chemical weathering. In detailed soil classification one needs to recognize about five groups of till according to texture: (1) Coarse textured, loose, porous till, consisting mainly of a mixture of sand, gravel, cobbles, and boulders; (2) sandy till with some gravel and perhaps a few stones and a little clay; (3) medium textured, gritty till having a relatively even mixture of sand, silt, and clay, with or without stones and boulders; (4) medium textured silty till that is relatively free of gritty particles; and (5) fine textured till having a predominance of silt and clay.

Glaciofluvial deposits.—These deposits are made up of materials produced by glaciers and carried, sorted, and deposited by water that originated mainly from the melting of glacial ice.

The most important of these is *glacial outwash*. This is a broad term including all of the material swept out, sorted, and deposited beyond the glacial ice front by streams of melt water. Commonly, this outwash exists in the form of plains, valley trains, or deltas in old glacial lakes. The valley trains of outwash may extend far beyond the farthest advance of the ice.

Especially near the moraines, poorly sorted outwash materials may exist in kames, eskers, and crevasse-fills.

---

[5] In the Middle West, the term *gumbotil* is applied to tenacious clays, generally gray, plastic when wet, and hard when dry, which have been weathered from Nebraskan, Kansan, and Illinoian till during the interglacial periods.

Glacial beach deposits.—These consist of gravel and sand and mark the beach lines of former glacial lakes. Depending upon the character of the original drift, they may be sandy, gravelly, cobbly, or stony.

Glaciolacustrine materials.—These materials range from fine clays to sand. They are derived from glaciers and reworked and laid down in glacial lakes. Many of them are interbedded or laminated. The fine horizontal markings exposed in a section of glaciolacustrine clay, each related to one year's deposition and one season's glacial-ice melt, are called *varves*.

Fine examples of all the glacial materials and forms described in preceding paragraphs may be found. Yet in many places it is not easy to distinguish definitely among the kinds of drift on the basis of mode of origin and land form. In places, for example, pitted outwash plains can scarcely be distinguished from sandy till in terminal moraines. Often it is difficult to distinguish between wave-cut till and lacustrine materials. We must continually recall that these names connote only a little about the actual characteristics of the parent material. Certainly mode of origin of the parent material is not a sufficient basis, by itself, for separating soil classificational units.

MATERIALS MOVED AND REDEPOSITED BY GRAVITY

As strictly defined by some, *colluvium* is the unsorted or slightly sorted material at the base of slopes, accumulated largely as rock fragments that have fallen down the slope under the influence of gravity. In its extreme form this material is called *talus*. Rock fragments are angular in contrast to the rounded, water-worn cobbles and stones in alluvial terraces and glacial outwash. As mentioned before, colluvium is used generally for that part of the poorly sorted local alluvium that has accumulated at the base of slopes, in depressions, or along tiny streams, through gravity, soil creep, and local wash.

ORGANIC MATERIALS

In moist situations where organic matter forms more rapidly than it decomposes, peat deposits are formed. These peats become, in turn, parent material for soils. If the organic remains are sufficiently fresh and intact to permit identification of plant forms, the material is regarded as *peat*. If, on the other hand, the peat has undergone sufficient decomposition to make recognition of the plant parts impossible, the decomposed material is called *muck*. Generally speaking, muck has a higher mineral or ash content than peat, because in the process of decomposition the ash that was in the vegetation accumulates. Yet total mineral or ash content is not a dependable guide for distinguishing between peat and muck. Besides the accumulation of minerals through the decomposition of vegetation, large amounts of mineral matter may be introduced into peat formations by wash from surrounding uplands, by wind, and as volcanic ash. Nearly raw peat may contain 50 percent mineral matter as volcanic ash with only a small influence on the character of the peat.

The color, texture, compactness, and other characteristics of peat materials in soils need to be described. The principal general classes of peat, mainly according to origin, are (1) woody, (2) fibrous, (3) moss, (4) sedimentary, and (5) colloidal.

CHARACTERISTICS AND ORIGIN OF THE PARENT MATERIAL

Both consolidated and unconsolidated materials beneath the solum that influence the genesis and behavior of the soil need to be described in standard terms. Besides the observations themselves, the scientist should record his judgment about the origin of the parent material from which the solum has developed; yet the observed facts need to be separated clearly from inferences and, where important, an indication of the relative probability of the relationships suggested.

The hardness, lithological composition, and permeability of the material directly beneath the solum are especially important. Evidence of stratification of the material—textural banding, stone lines, and the like—need to be noted. Many soils have obviously developed from stratified parent material; others seem to have developed from uniform material like that directly beneath the solum, although one can rarely be certain without chemical, physical, and mineralogical data on samples of the horizons. As weathering and soil formation go forward on interbedded geological formations, with natural erosion, sola developed from materials weathered from one kind of rock, limestone let us say, are underlain by those weathered from another, say shale or sandstone. Commonly, the upper layers of outwash deposits were laid down from more slowly moving water and are finer in texture than the lower layers. Wind-blown fines and volcanic ash are laid down in blankets of varying thickness over other rock formations. The examples of such complications are nearly endless. Then, too, these geological changes often go forward along with soil formation. Where loess or ash are quickly dropped on old soils, buried soils may be well-preserved. Elsewhere the accumulation of mineral material on the top of the soil is so slow that the solum thickens only gradually. In such places the material beneath the solum was once a part of it and has now been buried beyond the influence of the biological forces.

Where hard rocks or other strongly contrasting materials lie near enough to the surface to affect the behavior of the soil, their depths need to be measured accurately; for the depth of the solum, or of solum and parent material, over such nonconforming formations is an important criterion for series and phase distinctions.

LAND FORM, RELIEF, AND DRAINAGE

Its land form is an essential part of a soil, conceived as a three-dimensional landscape resulting from the synthetic effect of all the materials and processes in its environment. Kinds of soil profiles are associated with kinds of land form that influence their genesis. Although, like other features of the soil, land form by itself is not always a sufficient basis for differentiating between soil series, it is usually associated with other differentiating characteristics. Important differences in both parent material and soil profile are commonly covariant with differences in land form.

Most soil series and types have a relatively narrow range in land form. Yet there are exceptions. Soils of two areas may be developed from deep loess, let us say, laid down on a ground moraine in one area and over a terrace in the other. Soil profiles, slopes, and other characteristics may be similar in the two areas, yet the land over the old terrace may have better water supplies in the substratum. In such an instance, the soil series should be subdivided into phases, the typical (phase) on the ground moraine and a *terrace phase* for the soil on the old terrace.

The importance of land form is being recognized increasingly by soil scientists in soil classification and interpretation. Materials in terraces, volcanic ash deposits, and other formations of differing ages and origins that appear to be similar in the field may have significantly different chemical compositions. Where substantial differences exist in texture, clay minerals, or calcium content, the materials themselves and the soils developed from them are easily distinguished; yet, differences in cobalt and other trace elements of great importance to soil use and management sometimes are not associated with other characteristics of the material recognizable in the field. In many such instances, geological origin is associated with land form, which, in turn, serves as the basis of prediction to farmers and agricultural advisers.

Other important examples, among many, that show the need for careful studies of land form may be found in areas of old valley fills made up of gently sloping coalescing fans of unlike origin and stratigraphy. A large part of the irrigated soils of the world are in such valleys. A dependable classification of these valley soils is greatly facilitated by a clear understanding of the origin of the various surfaces, especially as these relate to predictions of drainage conditions and problems that develop when water is supplied.

Land forms should be named and described in the standard terms used and accepted by physiographers and geomorpholo-

FIGURE 24.—Characteristic microrelief of the gilgai type: Upper, on Irving clay near Millican, Tex.; and lower, on Bell clay 15 miles southwest of College Station, Tex.

gists. Each soil survey party should use the most authoritative texts and monographs that apply to the survey area.[1]

RELIEF

Relief is sometimes used broadly to indicate simply the differences in elevation within an area or perhaps only the difference between the highest and lowest altitude of an area. More precisely, however, relief implies relative elevation and has been defined as the elevations or inequalities of a land surface considered collectively.

Microrelief refers to small-scale differences in relief. In areas of similar macrorelief, the surface may be nearly uniform or it may be interrupted by mounds, swales, or pits that are a few feet across and have significant differences in elevation of only 1 to 3 feet or even less (figs. 24 and 25).

FIGURE 25.—Characteristic microrelief of truncated solodized-Solonetz. The low places are sometimes called scabby spots. Western North Dakota.

Examples include (1) the relief of Ground-Water Podzols with characteristic cradle knolls, (2) truncated solodized-Solonetz with low bare spots, (3) puff Solonchak with mounds, (4) the small mounds, *coppice mounds,* of soil material stabilized around

---

[1] Some useful general texts are the following:

COTTON, C. A. CLIMATIC ACCIDENTS IN LANDSCAPE-MAKING. 354 pp., illus. Christchurch, New Zealand. 1942.
——— LANDSCAPE AS DEVELOPED BY THE PROCESSES OF NORMAL EROSION. Ed. 2, 509 pp. New York. 1948.
FENNEMAN, N. M. PHYSIOGRAPHY OF WESTERN UNITED STATES. 534 pp., illus. New York. 1931.
——— PHYSIOGRAPHY OF EASTERN UNITED STATES. 714 pp., illus. New York. 1938.
LOBECK, A. K. GEOMORPHOLOGY. 731 pp., illus. New York. 1939.
VON ENGELN, O. D. GEOMORPHOLOGY. 655 pp., illus. New York. 1942.

desert shrubs, and (5) the *gilgai*[2] microrelief of clays that have high coefficients of expansion and contraction with changes in moisture. Such microrelief consists of either a succession of enclosed micro-basins and micro-knolls in nearly level areas or of micro-valleys and micro-ridges that run with the slope.

Topography had a general connotation similar to relief, but has come to be used for the features disclosed on a contour map—even by some people for all the natural and cultural features considered collectively that are ordinarily shown on a topographic map. In soil descriptions the more specific terms—relief, physiography, land form, or soil slope—should be used rather than topography.

Soil slope refers to the incline of the surface of the soil area. It is an integral part of any soil as a natural body, not something apart from it. A simple, or single, slope is defined by its gradient, shape, and length. Depending upon the detail of mapping and the character of the soil areas, slopes may be defined as single or complex, or as patterns of slope classes.

RELIEF AND GENETIC PROFILES

Relief influences soil formation primarily through its effects upon drainage, runoff, and erosion,[3] and secondarily through variations in exposure to the sun and wind and in air drainage.

Theoretically, at least, the water falling on a perfectly level surface of permeable soil material is admitted until the material is saturated, or sealed, and then collects on the surface as a sheet. Uniformly flat and permeable soils are rare indeed. Rain water collects in depressions however slight, and penetrates some soils more rapidly than others. Because of runoff, strongly sloping soils receive less water than the average, and soils in depressions more.

The amount of water entering and passing through the soil depends upon the permeability of both solum and substrata, the relief, and the climate. In regions of nearly continuous rainfall, even strongly sloping soils may be very poorly drained. Nearly level soils on exceedingly pervious materials are excessively drained, even in humid climates, unless the water table is high. Thus, the specific relationships existing between relief or soil slope and soil genesis in one combination of climate and soil material cannot be applied to another significant combination.

In relation to soil genesis, four broad relief positions may be recognized. The definitions of these positions in terms of single or complex slopes vary among climatic regions and even on different geological materials within one region. Considering all

---

[2] The name *gilgai* is adopted from Australia, where this phenomenon is extensive and developed in extreme degrees, with microrelief up to 2 feet. Other common names with similar or overlapping connotations are hog-wallowed, crab-holey, hush-a-bye, buffalo-wallowed, Bay of Biscay, self-swallowing, self-plowing, self-mulching, tiger-striped, leopard-spotted, puffed, corrugated, and pits-and-mounds.

[3] In this discussion the reference is to water erosion, not soil blowing.

possible combinations of climate and parent material in the world, soils in each of these four relief positions have a rather wide range of slope. Within each, and between them, intermediate positions need to be recognized in detailed classification. The four broad relief positions are described in the numbered paragraphs following.

1. **Normal relief.**—In this position are sloping uplands with medium runoff. Under the native vegetation, normal erosion removes materials as the solum deepens, thus bringing relatively new minerals into the soil from beneath.[4] This is the relief position of the normal soil, including modal representatives of the zonal great soil groups. The actual soil slope, in quantitative terms, varies with different combinations of climate and parent material.

2. **Subnormal relief.**—In this position are the nearly flat to sloping uplands with slow to very slow runoff. Erosion under the native vegetation is so slow that in humid regions the leached materials accumulate on the surface. The solum is relatively fixed and does not gradually move down as in many soils in the normal position. Given the necessary time, claypans and hardpans generally form from materials of mixed chemical and mechanical composition. Soils in this position often have fluctuating water tables, or perched water tables, near the surface part of the time. Planosols and Ground-Water Laterite soils are typically found in this position. Soils characteristic of this relief position may be found on fairly strong slopes in very humid regions and on seepy slopes.

3. **Excessive relief.**—This is the relief position for hills and hilly uplands that have rapid to very rapid runoff and more erosion than areas in the associated normal position. Soil development is stunted because of rapid erosion, reduced percolation of the water through the soil, and lack of water in the soil for the vigorous growth of the plants responsible for soil formation. Lithosols and the lithosolic associates of other soils are characteristic of this relief position. Other things being equal, the minimum slope is relatively low on very slowly permeable materials in dry regions and relatively great on permeable materials in humid regions.

4. **Flat or concave relief.**—In this relief position are nearly flat or depressed lowlands with either very slow runoff or none at all, excess water all or part of the time, and no natural erosion. Such lands retain all or nearly all of the water that falls as rain and often receive a considerable additional amount from adjacent uplands. The hydromorphic and halomorphic intrazonal soils are

---

[4] The amount and character of natural erosion varies widely among the great soil groups. On Red Latosols, for example, it is relatively great, and on Chernozem relatively small or even insignificant. On some soils, like grassy Tundra, for example, natural erosion takes the form of a succession of slips rather than sheet wash. (See the first part of the section on Accelerated Soil Erosion.)

typically in this position. Soils characteristic of this position may be found on strong slopes in very humid regions of nearly continuous rainfall.

Within any soil zone one may find a group of strongly contrasting soil series that extend across all of the four relief positions described, yet are developed from similar parent material. Such a group of soil series is called a catena.[5]

Attempts have been made to develop uniformly defined stages or kinds of profiles, often indicated by numbers, according to evidences of natural drainage and land form or relief. Such schemes are appealing as guides to classification and for remembering characteristics, but they are not recommended. They are apt to be misused. Profile features result from such a wide variety of genetic factors that parallel analogs do not necessarily exist in different soil regions, or even on different parent materials within the same soil region. One catena can be adequately represented by four or five profiles, while another may need ten. If a uniform scheme has enough stages to accommodate the second catena, it may lead the field scientist to look for and to establish too many stages in the first catena, or to make the distinctions in the wrong places. Each catena needs to be defined by itself.

SOIL SLOPE CHARACTERISTICS

In defining soil classificational units, especially in detailed soil surveys, soil slope is given special attention. Within the permissible slope ranges of many soil types, phases need to be defined in terms of slope gradient that indicate differences significant to use and management. As with other important soil characteristics, the relative significance of differences in slope depends upon the other characteristics of the soil. Broad classes of soil slope, defined in terms of percentage alone without reference to other soil characteristics, have no consistent relationship to the capabilities of the soil for use. Thus, the definitions of slope classes must be adjusted among soil types, so that boundaries between soil areas are placed where the significant changes occur in soil slope for the particular kind of soil and so that insignificant boundaries are not added to the soil map.

Up to the present time, slope gradient—this one characteristic of soil slope—has perhaps been given undue emphasis over the other slope characteristics—shape, length, and pattern. The nomenclature for classes of soil slope does provide for recognizing units consisting (1) primarily of single slopes and (2) primarily of slope complexes. In actual practice, consideration is given to the relief of the terrain as a whole as well as to that of an individual soil area within it. That is, in a rolling terrain, the slope of a particular soil area is designated in the complex group

---

[5] In East Africa, catena is used in a somewhat broader sense for groups of soils over a range in relief, but from similar or unlike parent materials. See MILNE, G., in collaboration with BECKLEY, V. A., JONES, G. H. GETHIN, MARTIN, W. S., GRIFFITH, G., and RAYMOND, L. W. A PROVISIONAL SOIL MAP OF EAST AFRICA (KENYA, UGANDA, TANGANYIKA, AND ZANZIBAR) WITH EXPLANATORY MEMOIR. 34 pp., illus. London. 1936.

even though it is single if considered only by itself. In contrast, soil slopes on fans and mountain foot slopes are regarded as single.

Ranges in soil slope are described for each mapping unit. The significant features of soil slope cannot be worked into the nomenclature except as they are included in the description of the classificational units, especially those of series and types. Even though phases within different soil types or series are given the same adjective in their name, as for example "slope" or "sloping," this does not and cannot mean that there are no other important differences in slope characteristics between the two units or even that the two are entirely similar in the gradient of slope. Often slope characteristics even more important than gradient, such as shape, length, direction, and pattern of slopes, are implied by the soil series name rather than by the adjective used in the phase name that refers to soil slope alone. Thus, the slope classes must be looked upon simply as convenient units of slope gradient, arbitrarily limited in terms of percentage, and somewhat analogous, for example, to the classes defined in terms of pH, which are used for expressing the acidity of soil horizons as "medium acid," "strongly acid," and the like.

In studying and describing the soil, important practical aspects of soil slope, besides its relation to soil genesis, need to be given consideration under the probable conditions of use and management: these are (1) the rate and amount of runoff, (2) the erodibility of the soil, and (3) use of agricultural machinery. None of these varies as a linear function of slope gradient alone, except where other characteristics of the slope and other soil characteristics are similar. It is well known that some soils, if cultivated, are not subject to erosion at 1 percent slope but may be at 2 percent; whereas others, such as some of the highly pervious Latosols of the humid tropics, are not subject to significant accelerated erosion even with soil slopes of 40 percent or more. The use of machinery and the rapidity and amount of runoff also depend upon many other soil characteristics besides slope gradient. Thus, in arriving at the definition for any soil unit, or of a phase, in terms of percentage of slope gradient, all important soil characteristics in relation to all significant aspects of soil use must be evaluated.

Classes by soil slope gradient.—Soil slope is normally measured by the hand level (fig. 26) and expressed in terms of percentage— the difference in elevation in feet for each 100 feet horizontal. Thus, a soil slope of 45° is one of 100 percent since the difference in elevation of two points 100 feet apart horizontally is 100 feet.

Slope classes have been established with alternative minimum and maximum limits in terms of gradient, so that all soil slopes within a given class, as named, will fall within broad limits and yet allow enough flexibility to make narrow definitions and subdivisions as needed for specific application to different soil types.

The slope classes provide for the recognition of either single or complex slopes as appropriate. The distinction is not mandatory. Generally, the terms for single slopes are used except in

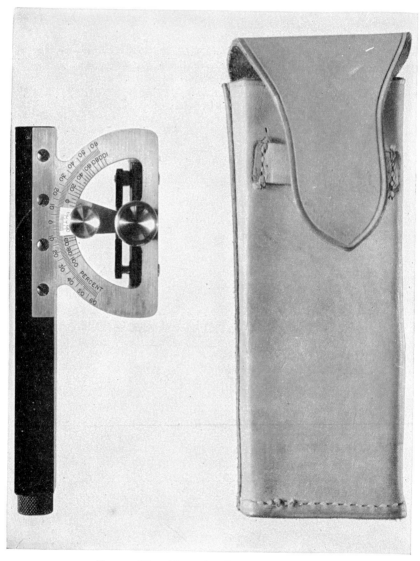

FIGURE 26.—Abney hand level with case.

areas where long established usage of terms for complex slopes make their use much more meaningful or where soil relief is very complex, as in areas of dunes and karst sinkholes. The soil slope classes are not always directly translatable into mapping units.

Slope classes are designated in the numbered paragraphs following.

1. *A class.*—In this class are level or nearly level soil areas on which runoff is slow or very slow. The soil slope alone offers no

difficulty in the use of agricultural machinery; nor is there likelihood of significant water erosion except possibly on very long slopes of highly erodible soils.

Limits	*Names*
Lower—0 percent.	Single slopes—level; or level and nearly level.[1]
Upper—1 to 3 percent.	Complex slopes—level; or level and nearly level.

[1] Where subdivisions are necessary in extremely detailed classification.

2. *B class.*—This class consists of gently undulating, undulating, or gently sloping soil areas on which runoff is slow or medium for most soils. All types of ordinary agricultural machinery may be used without difficulty, insofar as slope is concerned. Soils with B slopes vary widely in erodibility, depending upon the other soil characteristics. On some, erosion offers no serious problem; on many, relatively simple precautions are all that is needed; while for use under cultivation some very erodible soils need protection by terraces, or by other means, depending on the other features of the soil and the set of soil management practices.

Limits	*Names*
Lower—1 to 3 percent.	Single slopes—gently sloping; or very gently sloping and gently sloping.
Upper—5 to 8 percent.	Complex slopes—undulating; or gently undulating and undulating.

3. *C class.*—In this class are gently rolling, rolling, or moderately and strongly sloping soil areas on which runoff is medium to rapid for most soils. Insofar as slope is concerned, all types of farm machinery can be used successfully although some difficulty may be had in using the large and heavy types. Soils with C slope vary widely in erodibility under cultivation, depending upon the other soil characteristics and the management practices. On a few, erosion offers no serious problem, or else can be controlled by relatively simple practices; while others need careful management in which close-growing crops are used most of the time, with supplemental strip cropping or terracing where the soils are otherwise suitable.

Limits	*Names*
Lower— 5 to 8 percent.	Single slopes—sloping; or sloping and strongly sloping.
Upper—10 to 16 percent.	Complex slopes—rolling; or gently rolling and rolling.

4. *D class.*—This class is made up of very strongly sloping or hilly soil areas on which runoff is rapid or very rapid on most soils. Unless the slopes are very complex, most farm machinery can be used, but with difficulty, especially for the heavier types. Soils with D slopes are likely to erode under clean cultivation, except for the most pervious ones, like well-developed Latosols, for example. There are many exceptions, but the separation between those soils suited to ordinary rotations that include intertilled crops and those soils suited only to pasture or to rotations dominated by sod-forming crops commonly comes at the dividing point between C and D classes of soil slope.

Limits	Names
Lower—10 to 16 percent.	Single slope—moderately steep.
Upper—20 to 30 percent.	Complex slope—hilly.

5. *E class.*—In this class are steeply sloping or very hilly soil areas on which runoff is very rapid on most soils. Only the lightest types of agricultural machinery can be used. The arability of soils with E class slope varies widely. If the soils are highly fertile and permeable, they may support good grass, orchards, or even intertilled crops with a proper set of management practices. With many hilly soils, the distinction between areas useful for pasture and those suited only to forests coincides with the dividing point between the D and E classes of soil slope.

Limits	Names
Lower—20 to 30 percent.	Single slope—steep.
Upper—45 to 65 percent.	Complex slope—steep.

6. *F class.*—This class is used where the soils are unusually fertile and permeable and distinctions in soil slope above the E class therefore may be needed. Ordinarily, soils with such slopes are lithosolic and are included in the appropriate miscellaneous land type.

Limits	Names
Lower—45 to 65 percent.	Very steep.
Upper—None.	

The use of slope classes as a basis for phase distinction is discussed in a later section of this *Manual*. If properly defined, where variations in slope are significant, each slope class within a soil type can be given a specific set of yield estimates, productivity ratings, and management recommendations.

In the definition of detailed soil classificational and mapping units, the names for single slopes are more commonly appropriate than the names for complex slopes, although both need to be used, depending upon the features of soil slope besides gradient.[6] For soil associations, the names of the complex slopes are most commonly meaningful.

Other characteristics of soil slope.—In the description of soils in the field and in the definition of classificational units, the length and shape of slopes need to be described. Other things being equal, soils at the lower parts of long slopes are more likely to be gullied because of the concentration and velocity of the water. Concentration of water and other factors being equal, cutting is more likely on the convex slopes and filling on the concave slopes. For detailed description and definition of slopes and land form, the names and definitions employed by the geomorphologists are

---

[6] Except in highly detailed special soil surveys, however, it is not appropriate to have within one soil type two soil slope phases having the same slope class and differentiated on the basis of single versus complex slopes alone. For very highly detailed surveys in areas to be irrigated, the following distinctions according to shape of slope have been recognized: (1) Single slopes, (2) undulating, with short gentle slopes in all directions, (3) convex slopes, (4) concave slopes, and (5) concave-convex slopes on an incline, or inclined corrugations.

used. Regular patterns of slope are characteristic of most soil series, and especially of soil associations.

With accurate mapping and classification of intermittent drainage, a skilled reader of soil maps can visualize length and direction of soil slope from a detailed soil map.

ELEVATION

It is often necessary to observe the elevation where soils are studied, either from a topographic map or with a barometer, in order to correlate soil descriptions with each other and with the other observations of geology, land form, and climate.

EXPOSURE

In describing soils in the field, notes need to be taken of significant differences in exposure to wind and especially to sun that may have an important bearing on soil climate and vegetation at the particular spot. Near the critical limits of temperature, length of day, and moisture, quite different soils may be found on the north and south slopes of similar geological materials. Then too, near the critical boundaries between shrubs and trees or between grass and trees, strong winds favor the low vegetation. The skilled map reader can interpret exposure from a detailed soil map with well-defined units and a complete pattern of classified intermittent streams.

The climatic pattern of many mountainous regions is so variable within short distances that unless soil observations are carefully located in relation to elevation and exposure, they cannot be correlated with general climatic conditions.

SOIL DRAINAGE

Soil drainage, in a dynamic or active sense, refers to the rapidity and extent of the removal of water from the soil, in relation to additions, especially by surface runoff and by flow through the soil to underground spaces. Yet evaporation and transpiration contribute to water loss. Thus a nearly level Sierozem soil, having neither runoff nor percolation to the deep substratum, is well-drained because the water from all rains can distribute itself within the solum and move out by evaporation and transpiration without appreciable reduction in aeration of the soil material.

Soil drainage, as a condition of the soil, refers to the frequency and duration of periods when the soil is free of saturation or partial saturation. Such conditions can be accurately measured, although the field scientist shall need to estimate them by inference.

Accurate appraisals of the drainage conditions of soils are necessary in both soil descriptions and definitions. The problem is far more complicated than it may first appear to be. One may observe certain direct evidences of drainage or a lack of it, such as saturated soil at various times after rains or after additions of irrigation water, water-table levels, pools of surface water, and the like. Variations in soil drainage can be related by inference to differences in soil color and patterns of soil color. Mottling, the gray colors that accompany gleying, and the organic-rich material characteristic of many poorly drained soils are all good evidences, but not infallible ones. Other influences may cause similar evidences. Then too, soil slope and the texture, structure, and other characteristics of the horizons of the soil profile are useful as a basis for predicting permeability of the soil and drainage conditions. Here again, however, the scientist must consider climate, water-table levels, and other factors along with these evidences. Thus, the assessment of drainage is partly a matter of direct observation and partly a matter of inference from a large group of observations.

The concept of soil drainage is a broad one. Certain narrower aspects need to be defined first: (1) Runoff, (2) internal soil drainage, and (3) soil permeability. These last two are over-lapping, but not identical qualities. That is, a slowly permeable soil may have medium internal drainage under the natural rain-fall and slow internal drainage under irrigation. A soil of similar permeability may be regarded as having very slow internal drain-age in a wet climate. The first quality, runoff, or external drainage, is closely related to soil slope; yet a rapidly permeable, nearly level soil may have slow runoff, as contrasted to rapid runoff on a slowly permeable soil of similar slope. A slowly permeable soil and rapidly permeable soil may both have very slow internal drainage because of a high water table. If this is lowered by tiling and ditching, the one may have slow internal drainage and the other rapid internal drainage after reclamation. It is important to be able to predict the *potential* internal drainage of poorly drained soils prior to reclamation.

Ordinarily, in soil descriptions, indication of the general soil drainage class, or that and permeability class, is sufficient. In detailed studies, however, and especially in predicting soil drain-age under significantly changed conditions to be brought about through reclamation works for irrigation, drainage, and water control by dikes, separate indication of the classes of runoff and of internal drainage should be given also. An indication of the permeability of naturally poorly drained soils is essential to predictions of their suitability for use after artificial drainage.

RUNOFF

Runoff,[7] sometimes called surface runoff or external soil drain-age, refers to the relative rate water is removed by flow over the surface of the soil. This includes water falling as rain as well as water flowing onto the soil from other soils. Where needed for clear descriptions, six classes are recognized on the basis of the relative flow of water from the soil surface as determined by the characteristics of the soil profile, soil slope, climate, and cover.

---

[7] Sometimes the term "runoff" is applied to whole watersheds to refer to all the water entering stream flow, including that from springs. If any possibility of confusion exists, the term "surface runoff" should be used instead of "runoff" in soil descriptions and interpretations.

0. *Ponded.*—None of the water added to the soil as precipitation or by flow from surrounding higher land escapes as runoff. The total amount of water that must be removed from ponded areas by movement through the soil or by evaporation is usually greater than the total rainfall. Ponding normally occurs in depressed areas and may fluctuate seasonally.

1. *Very slow.*—Surface water flows away so very slowly that free water lies on the surface for long periods or enters immediately into the soil. Much of the water either passes through the soil or evaporates into the air. Soils with very slow surface runoff are commonly level to nearly level or very open and porous.

2. *Slow.*—Surface water flows away so slowly that free water covers the soil for significant periods or enters the soil rapidly and a large part of the water passes through the profile or evaporates into the air. Soils with a slow rate of surface runoff are either nearly level or very gently sloping, or absorb precipitation very rapidly. Normally there is little or no erosion hazard.

3. *Medium.*—Surface water flows away at such a rate that a moderate proportion of the water enters the soil profile and free water lies on the surface for only short periods. A large part of the precipitation is absorbed by the soil and used for plant growth, is lost by evaporation, or moves downward into underground channels. With medium runoff, the loss of water over the surface does not reduce seriously the supply available for plant growth. The erosion hazard may be slight to moderate if soils of this class are cultivated.

4. *Rapid.*—A large proportion of the precipitation moves rapidly over the surface of the soil and a small part moves through the soil profile. Surface water runs off nearly as fast as it is added. Soils with rapid runoff are usually moderately steep to steep and have low infiltration capacities. The erosion hazard is commonly moderate to high.

5. *Very rapid.*—A very large part of the water moves rapidly over the surface of the soil and a very small part goes through the profile. Surface water runs off as fast as it is added. Soils with very rapid rates of runoff are usually steep or very steep and have low infiltration capacities. The erosion hazard is commonly high or very high.

SOIL PERMEABILITY[8]

Soil permeability is that quality of the soil that enables it to transmit water or air. It can be measured quantitatively in terms of rate of flow of water through a unit cross section of saturated soil in unit time, under specified temperature and hydraulic conditions. Percolation under gravity with a $\frac{1}{2}$-inch head and drainage through cores can be measured by a standard procedure involving presaturation of samples. Rates of percolation are expressed in inches per hour.

---

[8] R. D. Hockensmith, Soil Conservation Service, made valuable suggestions concerning soil permeability.

In the absence of precise measurements, soils may be placed into relative permeability classes through studies of structure, texture, porosity, cracking, and other characteristics of the horizons in the soil profile in relation to local use experience. The observer must learn to evaluate the changes in cracking and in aggregate stability with moistening. If predictions are to be made of the responsiveness of soils to drainage or irrigation, it may be necessary to determine the permeability of each horizon and the relationship of the soil horizons to one another and to the soil profile as a whole. Commonly, however, the percolation rate of a soil is set by that of the least permeable horizon in the solum or in the immediate substratum.

The infiltration rate, or entrance of water into surface horizons, or even into the whole solum, may be rapid; yet permeability may be slow because of a slowly permeable layer directly beneath the solum that influences water movement within the solum itself. The rate of infiltration and the permeability of the plow layer may fluctuate widely from time to time because of differences in soil management practices, kinds of crops, and similar factors.

Sets of relative classes of soil permeability are as follows:

		Possible rates in inches per hour[1]
Slow:		
1.	*Very slow*	less than 0.05
2.	*Slow*	0.05 to 0.20
Moderate:		
3.	*Moderately slow*	0.20 to 0.80
4.	*Moderate*	0.80 to 2.50
5.	*Moderately rapid*	2.50 to 5.00
Rapid:		
6.	*Rapid*	5.00 to 10.00
7.	*Very rapid*	over 10.00

[1] Very tentatively suggested rates through saturated undisturbed cores under a ½-inch head of water.

INTERNAL SOIL DRAINAGE

Internal soil drainage is that quality of a soil that permits the downward flow of excess water through it. Internal drainage is reflected in the frequency and duration of periods of saturation with water. It is determined by the texture, structure, and other characteristics of the soil profile and of underlying layers and by the height of the water table, either permanent or perched, in relation to the water added to the soil. Thus, a soil of medium internal drainage may be similar in permeability to one of slow internal drainage that has a more moist climate.

As needed, six relative classes of internal drainage are recognized and defined in the following paragraphs.

0. *None.*—No free water passes through the soil mass. In humid regions, the water table is at or near the surface most of the year. Even sandy or gravelly soils may have this natural drainage condition, but when they are drained—when the water table is lowered—they may become moderately or even rapidly drained internally.

1. *Very slow.*—The rate of internal drainage is much too slow for the optimum growth of the important crops in humid regions, and may even be too slow for the optimum growth of crops on soils of the semiarid regions. Soils may be saturated with water in the root zone for a month or two. Most soils of very slow internal drainage are blotched or mottled in nearly all parts of the profile, although some have dominantly gray surface soils and upper subsoils, and others have dark-colored surface soils that are high in organic matter. A high water table, or a very slowly permeable horizon, or both, may be responsible for very slow internal soil drainage.

2. *Slow.*—In slow internal drainage, the rate of movement of water through the soil is not so fast as in medium drainage but faster than in very slow drainage. Saturation with water occurs for periods of a week or two—long enough to affect adversely the roots of many crop plants. The rate of drainage is usually somewhat too slow for the optimum growth of the important crops[9] of the region. This is especially true in the humid temperate region, where most soils having slow internal drainage have black or gray A horizons. Mottling or blotching occurs in the lower A or upper B horizons as well as in the lower B and C horizons. Many soils with slow internal drainage have relatively high permanent water tables, or a fluctuating water table.

3. *Medium.*—Internal drainage is not so free as in rapid drainage but is freer than in slow drainage. Saturation with water is limited to a few days—less time than is required for it to injure the roots of crop plants. Internal drainage is about optimum for the growth of the important crops under humid conditions. Most soils of medium internal drainage are free of mottling and blotching throughout the A horizon and all or most of the B horizon.

4. *Rapid.*—The horizons somewhat restrict the movement of water through the soil as compared to very rapid drainage. Saturation with water is restricted to a few hours. Internal drainage is somewhat too rapid for the optimum growth of the important crops of the region.

5. *Very rapid.*—The rate of movement of water through the profile is very rapid, usually because of its high porosity, and the soil is never water-saturated. Internal drainage is too rapid for the optimum growth of most of the important crops adapted to the region. Most soils with very rapid internal drainage are free to a depth of several feet of those characteristic blotches or mottlings that suggest impeded drainage. The permanent water table is usually several feet beneath the surface.

SOIL-DRAINAGE CLASSES

On the basis of the observations and inferences used to obtain classes of runoff, soil permeability, and internal soil drainage,

---

[9] The reference to "important crops" is a general one, with exceptions for water-loving sorts like paddy rice.

general relative soil-drainage classes are described below. The soil-drainage class needs to be given in each soil description. Except in very young soils, the natural drainage conditions are usually reflected in soil morphology. Since their formation some soils have had their drainage markedly altered, either naturally or by irrigation or drainage structures. Seven classes of soil drainage are used in soil descriptions and definitions to describe the natural drainage under which the soil occurs.

In the numbered paragraphs following, each of the seven soil-drainage classes is defined first in broad general terms and then in terms of the morphological relationships existing among podzolic soils and among the dark-colored soils of the grasslands. Some relationships to the production of crops, especially of corn and small grains, are suggested. Examples of soil series that fall in each class are added in parentheses.

0. **Very poorly drained.**—Water is removed from the soil so slowly that the water table remains at or on the surface the greater part of the time. Soils of this drainage class usually occupy level or depressed sites and are frequently ponded. Very poorly drained soils in the podzolic soil regions commonly have dark-gray or black surface layers and are light gray, with or without mottlings, in the deeper parts of the profile. In the grassland regions, very poorly drained soils commonly have mucky surfaces with distinct evidences of gleying. These soils are wet enough to prevent the growth of important crops (except rice) without artificial drainage. (Portsmouth, Toledo, Brookston, Westland, Abington, Pamlico muck, and Everglades peat)

1. **Poorly drained.**—Water is removed so slowly that the soil remains wet for a large part of the time. The water table is commonly at or near the surface during a considerable part of the year. Poorly drained conditions are due to a high water table, to a slowly permeable layer within the profile, to seepage, or to some combination of these conditions. In the podzolic soil region, poorly drained soils may be light gray from the surface downward, with or without mottlings. Among the dark-colored soils of the grasslands, poorly drained soils commonly have slightly thickened dark-colored surface layers. The large quantities of water that remain in and on the poorly drained soils prohibit the growing of field crops under natural conditions in most years. Artificial drainage is generally necessary for crop production, provided other soil characteristics are favorable. (Henry, Waverly, Myatt, Melvin, Webster, Loy, Clermont, Bethel, Delmar, and Wehadkee)

2. **Imperfectly or somewhat poorly drained.**—Water is removed from the soil slowly enough to keep it wet for significant periods but not all of the time. Imperfectly drained soils commonly have a slowly permeable layer within the profile, a high water table, additions through seepage, or a combination of these conditions. Among the podzolic soils, somewhat poorly drained soils are uniformly grayish, brownish, or yellowish in the upper A horizon

and commonly have mottlings below 6 to 16 inches in the lower A and in the B and C horizons. Among the dark-colored soils of the grasslands, somewhat poorly drained soils have thick, dark A horizons, high in organic matter, and faint evidences of gleying immediately beneath the A horizon. The growth of crops is restricted to a marked degree, unless artificial drainage is provided. This is the lowest drainage class in which a zonal soil retains enough of its characteristics to be classed in that order. Many soils with this drainage class cannot be placed in the zonal order. (Taft, Calloway, Pheba, Fincastle, Lawrence, Crosby, Vigo, and Odell)

3. **Moderately well drained.**—Water is removed from the soil somewhat slowly, so that the profile is wet for a small but significant part of the time. Moderately well drained soils commonly have a slowly permeable layer within or immediately beneath the solum, a relatively high water table, additions of water through seepage, or some combination of these conditions. Among podzolic soils, moderately well drained soils have uniform colors in the A and upper B horizons, with mottling in the lower B and in the C horizons. Among the dark-colored soils of the grasslands, profiles have thick, dark A horizons and yellowish or grayish faintly mottled B horizons. (Grenada, Tilsit, Richland, Muscatine, Gibson, Bronson, Bedford, and Ellsworth)

4. **Well-drained.**[10]—Water is removed from the soil readily but not rapidly. Well-drained soils are commonly intermediate in texture, although soils of other textural classes may also be well drained. Among the podzolic soils, well-drained soils are free of mottlings (except for fossil gley), and horizons may be brownish, yellowish, grayish, or reddish. They may be mottled deep in the C horizon or below depths of several feet. Among the dark-colored soils of the grasslands, well-drained soils have thick, dark A horizons, reddish, brownish, or yellowish B horizons, and C horizons that may or may not be mottled. Well-drained soils commonly retain optimum amounts of moisture for plant growth after rains or additions of irrigation water. This is the characteristic drainage of modal representatives of the zonal great soil groups. (Baxter, Ruston, Vicksburg, Cecil, Memphis, Tama, Fayette, Barnes, Williams, Miami, Russell, Cincinnati, and Holdrege)

5. **Somewhat excessively drained.**—Water is removed from the soil rapidly. Some of the soils are lithosolic. Many of them have little horizon differentiation and are sandy and very porous. Among podzolic soils, somewhat excessively drained types are free of mottling throughout the profile and are brown, yellow, gray, or red. Among the dark-colored soils of the grasslands, many profiles have relatively thin A horizons, brownish, yellowish, grayish, or reddish thin B horizons, and no mottlings within the solum. Only a narrow range of crops can be grown on these soils,

---

[10] A well-drained soil has "good" drainage.

and the yields are usually low without irrigation. (Bruno, Dickinson, Flasher, and Oshtemo)

6. **Excessively drained.**—Water is removed from the soil very rapidly. Excessively drained soils are commonly Lithosols or lithosolic, and may be steep, very porous, or both. Shallow soils on slopes may be excessively drained. Among podzolic soils, excessively drained types are commonly brownish, yellowish, grayish, or reddish in color and free of mottlings throughout the profile. Among the dark-colored soils of the grasslands, profiles commonly have thin A horizons (except for sand types that may have thick ones). Enough precipitation is commonly lost from these soils to make them unsuitable for ordinary crop production. (Guin, Muskingum, Hamburg, Plainfield, Coloma, and Chelsea)

ALTERED DRAINAGE

Notes on altered drainage are needed to indicate changed drainage conditions where there has been no corresponding change in soil morphology. Such changes are commonly due to reclamation, as in artificial drainage or irrigation, but they may also be due to a natural deepening of the stream channels or to the filling of depressions. Altered drainage conditions need to be described, as they affect potentialities for crop production. Usually the same relative terms can be used for altered drainage as those used for natural drainage.

Descriptions and definitions of altered drainage conditions may serve as the basis for the establishment of drained or waterlogged phases of soil types or series.

INCIDENCE OF FLOODING

The descriptions and definitions of soils subject to flooding need to include statements describing the frequency and regularity of flooding in as much relevant detail as the available evidence permits. The following general classes are suggested:

1. Floods frequent and irregular, so that any use of the soil for crops is too uncertain to be practicable.

2. Floods frequent but occurring regularly during certain months of the year, so that the soil may be used for crops at other times.

3. Floods may be expected, either during certain months or during any period of unusual meteorological conditions, often enough to destroy crops or prevent use in a specified percentage of the years.

4. Floods rare, but probable during a very small percentage of the years.

IDENTIFICATION AND NOMENCLATURE
OF SOIL HORIZONS

The description of a soil profile consists mainly of descriptions of its several horizons. A *soil horizon* may be defined as a layer of soil, approximately parallel to the soil surface, with characteristics produced by soil-forming processes. One soil horizon is commonly differentiated from an adjacent one at least partly on the basis of characteristics that can be seen in the field. Yet laboratory data are sometimes required for the identification and designation of horizons as well as for their more detailed characterization. The *soil profile,* as exposed in a cut or section, includes the collection of all the genetic horizons, the natural organic layers on the surface, and the parent material or other layers beneath the solum that influence the genesis and behavior of the soil.

Besides genetic soil horizons, many soils have layers inherited from stratified parent material. In making soil examinations, all distinguishable layers, or horizons, are separately described, regardless of genesis. These descriptions need to be completely objective and clearly able "to stand on their own," regardless of presumed genesis or nomenclature. Objective descriptions are the basic stuff of soil classification. Nothing can substitute for them. The more laboratory data there are available on collected samples, the more important the descriptions become; without them, the laboratory data cannot be safely interpreted, if indeed, they are relevant at all.

The profiles of numerous soils having properties quite unlike those of the original material have some characteristics due partly to inheritance from stratified parent material as well as to soil-forming processes, as in an alluvial terrace; or even partly to geological processes accompanying soil formation. That is, a soil with a well-developed profile may be gradually covered with volcanic ash, loess, wind-blown sand, or alluvium, for example, without seriously injuring the vegetation. The surface horizon becomes thickened and the lower part of the soil profile gradually passes beyond reach of active soil-forming processes.

Soil profiles vary in an almost endless number of ways. The important characteristics to be described have already been listed, and separate sections of this *Manual* explain the classes and terms for describing each one. Soil profiles vary widely in thickness, from mere films to those many feet thick. Generally in temperate regions, soil profiles need to be examined to depths of 3 to 5 feet. Normal soils are thinner toward the poles and thicker toward the Equator. Yet even in temperate regions, deeper layers, say to 6 feet or more, may be so important to soil drainage that they need to be examined, especially in the study and mapping of soils to predict their response to reclamation through irrigation or drainage.

173

Soil profiles vary widely in the degree to which genetic horizons are expressed. On nearly fresh geological formations, like new alluvial fans, sand drifts, or blankets of volcanic ash, no genetic horizons may be distinguished at all. As soil formation proceeds, they may be detected in their early stages only by laboratory study of the samples, and then later with gradually increasing clarity in the field.

In describing a soil profile, one usually locates the boundaries between horizons, measures their depth, and studies the profile as a whole before describing and naming the individual horizons.

NOMENCLATURE OF SOIL HORIZONS

It is not absolutely necessary to name the various soil horizons in order to make a good description of a soil profile. Yet the usefulness of profile descriptions is greatly increased by the proper use of genetic designations, like A, B, and C. Such interpretations show the genetic relationships among the horizons within a profile, whereas simple numbers like 1, 2, 3, 4, and 5, or undefined letters, like a, b, c, and so on, tell us nothing but depth sequence. The genetic designations make possible useful comparisons among soils. One cannot usefully compare arbitrarily defined "12- to 24-inch" layers of different soils, but B horizons can be usefully compared.

Since the advantage of letter designations is to show relationships among horizons, these designations must have genetic meaning. The application of any one of these letter designations to a soil horizon is an *interpretation* in addition to the description and not a substitute for it. The applicability of this interpretation is a matter of probability, not certainty. If the scientist can make no suggestions of genetic names—has no basis for them—the horizons should be simply numbered 1, 2, 3, and so on, from the topmost down to the lowest. If he is unable to suggest designations for some horizons and is exceedingly doubtful about others, he may (1) use numbers but put his best field estimate in parentheses after the number, such as $1(A_1)$, $2(A_2)$, 3, 4(B), 5, 6(C), and so on, or (2) use the designations followed by question marks (?) for the doubtful ones. Ordinarily the scientist can give designations to all horizons and indicate any serious uncertainty by question marks, as B_3 (?), for example, or uncertainty between two alternatives, as (B_2 or B_{2g}), for example.

Doubt about the designation of a horizon can often be removed, or at least reduced, if there are appropriate laboratory data to supplement the field observations. A final decision is often helped by the approximate field designation. While on the spot, looking at the profile as a whole, the scientist is making useful observations beyond those he can possibly write into a description. He should give his best estimate of the designation on the spot. Recognizing the uncertainty, further evidence may lead him to change the designation.

A general outline of the principal horizons and subhorizons is shown as a hypothetical soil profile in figure 27. No such profile

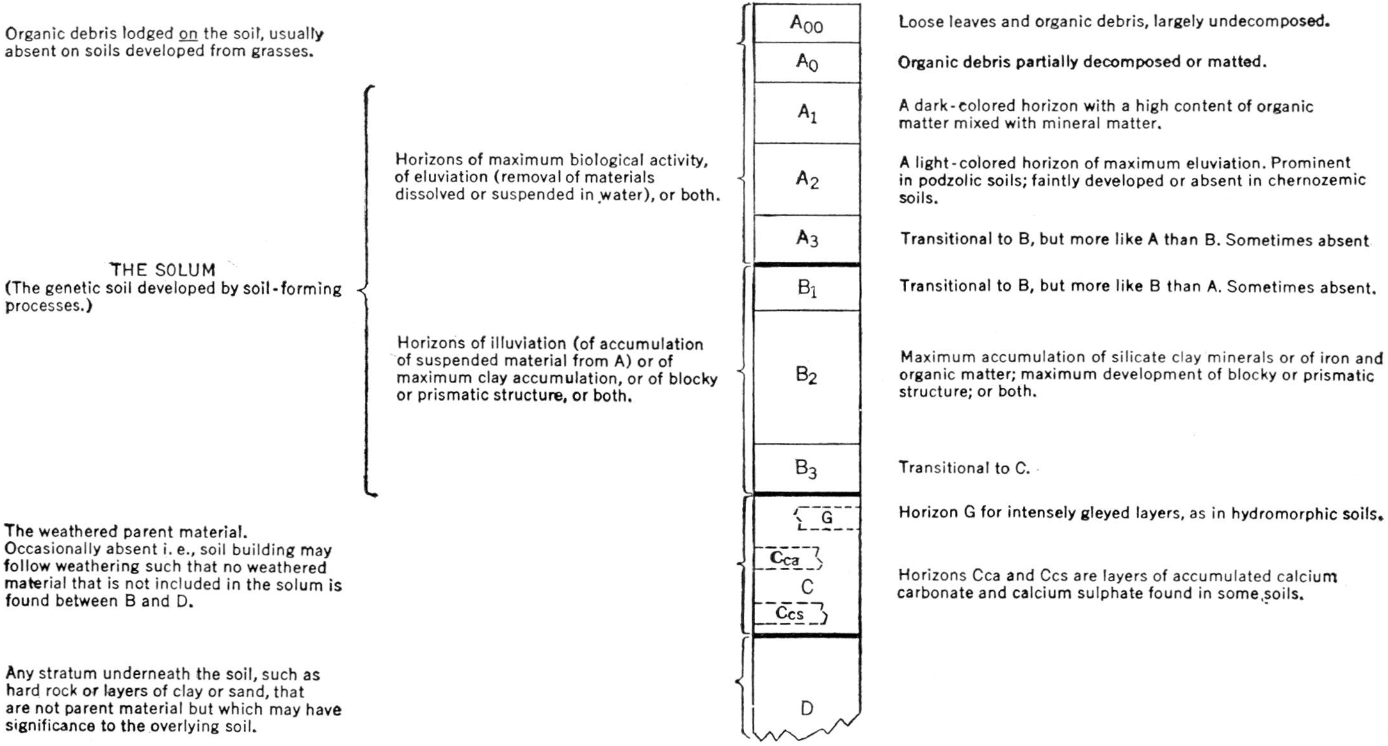

Horizon	Description
A_{00}	Loose leaves and organic debris, largely undecomposed.
A_0	Organic debris partially decomposed or matted.
A_1	A dark-colored horizon with a high content of organic matter mixed with mineral matter.
A_2	A light-colored horizon of maximum eluviation. Prominent in podzolic soils; faintly developed or absent in chernozemic soils.
A_3	Transitional to B, but more like A than B. Sometimes absent
B_1	Transitional to B, but more like B than A. Sometimes absent,
B_2	Maximum accumulation of silicate clay minerals or of iron and organic matter; maximum development of blocky or prismatic structure; or both.
B_3	Transitional to C.
G	Horizon G for intensely gleyed layers, as in hydromorphic soils.
C_{ca} C_{cs}	Horizons Cca and Ccs are layers of accumulated calcium carbonate and calcium sulphate found in some soils.
D	

Organic debris lodged on the soil, usually absent on soils developed from grasses.

Horizons of maximum biological activity, of eluviation (removal of materials dissolved or suspended in water), or both.

THE SOLUM
(The genetic soil developed by soil-forming processes.)

Horizons of illuviation (of accumulation of suspended material from A) or of maximum clay accumulation, or of blocky or prismatic structure, or both.

The weathered parent material. Occasionally absent i. e., soil building may follow weathering such that no weathered material that is not included in the solum is found between B and D.

Any stratum underneath the soil, such as hard rock or layers of clay or sand, that are not parent material but which may have significance to the overlying soil.

FIGURE 27.—A hypothetical soil profile having all the principal horizons. It will be noted that horizon B may or may not have an accumulation of clay. Horizons designated as C_{ca} usually appear between B_3 and C. The G may appear directly beneath the A.

could really exist in nature—the outline merely shows the relative positions of horizons. No one soil has all the various kinds of horizons in it. The simpler drawings in figure 28 present a few examples of how the horizons of actual profiles may be usefully designated. Capital letters are used for the main horizons, and lower-case letters and numbers in subscripts.

Originally the A–B–C nomenclature for soil horizons was applied in Russia to Chernozems. The A was used for the uniformly dark-colored surface soil, the C for the weathered material below the solum, and the B for the transitional horizon, as then regarded, between them. Later, these designations were used on Podzols and other podzolic soils in Russia and elsewhere in Europe; and the B became the layer of accumulation, especially of clay, iron oxide, and alumina. The early use of this nomenclature for soil horizons in the United States was adapted from its use in Europe on podzolic soils. Thus, at first, the notion became current that the B, to be a B, *had* to be a horizon of accumulation. During this early period, some even went so far as to designate the principal horizon of calcium carbonate accumulation in Chernozem and Chestnut soils as B!

Definitions have been expanded and revised since the earlier edition of this *Manual,* and further improvements may be hoped for. For example, the present definitions are not entirely adequate for many Tundra and Desert soils. Possibly additional symbols can be added usefully. Yet no set of symbols can substitute for adequate descriptions without becoming too unwieldy for accurate general use.

THE A_0 AND A_{00} HORIZONS

The A_0 and A_{00} horizons lie above the A_1 horizon of unplowed soils. They are not strictly parts of the A horizon or of the solum as herein defined, although, from some points of view, they might be so regarded.[1] The exclusion of these horizons from the solum in no way suggests that they are unimportant or that careful recognition is not essential to a useful description of many soils. Many important soil-forming processes owe their origin in part to materials produced in these layers. Although these horizons have typical thicknesses and characteristics for any one soil type under the normal undisturbed vegetation, their actual thicknesses vary widely because of fire and other common disturbances. These horizons are especially well developed in Podzols and are found on most unburned forested soils, although they are exceedingly thin on some. Thin but important A_0 or A_{00} horizons are occasionally found also on soils developed under grasses and desert shrubs.

A_{00} horizon.—This is a surface horizon consisting of relatively fresh leaves, twigs, and other plant remains, generally of the past year.

---

[1] Some letter other than A would be chosen by the authors for these layers if the use of A_0 and A_{00} were not so well established.

Issued May 1962

U.S. DEPARTMENT OF AGRICULTURE

Soil Conservation Service

Supplement to Agriculture Handbook No. 18

SOIL SURVEY MANUAL

(Replacing pages 173–188)

IDENTIFICATION AND NOMENCLATURE
OF SOIL HORIZONS

The description of a soil profile consists mainly of descriptions of its several horizons. A *soil horizon* may be defined as a layer of soil, approximately parallel to the soil surface, with characteristics produced by soil-forming processes. One soil horizon is commonly differentiated from an adjacent one at least partly on the basis of characteristics that can be seen in the field. Yet laboratory data are sometimes required for the identification and designation of horizons as well as for their more detailed characterization. The *soil profile*, as exposed in a cut or section, includes the collection of all the genetic horizons, the natural organic layers on the surface, and the parent material or other layers beneath the solum that influence the genesis and behavior of the soil.

Besides genetic soil horizons, many soils have layers inherited from stratified parent material. In making soil examinations, all distinguishable layers, or horizons, are separately described, regardless of genesis. These descriptions need to be completely objective and clearly able "to stand on their own," regardless of presumed genesis or nomenclature. Objective descriptions are the basic stuff of soil classification. Nothing can substitute for them. The more laboratory data there are available on collected samples, the more important the descriptions become; without them, the laboratory data cannot be safely interpreted, if indeed, they are relevant at all.

The profiles of numerous soils having properties quite unlike those of the original material have some characteristics due partly to inheritance from stratified parent material as well as to soil-forming processes, as in an alluvial terrace; or even partly to geological processes accompanying soil formation. That is, a soil with a well-developed profile may be gradually covered with volcanic ash, loess, windblown sand, or alluvium, for example, without seriously injuring the vegetation. The surface horizon becomes thickened and the lower part of the soil profile gradually passes beyond reach of active soil-forming processes.

Soil profiles vary in an almost endless number of ways. The important characteristics to be described have already been listed, and separate sections of this *Manual* explain the classes and terms for describing each one. Soil profiles vary widely in thickness, from mere films to those many feet thick. Generally in temperate regions, soil profiles need to be examined to depths of 3 to 5 feet. Normal soils are thinner toward the poles and thicker toward the Equator. Yet even in temperate regions, deeper layers, say to 6 feet or more, may be so important to soil drainage that they need to be examined, especially in the study and mapping of soils to predict their response to reclamation through irrigation or drainage.

Soil profiles vary widely in the degree to which genetic horizons are expressed. On nearly fresh geological formations, like new alluvial fans, sand drifts, or blankets of volcanic ash, no genetic horizons may be distinguished at all. As soil formation proceeds, they may be detected in their early stages only by laboratory study of the samples, and then later with gradually increasing clarity in the field.

In describing a soil profile, one usually locates the boundaries between horizons, measures their depth, and studies the profile as a whole before describing and naming the individual horizons.

DESIGNATIONS FOR HORIZONS AND LAYERS

It is not absolutely necessary to name the various soil horizons in order to make a good description of a soil profile. Yet the usefulness of profile descriptions is greatly increased by the proper use of genetic designations, like A, B, and C. Such interpretations show the genetic relationships among the horizons within a profile, whereas simple numbers like 1, 2, 3, 4, and 5, or undefined letters like a, b, c, and so on, tell us nothing but depth sequence. The genetic designations make possible useful comparisons among soils. One cannot usefully compare arbitrarily defined "12- to 24-inch" layers of different soils, but B horizons can be usefully compared.

It is assumed that each horizon or layer designation used is merely a symbol indicating the considered judgment of the person describing the soil relative to kind of departure from the original material from which it has formed, including the zero degree of departure in the case of R and some C layers. This implies that each symbol indicates merely an estimate, not a proven fact. It implies that when reading a symbol one must reconstruct mentally the character of the parent material, for this was done when the designation was assigned. It implies that the processes that have caused change need not be known. It also implies that specific morphology need not be consistent from profile to profile and that morphology relative to an estimated parent material is the criterion for judgment. The parent material of the horizon in question, not the material in the horizon or layer designated by the symbol C, is used as the basis of comparison. Morphology is interpreted relative to this assumed parent material, not in terms of absolute values of properties.

CONVENTIONS GOVERNING USE OF SYMBOLS

1. Capital letter symbols include O, A, B, C, and R. They indicate dominant kinds of departures from the parent material. More than one kind of departure may be indicated by a single capital letter,

providing these departures are within the limits of the definitions given further along in this chapter.

2. In a description of a given profile, if a horizon designated by O, A, or B is subdivided, the subdivisions are indicated by placing an arabic number after the capital letter. Thus, symbols such as O1, O2, A1, A2, A3, B1, B2, and B3 are obtained. Each symbol derived in this way stands for an integral unit, and each unit requires its own definition. A given arabic numeral therefore has different implication when combined with different capital letters. Thus, the symbols O1, O2, A1, and A2 indicate specific kinds of O and A master horizons. The symbols A3, B1, and B3 are transitional horizons. Likewise, the symbol B2 indicates that part of the B horizon that is of a nature not transitional either to A or to C. Even if both B1 and B3 are absent, if the B horizon of a given profile is subdivided, the symbol B2, not B, is used. The symbols O, A, and B each indicate a unit that, according to need, can have several subdivisions or none. The symbol C, however, indicates a unit that is not subdivided in the manner of O, A, and B. If a horizon is subdivided, this is done only in the manner described in the following paragraph 3, and the arabic numeral assigned has no consistent meaning except vertical sequence.

3. Vertical subdivision within an otherwise undifferentiated horizon is indicated by primary or secondary arabic numbers assigned, in order, from the topmost subdivision downward. These are not used with O, A, or B without a primary arabic number. Thus, secondary numbers are used with O1, O2, A1, A2, A3, B1, B2, B3, and C. Primary arabic numbers are used with C and Ap. Thus, we use C1 and C2, Ap1 and Ap2, but A11 and A12, B21, B22 or B23, as needed, without consistence in meaning beyond the fact that we have made a subdivision. The reason for the subdivision may be indicated in the text of the description or by a lower case letter suffix.

4. Lower case letters are used as suffixes to indicate selected subordinate departures from the assumed parent material or to indicate selected, specific kinds of major departures from the definition assigned to the symbol O, A, B, C. These are regarded as alternatives to narrative statements of equivalent interpretations in the profile description. These suffixes follow the arabic number in the letter-number combined symbols discussed under item 2 above (A2g or B3ca), or they may follow the capital letter of a master horizon if it is not subdivided (Bt or Ap). These suffixes also follow arabic numbers used solely for vertical subdivision described under item 3 above, as A21g and A22g or C1ca and C2ca. An exception is made with the lower case letter p. This is used only with the letter A (Ap) and is comparable to the A1 or A2.

5. Roman numerals are prefixed to the master horizon or layer designations (O, A, B, C, R) to indicate lithologic discontinuities either within or below the solum. The first, or uppermost, material is not numbered, for the Roman numeral I is understood; the second contrasting material is numbered II, and others encountered are numbered III, IV, and so on, consecutively with depth. Thus, for example, a sequence from the surface downward might be A2, B1, IIB2, IIB3, IIC1, IIIC2.

A lithologic discontinuity is a significant change in particle size distribution or mineralogy that indicates a difference in the material from which the horizons have formed. A change in the clay content associated with an argillic horizon (textural B) does not indicate a difference in parent material. Appearance of gravel, or a change in the ratios between the various sand separates, will normally suggest a difference in parent materials. One purpose in identifying lithologic discontinuities is to distinguish between those differences between horizons that are the result of pedo-genesis and those that are geologic. Consequently, a designation with a different Roman number would not normally be used for a buried soil in a thick loess deposit. The difference between the properties of the buried soil and the overlying loess are presumably the result of pedo-genesis. But a stone line usually indicates a need for another Roman number. The material above the stone line is presumed to be transported. If the transport was by wind or water, one must suspect that during the movement there was some sorting of the material according to size.

6. An illuvial or B horizon (together with its overlying eluvial or A horizon if one is present) is called a sequum. If more than one sequum is present in vertical sequence, the lower sequum is given A and B designations with a prime accent, as A′2, B′2. The prime accents are not used however for buried soils. These carry the lower case letter b.

MASTER HORIZONS AND LAYERS

Organic horizons

O—Organic horizons of mineral soils. Horizons: (1) formed or forming in the upper part of mineral soils above the mineral part; (2) dominated by fresh or partly decomposed organic material; and (3) containing more than 30 percent organic matter if the mineral fraction is more than 50 percent clay, or more than 20 percent organic matter if the mineral fraction has no clay. Intermediate clay content requires proportional organic-matter content

The O horizons may be present at the surface horizon of mineral soils, or at any depth beneath the surface in buried soils, but they have been formed from organic litter derived from plants and animals and deposited on the surface. The O horizons do not include soil horizons formed by illuviation of organic material into mineral material, nor do they include horizons high in organic matter formed by a decomposing root mat below the surface of a mineral material.

Because organic horizons at the surface may be rapidly altered in thickness or be destroyed by fire or by the activities of man or other animals, the depth limits of organic horizons that are at the surface are always measured upward from the top of the underlying mineral material. Two subdivisions are recognized:

O1—Organic horizons in which essentially the original form of most vegetative matter is visible to the naked eye

Aoo

Identifiable remains of soil fauna, or their excrement, may be present, and the horizon may be filled with fungal hyphae. The vegetative matter may be essentially unaltered, as freshly fallen leaves, or may be leached of its most soluble constituents and discolored. The O1 corresponds to the L and some F layers mentioned in literature on forest soils and to the horizon formerly called Aoo.

Ao

O2—**Organic horizons in which the original form of most plant or animal matter cannot be recognized with the naked eye**

Remains of parts of plants and animals commonly can be identified with magnification, and excrement of soil fauna is commonly a large part of the material present. The O2 corresponds to the H layer and some F layers described in literature on forest soils and to the horizon formerly called Ao.

The organic horizons in organic soils are not defined here. They are currently under discussion. The organic B horizons in mineral soils are defined under B horizon, along with the mineral horizons.

Mineral horizons and layers

Mineral horizons contain less than 30 percent organic matter if the mineral fraction contains more than 50 percent clay or less than 20 percent organic matter if the mineral fraction has no clay. Intermediate clay content requires proportional content of organic matter.

A—**Mineral horizons consisting of: (1) horizons of organic-matter accumulation formed or forming at or adjacent to the surface; (2) horizons that have lost clay, iron, or aluminum with resultant concentration of quartz or other resistant minerals of sand or silt size; or (3) horizons dominated by 1 or 2 above but transitional to an underlying B or C**

A1—**Mineral horizons, formed or forming at or adjacent to the surface, in which the feature emphasized is an accumulation of humified organic matter intimately associated with the mineral fraction**

The mineral particles have coatings of organic material, or the soil mass is darkened by organic particles; the horizon is as dark as, or darker than, adjacent underlying horizons. The mineral fraction may be unaltered or may have been altered in a manner comparable to that of A2 or B. The organic fraction is assumed to have been derived from plant and animal remains deposited mechanically on the surface of the soil, or deposited within the horizon without translocation of humified material through an intervening horizon that qualifies for a horizon designation other than A1.

A2—**Mineral horizons in which the feature emphasized is loss of clay, iron, or aluminum, with resultant concentration of quartz or other resistant minerals in sand and silt sizes**

Such horizons are commonly but not necessarily lighter in color than an underlying B. In some soils the color is determined by that of the primary sand and silt particles, but in many soils, coats of iron or other compounds, apparently released in the horizon and not translocated, mask the color of the primary particles. An A2 is most commonly differentiated from an overlying A1 by lighter color and is generally measurably lower in organic matter. An A2 is most commonly differentiated from an underlying B in the same profile by lighter color, or coarser texture, or both. A2 horizons are commonly near the surface, below an O or A1 horizon and above a B, but the symbol A2 may be used either above or below subsurface horizons; position in the profile is not diagnostic. For horizons at the surface that would qualify equally well as either A1 or A2, the designation A1 is given preference over A2.

A3—**A transitional horizon between A and B, and dominated by properties characteristic of an overlying A1 or A2 but having some subordinate properties of an underlying B**

No distinction is made between the different kinds of horizons that are transitional from A1 or A2 to different kinds of B; they obviously may be quite unlike one another, but the burden of characterization rests on the description of the transitional horizon, plus inferences that can be made after noticing the symbols assigned to the overlying and underlying horizons. The symbol A3 normally is used only if the horizon is underlain by a B horizon. However, where the profile is truncated from below in small places by rock, so as to eliminate the horizon that would be designated B, the symbol A3 may be used for the horizon that is above the rock. For example, in one part of a pedon, a horizon may be transitional between A and B, and thus appropriately designated A3. But, in another part of the same pedon, the same horizon rests on rock, and may appropriately be called A3, even though there is no underlying B.

The symbol A3 is confined to those kinds of transitional zones in which some properties of the underlying B are superimposed on properties of A throughout the soil mass. Those kinds of "transitional horizons" in which parts that are characteristic of A enclose parts characteristic of B are classified as A and B.

AB—A horizon transitional between A and B, having an upper part dominated by properties of A and a lower part dominated by properties of B, and the two parts cannot conveniently be separated into A3 and B1

Such combined horizons are normally thin; they should be separated if thick enough to permit separation.

A&B—Horizons that would qualify for A2 except for included parts constituting less than 50 percent of the volume that would qualify as B

Commonly, A and B horizons are predominantly A2 material partially surrounding thin, columnar-like upward extensions of the B or wholly surrounding small, isolated spheres, elipsoids, or other bodies that would qualify as B. In such horizons the A2 appears to be encroaching on an underlying B.

AC—A horizon transitional between A and C, having subordinate properties of both A and C, but not dominated by properties characteristic of either A or C

B—Horizons in which the dominant feature or features is one or more of the following: (1) an illuvial concentration of silicate clay, iron, aluminum, or humus, alone or in combination; (2) a residual concentration of sesquioxides or silicate clays, alone or mixed, that has formed by means other than solution and removal of carbonates or more soluble salts; (3) coatings of sesquioxides adequate to give conspicuously darker, stronger, or redder colors than overlying and underlying horizons in the same sequum but without apparent illuviation of iron and not genetically related to B horizons that meet requirements of 1 or 2 in the same sequum; or (4) an alteration of material from its original condition in sequums lacking conditions defined in 1, 2, and 3 that obliterates original rock structure, that forms silicate clays, liberates oxides, or both, and that forms granular, blocky, or prismatic structure if textures are such that volume changes accompany changes in moisture.

It is obviously necessary to be able to identify the kind of B before one can establish that a horizon qualifies as B. There is no common diagnostic property or location in the profile by means of which all kinds of B can be identified. There are, however, marginal cases in which a horizon might qualify as either of two kinds of B. In such cases, the horizon description should indicate the kind of B that characterizes the dominant condition, in the judgment of the person describing the soil. Laboratory work may be needed for identification of the kind of B, or even to determine that a given horizon is a B.

B1—A transitional horizon between B and A1 or between B and A2 in which the horizon is dominated by properties of an underlying B2 but has some subordinate properties of an overlying A1 or A2

An adjacent overlying A1 or A2 and an adjacent underlying B2 are essential to characterization of a horizon as B1 in a virgin soil. In a few instances the horizon may still be recognized in a truncated soil by comparing the truncated profile with a profile of the same soil that has not been truncated. The symbol B1 is confined to those kinds of transitional horizons in which some properties of the overlying, adjacent A1 or A2 are superimposed on properties of B throughout the mass of the transitional horizon. Those kinds of transitional horizons containing parts characteristic of B, separated by abrupt boundaries from parts characteristic of an overlying A2, are classified as B&A.

B&A—Any horizon qualifying as B in more than 50 percent of its volume including parts that qualify as A2

Such horizons commonly have many vertical tongues of A2 material that extend downward into the B from the A2 or they have thin horizontal bands of A2-like material, which lie between thicker bands of B and are connected with tongues extending from the A2. Tubes filled with A1 material, as in krotovinas or earthworm channels, in a B horizon should be described but should not be designated as B and A. Many B horizons have A2-like material in widely spaced narrow cracks. Such features should be described, but the horizon should be designated as B and A only if the A2 material constitutes more than 10 percent of the volume of the horizon.

B2—That part of the B horizon where the properties on which the B is based are without clearly expressed subordinate characteristics indicating that the horizon is transitional to an adjacent overlying A or an adjacent underlying C or R

This does not imply that the B2 horizon in a given profile must express to uniform degree the properties diagnostic of B or that it must be confined to a zone of maximum expression in the absolute sense. The horizon B3, which is transitional from B2 to C, commonly exhibits the subordinate properties of C by expressing in lower degree the properties of an adjacent B2. Before the designation B3 is justified, the degree of expression of B2 must be low enough that the properties of C are clearly evident. The definition does not imply that a given kind of B2 has the same degree of expression in all profiles. In some profiles the most strongly expressed part of the B horizon, which would be designated B2, may be as weakly expressed as B3 in other profiles. The designation B2 is used strictly within the frame of reference of a single profile and not in an absolute sense of degree.

B3—A transitional horizon between B and C or R in which the properties diagnostic of an overlying B2 are clearly expressed but are associated with clearly expressed properties characteristic of C or R

The designation B3 is used only if there is an overlying B2; this applies even though the properties diagnostic of B are weakly expressed in the profile. Where an underlying material presumed to be like the parent material of the solum is absent, as in A–B–IIC profiles, B3 is used below B2 in the sense of a horizon transitional to an assumed original parent material. Use of the symbol IIC involves an estimate of at least the gross character of the parent material of the horizons above it. B3 in such cases is based on this estimate of the properties of the parent material of the B. B3 is not used as a horizon transitional from IB2 to IIC or IIR.

C—A mineral horizon or layer, excluding bedrock, that is either like or unlike the material from which the solum is presumed to have formed, relatively little affected by pedogenic processes, and lacking properties diagnostic of A or B but including materials modified by: (1) weathering outside the zone of major biological activity; (2) reversible cementation, development of brittleness, development of high bulb density, and other properties characteristic of fragipans; (3) gleying; (4) accumulation of calcium or magnesium carbonate or more soluble salts; (5) cementation by such accumulations as calcium or magnesium carbonate or more soluble salts; or (6) cementation by alkali-soluble siliceous material or by iron and silica

This definition is intended to exclude horizons that meet the requirements of A or B but to include certain kinds of alteration that, historically, have been considered to be little influenced by the activity of organisms. These alterations include chemical weathering deep in the soil. Some soils are presumed to have developed in materials already highly weathered, and such weathered material that does not meet requirements for A or B is considered C. Development of the firmness, brittleness, and high density characteristic of fragipans is, by itself, not a criterion of A or B. Fragipans that have distinct silicate clay concentrations are to be indicated as Bx or simply as B. Fragipans lacking such clay concentration, however, are considered to be within the definition of C and are designated Cx. Accumulations of carbonates, gypsum, or more soluble salts are permitted in C if the material is otherwise considered to be little affected by other processes that have contributed to genesis of associated horizons. Such horizons are designated as Cca, Ccs, Csa. Even induration by such materials is permitted and this can be indicated by the suffix m, as in Ccam. Induration by alkali-soluble siliceous material is also permitted and may be indicated by Csim. Induration by iron and silica does not exclude the horizon from C, and horizons or layers thus indurated would be designated Cm. Horizon C, as defined, is intended to include the diagnostic horizons indicated by ca, cs, and sa, and the alkali-soluble pans, the iron-silica pans, and the fragipans, provided these layers do not meet the requirements of B. The C horizon now includes the contrasting layers of unconsolidated material formerly designated as D. It also includes the former G horizon, if that horizon cannot be designated as A or B. Historically, C has often incorrectly been called parent material. In fact it is impossible to find the parent material from which the A and B horizons have developed; that material has been altered. For this reason, C never was parent material, but was merely presumed to be like parent material. As C is now defined, even this assumption is dropped.

The differentiation between C1 and C2 that was formerly made has been dropped because it is untenable when applied to the variety of conditions recognized as C. Deletion of C1 makes arabic numerals applied to C indicative only of vertical sequence within C.

R—Underlying consolidated bedrock, such as granite, sandstone, or limestone. If presumed to be like the parent rock from which the adjacent overlying layer or horizon was formed, the symbol R is used alone. If presumed to be unlike the overlying material, the R is preceded by a Roman numeral denoting lithologic discontinuity as explained under the heading

SYMBOLS USED TO INDICATE DEPARTURES SUBORDINATE TO THOSE INDICATED BY CAPITAL LETTERS

The following symbols are to be used in the manner indicated under the heading Conventions Governing Use of Symbols.

b—Buried soil horizon

This symbol is added to the designation of a buried genetic horizon or horizons. Horizons of another solum may or may not have formed in the overlying material, which may be similar to, or different from, the assumed parent material of the buried soil.

ca—An accumulation of carbonates of alkaline earths, commonly of calcium

This symbol is applied to A, B, or C horizons. Possible combinations are A1ca, A3ca, B1ca, B2ca, B3ca. A2ca is probably also possible where accumulation has occurred in an A2 formed under different conditions, but it is not common. The presence of secondary carbonates alone is not adequate to justify the use of the ca symbol. The horizon must have more carbonates than the parent material is presumed to have had.

cs—An accumulation of calcium sulfate

This symbol is used in a manner comparable to that of ca. Calcium sulfate accumulations commonly occur in the C below ca accumulations in chernozemic soils but may occur in other horizons as well. Before the symbol cs is used, the horizon must have more sulfates than the parent material is presumed to have had.

cn—Accumulations of concretions or hard nonconcretionary nodules enriched in sesquioxides with or without phosphorus.

The nodules indicated by the symbol cn must be hard when dry but need not be indurated. The horizon description should characterize the nodules. Nodules, concretions, or crystals do not qualify as cn if they are of dolomite or more soluble salts, but they do qualify if they are of iron, aluminum, manganese, or titanium.

f—Frozen soil

The suffix f is used for soil that is thought to be permanently frozen.

g—Strong gleying

The suffix g is used with a horizon designation to indicate intense reduction of iron during soil development, or reducing conditions due to stagnant water, as evidenced by base colors that approach neutral, with or without mottles. In aggregated material, ped faces in such horizons generally have chroma of 2 or less as a continuous phase, and commonly have few or faint mottles. Interiors of peds may have prominent and many mottles but commonly have a network of threads or bands of low chroma surrounding the mottles. In soils that are not aggregated, a base chroma of 1.0 or less, with or without mottles, is indicative of strong gleying. Hues bluer than 10Y are also indicative of strong gleying in some soils. Horizons of low chroma in which the color is due to uncoated sand or silt particles are not considered strongly gleyed. Although gleying is commonly associated with wetness, especially in the presence of organic matter, wetness by itself is not a criterion of gleying. The symbol g may be applied to any of the major symbols for mineral horizons and should follow the horizon designations, as A2g, A21g, A3g, B1g, B2g, B3g, and Cg. Bg may be used where B horizons cannot be subdivided into B1, B2, and B3.

No lower case letter is used as a suffix with horizon designations to indicate reduction of iron less intense than that indicated by g. Not given a special designation but described in detail is the condition generally associated with (1) common to many, distinct to prominent mottles on base colors of chroma stronger than 2 in unaggregated material, or (2) evidenced by base chroma greater than 2 with few to common, faint to distinct mottles on ped faces and common to many distinct to prominent mottles in ped interiors in well-aggregated material.

h—Illuvial humus

Accumulations of decomposed illuvial organic matter, appearing as dark coatings on sand or silt particles, or as discrete dark pellets of silt size, are indicated by h. If used, this suffix follows the letter B or a subdivision of B, as Bh or B2h.

ir—Illuvial iron

Accumulations of illuvial iron as coatings on sand or silt particles or as pellets of silt size; in some horizons the coatings have coalesced, filled pores, and cemented the horizon.

m—Strong cementation, induration

The symbol m is applied as a suffix to horizon designations to indicate irreversible cementation. The symbol is not applied to indurated bedrock. Contrary to previous usage, m is not used to indicate firmness, as in fragipans, but is confined to indurated horizons which are essentially (more than 90 percent) continuous, though they may be fractured.

p—Plowing or other disturbance

The symbol p is used as a suffix with A to indicate disturbance by cultivation or pasturing. Even though a soil has been truncated and the plow layer is clearly in what was once B horizon, the designation Ap is used. When an Ap is subdivided, the arabic number suffixes follow, as Ap1 and Ap2, for the Ap is considered comparable to A1, A2, or B2.

sa—An accumulation of salts more soluble than calcium sulfate

This symbol may be applied to the designation of any horizon and in its manner of use is comparable to that described for ca or cs. If the symbol is used, the horizon must have more salt than the parent material is presumed to have had.

si—Cementation by siliceous material, soluble in alkali. This symbol is applied only to C

The cementation may be nodular or continuous. If the cementation is continuous the symbol sim is used.

t—Illuvial clay

Accumulations of translocated silicate clay are indicated by the suffix t (Ger. ton, clay). The suffix t is used only with B, as B2t, to indicate the nature of the B.

x—Fragipan character

The symbol x is used as a suffix with horizon designations to indicate genetically developed properties of firmness, brittleness, high density, and characteristic distribution of clay that are diagnostic of fragipans. Fragipans, or parts of fragipans, may qualify as A2, B, or C. Such horizons are classified as A2, B, or C, and the symbol x is used as a suffix to indicate fragipan character. Unlike comparable use of supplementary symbols, the symbol x is applied to B without the connotative arabic numeral normally applied to B. Arabic numerals used with C to indicate only vertical subdivision of the horizon precede the x in the symbol, as C1x, C2x.

All lower case symbols except p follow the last arabic number used, as B3ca, A2g, A21g. If the horizon is not subdivided, the symbol follows the capital letter, as Cg, Bt. The symbol p is restricted to use with A because of the common difficulty of deciding which horizons have been included in the plow layer.

It will be noted that the connotation of the symbol m has been changed to prohibit its use with "fragipans" and that definitions of the other symbols have been modified or elaborated. The symbols si and x have been added, and the symbols r, G, D, M, and u have been dropped.

SUBDIVISION OF HORIZONS

In a single profile it is often necessary to subdivide the horizons for which designations are provided, for example, to subdivide Ap, A1, A2, A3, B1, B2, B3, or C so that detailed studies of morphology, sampling, and similar work can be correctly recorded. In some cases, such subdivision is arbitrary in relation to differences observable in the field; in others, it may be needed to differentiate within a horizon on bases not provided by unique horizon symbols. In all such cases, the subdivisions are numbered consecutively, with arabic numbers, from the top of the horizon downward, as B21, B22, B23. If the suffixes consisting of lower-case letters are being used, the arabic numbers precede all lower-case suffixes except p as B21t, C1g, C2g, but Ap1, Ap2.

LITHOLOGIC DISCONTINUITES

Roman numerals are prefixed to the appropriate horizon designations when it is necessary to number a series of layers of contrasting material consecutively from the surface downward. A soil that is all in one kind of material is all in material designated by the numeral I. This numeral therefore can be omitted from the symbol, as it is understood that all the material is I. Similarly, the uppermost material in a profile having two or more contrasting materials is always designated I. Consequently, for the topmost material, the numeral I can be omitted from the symbol because it is always understood. Numbering starts with the second layer of contrasting material, which is designated II, and each contrasting material below this second layer is numbered consecutively, III, IV, and so on, downward as part of each horizon designation. Even though a layer below a layer designated by II is similar to the topmost layer, it is given the appropriate consecutive number in the sequence. Where two or more horizons developed in one of the numbered layers, the Roman number is applied to all the horizon designations in that material.

Following are two examples of horizon sequences using this convention:

A1—A2—B1—B21—IIB22—IIB3—IIC1—IIIC2.
A1—A2—B1—B2—IIA'2—IIB'x—IICIx—IIIC2x—IIIC3—IVR.

In the first example, the first contrasting layer is unnumbered; the second layer, starting in the B2, is indicated by Roman II, as IIB22; the third, within the C, by the symbol IIIC. In the second example, the first contrasting layer is unnumbered; the second, starting at the top of A'2, is numbered II; the third, starting in the middle of the fragipan is numbered III, even though the fragipan is partly in C; and the fourth, starting below C, is indicated by IVR. Note that arabic numerals are used independently of the Roman numerals, in the conventional manner, both as connotative symbols and for vertical subdivision.

THE SOLUM

The solum may be defined simply as the genetic soil developed by soil-building forces. In normal soils, the solum includes the A and B horizons, or the upper part of the soil profile above the parent material.

Although the concept of *solum* is commonly understood by soil scientists, this definition is deceptively simple. Especially in some of the intrazonal soils, the actual sola are not easily determined; and in some soils their lower limits can be set only arbitrarily, say at 6 feet or 2 meters, or at the lower limit of plant roots. Used with such soils, the term "solum" may need to be defined in relation to the particular soil.

These difficulties concerning the solum arise mainly from the fact that the processes of soil formation often merge with broad geological processes. Although it is important to distinguish between geological and soil-forming processes, it is equally important to recognize that they usually go on together and that soils are being influenced by both. It is of little use to argue semantically about certain phenomena in the profile that are the result of combinations of the two sets of processes or that can be ascribed sometimes to one and sometimes to the other. These difficulties are illustrated by some common examples in the paragraphs following.

Croûte calcaire.—Croûte calcaire, or hardened caliche, is often found in thick masses overlain by only a few inches of soil. The common Cca horizons of Chernozems, let us say, are easily conceived as part of the soil profile, although they are not within the solum.[1] Their genesis and relationships to the solum raise no particular difficulties. It is another matter, however, to include some 10 to 25 feet of croûte calcaire under a Reddish-Brown soil as a part of its

---

[1] Admittedly this may appear to be somewhat arbitrary. In many Chernozems and Chestnut soils it may seem that the solum could be defined to include the Cca; but in some developed from materials low in calcium the Cca comes deep within the C, far below the solum.

profile. Doubtless this croûte calcaire is related to the solum and should be described in any description of the soil profile; but certainly broad long-time geological processes have been at work, as well as soil-forming processes.

Laterite.—Laterite includes the sesquioxide-rich, highly weathered clayey material that is hardened irreversibly to concretions, hardpans, or crusts when dehydrated, and hardened relicts of such materials more or less mixed with quartz and other diluents. Laterite is found in many soils and is a distinguishing feature of Ground-Water Laterite soil. In the profile of a Ground-Water Laterite soil one may designate the horizons easily as A1, A2, A3, and B1, down into the B2 or, perhaps, into the B3. The same material may continue practically without change for another 25 feet or so with no definite place for dividing the solum from the material underneath it. It would be unreasonable to exclude the upper part of the laterite from the solum; and it seems unreasonable to include the lower part, far removed from the influence of organisms.

Gleyed soil material.—Gleyed soil material may begin a few inches below the surface of hydromorphic soils and, in some instances, continue on down for many feet essentially unchanged. Such conditions can arise through the gradual filling of a wet basin, with the A horizon gradually being added to at the surface and being gleyed beneath. Finally the A rests on a thick mass of gleyed material, which may be relatively uniform, especially in sandy types. Obviously the upper part belongs in the solum, while the lower part does not. This illustration does not extend to all gleyed soils. In many the gleyed horizon is clearly a part of the solum and has a clear lower boundary with the C.

Permafrost.—Permanently frozen ground under soils of the arctic and subarctic regions is called permafrost. The upper boundary, or *permafrost table*, is said to be coincident with the lower limits of seasonal thaws. The upper boundary of frozen ground varies, of course, from month to month during the summer and from year to year, depending upon the season. The soil that freezes and thaws seasonally is above the permafrost table. The frozen ground may extend downward many feet, even several hundred feet. Here again, the morphologist may properly place some part of the frozen ground in the soil profile, or even in the solum, as a kind of "thermal" hardpan, especially if it contains organic matter and bears a definite relationship to the upper horizons or solum. In many soils with permafrost, the permafrost table is deep beneath the solum, within the C or below it.

Some soils have no solum at all although they support plants. Examples include very young soils from recent accumulations of volcanic ash, alluvium, or loess. At least some time is required after vegetation has become established before recognizable genetic horizons are formed.

POPULAR TERMS FOR SOIL LAYERS

Several popular terms have long been used to refer to certain soil horizons or groups of horizons—terms that are exceedingly difficult to define precisely. They are very old and have been used by laymen in widely different senses.

Topsoil is a general term that is used in at least four senses: (1) For the surface plowed layer (Ap) and thus as a synonym for surface soil; (2) for the original or present A1 horizon, and thus exceedingly variable in depth among different soils; (3) for the original or present A horizon; and (4) for presumed fertile soil or soil material, usually rich in organic matter, used to top-dress road banks, parks, gardens, and lawns.

The authors know of no way to settle on a specific definition that would make the term even reasonably clear in soil descriptions. It should be avoided except as a top-dress material.

Surface soil refers to the soil ordinarily moved in tillage, or its equivalent in uncultivated soil, about 5 to 8 inches in thickness. The depth varies among different soil regions. If the term is used without qualification, reference is made to the existing surface soil, regardless of origin. If reference is made to a former condition, the term needs to be modified to *original surface soil*, as in the statement, "50 percent of original surface soil has been lost by sheet erosion."

Subsurface soil refers to that part of the A horizon below the surface soil. In soils of weak profile development subsurface soil can be defined only in terms of arbitrary depths.

Subsoil refers to the B horizon of soils with distinct profiles. In soils with weak profile development, subsoil can be defined as the soil below the surface soil in which roots normally grow or in terms of arbitrary depths. It is a poor term inherited from the days when "soil" was conceived only as the plowed soil; hence that under it was "subsoil."

Substratum is any layer beneath the solum, either conforming (C or R) or unconforming.

MEASUREMENT OF HORIZONS

The designations and descriptions of several horizons of the soil profile follow their identification and location within the profile. The description of the profile as a whole can be aided greatly by a scaled diagram, sketch, or photograph on which the horizon boundaries are shown.[2]

DEPTH AND THICKNESS

The profile description needs to include for each horizon (or layer) both (1) thickness in inches (or centimeters) and (2) depth of horizon boundaries below the top of A1.[3] If both sets of figures vary widely, it will be necessary to give the two sets separately to avoid confusion.

---

[2] The reader will find many schemes for measuring horizons in various publications. The best ones are those coupled with conventional outlines of soil characteristics so that none is inadvertently omitted. C. C. Nikiforoff outlined an excellent scheme in his METHOD OF RECORDING SOIL DATA. Soil Sci. Soc. America Proc. 1: 307–317. 1936. The scheme he outlines needs only revision in classes and grades of horizon characteristics to bring it up to date with current practices. (See also p. 137.)

[3] This standard applies to all soils except Bogs and Half Bogs, in which the measurement begins at the top of the peat or muck, not counting fresh leaves or twigs. In other soils, if the A1 is missing, the measurement is taken from the top of the AP or other surface horizon, say the A2 in severely burned podzolic soils or the B2 of a truncated profile if it now lies at the surface.

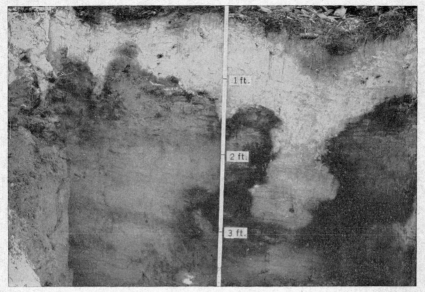

FIGURE 29.—Profile of a Podzol or sandy material illustrating an exceedingly irregular horizon boundary.

The upper boundary of a B2 horizon, for example, may lie from 10 to 18 inches beneath the top of A1, and the lower boundary from 20 to 32 inches below the top of the A1; while the thickness may vary from 8 to 16 inches, not 2 to 22 inches as might be interpreted from the figures for depth below the top of the A1. Even the figures for thickness and for depth do not describe very irregular horizons adequately. The main body of the A2 of a Podzol, for example, may be 5½ to 8½ inches thick, with an upper boundary ¼ to ½ inch deep, and a lower boundary generally 5 to 8 inches deep but with irregular tongues extending down to 18 inches. The lower boundary of the underlying B2 may vary similarly—as little as 10 inches deep to as much as 24 inches, but with a thickness of only 4 inches to not more than 12 inches.

In sandy Podzols with microrelief it is not unusual to find tongues of A2 actually bending under the B2 in such a way that a vertical cut into the soil will pass through A1, A2, B2, back into a bulging tongue of A2, then into B2 again, and finally through the B3 into the C. This example illustrates the need for a considerable trench for examining soil profiles and especially for taking samples, else serious errors may rise. Many soil horizons have similar tongues or other discontinuities, such as the common krotovinas of Chernozem and Chestnut soils, for example.

HORIZON BOUNDARIES

Horizon boundaries vary (1) in distinctness, and (2) in surface topography. Some boundaries are clear and sharp, as those between A2 and B2 horizons in most solodized-Solonetz and well-developed Podzols. Again they may be diffuse, with one horizon gradually merging into another, as between the A1 and A3 of Chernozem or the B2 and B3 of many Latosols. With these diffuse horizons, the location of the boundary requires time-consuming comparisons of small samples of soil from various parts of the profile until the midpoints are established. Small markers can be inserted until all horizons of the profile are worked out; then measurements can be taken; and finally the individual horizons can be described and sampled. Sampling can often begin with the lowest horizon to good advantage.

The distinction of the horizons to the observer depends partly upon the contrast between them—some adjacent ones are highly contrasting in several features—and partly upon the width of the boundary itself or the amount of the profile in the transition between one horizon and the next. The characteristic widths of boundaries between soil horizons may be described as (1) *abrupt*, if less than 1 inch wide; (2) *clear*, if about 1 to 2½ inches wide; (3) *gradual*, if 2½ to 5 inches wide; and (4) *diffuse*, if more than 5 inches wide.

The topography of different soil horizons varies, as well as their distinctness. Although observations of soil horizons are made in profiles or sections, and so photographed or sketched, we must continually recall that they are not "bands" (or literally "horizons" as that word is understood in everyday speech) but rather three-dimensional layers that may be smooth or exceedingly irregular. Horizon boundaries may thus be described as (1) *smooth*, if nearly a plane; (2) *wavy* or undulating, if pockets are wider than their depth; (3) *irregular*, if irregular pockets are deeper than their width; and (4) *broken*, if parts of the horizon are unconnected with other parts, as the B_2 in the limestone cracks of a truncated Terra Rossa.

HORIZONTAL VARIATIONS

The profiles of soils having well-developed microrelief cannot be satisfactorily described from pits. To describe such soils, or to understand how one soil profile merges into another at the soil boundary, a long trench is dug so that horizons may be measured, described, sketched, and sampled at appropriate horizontal intervals. Small stakes may be set on the margin of the trench at 6- or 12-inch intervals as reference points. Using one stake as a zero point, the relative elevations of the others can be measured with an ordinary surveyor's level or Y-level.

For the purpose of observing any horizontal cracking or patterns in the soil, it is often revealing to remove soil horizons, one by one from the top down, from an area of a square yard or more. One may, for example, discover gross hexagonal cracking of hardpans or claypans, unsuspected from the vertical cut alone, that suggest previous influences of freezing, moistening, or desiccation that have been interrupted by coverings now changed to a part of the solum.

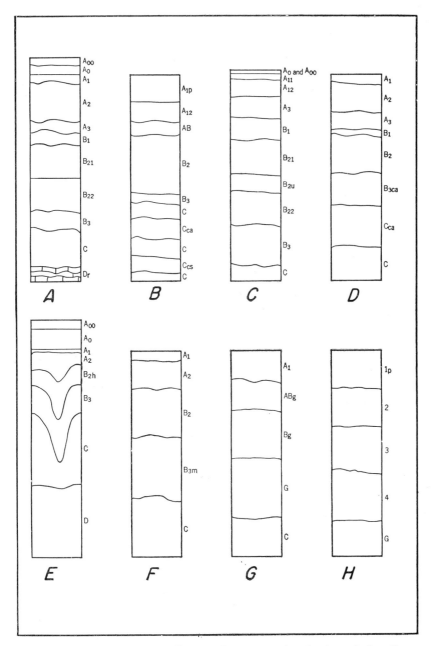

FIGURE 28.—Hypothetical profiles to illustrate a few horizon designations: A, Gray-Brown Podzolic; B, Chernozem (cultivated); C, Latosol; D, solodized-Solonetz; E, Podzol; F, Planosol; G, Humic Gley (Wiesenboden); H, Bog.

A_0 **horizon.**—This is a surface horizon, below the A_{00} if present, and above A_1; it consists of partly decomposed or matted plant remains.

The letters L, F, H, or others to indicate the character of the organic material may be used in the description of A_{00}, A_0, and A_1 horizons in addition to the designations suggested, but not in place of them.[2] Subdivisions of A_0 horizons are made as they are for any others.

The A_0 and A_{00} horizons are measured *upward* from the top of the A_1, if present, otherwise from the upper mineral soil horizon. It is important to observe this convention. The thickness of the A_0 and A_{00} horizons varies so greatly with fire that the surface of the A_1, or upper mineral soil, must be used as a general reference point rather than the upper surface of the A_{00}.

THE A HORIZON

The *A horizon* is a master horizon consisting of (1) one or more surface mineral horizons of maximum organic accumulation; or (2) surface or subsurface horizons that are lighter in color than the underlying horizon and which have lost clay minerals, iron, and aluminum with resultant concentration of the more resistant minerals; or (3) horizons belonging to both of these categories.

The A horizon, and especially the A_1, is the horizon of maximum biological activity and is subject to the most direct influences of climate, plants, animals, and other forces in the environment. In a sense, the A protects the rest of the soil; and in it many of the most important soil-building forces have their origin.

When the A horizon is used without subscript numbers, it refers collectively to all the subhorizons in it, excluding A_0 and A_{00}. The subhorizons are named and described in the following paragraphs.

A_1 **horizon.**—This is a surface mineral soil horizon having a relatively high content of organic matter mixed with mineral matter, usually dark in color. It may or may not be a horizon of eluviation. In nearly all soils it is the horizon of maximum biological activity and is subject to the greatest changes in temperature and moisture content. It is very thick in Chernozems and exceedingly thin in many Podzols. In some Podzols, Ground-Water Podzols, Ground-Water Laterites, and other soils, it is destroyed by repeated fires. Measurements of all horizons are referred to the top of the A_1, if present.

A_2 **horizon.**—This surface or subsurface horizon, usually lighter in color than the underlying horizon, has lost clay minerals, iron, or aluminum, or all three, with the resultant concentration of the more resistant minerals. It is a horizon of eluviation—of leaching of materials out in solution and suspension.[3] Much of

---

[2] HEIBERG, S. O., and CHANDLER, R. F., JR. A REVISED NOMENCLATURE OF FOREST HUMUS LAYERS FOR THE NORTHERN UNITED STATES. Soil Science 52 (2): 87–99, illus. 1941; and LUNT, H. A. THE FOREST SOILS OF CONNECTICUT. Conn. Agr. Expt. Sta. Bul. 523, 99 pp., illus. 1948.

[3] A horizon within B or C resulting, for example, from leaching by water moving laterally through a gleyed layer, may fall within this concept of an A_2 horizon.

the dissolved and dispersed material, including clay, moves completely out of the whole soil, not simply into the B horizon. The A_2 is the principal gray or light-colored leached layer in Podzols (bleicherde), solodized-Solonetz, Planosols, and podzolic soils generally.

A_3 horizon.—This is a horizon transitional to the B but more like the A than B. (If a transitional horizon between A and B is not clearly divided, and especially where it is thin, it may be designated AB).

A_p horizon.—This is a plowed or otherwise mixed surface horizon including more than the original A_1 horizon. The subscript letter p indicates disturbance, usually by cultivation but occasionally by pasturing. Where the plow layer is entirely within the A_1 horizon, it is designated as A_{1p}.

THE B HORIZON

The B horizon is a master horizon of altered material characterized by (1) an accumulation of clay, iron, or aluminum, with accessory organic material[4]; or (2) more or less blocky or prismatic structure together with other characteristics, such as stronger colors, unlike those of the A or the underlying horizons of nearly unchanged material; or (3) characteristics of both these categories. Commonly, the lower limit of the B horizon corresponds with the lower limit of the solum. (See discussion of solum.)

Actually the accumulation of clay and the development of blocky or prismatic structure are covariant in many soils, but not in all of them. The relatively small accumulations of total clay in the B horizons of typical Chernozem and Chestnut soils, and in some Podzols, are not primarily responsible for their designation as B horizons.

Commonly the B is called an illuvial horizon, in the sense that colloidal material carried in suspension from overlying horizons has lodged in it. We must recall, however, that the clay in B horizons may also originate from differences of residual clay formation in place or by recombination of soluble materials brought into it in true solution. Texture differences between A and B horizons may also arise partly from differential destruction of clay, as in Red-Yellow Podzolic soils for example, as well as from illuviation and residual formation in place. When B horizon is used without subscript number or letter, it refers collectively to all the subhorizons in it. These subhorizons are named and defined as follows:

B_1 horizon.—This horizon is transitional to the A above, but more like the B than A.

B_2 horizon.—This is the subhorizon of (1) maximum accumulation of silicate clay minerals or of iron and organic material; or (2) maximum development of blocky or prismatic structure; or

---

[4] Organic material is the chief added constituent in the B horizon of some Ground-Water Podzols and in "humus" Podzols.

may have characteristics of both. In B_2 horizons having both these features, but separated, the horizons need to be subdivided into B_{21} and B_{22}, as appropriate.

B_3 horizon.—The B_3 horizon is transitional to the C horizon, but more like the B than C.

THE C HORIZON

The *C horizon*[5] is a layer of unconsolidated material, relatively little affected by the influence of organisms and presumed to be similar in chemical, physical, and mineralogical composition to the material from which at least a portion of the overlying solum has developed. Any slight alteration of the upper part of the C, such as reduction of calcium carbonate content in glacial till, unaccompanied by other changes, is designated as C_1.

THE D LAYER

The *D layer* is any stratum underlying the C, or the B if no C is present, which is unlike C, or unlike the material from which the solum has been formed. The designation D_r is for consolidated parent rock like that from which the C has developed or like that from which the parent material of the solum has developed if no C is present.

OTHER HORIZONS

Besides the common horizons already defined, there are others that occur importantly but less regularly.

G horizon.—This is a layer of intense reduction, characterized by the presence of ferrous iron and neutral gray colors[6] that commonly change to brown upon exposure to the air. It is a characteristic horizon in soils developed wholly or partly by gleying. This process involves saturation of the soil with water for long periods in the presence of organic matter. One may speak appropriately of a "gley (glā) soil" but hardly so of a "gley horizon," since the genesis of the whole profile is involved. Besides the G, other horizons may be somewhat gleyed, indicated by the subscript *g*. Occasionally it may be necessary to differentiate in the description between fossil gley and active gley. Intergrades between B and G and between C and G may be indicated as BG and CG if more strongly gleyed than indicated by B_g and C_g.

The G horizon is usually included as a part of the solum, along with A and B, but those G horizons occurring within the C or beneath it are not.

---

[5] Although commonly used and understood, the C is not strictly a soil horizon as herein defined, partly because it is little modified by biological processes in soil formation, and partly because it often has an undetermined lower limit.

[6] Some G horizons have olive colors—a few too nearly green for the standard color chart.

C_{ca} **horizon.**[7]—This is a layer of accumulated calcium carbonate below the solum and within the C. Such horizons are characteristic of most chernozemic and other soils of subhumid and semiarid regions. The C_{ca} horizon is not always clearly expressed in Chernozems and sometimes can be detected only by laboratory methods. It is found in some Prairie soils and in some podzolic soils, especially those developed from highly calcareous unconsolidated material. It is often referred to loosely as the "lime horizon" or the "lime zone." This layer may be thin or thick, and soft or very hard. Generally, the thickness and hardness increase from cool to warm climates. In cool and cool-temperate regions the hard layers are found mostly in gravel. In warm semiarid regions this layer becomes so thick that it can no longer be regarded strictly as a soil horizon. Although the explanation of its genesis is not wholly settled, broad geological processes have undoubtedly contributed, as well as those included under soil formation. The term *caliche* is applied to C_{ca} horizons, especially to the thick ones in the warm countries of the Western Hemisphere. For the hardened ones, *croûte calcaire* is an alternative term for *hardened caliche.*

Formerly C_c was used for what is now designated as C_{ca}. The subscript *ca* can also be used for accumulations of calcium carbonate in other horizons or layers.

C_{cs} **horizon.**—This is a layer of accumulated calcium sulfate within the C. Such horizons commonly occur beneath the C_{ca} horizons of chernozemic soils. The subscript *cs* may also be used for accumulations of calcium sulfate in other horizons or layers.

LETTER SUBSCRIPTS

Letter subscripts may be helpful in indicating processes that have been active within a horizon, or layer, but they are not necessary and cannot substitute for a proper description. Several suggested ones follow:

b: A subscript to add to the genetic designation of a buried soil horizon. Thus beneath one solum, or part of one, buried horizons are designated as A_{1b}, B_{2b}, and so on.

ca: An accumulation of calcium carbonate, as in D_{ca} or B_{3ca}.

cn: Accumulations of concretions rich in iron, iron and manganese, or iron and phosphate (like *perdigons*, for example, or the "shot" in some soils of the Pacific Northwest).

cs: An accumulation of calcium sulfate (gypsum), as in D_{cs}.

f: Frozen soil, as C_f under Tundra.[8]

g: A gleyed (glåde) horizon, as B_g or B_{3g}.

---

[7] The use of *ca* as an abbreviation of calcium carbonate is preferred as a subscript to Ca, the chemical symbol, partly to have all letter subscripts uncapitalized.

[8] Permafrost is reserved for permanently frozen ground. A profile description can only indicate whether the soil is frozen at the time of the examination.

h*:[9] Outstanding accumulation of decomposed organic matter for the horizon, as in the B_2 of a "humus" Podzol, making it B_{2h}.

ir*: Outstanding accumulation of finely disseminated iron for the horizon, as in the B_2 of an "iron" Podzol, making it B_{2ir}.

m: A subscript (suggesting "massive") for indurated horizons composed mainly of silicate minerals, such as fragipans, within the solum or beneath it, which are indurated much more than horizons normally having the principal horizon designation given. Such an indurated horizon is given its appropriate designation, such as B, B_2, C, or G, and then the subscript is added to form B_m, B_{2m}, C_m, or G_m.[10]

p: Indicates plowing or other disturbance, especially of the A horizon.

r: A subscript applied to a D layer of hard rock like that from which the C has developed.

sa: An accumulation of soluble salts, other than calcium carbonate or calcium sulfate.

t*: Outstanding accumulation of clay for the horizon, as in the B_2 horizon of podzolic soil richer in clay than the B_2 horizon of the associated normal soil, making it B_{2t}. (From *Ton*—clay in German.)

u: Unconformable layer with inherited characteristics unlike those of the adjacent soil material, such as a stone line within a B horizon, making it B_{3u}.

The letter designations do not provide for all situations. For example, the A_1 of humus Podzols may be thickened from 4 inches to 20 inches through long treatment with earth-containing compost. All sorts of partially truncated profiles may have been buried. Where such generally unusual soils are important in a local survey area, special symbols may be added that do not conflict with the ones given above. A small subscript, *an* for example, may be used for man-made or anthropic layers beneath A_p, if present, and above the undisturbed layers. Thus an anthropic humus Podzol may have horizons A_{1anp}, A_{1an}, A_1, A_2, B_2, B_3, and C.

Further, the A–B–C nomenclature of soil horizons has been applied mainly to those consisting largely of mineral matter. The dominantly organic layers of hydromorphic soils, Bogs and Half Bogs, are not logically assigned one of these designations. The separate layers of these soils are simply numbered 1, 2, 3, and

---

[9] Subscripts marked with the asterisk (*) are ordinarily used only for B horizons.

[10] In some instances it may be difficult to assign an appropriate major designation, such as A, B, C, G, or D, to a prominently indurated horizon or layer. In such instances, if the induration is irreversible, the horizon can be given the designation M. The use of this designation should be carefully restricted. It is not used to indicate hard layers composed mainly of calcium carbonate, nor for that induration characteristic of the genetic horizon, as in B_2 (ortstein) of typical sandy Podzols and Ground-Water Podzols.

so on, down to the C or D, or to the limit of examination in a Bog soil and to the G or C in a Half Bog soil. A surface plowed layer, if still peat, muck, or peaty muck, may be designated 1_p; while the mixed organic and mineral surface of a cultivated Half Bog soil or cultivated burned Bog soil is designated A_p.

SUBDIVISIONS OF HORIZONS

The need often arises to subdivide the main horizons further, especially in detailed studies of soil morphology. In the collection of samples for research in soil genesis, thick horizons may include significant differences and may be subdivided arbitrarily for two or more samples. It is important that these subdivisions be clearly designated within the general system of horizon nomenclature. To do this, numbers 1, 2, 3, and so on are added to the complete horizon subscript. Thus three subdivisions of an A_0 horizon are indicated as A_{01}, A_{02}, and A_{03}. Two subdivisions of B_2 may be indicated as B_{21} and B_{22}. Such numbers in the subscript should follow any of the small letters used in the subscript. Thus subdivisions of A_{1p} become A_{1p1} and A_{1p2}. A buried B_2 horizon, subdivided into two parts, is labeled B_{2b1} and B_{2b2}.

THE SOLUM

The solum may be defined simply as the genetic soil developed by soil-building forces. In normal soils, the solum includes the A and B horizons, or the upper part of the soil profile above the parent material.

Although the concept of *solum* is commonly understood by soil scientists, this definition is deceptively simple. Especially in some of the intrazonal soils, the actual sola are not easily determined; and in some soils their lower limits can be set only arbitrarily, say at 6 feet or 2 meters, or at the lower limit of plant roots. Used with such soils, the term "solum" may need to be defined in relation to the particular soil.

These difficulties concerning the solum arise mainly from the fact that the processes of soil formation often merge with broad geological processes. Although it is important to distinguish between geological and soil-forming processes, it is equally important to recognize that they usually go on together and that soils are being influenced by both. It is of little use to argue semantically about certain phenomena in the profile that are the result of combinations of the two sets of processes or that can be ascribed sometimes to one and sometimes to the other. These difficulties are illustrated by some common examples in the paragraphs following.

Croûte calcaire.—Croûte calcaire, or hardened caliche, is often found in thick masses overlain by only a few inches of soil. The common C_{ca} horizons of Chernozems, let us say, are easily conceived as part of the soil profile, although they are not within the solum.[11] Their genesis and relationships to the solum raise no particular difficulties. It is another matter, however, to include some 10 to 25 feet of croûte calcaire under a Reddish-Brown soil as a part of its profile. Doubtless this croûte calcaire is related to the solum and should be described in any description of the soil profile; but certainly broad long-time geological processes have been at work, as well as soil-forming processes.

Laterite.—Laterite includes the sesquioxide-rich, highly weathered clayey material that is hardened irreversibly to concretions, hardpans, or crusts when dehydrated, and hardened relicts of such materials more or less mixed with quartz and other diluents. Laterite is found in many soils and is a distinguishing feature of Ground-Water Laterite soil. In the profile of a Ground-Water Laterite soil one may designate the horizons easily as A_1, A_2, A_3, and B_1, down into the B_2 or, perhaps, into the B_3. The same material may continue practically without change for another 25 feet or so with no definite place for dividing the solum from the material underneath it. It would be unreasonable to exclude the upper part of the laterite from the solum; and it seems unreasonable to include the lower part, far removed from the influence of organisms.

Gleyed soil material.—Gleyed soil material may begin a few inches below the surface of hydromorphic soils and, in some instances, continue on down for many feet essentially unchanged. Such conditions can arise through the gradual filling of a wet basin, with the A horizon gradually being added to at the surface and being gleyed beneath. Finally the A rests on a thick mass of gleyed material, which may be relatively uniform, especially in sandy types. Obviously the upper part belongs in the solum, while the lower part does not. This illustration does not extend to all gleyed soils. In many the G horizon is clearly a part of the solum and has a clear lower boundary with the C.

Permafrost.—Permanently frozen ground under soils of the arctic and subarctic regions is called permafrost. The upper boundary, or *permafrost table,* is said to be coincident with the lower limits of seasonal thaws. The upper boundary of frozen ground varies, of course, from month to month during the summer and from year to year, depending upon the season. The soil that freezes and thaws seasonally is above the permafrost table. The frozen ground may extend downward many feet, even several hundred feet. Here again, the morphologist may properly place some part of the frozen ground in the soil profile, or even in the solum, as a kind of "thermal" hardpan, especially if it contains organic matter and bears a definite relationship to the

[11] Admittedly this may appear to be somewhat arbitrary. In many Chernozems and Chestnut soils it may seem that the solum could be defined to include the C_{ca}; but in some developed from materials low in calcium the C_{ca} comes deep within the C, far below the solum.

upper horizons or solum. In many soils with permafrost, the permafrost table is deep beneath the solum, within the C or below it.

Some soils have no solum at all although they support plants. Examples include very young soils from recent accumulations of volcanic ash, alluvium, or loess. At least some time is required after vegetation has become established before recognizable genetic horizons are formed.

POPULAR TERMS FOR SOIL LAYERS

Several popular terms have long been used to refer to certain soil horizons or groups of horizons—terms that are exceedingly difficult to define precisely. They are very old and have been used by laymen in widely different senses.

Topsoil is a general term that is used in at least four senses: (1) For the surface plowed layer (A_p) and thus as a synonym for surface soil; (2) for the original or present A_1 horizon, and thus exceedingly variable in depth among different soils; (3) for the original or present A horizon; and (4) for presumed fertile soil or soil material, usually rich in organic matter, used to top-dress road banks, parks, gardens, and lawns.

The authors know of no way to settle on a specific definition that would make the term even reasonably clear in soil descriptions. It should be avoided except as a top-dress material.

Surface soil refers to the soil ordinarily moved in tillage, or its equivalent in uncultivated soil, about 5 to 8 inches in thickness. The depth varies among different soil regions. If the term is used without qualification, reference is made to the existing surface soil, regardless of origin. If reference is made to a former condition, the term needs to be modified to *original surface soil*, as in the statement, "50 percent of original surface soil has been lost by sheet erosion."

Subsurface soil refers to that part of the A horizon below the surface soil. In soils of weak profile development subsurface soil can be defined only in terms of arbitrary depths.

Subsoil refers to the B horizon of soils with distinct profiles. In soils with weak profile development, subsoil can be defined as the soil below the surface soil in which roots normally grow or in terms of arbitrary depths. It is a poor term inherited from the days when "soil" was conceived only as the plowed soil; hence that under it was "subsoil."

Substratum is any layer beneath the solum, either conforming (C) or unconforming (D).

MEASUREMENT OF HORIZONS

The designations and descriptions of several horizons of the soil profile follow their identification and location within the profile. The description of the profile as a whole can be aided greatly by a scaled diagram, sketch, or photograph on which the horizon boundaries are shown.[12]

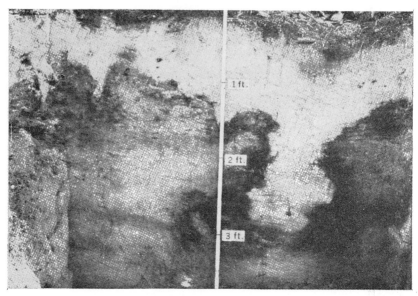

FIGURE 29.—Profile of a Podzol on sandy material illustrating an exceedingly irregular horizon boundary.

DEPTH AND THICKNESS

The profile description needs to include for each horizon (or layer) both (1) thickness in inches (or centimeters) and (2) depth of horizon boundaries below the top of A_1.[13] If both sets of figures vary widely, it will be necessary to give the two sets separately to avoid confusion. The upper boundary of a B_2 horizon, for example, may lie from 10 to 18 inches beneath the top of A_1, and the lower boundary from 20 to 32 inches below the top of the A_1; while the thickness may vary from 8 to 16 inches, not 2 to 22 inches as might be interpreted from the figures for depth below the top of the A_1. Even the figures for thickness and for depth do not describe very irregular horizons adequately. The main body of the A_2 of a Podzol, for example, may be $5\frac{1}{2}$ to

[12] The reader will find many schemes for measuring horizons in various publications. The best ones are those coupled with conventional outlines of soil characteristics so that none is inadvertently omitted. C. C. Nikiforoff outlined an excellent scheme in his METHOD OF RECORDING SOIL DATA. Soil Sci. Soc. America Proc. 1: 307–317. 1936. The scheme he outlines needs only revision in classes and grades of horizon characteristics to bring it up to date with current practices. (See also p. 137.)

[13] This standard applies to all soils except Bogs and Half Bogs, in which the measurement begins at the top of the peat or muck, not counting fresh leaves or twigs (A_{00}). In other soils, if the A_1 is missing, the measurement is taken from the top of the A_p or other surface horizon, say the A_2 in severely burned podzolic soils or the B_2 of a truncated profile if it now lies at the surface.

$8\frac{1}{2}$ inches thick, with an upper boundary $\frac{1}{4}$ to $\frac{1}{2}$ inch deep, and a lower boundary generally 5 to 8 inches deep but with irregular tongues extending down to 18 inches. The lower boundary of the underlying B_2 may vary similarly—as little as 10 inches deep to as much as 24 inches, but with a thickness of only 4 inches to not more than 12 inches.

In sandy Podzols with microrelief it is not unusual to find tongues of A_2 actually bending under the B_2 in such a way that a vertical cut into the soil will pass through A_1, A_2, B_2, back into a bulging tongue of A_2, then into B_2 again, and finally through the B_3 into the C (fig. 29). This example illustrates the need for a considerable trench for examining soil profiles and especially for taking samples, else serious errors may rise. Many soil horizons have similar tongues or other discontinuities, such as the common krotovinas of Chernozem and Chestnut soils, for example.

HORIZON BOUNDARIES

Horizon boundaries vary (1) in distinctness, and (2) in surface topography. Some boundaries are clear and sharp, as those between A_2 and B_2 horizons in most solodized-Solonetz and well-developed Podzols. Again they may be diffuse, with one horizon gradually merging into another, as between the A_1 and A_3 of Chernozem or the B_2 and B_3 of many Latosols. With these diffuse horizons, the location of the boundary requires time-consuming comparisons of small samples of soil from various parts of the profile until the midpoints are established. Small markers can be inserted until all horizons of the profile are worked out; then measurements can be taken; and finally the individual horizons can be described and sampled. Sampling can often begin with the lowest horizon to good advantage.

The distinction of the horizons to the observer depends partly upon the contrast between them—some adjacent ones are highly contrasting in several features—and partly upon the width of the boundary itself or the amount of the profile in the transition between one horizon and the next. The characteristic widths of boundaries between soil horizons may be described as (1) *abrupt*, if less than 1 inch wide; (2) *clear*, if about 1 to $2\frac{1}{2}$ inches wide; (3) *gradual*, if $2\frac{1}{2}$ to 5 inches wide; and (4) *diffuse*, if more than 5 inches wide.

The topography of different soil horizons varies, as well as their distinctness. Although observations of soil horizons are made in profiles or sections, and so photographed or sketched, we must continually recall that they are not "bands" (or literally "horizons" as that word is understood in everyday speech) but rather three-dimensional layers that may be smooth or exceedingly irregular. Horizon boundaries may thus be described as (1) *smooth*, if nearly a plane; (2) *wavy* or undulating, if pockets are wider than their depth; (3) *irregular*, if irregular pockets are deeper than their width; and (4) *broken*, if parts of the horizon are unconnected with other parts, as the B_2 in the limestone cracks of a truncated Terra Rossa.

HORIZONTAL VARIATIONS

The profiles of soils having well-developed microrelief cannot be satisfactorily described from pits. To describe such soils, or to understand how one soil profile merges into another at the soil boundary, a long trench is dug so that horizons may be measured, described, sketched, and sampled at appropriate horizontal intervals. Small stakes may be set on the margin of the trench at 6- or 12-inch intervals as reference points. Using one stake as a zero point, the relative elevations of the others can be measured with an ordinary surveyor's level or Y-level.

For the purpose of observing any horizontal cracking or patterns in the soil, it is often revealing to remove soil horizons, one by one from the top down, from an area of a square yard or more. One may, for example, discover gross hexagonal cracking of hardpans or claypans, unsuspected from the vertical cut alone, that suggest previous influences of freezing, moistening, or desiccation that have been interrupted by coverings now changed to a part of the solum.

SOIL COLOR

Color is the most obvious and easily determined of soil characteristics. Although it has little direct influence on the functioning of the soil, one may infer a great deal about a soil from its color, if it is considered with the other observable features. Thus the significance of soil color is almost entirely an indirect measure of other more important characteristics or qualities that are not so easily and accurately observed. Color is one of the most useful and important characteristics for soil identification, especially when combined with soil structure.

SIGNIFICANCE OF COLOR

The content of organic matter in soil, for example, is a characteristic that is commonly indicated only approximately by soil color. Generally in temperate climates dark-colored soils are relatively higher in organic matter than light-colored soils. In well-drained soils, the colors usually range from very pale brown, through the intermediate browns, to very dark brown or black, as organic matter increases. The most stable part of decomposed organic matter, humus, is darker than the raw or less well decomposed plant remains. Raw peat is brown, whereas the well-decomposed and more fertile organic soil produced from peat is black or nearly so.

As organic matter is neither all of the same color nor the only coloring matter in soils, soil color by itself is not an exact measure of this important constituent. Well-drained soils of the same relatively high content of organic matter are browner, less nearly black, under high annual temperatures than those of cool regions. Yet the dark clays of warm-temperate and tropical regions, which include some of the blackest soils in the world, seldom contain as much as 3 percent organic matter. Their color may range from medium gray to black with little or no change in the total content of organic matter. Self-mulching black clays with 2 or 3 percent of organic matter may lie side by side with reddish-brown latosolic soils having two or three times as much organic matter. Dark-colored soils low in organic matter may contain compounds of iron and humus, elemental carbon, compounds of manganese, and magnetite. Depth of color depends upon the nature and distribution of the organic matter as well as upon the total amount. In highly alkaline Solonetz soils, for example, the highly dispersed organic matter apparently coats each soil grain. Such soils are nearly black at relatively low contents of total organic matter.

The red color of soils is generally related to unhydrated iron oxide, although manganese dioxide and partially hydrated iron oxides may also contribute red colors. Since unhydrated iron oxide is relatively unstable under moist conditions, red color usually indicates good drainage and good aeration. Strongly red soils are

189

expected on convex surfaces underlain by pervious rocks. Yet many red soils owe their color to inheritance from the parent material and not to soil-forming processes, since the redness in some rocks may persist for centuries even under moist conditions.[1]

In regions where the normal soils have red color, the well-developed red color is one indication that the soils are relatively old or at least that the soil material has been subjected to relatively intense weathering for a considerable time. Yet occasionally red colors develop very rapidly. Other things being equal, the red and yellow colors in soil generally increase both in prevalence and in intensity in going from cool regions toward the Equator. The intensity of weathering increases with temperature. Then too, many very old land surfaces may be found in warm regions, especially as contrasted with glaciated cool and temperate regions.

The yellow color in soils is also largely due to iron oxides.[2] Yellow colors in the deeper horizons usually indicate a somewhat more moist soil climate than do red colors. The general climatic differences may be in humidity and cloudiness rather than in rainfall. Where associated red and yellow soils are developed from the same kind of parent material, the yellow soils commonly occupy the less convex and more moist sites. Other things being equal, yellow colors are also more common than red colors in regions of high humidity and heavy cloud cover. Apparently, however, it takes a long time to change a yellow soil to a red one, since strongly sloping yellow soils may be found in regions of geologically recent uplift and rapid dissection.

Iron oxides occur in all colors ranging from yellow at the one extreme to red at the other. Thus many brown soils contain relatively large amounts of iron oxides in addition to organic matter.

Well-drained yellowish sands owe their colors to the fact that small amounts of organic matter and other coloring material such as iron oxide are mixed with large amounts of nearly white sand.

Gray and whitish colors of soils are caused by several substances, mainly quartz, kaolin and other clay minerals, carbonates of lime and magnesium, gypsum, various salts, and compounds of ferrous iron. The grayest colors (chromas of less than 1,

---

[1] Soils owing their color to inheritance from the parent material rather than from soil-forming processes are referred to as *lithochromic.*

[2] In the past red colors have been ascribed to unhydrated and yellow colors to hydrated iron oxides. It seems clear that red colors are due to unhydrated iron oxides, but a yellow color is more difficult to explain. Recent evidence suggests that some yellow soils lack hydrated iron oxides. This raises a question about the general occurrence of such oxides in well-drained soils. Although the question may not be answered one way or another at the present time, alternative explanations for yellow colors need to be examined. It is known that the particle size of some colloidal precipitates affects the color, and this may also be true of colloidal iron oxides in soils. Moreover, there is evidence that the ferric oxide in these Red-Yellow Podzolic soils of the southeastern part of the United States that have red B horizons is reduced more easily than is the ferric oxide in the associated soils with yellow B horizons. It has been suggested that the yellow color in some profiles may be due to a solid-solution mixture of iron and aluminum oxides.

values of 2.5 to 7.5) that occur in soils are those of permanently saturated G horizons. In these, the iron is in the ferrous form. Some soils are so rich in these compounds as to have nearly pure gray colors that appear bluish.[3]

Imperfectly and poorly drained soils are nearly always mottled with various shades of gray, brown, and yellow, especially within the zone of fluctuation of the water table. In the presence of organic matter, the proportion of gray generally increases with increasing wetness. Wet materials without organic matter rarely have the very light-gray color.

A light-gray color may indicate a very low content of organic matter and iron, as in the A_2 horizons of the Podzol, or in sands that consist almost wholly of quartz. Irregular layers of white clay, from which the iron has been removed, are commonly found in the lower parts of Ground-Water Laterite soils and Latosols. In arid and semiarid regions, certain soil horizons may be white or nearly white because of the very high content of calcium carbonate, gypsum, or other salts.

Nearly white colors sometimes occur as an inheritance from the parent material, as in Lithosols or Regosols on marls or other white rocks. The failure of soils to accumulate organic matter ordinarily indicates an environment unfavorable to plants and micro-organisms. White soils are almost invariably unproductive naturally, although a few are responsive to good management, such as some weakly developed Rendzinas.

COLOR PATTERNS

Nearly every soil profile consists of several horizons differing in color. For every soil examined and described in the field, the complete color profile should be presented. A single horizon may be uniform in color or it may be streaked, spotted, variegated, or mottled in many ways. Local accumulations of lime or organic matter may produce a spotted appearance. Streaks or tongues of color may result from the seeping downward of colloids, organic matter, or iron compounds from overlying horizons. Certain combinations of mottled colors, mainly the grays and browns, indicate impeded drainage. The word "mottled" means marked with spots of color. Some mottled colors occur unassociated with poor drainage, either past or present. A mottled or variegated pattern of colors occurs in many soil horizons and especially in parent materials that are not completely weathered.

Mottling in soils is described by noting: (1) The color of the matrix and the color, or colors, of the principal mottles, and (2) the pattern of the mottling. The color of the mottles may be

---

[3] The usual color of G horizons is of yellow hue, generally about 2.5Y, but of such weak chroma as to suggest the complementary hue in contrast to other stronger colors that predominate in the background against which the soils are viewed. The hue complementary to 10YR, the most usual in soil, is 10B, a blue. Before alteration from exposure to the air, the chroma of G horizons generally is less than 1; with exposure to air the color changes rapidly, sometimes within a few minutes. Few air-dry samples of G horizons have chromas of less than 1.

defined by using the Munsell notation, as with other soil masses; but usually it is sufficient and even better to use the standard linguistic equivalents, since precise measurement of the color of the mottles is rarely significant. In fact, descriptions of soil horizons containing several Munsell notations are difficult to read rapidly.

The pattern of mottles can be conveniently described by three sets of notations: contrast, abundance, and size.[4]

Contrast.—Contrast may be described as *faint, distinct*, or *prominent* as follows:

> *Faint:* Indistinct mottles are evident and recognizable only with close examination. Soil colors in both the matrix and mottles have closely related hues and chromas.
>
> *Distinct:* Although not striking, the mottles are readily seen. The hue, value, and chroma of the matrix are easily distinguished from those of the mottles. They may vary as much as one or two hues or several units in chroma or value. The pattern may be one of a continuous matrix with mottles or one of mixtures of two or more colors.
>
> *Prominent:* The conspicuous mottles are obvious and mottling is one of the outstanding features of the horizon. Hue, chroma, and value may be several units apart. The pattern may be one of a continuous matrix with contrasting mottles or one of mixtures of two or more colors.

Abundance.—Abundance of mottles can be indicated in three general classes as: *few, common,* and *many,* based upon the relative amount of mottled surface in the unit area of the exposed soil horizon, as follows:[5]

> *Few:* Mottles occupy less than about 2 percent of the exposed surface.
>
> *Common:* Mottles occupy about 2 to 20 percent of the exposed surface.
>
> *Many:* Mottles occupy more than 20 percent of the exposed surface. This last class can be further subdivided according to whether (a) the mottles set in a definite matrix or (b) there is no clear matrix color.

Size.—Size refers to the approximate diameters of individual mottles. Three relative size classes can be used as follows:

> *Fine:* Mottles less than 5 mm. in diameter along the greatest dimension.
>
> *Medium:* Mottles range between 5 and 15 mm. in diameter along the greatest dimension.
>
> *Coarse:* Mottles are greater than 15 mm. in diameter along the greatest dimension.

In the detailed examination of some soil horizons, it may be necessary to add still further notes on the mottling to indicate whether or not the boundaries of the mottles are sharp (knife-edge), clear (less than 2 mm. wide), or diffuse (more than 2 mm. wide). Although many mottles are roughly circular in cross-section, others are elongated and merge into streaks or tongues. Although, normally, mottling carries no inferences of differences in texture as compared to the matrix, many soils show mottling in a freshly exposed horizon because of the slicing of incipient concretions.

---

[4] This discussion is based on a recent paper: SIMONSON, R. W. DESCRIPTION OF MOTTLING IN SOILS. Soil Science. 7: 187–192. 1951.

[5] The suggested limits are tentative only. More research is needed to establish the most useful size classes and number of classes.

In soil descriptions the mottling can be most conveniently described by describing the mottles as to abundance, size, contrast, and color, such as, ". . . brown silt loam with few, fine, distinct reddish-brown and dark-gray mottles."

In verbal descriptions of soil mottling intended for the general reader, part of the detail needed in detailed soil morphology and correlation may be omitted. Thus, starting with the classes according to abundance, descriptions may be written as follows:

1. *Few:* ". . . brown silt loam, slightly mottled with red and yellow."
2. *Common:* ". . . brown silt loam, mottled with red and yellow."
3. *Many:*
   (a) If the matrix is clearly apparent: ". . . brown silt loam, highly mottled with red and yellow."
   (b) If no clear matrix exists: ". . . mottled red, yellow, and brown silt loam."

If contrast is not clearly shown by the color names, "faintly" or "prominently" may be added. Faint mottling can be implied as ". . . brown silt loam, mottled with shades."

If size is important "finely" or "coarsely" may be added, as ". . . coarsely mottled red and yellow clay", or ". . . brown silt loam finely and slightly mottled with reddish brown." Usually such distinctions are more confusing than helpful to the lay reader.

In the description of soil color, special notice should be taken of any relationships between the color pattern and structure or porosity. Structural aggregates in the soil must be broken to determine whether the color is uniform throughout. The black or dark-brown surface color of soil granules is often due to a thin coating, though the basic color of the soil material is brown or yellow. When such granules are crushed, the mass of soil is lighter in color than the original surfaces of the aggregates. Marked contrast between the color of the soil aggregates and the color of the soil when crushed is common. Coatings of red color often cover structural particles or sand grains; and a gray color may be due to a thin film of leached soil around darker aggregates.

EFFECTS OF MOISTURE

Soil color changes with the moisture content, very markedly in some soils and comparatively little in others. Between dry and moist, soil colors commonly are darker by $\frac{1}{2}$ to 3 steps in value and may change from $-\frac{1}{2}$ to $+2$ steps in chroma. Seldom are they different in hue. Some of the largest differences in value between the dry and moist colors occur in gray and grayish-brown horizons having moderate to moderately low contents of organic matter.

Reproducible quantitative measurements of color are obtained at two moisture contents: (1) Air dry, and (2) field capacity. The latter may be obtained with sufficient accuracy for color measurements by moistening a sample and reading the color as soon as visible moisture films have disappeared. Both the dry and the moist colors are important. In most notes and soil descriptions, unless stated otherwise, colors are given for moist soils.

Comparisons of color among widely separated soils are facilitated by using the color designation of freshly broken surfaces of air-dry samples. Official descriptions for technical use, such as series descriptions, should include the moist colors, and preferably, both dry and moist colors if significantly unlike.

DETERMINATION OF SOIL COLOR

Soil colors are most conveniently measured by comparison with a color chart. The one generally used with soil is a modification of the Munsell color chart and includes only that portion needed for soil colors, about one-fifth of the entire range of color.[6] It consists of some 175 different colored papers, or chips, systematically arranged, according to their Munsel notations, on cards carried in a loose-leaf notebook. The arrangement is by *hue, value,* and *chroma*—the three simple variables that combine to give all colors. *Hue* is the dominant spectral (rainbow) color; it is related to the dominant wavelength of the light. *Value* refers to the relative lightness of color and is a function (approximately the square root) of the total amount of light. *Chroma* (sometimes called saturation) is the relative purity or strength of the spectral color and increases with decreasing grayness.

In the soil color chart, all colors on a given card are of a constant hue, designated by the symbol in the upper right-hand corner of the card. Vertically, the colors become successively lighter by visually equal steps; their value increases. Horizontally, they increase in chroma to the right and become grayer to the left. The value and chroma of each color in the chart is printed immediately beneath the color. The first number is the value, and the second is the chroma. As arranged in the chart the colors form three scales: (1) Radial, or from one card to the next, in hue; (2) vertical in value; and (3) horizontal in chroma.

The nomenclature for soil color consists of two complementary systems: (1) Color names, and (2) the Munsell notation of color. Neither of these alone is adequate for all purposes. The color names are employed in all descriptions for publication and for general use. The Munsell notation is used to supplement the color names wherever greater precision is needed, as a convenient abbreviation in field descriptions, for expression of the specific relations between colors, and for statistical treatment of color data. The Munsell notation is especially useful for international correlation, since no translation of color names is needed. The names for soil colors are common terms now so defined as to obtain uniformity and yet accord, as nearly as possible, with past usage by soil scientists. Bizarre names like "rusty brown," "tan," "mouse gray," "lemon yellow," and "chocolate brown" should never be used.

The soil color names and their limits are given in the name-diagrams, figures 30 to 36.

---

[6] The appropriate color chips separately, or mounted by hues on special cards (4¼ by 7¼ inches) for a loose-leaf notebook, may be obtained from the Munsell Color Company, Inc., 10 East Franklin Street, Baltimore 2, Md.

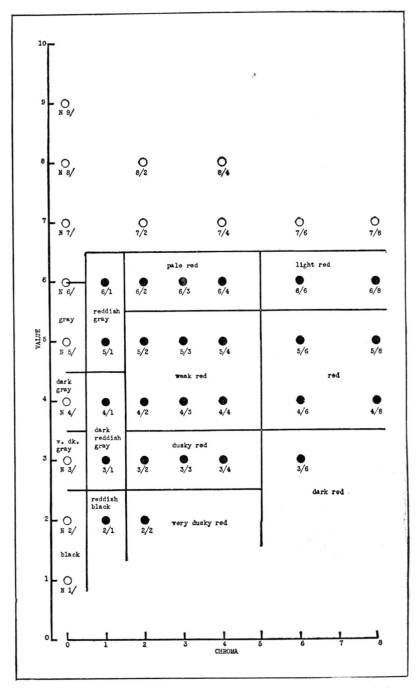

FIGURE 30.—Soil color names for several combinations of value and chroma and hue 10R.

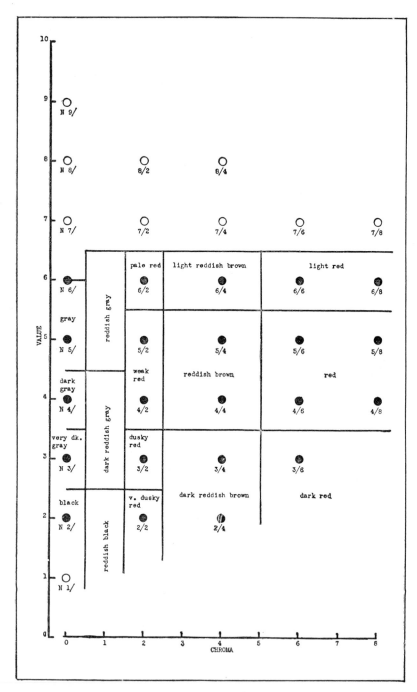

FIGURE 31.—Soil color names for several combinations of value and chroma and hue 2.5YR.

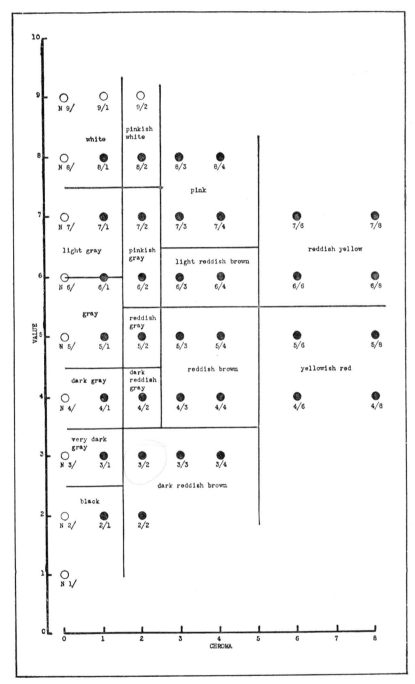

FIGURE 32.—Soil color names for several combinations of value and chroma and hue 5YR.

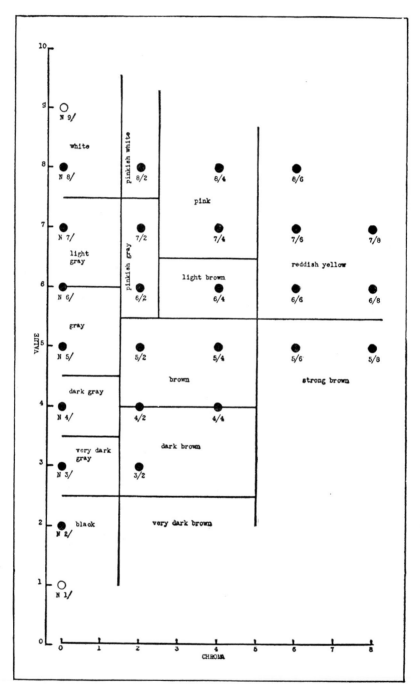

FIGURE 33.—Soil color names for several combinations of value and chroma and hue 7.5YR.

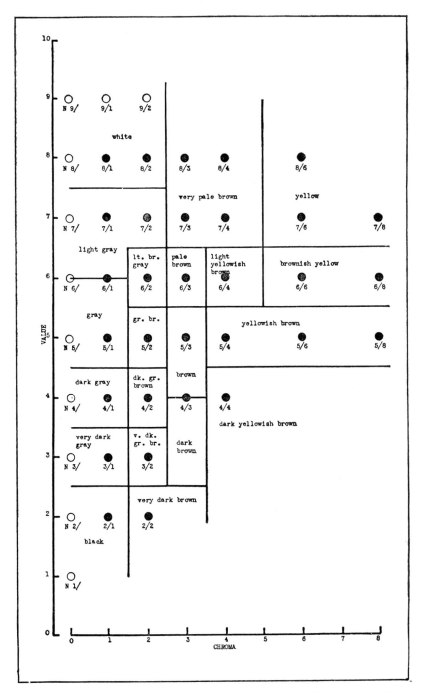

FIGURE 34.—Soil color names for several combinations of value and chroma and hue 10YR.

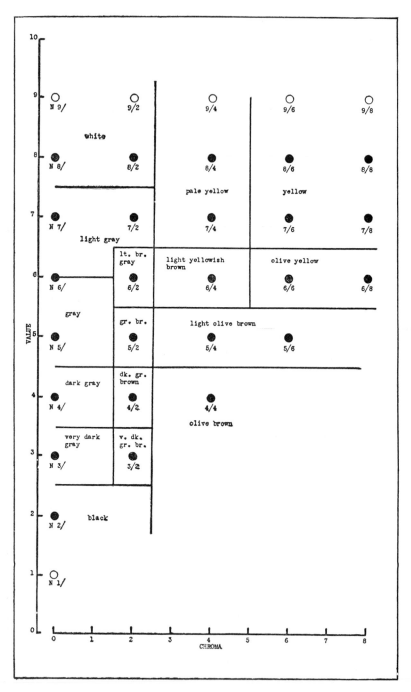

FIGURE 35.—Soil color names for several combinations of value and chroma and hue 2.5Y.

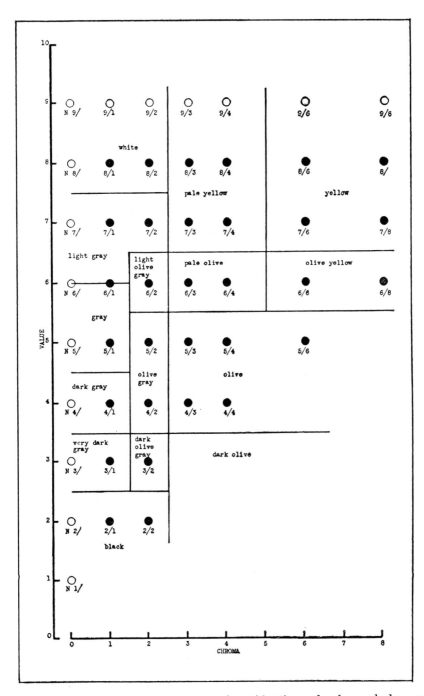

FIGURE 36.—Soil color names for several combinations of value and chroma and hue 5Y.

The Munsell notation for color consists of separate notations for hue, value, and chroma, which are combined in that order to form the color designation. The symbol for hue is the letter abbreviation of the color of the rainbow (R for red, YR for yellow-red, or orange, Y for yellow) preceded by numbers from 0 to 10. Within each letter range, the hue becomes more yellow and less red as the numbers increase. The middle of the letter range is at 5; the zero point coincides with the 10 point of the next redder hue. Thus 5YR is in the middle of the yellow-red hue, which extends from 10R (zero YR) to 10YR (zero Y).

The notation for value consists of numbers from 0, for absolute black, to 10, for absolute white. Thus a color of value 5/ is visually midway between absolute white and absolute black. One of value 6/ is slightly less dark, 60 percent of the way from black to white, and midway between values of 5/ and 7/.

The notation for chroma consists of numbers beginning at 0 for neutral grays and increasing at equal intervals to a maximum of about 20, which is never really approached in soil. For absolute achromatic colors (pure grays, white, and black), which have zero chroma and no hue, the letter N (neutral) takes the place of a hue designation.

In writing the Munsell notation, the order is hue, value, chroma, with a space between the hue letter and the succeeding value number, and a virgule between the two numbers for value and chroma. If expression beyond the whole numbers is desired, decimals are always used, never fractions. Thus the notation for a color of hue 5YR, value 5, chroma 6, is 5YR 5/6, a yellowish-red. The notation for a color midway between the 5YR 5/6 and 5YR 6/6 chips is 5YR 5.5/6; for one midway between 2.5YR 5/6 and 5YR 6/8, it is 3.75YR 5.5/7. The notation is decimal and capable of expressing any degree of refinement desired. Since color determinations cannot be made precisely in the field— generally no closer than half the interval between colors in the chart—expression of color should ordinarily be to the nearest color chip.

In using the color chart, accurate comparison is obtained by holding the soil sample above the color chips being compared. Rarely will the color of the sample be *perfectly* matched by any color in the chart. The probability of having a perfect matching of the sample color is less than one in one hundred. It should be evident, however, which colors the sample lies between, and which is the closest match. The principal difficulties encountered in using the soil color chart are (1) in selecting the appropriate hue card, (2) in determining colors that are intermediate between the hues in the chart, and (3) in distinguishing between value and chroma where chromas are strong. In addition, the chart does not include some extreme dark, strong (low value, high chroma) colors occasionally encountered in moist soils. With experience, these extreme colors lying outside the range of the chart can be estimated. Then too, the ability to sense color differences varies among people, even among those not regarded as color blind.

While important details should be given, long involved designations of color should generally be avoided, especially with variegated or mottled colors. In these, only the extreme or dominant colors need be stated. Similarly, in giving the color names and Munsell notations for both the dry and moist colors, an abbreviated form, such as "reddish brown (5YR 4/4; 3/4, moist)," simplifies the statement.

By attempting detail beyond the allowable accuracy of field observations and sample selection, one may easily make poorer soil descriptions than by expressing the dominant color simply. In all descriptions, terms other than the ones given on these charts should be used only in rare instances, and then only as supplemental expressions in parentheses where some different local usage is common.

SOIL TEXTURE, COARSE FRAGMENTS, STONINESS, AND ROCKINESS

Soil texture refers to the relative proportions of the various size groups of individual soil grains in a mass of soil. Specifically, it refers to the proportions of clay, silt, and sand below 2 millimeters in diameter.

The presence of coarse particles larger than very coarse sand (or 2 mm.) and smaller than 10 inches is recognized by modifiers of textural class names, like *gravelly* sandy loam or *cobbly* loam.

General classes of still larger particles—stones or rock outcrops—are defined in terms of the influence they have on soil use, and in specific physical terms for individual soil series. Although distinctions within a type, series, family, or great soil group according to stoniness or rockiness are *phases,* these are indicated in soil types by an additional adjective added to the soil class name. Thus, Gloucester stony loam and Gloucester very stony loam are two phases of Gloucester loam which could be written more accurately and more clumsily Gloucester loam, stony phase, and Gloucester loam, very stony phase.

Actually, of course, sharp distinctions among the size groups of particles are more or less arbitrary. They have been arrived at after many, many trials in developing classes that can be used consistently and conveniently to define soil classificational and mapping units in such ways that they can be given the most specific interpretations.

The discussion of particle size is therefore presented under three principal headings: (1) The designation of soil textural class based primarily upon the proportion of clay, silt, and sand; (2) the definition of groups of coarse fragments having diameters less than 10 inches that may be regarded as a part of the soil mass and modify the textural class; and (3) the definition of classes of stoniness and rockiness for stones over 10 inches in diameter and for bedrock not considered a part of the soil mass.

SOIL TEXTURAL CLASS

The texture of a soil horizon is, perhaps, its most nearly permanent characteristic. Structure can be quickly modified by management. Often the texture of the plowed layer of an arable soil is modified, not by changes within the surface layer, but by the removal of surface horizons and the development of a new surface soil from a lower natural horizon of different texture, or by the addition of a new surface horizon, say of wind-blown sand or of silt loam settling out of muddy irrigation water. Soil blowing during drought may change soil texture by removing the fine particles from the exposed soil, leaving the surface soil richer in sand and coarse fragments than before.

Although texture is a seemingly simple basic concept in soil science, its consistent application has not been easy. Texture is so basic that terms like sand, clay, and loam are very old indeed. Since both consistence and structure are very important properties related partly to texture, the textural terms, as used earlier, had some connotations of these qualities as well as of texture. As long as their use was confined to soils in Britain and in the eastern part of the United States, the lack of correspondence between field designations of soil textural class and actual size distribution as shown by mechanical analysis was not obviously great. Yet structure and consistence depend on the kind and condition of the clay as well as on the amount of clay, on other soil constituents, and on the living tissue in the soil. As soil scientists began to deal with all soils, many of which are quite unlike the podzolized soils of the temperate forested regions, it became clear that structure, consistence, and texture had to be measured separately. Then too, early dispersion methods were so inadequate that fine granules of clay were actually reported as silt or sand.

Common sources of confusion and error are the agricultural connotations that were associated with the soil textural class names as formerly used. Clay soils were supposed to be sticky and easily puddled; sand soils were supposed to be loose, structureless, and droughty. Such connotations do not hold generally, however, and must be dissociated from general soil textural class names. Among some soil groups, clay soils are sticky and easily puddled, but among others they are not at all. Many sand soils are loose, structureless, and droughty, but some are not. As with each other soil characteristic, no direct relationship that can be applied generally to all soils exists between soil textural class and fertility, productivity, or other inferred qualities. To make such inferences we must also know the other important soil characteristics. Unfortunately, these erroneous correlations are well fixed in some textbooks and other books about soils for farmers and gardeners. Within the universe that the authors of these books actually consider, say Britain and the northeastern part of the United States, the correlations may be approximately correct for most soils; but the writers do not thus clearly limit their universe. As applied to the arctic, the tropics, and the desert they are often seriously wrong, even for the principal soils. Standardization of soil textural class names in terms of size distribution alone is clearly essential if soils of widely different genetic groups are to be compared.

SOIL SEPARATES

Soil separates are the individual size-groups of mineral particles. Sometimes the large sizes—coarse fragments—are included, but usually the groups of particles below 2 mm. in diameter are the only ones called soil separates. Since so many of the chemical and physical reactions in soils occur mainly on the surface of the grains, the fine part is most important. Only 4 pounds of dry clay particles having a diameter of 0.001 mm. have a total surface area of about an acre. The amount of surface exposed per unit weight drops very rapidly with increasing diameter until above 0.005 mm. in diameter the differences are small.

Two schemes are in common use: (1) The International system proposed by Atterberg and (2) the scheme used in the United States Department of Agriculture, which is now essentially consistent with the International system but makes more separations. Mechanical analyses of soils in the Department are reported in both systems as shown in table 2 and figure 37.

TABLE 2.—*Size limits of soil separates from two schemes of analysis*

U. S. Department of Agriculture scheme		International scheme	
Name of separate	Diameter (range)	Fraction	Diameter (range)
	Millimeters		*Millimeters*
Very coarse sand[1]...	2.0 –1.0		
Coarse sand	1.0 – .5	I	2.0–0.2
Medium sand	.5 – .25		
Fine sand	.25– .10	II	.20–.02
Very fine sand......	.10– .05		
Silt	.05– .002	III	.02–.002
Clay	Below .002	IV	Below .002

[1] Prior to 1947 this separate was called fine gravel. Now fine gravel is used for coarse fragments from 2 mm. to ½ inch in diameter.

TEXTURAL CLASS NAMES AND THEIR DEFINITIONS

Rarely, if ever, do soil samples consist wholly of one separate. Classes of soil texture are based on different combinations of sand, silt, and clay. The basic classes in order of increasing proportions of the fine separates are sand, loamy sand, sandy loam, loam, silt loam, silt, sandy clay loam, clay loam, silty clay loam, sandy clay, silty clay, and clay. Those with the term "sand" in the name are modified for very fine, fine, coarse, or very coarse sand.[1] In these class names the word "loam" appears. This is an old English word formerly applied to crumbly soils rich in humus. It is still used by some in that sense. In soil classification, however, it is used only in soil textural class names.[2]

The basic soil textural class names in present use are defined in terms of *size distribution* as determined by mechanical analysis in the laboratory.[3]

The definitions of these classes developed since the earlier edition of this *Manual* have resulted from long experience and much

[1] It will be noted that the terms "clay," "silt," "very fine sand," "fine sand," and "coarse sand" are used for both soil separates and for specific soil classes.

[2] Unfortunately, old and misleading names like "desert loams," "tropical red loams," and "brown loams" still persist as group names for soils varying widely from loam in texture.

[3] For accepted methods now in use see KILMER, V. J., and ALEXANDER, L. T. METHODS OF MAKING MECHANICAL ANALYSIS OF SOILS. Soil Sci. 68: 15–24. 1949.

Survey No. ....   Field No. ....   Laboratory No. ....

Locality ....

Soil type ....   Depth ....

MECHANICAL ANALYSIS

U. S. DEPARTMENT AGRICULTURE CLASSIFICATION

Diameter (mm)	Conventional Names		Percent
2-1	Very coarse sand	=	
1-0.5	Coarse sand	=	
0.5-0.25	Medium sand	=	
0.25-0.1	Fine sand	=	
0.1-0.05	Very fine sand	=	
0.05-0.002	[1]Silt	=	
Less than 0.002	[1]Clay	=	
TOTAL (Calculated on basis of organic-free oven-dry sample)		=	

OTHER CLASSES

Less than 0.005 mm	=
Greater than 2.0 mm	=
Organic carbon	=
pH	=

[1] NOTE.—Previous to Jan. 1, 1938, 0.05-0.005 mm was called silt; less than 0.005 mm, clay; and less than 0.002 mm, colloid.

GPO   16—27735-3

INTERNATIONAL CLASSIFICATION

Fraction	Diameter (mm)		Percent
I	2.0-0.2	=	
II	0.2-0.02	=	
III	0.02-0.002	=	
IV	Less than 0.002	=	
TOTAL (Calculated on basis of organic-free oven-dry sample)		=	

REMARKS:

Date reported ....

MECHANICAL ANALYSIS LABORATORY

FIGURE 37.—In the Division of Soil Survey the mechanical analysis of each soil sample is reported on a card like this.

special research to establish boundaries between classes so that they have the maximum general use for soil definitions and interpretations. Using the results of this research had the effect of some nearly drastic modifications in the old definitions of class names in terms of actual percentages of sand, silt, and clay as determined in the laboratory, and some modifications in field definitions based upon feel. Whereas laboratory data from mechanical analyses were formerly regarded as general guides only to soil textural class names, they are now regarded as absolute guides to soils of the mainland of the United States. At the same time one cannot say that the standards are yet perfect. Especially may further improvements be expected in the designations used for the textural class of Tundra soils and of Latosols in which the clays generally have different mineralogical compositions from those of soils in temperate regions. Textural class names must be defined wholly in terms of size distribution, however, and not used to express differences in consistence or structure; else the names will lose their fundamental significance.

Definitions of the basic classes are set forth in graphic form in figure 38, in terms of clay, below 0.002 mm; silt, 0.002 to 0.05 mm;

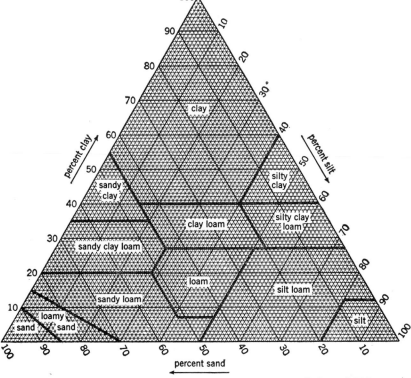

FIGURE 38.—Chart showing the percentages of clay (below 0.002 mm.), silt (0.002 to 0.05 mm.), and sand (0.05 to 2.0 mm.) in the basic soil textural classes.

and sand 0.05 to 2.0 mm. Although much improved over previous charts, this one is still tentative. Those frequently interpreting laboratory data into soil textural class names will find an enlarged copy of this triangle useful. Verbal definitions of the soil textural classes, defined according to size distribution of mineral particles less than 2 millimeters in diameter, are as follows:

Sands.—Soil material that contains 85 percent or more of sand; percentage of silt, plus 1½ times the percentage of clay, shall not exceed 15.

> *Coarse sand:* 25 percent or more very coarse and coarse sand, and less than 50 percent any other one grade of sand.
> *Sand:* 25 percent or more very coarse, coarse, and medium sand, and less than 50 percent fine or very fine sand.
> *Fine sand:* 50 percent or more fine sand (or) less than 25 percent very coarse, coarse, and medium sand and less than 50 percent very fine sand.
> *Very fine sand:* 50 percent or more very fine sand.

Loamy sands.—Soil material that contains at the upper limit 85 to 90 percent sand, and the percentage of silt plus 1½ times the percentage of clay is not less than 15; at the lower limit it contains not less than 70 to 85 percent sand, and the percentage of silt plus twice the percentage of clay does not exceed 30.

> *Loamy coarse sand:* 25 percent or more very coarse and coarse sand, and less than 50 percent any other one grade of sand.
> *Loamy sand:* 25 percent or more very coarse, coarse, and medium sand, and less than 50 percent fine or very fine sand.
> *Loamy fine sand:* 50 percent or more fine sand (or) less than 25 percent very coarse, coarse, and medium sand and less than 50 percent very fine sand.
> *Loamy very fine sand:* 50 percent or more very fine sand.

Sandy loams.—Soil material that contains either 20 percent clay or less, and the percentage of silt plus twice the percentage of clay exceeds 30, and 52 percent or more sand; or less than 7 percent clay, less than 50 percent silt, and between 43 percent and 52 percent sand.

> *Coarse sandy loam:* 25 percent or more very coarse and coarse sand and less than 50 percent any other one grade of sand.
> *Sandy loam:* 30 percent or more very coarse, coarse, and medium sand, but less than 25 percent very coarse sand, and less than 30 percent very fine or fine sand.
> *Fine sandy loam:* 30 percent or more fine sand and less than 30 percent very fine sand (or) between 15 and 30 percent very coarse, coarse, and medium sand.
> *Very fine sandy loam:* 30 percent or more very fine sand (or) more than 40 percent fine and very fine sand, at least half of which is very fine sand and less than 15 percent very coarse, coarse, and medium sand.

Loam.—Soil material that contains 7 to 27 percent clay, 28 to 50 percent silt, and less than 52 percent sand.

Silt loam.—Soil material that contains 50 percent or more silt and 12 to 27 percent clay (or) 50 to 80 percent silt and less than 12 percent clay.

Silt.—Soil material that contains 80 percent or more silt and less than 12 percent clay.

Sandy clay loam.—Soil material that contains 20 to 35 percent clay, less than 28 percent silt, and 45 percent or more sand.

Clay loam.—Soil material that contains 27 to 40 percent clay and 20 to 45 percent sand.

Silty clay loam.—Soil material that contains 27 to 40 percent clay and less than 20 percent sand.

Sandy clay.—Soil material that contains 35 percent or more clay and 45 percent or more sand.

Silty clay.—Soil material that contains 40 percent or more clay and 40 percent or more silt.

Clay.—Soil material that contains 40 percent or more clay, less than 45 percent sand, and less than 40 percent silt.

Necessarily these verbal definitions are somewhat complicated and, perhaps, not entirely adequate for unusual mixtures near the boundaries between classes. Some of the definitions are not entirely mutually exclusive, but the information needed to make them so is lacking. Departures from these definitions should be made only after careful joint research between field and laboratory scientists.

In addition to these basic soil textural class names, modified according to the size group of the sand fraction, other terms are also added as modifiers.

Muck, peat, mucky peat, and *peaty muck* are used in place of the textural class names in organic soils—muck for well-decomposed soil material, peat for raw undecomposed material, and peaty muck and mucky peat for intermediate materials. Former definitions have also specified a higher mineral content for muck than for peat. This cannot be followed, however, since many raw peats contain high amounts of mineral matter dropped from the air or washed in by water. The word "mucky" is used as an adjective on the textural class name for horizons of mineral soils, especially of Humic-Gley[4] soils that contain roughly 15 percent or more of partially decomposed organic matter. Horizons designated "mucky loam" or "mucky silt loam" are intergrades between muck and the soil textural class.

The terms for coarse fragments, outlined in the following section, are also added as adjectives to the soil class name and become a part of it. Thus a "gravelly sandy loam" has about 20 percent or more of gravel in the whole soil mass. The basic soil textural class name, however, is determined from the size distribution of the material below 2 mm. in diameter. That is, the percentages used for the standard soil class designations are net after the coarse fragments are excluded.

Phase names for stoniness and rockiness, although not a part of textural soil class names, are used to modify the soil-class part of a soil-type name, as for example, Gloucester *very stony* loam. In the descriptions of all soil horizons, particles larger than 10 inches are excluded from the soil textural class name. It needs to be recalled that classes of stoniness and rockiness are separate from soil class and have a separate place in soil descriptions.

Terms besides those herein defined, such as "wet," "ashy," "cindery," and the like, should be avoided in soil-class names or as modifiers of soil class in soil-type names.

---

[4] Tentative name for soils now included with Wiesenboden and for some included in Half Bog.

FIELD DETERMINATION OF SOIL TEXTURAL CLASS

The determination of soil class is still made in the field mainly by feeling of the soil with the fingers, sometimes supplemented by examination under the hand lens. This requires skill and experience, but good accuracy can be had if the field scientist frequently checks against laboratory results, especially for each soil varying widely from other soils of the area in structure, consistence, and content of organic matter. Moist soil feels different to the fingers than dry soil. Frequently clay particles are grouped into small hard aggregates that give a feel of silt or sand when dry. Because of differences in relative size within the clay fraction itself, soil horizons of similar total clay content vary in physical properties. Variations in kind of clay or in other constituents may give a soil unusual hardness, suggesting a high amount of clay, or an unusual granulation, suggesting a low amount of clay. The soil must be well moistened and rubbed vigorously between the fingers for a proper designation of textural class by feel.

For many years, the field determination of soil textural class actually took precedence over the results of mechanical analyses, which served only as general guides. Some 25 years ago the late Professor C. F. Shaw[5] worked out the following definitions of the basic soil textural classes in terms of field experience and feel:

Sand: Sand is loose and single-grained. The individual grains can readily be seen or felt. Squeezed in the hand when dry it will fall apart when the pressure is released. Squeezed when moist, it will form a cast, but will crumble when touched.

Sandy loam: A sandy loam is a soil containing much sand but which has enough silt and clay to make it somewhat coherent. The individual sand grains can readily be seen and felt. Squeezed when dry, it will form a cast which will readily fall apart, but if squeezed when moist a cast can be formed that will bear careful handling without breaking.

Loam: A loam is a soil having a relatively even mixture of different grades of sand and of silt and clay. It is mellow with a somewhat gritty feel, yet fairly smooth and slightly plastic. Squeezed when dry, it will form a cast that will bear careful handling, while the cast formed by squeezing the moist soil can be handled quite freely without breaking.

Silt loam: A silt loam is a soil having a moderate amount of the fine grades of sand and only a small amount of clay, over half of the particles being of the size called "silt." When dry it may appear cloddy but the lumps can be readily broken, and when pulverized it feels soft and floury. When wet the soil readily runs together and puddles. Either dry or moist it will form casts that can be freely handled without breaking, but when moistened and squeezed between thumb and finger it will not "ribbon" but will give a broken appearance.

Clay loam: A clay loam is a fine textured soil which usually breaks into clods or lumps that are hard when dry. When the moist soil is pinched between the thumb and finger it will form a thin "ribbon" which will break readily, barely sustaining its own weight. The moist soil is plastic and will form a cast that will bear much handling. When kneaded in the hand it does not crumble readily but tends to work into a heavy compact mass.

Clay: A clay is a fine textured soil that usually forms very hard lumps or clods when dry and is quite plastic and usually sticky when wet. When the moist soil is pinched out between the thumb and fingers it will form a long, flexible "ribbon." Some fine clays very high in colloids are friable and lack plasticity in all conditions of moisture.

[5] SHAW, C. F. A DEFINITION OF TERMS USED IN SOIL LITERATURE. 1st Internatl. Cong. Soil Sci. Proc. and Papers 5: 38–64. Washington. 1928.

Such definitions are suggestive only. None could be made in these or similar terms that would apply adequately to all soils. Variations in the kind of clay mineral and in the proportion of different exchangeable cations in the clay are too great among the great soil groups. Such kinds of definitions are limited to a group of similar soils.

The dependable definitions, the standards, are those developed from mechanical analyses. Each soil scientist must work out for himself the ability to determine soil class by feel, within each genetic soil group according to the standards established by mechanical analysis. In the progress of soil surveys, samples of soil horizons of doubtful texture should be forwarded to the laboratory and given high priority so that results may be sent back to the field at once to serve as guides. Soil scientists must recall that soil horizons of the same soil textural class, but in different great soil groups, may have a different feel. The scientist needs to adjust his field criteria, not the size-distribution standards.

GENERAL GROUPING OF SOIL TEXTURAL CLASSES

The need for fine distinctions in the texture of soil horizons results in a large number of soil textural classes. Often it is convenient to speak generally of a broad group of textural classes. Although the terms "heavy" and "light" have been used for many years, they are confusing, since the terms arose from the power required in plowing, not the actual weight of the soil. According to local usage in a few places, "light" soils are those low in productivity, including especially ones of clay texture.

An outline of acceptable general terms, in three classes and in five, in relation to the basic soil textural class names, is shown as follows:

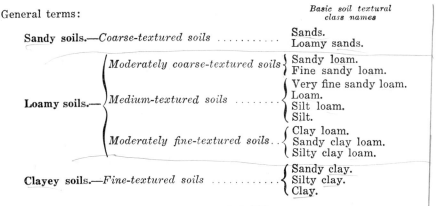

General terms:		Basic soil textural class names
Sandy soils.—*Coarse-textured soils*		Sands. Loamy sands.
Loamy soils.—	*Moderately coarse-textured soils*	Sandy loam. Fine sandy loam.
	Medium-textured soils	Very fine sandy loam. Loam. Silt loam. Silt.
	Moderately fine-textured soils . .	Clay loam. Sandy clay loam. Silty clay loam.
Clayey soils.—*Fine-textured soils*		Sandy clay. Silty clay. Clay.

COARSE FRAGMENTS

Significant proportions of fragments coarser than very coarse sand and less than 10 inches, if rounded, or 15 inches along the longer axis, if flat, are recognized by an appropriate adjective in the textural soil-class name. Such fragments are regarded as a part of the soil mass. They influence moisture storage, infiltration, and runoff. They influence root growth, especially through their dilution of the mass of active soil. They protect the fine particles from wash and blowing. They are moved with the soil mass in tillage.

Many names and standards have been proposed by geologists and soil scientists for these fragments. Fine distinctions are easily made (but not always easily mapped) because the fragments are easy to see; but finer distinctions than those set forth in table 3 have little or no real significance to soil genesis or behavior. Other variables, like the mineralogy of the clays or the nature of the organic matter, are far more important. The scientist must guard against making finer distinctions among the coarse fragments than those of real significance, simply because he can see them easily in the field.

The accepted adjectives to include in textural soil class names and the size limits of classes of coarse fragments are set forth in outline form in table 3. This table includes the probable maximum of detail required for detailed basic soil surveys. In situations where no useful purpose is served by developing separate mapping units to indicate the separate classes, the classes are grouped and a name given the soil type or soil phase that most clearly indicates the situation. Thus a cobbly loam or a stony phase may include other fragments also listed in the two right hand columns. In this section we shall concern ourselves only with fragments smaller than stones.

TABLE 3.—*Names used for coarse fragments in soils* [1]

Shape and kind of fragments	Size and name of fragments		
	Up to 3 inches in diameter	*3 to 10 inches in diameter*	*More than 10 inches in diameter*
Rounded and subrounded fragments (all kinds of rock).	Gravelly_____	Cobbly_____	Stony (or bouldery). [2]
Irregularly shaped angular fragments:			
Chert_____	Cherty_____	Coarse cherty.	Stony.
Other than chert_____	(Angular) gravelly.	Angular cobbly.[3]	Do.
	Up to 6 inches in length	*6 to 15 inches in length*	*More than 15 inches in length*
Thin, flat fragments:			
Thin, flat sandstone, limestone, and schist.	Channery___	Flaggy_____	Stony.
Slate_____	Slaty_____	_____do_____	Do.
Shale_____	Shaly_____	_____do_____	Do.

[1] The individual classes are not always differentiating characteristics of mapping units.
[2] Bouldery is sometimes used where stones are larger than 24 inches.
[3] Formerly called "stony."

The adjectives listed in the first two columns of table 3 are incorporated into the soil textural class designations of horizons when the soil mass contains significant proportions of the fragments, above 15 to 20 percent by volume, depending upon the other soil characteristics. These class names become parts of soil-type names. Where the coarse fragments make up 90 percent or more of the soil mass by volume in the upper 8 inches, the land is classified in the appropriate miscellaneous land type.[6] If necessary to make distinctions of clear significance, another subdivision can be made of the coarse fragments at about 50 percent to give, for example, gravelly loam (20 to 50 percent gravel) and very gravelly loam (50 to 90 percent gravel). The other defined fragments may be handled similarly.

The recommended terms to apply to soil containing above 15 to 20 percent coarse fragments smaller than stones, and less than 90 percent, are defined as follows:

Channery: Soils contain fragments of thin, flat sandstone, limestone, or schist up to 6 inches along the longer axis. A single piece is a *fragment.*

Cherty: Soils have angular fragments that are less than 3 inches in diameter, more than 75 percent of which are chert; *coarse cherty* soils have fragments of 3 to 10 inches (fig. 39). Unless the size distinction is significant to the use capability of the soil, the *cherty* soil includes the whole range up to 10 inches. Most cherty soils are developed from weathered cherty limestone. A single piece is a *chert fragment.*

FIGURE 39.—Fullerton coarse cherty fine sandy loam in Jefferson County, Tenn.

---

[6] Formerly, some soils having a high proportion of gravel or pebbles in the surface 8 inches were given a textural class name of "gravel," as in Rodman gravel. It is recommended that such soils be classified as gravelly loam, gravelly sandy loam, or gravelly sand, if they have less than 90 percent pebbles, or with the appropriate miscellaneous land type if they have more.

Cobbly: Soils have rounded or partially rounded fragments of rock ranging from 3 to 10 inches in diameter. *Angular cobbly,* formerly included as stony, is similar to cobbly except that fragments are not rounded. A single piece of either is a *cobblestone* or *small stone.*

Flaggy: Soils contain relatively thin fragments 6 to 15 inches long of sandstone, limestone, slate, or shale, or, rarely, of schist. A single piece is a *flagstone.*

Gravelly: Soils have rounded or angular fragments, not prominently flattened, up to 3 inches in diameter. If 75 percent or more of the fragments is chert, the soils are called *cherty.* In descriptions, soils with pebbles mostly over 2 inches in diameter may be called *coarsely gravelly* soils, and those with pebbles mostly under one-half inch in diameter may be called *finely gravelly* soils. An individual piece is a *pebble.* The term "gravel" refers to a mass of pebbles.

Shaly: Soils have flattened fragments of shale less than 6 inches along the longer axis. A single piece is a *shale fragment.*

Slaty: Soils contain fragments of slate less than 6 inches along the longer axis. A single piece is a *slate fragment.*

Stony: Soils contain rock fragments larger than 10 inches in diameter, if rounded, and longer than 15 inches along the longer axis, if flat. Classes are outlined in the following section.

STONINESS AND ROCKINESS

Stones larger than 10 inches in diameter and rock outcrops are not regarded as part of the soil mass as defined by soil textural classes. They have an important bearing on soil use, however, because of their interference with the use of agricultural machinery and their dilution of the soil mass. In fact, stoniness, rockiness, or both, are the differentiating criteria between classes of arable soil and between arable and nonarable soil in many places. In large part the soils developed from glacial till, for example, especially where the till is thin, have characteristics that make them highly responsive to management, except for stoniness. Soil scientists have sometimes neglected this factor, perhaps in part because it is a difficult problem to deal with in the field. Several otherwise useful published soil surveys have failed in their objectives because of the failure to establish meaningful classes of stoniness. Although detailed attention was given soil color, texture, parent material, slope, erosion, depth, and the like, stoniness was so carelessly evaluated that the maps cannot be used to distinguish between potential cropland, pasture land, and forest land, in descending order of intensity.

The suggestions that follow differentiate between loose stones and fixed stones and provide classes within each as required in detailed basic surveys. Admittedly the suggestions are especially aimed to deal with the most complicated situations—where both loose stones and fixed stones exist and influence soil-use capability differently and where the soils are otherwise suitable for intensive use. Generally, loose stones are scattered over the soil area, while rock ledges are more concentrated in strips with relatively rock-free soil between. Such situations are most common in glaciated regions with thin drift, as in New England and parts of the northern Lake States.

Outside the glaciated regions, loose stones are less abundant, although by no means uncommon. In some sections of the country, soils containing fixed stones (rocky soils as here defined), some loose fragments 3 to 10 inches in diameter, and some stones have been called stony for many years. Where no useful purpose is served by dividing into additional types and phases, it should not be done. Thus the classes proposed for stoniness and rockiness may be grouped in the definition of any individual mapping unit.

STONINESS

Stoniness refers to the relative proportion of stones over 10 inches in diameter in or on the soil. The significance of a given number or amount of stones depends upon the other soil characteristics. That is, if a soil is not suited to cultivated crops anyway, the presence of enough stones to interfere with cultivation is not significant and should not be used as a basis for a soil phase separation. If a soil is exceedingly responsive to management for improved pasture, let us say, differences between even high degrees of stoniness are significant and may separate mapping units, as for example, an extremely stony phase of a soil type from the miscellaneous land type, Stony land.

The limits of the classes of stoniness are defined broadly in absolute terms and more specifically in terms of soil use wherever the other soil characteristics are favorable for crops or improved pasture. The able soil classifier avoids fine distinctions according to stoniness where they are not significant as clearly as he recognizes them where they are significant. This means that in the descriptive soil legend and in the soil survey report, stony phases need to be defined *within* the soil series and types. The classes of stoniness are used in definitions of all units of soil classification and may become one criterion for soil series as well as the sole criterion for distinctions among phases within the soil series or soil types.

Classes of stoniness are outlined as follows:

Class 0: No stones or too few to interfere with tillage. Stones cover less than 0.01 percent of the area.

Class 1: Sufficient stones to interfere with tillage but not to make intertilled crops impracticable. (If stones are 1 foot in diameter and about 30 to 100 feet apart, they occupy about 0.01 to 0.1 percent of the surface, and there are about 0.15 to 1.5 cubic yards per acre-foot.) (See fig. 40.)

Class 2: Sufficient stones to make tillage of intertilled crops impracticable, but the soil can be worked for hay crops or improved pasture if other soil characteristics are favorable. (If stones are 1 foot in diameter and about 5 to 30 feet apart, they occupy about 0.1 to 3 percent of the surface, and there are about 1.5 to 50 cubic yards per acre-foot.) (See fig. 41.)

Class 3: Sufficient stones to make all use of machinery impracticable, except for very light machinery or hand tools where other soil characteristics are especially favorable for improved pasture. Soils with this class of stoniness may have some use for wild pasture or forests, depending on other soil characteristics. (If stones are 1 foot in diameter and about 2.5 to 5 feet apart, they occupy about 3 to 15 percent of the surface, and there are about 50 to 240 cubic yards per acre-foot.)

FIGURE 40.—An area of soil having class 1 stoniness, near the margin between class 1 and class 2.

FIGURE 41.—This photograph illustrates class 2 stoniness on a productive soil. On other soils it might be included in class 3.

Class 4: Sufficient stones to make all use of machinery impracticable; the land may have some value for poor pasture or for forestry. (If stones are 1 foot in diameter and are about 2.5 feet or less apart, they occupy 15 to 90 percent of the surface, and there are more than about 240 cubic yards per acre-foot.)

Class 5: Land essentially paved with stones that occupy more than 90 percent of the exposed surface (Rubble).

It should be emphasized that these classes are for general application in soil descriptions. They may or may not be used as phase distinctions. In other words a mapping unit may be defined in terms of more than one class of stoniness. Some individual soils may be defined in terms of classes of stoniness, classes of rockiness, and classes of coarse fragments. Stoniness is not a part of the soil textural class. The terms "stony," very stony," or "exceedingly stony" may modify the soil textural class name in the soil type; but this is simply a brief way of designating stony phases.[7] Soil series descriptions need to include the range of stoniness in terms of classes 0, 1, 2, and 3.

Distinctions between classes 0 and 1 are commonly the basis for stony phases of soil types, and between classes 1 and 2, of very stony phases. Distinctions between soil series and the miscellaneous land type, Stony land, usually come between classes 2 and 3, but may come between classes 3 and 4 if the soil is otherwise unusually responsive to management practices for improved pasture or for forestry.

If differences in potential use for wild pasture or for forestry, related to the parent material, exist among kinds of soil having class 3 stoniness, class 3 stoniness may be called Stony land, (series name) material.

If the distinction between class 3 and class 4 stoniness has no significance, all the land of both classes should be included as one unit, Stony land. But if land with class 3 stoniness is separated from that with class 4 stoniness, either as an extremely stony phase or as Stony land, (series name) material, or if a real difference exists of importance to grazing or forestry, class 4 is called Very stony land.

Land having class 5 stoniness is always called Rubble land, which may, in turn, be part of a complex mapping unit.

Some idealized relationship between the spacing of stones, area covered by stones, and cubic yards per acre in the surface foot are set forth in table 4. These values will vary, of course, with unevenness in spacing and with different sizes of stones.

The relation of classes of stoniness and of rockiness to one another and to some soil classificational units is set forth in table 5.

Areas of the units too small to be enclosed in boundaries are shown on the map by separate stone symbols for each stony phase (see p. 296 *et seq.*) with each symbol defined in terms of the area it represents (pl. 6). Areas of a stony phase enclosed within

---

[7] See section on Units of Soil Classification and Mapping.

boundaries but too small in total area for a place in the map legend are shown on the published map by symbols.

TABLE 4.—*Approximate spacings of stones and cubic yards of stones per acre-foot at selected percentages of area covered*

Diameter of stones (feet)	Spacing of stones from center to center (feet)	Area covered with stones (percent)	Stones per acre-foot (cubic yards)
2	11	3	97
	5	15	485
	2.7	50	1,616
1	5.5	3	48
	2.5	15	242
	1.3	50	808
0.5[1]	2.7	3	24
	1.2	15	121
	.7	50	404

[1] Cobbles.

ROCKINESS

Rockiness refers to the relative proportion of bedrock exposures, either rock outcrops or patches of soil too thin over bedrock for use, in a soil area. "Rocky" is used, perhaps arbitrarily, for soils having fixed rock (bedrock), and "stony" for soils having loose detached fragments of rock.

The classes of rockiness, as of stoniness, are given broad definitions in absolute terms and more specific definitions in terms of soil use for those soils otherwise suitable for crops or improved pasture. Soil areas having the same definitions in terms of area of bedrock exposure may vary widely in the depth of soils between the rock outcrops. Such distinctions need to be made within the soil series definitions. As with stoniness, the classes of rockiness are used in soil series descriptions and can become one criterion for series distinctions or the sole criterion for phase distinctions. Two or more classes may be combined in one mapping unit. Some mapping units may also have classes of stoniness and of coarse fragments.

The relationships to soil use suggested in the definitions of the classes apply mainly to areas of soil in humid regions that are otherwise responsive to management. The definitions of actual soil phases must take account of the alternative management practices that can be used for seeding, harvesting, weed control, and the like.

In each descriptive legend and soil survey report, rocky phases need to be defined specifically within each soil series or type.

The classes of rockiness are as follows:

Class 0: No bedrock exposures or too few to interfere with tillage. Less than 2 percent bedrock exposed.

Class 1: Sufficient bedrock exposures to interfere with tillage but not to make intertilled crops impracticable. Depending upon how the pattern affects tillage, rock exposures are roughly 100 to 300 feet apart and cover about 2 to 10 percent of the surface.

Class 2: Sufficient bedrock exposures to make tillage of intertilled crops impracticable, but soil can be worked for hay crops or improved pasture if the other soil characteristics are favorable. Rock exposures are roughly 30 to 100 feet apart and cover about 10 to 25 percent of the surface, depending upon the pattern (fig. 42).

FIGURE 42.—Area of soil with class 2 rockiness.

Class 3: Sufficient rock outcrop to make all use of machinery impracticable, except for light machinery where other soil characteristics are especially favorable for improved pasture. May have some use for wild pasture or forests, depending on the other soil characteristics. Rock exposures, or patches of soil too thin over rock for use, are roughly 10 to 30 feet apart and cover about 25 to 50 percent of the surface, depending upon the pattern.

Class 4: Sufficient rock outcrop (or of very thin soil over rock) to make all use of machinery impracticable. The land may have some value for poor pasture or for forestry. Rock outcrops are about 10 feet apart or less and cover some 50 to 90 percent of the area.

Class 5: Land for which over 90 percent of the surface is exposed bedrock (Rock outcrop).

The distinctions between classes 0, 1, and 2 are commonly the bases for phases of soil types.[8] As with stony phases, these terms are added as adjectives to the soil textural class part of the soil-

[8] See section on Units of Soil Classification and Mapping.

TABLE 5.—*Relation of classes of stoniness and rockiness[1] to one another and to some soil classificational units*

	Stoniness			Rockiness	
Class	Approximate percentage of surface covered	Modification in name of classificational unit to indicate degree of stoniness	Class	Approximate percentage of rock-exposed surface[4]	Modification in name of classificational unit to indicate degree of rockiness
0	Less than 0.01	No modification. Example: Gloucester loam.	0	Less than 2	No modification. Example: Hagerstown loam.
1	0.01 to 0.1	Stony (phase).[2] Example: Gloucester stony loam.	1	2 to 10	Rocky (phase).[2] Example: Hagerstown rocky loam.
2	0.1 to 3.0	Very stony (phase). Example: Gloucester very stony loam.	2	10 to 25	Very rocky (phase). Example: Hagerstown very rocky loam.
3	3 to 15	Any one of following: Extremely stony (phase). Example: Gloucester extremely stony loam. Stony land.[3] Stony land (Gloucester soil material).	3	25 to 50	Any one of following: Extremely rocky (phase). Example: Hagerstown extremely rocky loam. Rock land.[3] Rock land (Hagerstown material).
4	15 to 90	Either of following: Stony land.[3] Very stony land.	4	50 to 90	Rock land.[3]
5	Above 90	Rubble land.	5	Above 90	Rock outcrop.

[1] This table is a general guide in detailed basic surveys where it is important to differentiate among several classes and between stoniness and rockiness. With soils having rockiness, stoniness, and some coarse fragments, and for which separation by classes serves no useful purpose, stony phases may be recognized.

[2] The word "phase" usually can be omitted; but, for example, Gloucester stony loam is simply a short way of naming the unit, Gloucester loam, stony phase. Theoretically, at least, if all areas of a soil type have one class name of stoniness, say class 2, "very stony" is a descriptive adjective of the type and there are no phases of stoniness.

[3] Commonly, the distinction between classes 3 and 4 is not necessary, and the whole range of both classes is included as *Stony land* or *Rock land*.

[4] Including soil too thin over rock for useful plant growth.

type name to give names like Hagerstown rocky loam, Hagerstown very rocky loam, or Hagerstown extremely rocky loam. These are three phases, plus the unnamed nonrocky phase, within the Hagerstown loam.

The distinctions between classes 2 and 3 or between classes 3 and 4 are commonly the dividing lines between the soil series and the miscellaneous land type, Rock land. If the soil is not responsive to management for improved pasture with rockiness greater than class 2, the distinction is made there; and land with class 3 rockiness is designated as Rock land. If the soil is especially responsive to soil management practices for improved pasture and can be tilled with very light machinery, the soil is named and placed in an extremely rocky phase. If the land cannot be used practicably for improved pasture but the distinction between several kinds of Rock land with class 3 rockiness is important, a unit is designated as Rock land, (series name) soil material.

If distinctions between classes 3 and 4 of rockiness are not significant, all the land in both classes is called Rock land. If the distinction between these two classes is significant, land of class 3 rockiness may be indicated as an extremely rocky phase of a soil type or as Rock land, (series name) soil material, and the term Rock land reserved for that having class 4 rockiness.

Land with class 5 rockiness is always classified as Rock outcrop even though a little soil may be found between the outcrops or the ledges.

The relationship of classes of stoniness to classes of rockiness, and of these to some soil classificational units, is shown in table 5.

Areas of rocky phases too small to enclose with boundaries are not shown on the map. Instead symbols for rock outcrops and for rock ledges are used (pls. 4 and 6). In each survey, the area that each represents needs to be defined.

COMBINED CLASSES OF STONINESS AND ROCKINESS

Frequently it is necessary to combine classes of rockiness and stoniness. In such instances the combined influence of the two conditions on soil use needs to be considered. Soils having class 1 stoniness and class 1 rockiness might be named as a very stony and rocky phase of a soil type, or simply as a stony phase. Land having both class 2 rockiness or higher and class 2 stoniness or higher would doubtless need to be put into a miscellaneous land type, as Stony rock land.

SOIL STRUCTURE

Soil structure refers to the aggregation of primary soil particles into compound particles, or clusters of primary particles, which are separated from adjoining aggregates by surfaces of weakness. The exteriors of some aggregates have thin, often dark-colored, surface films which perhaps help to keep them apart. Other aggregates have surfaces and interiors of like color, and the forces holding the aggregates together appear to be wholly internal.

An individual natural soil aggregate is called a *ped*, in contrast to (1) a *clod*, caused by disturbance, such as plowing or digging, that molds the soil to a transient mass that slakes with repeated wetting and drying, (2) a *fragment* caused by rupture of the soil mass across natural surfaces of weakness, or (3) a *concretion* caused by local concentrations of compounds that irreversibly cement the soil grains together.

The importance of soil structure in soil classification and in influencing soil productivity can scarcely be overemphasized. The capability of any soil for the growth of plants and its response to management depends as much on its structure as on its fertility. Generally, in the United States, soils with aggregates of spheroidal shape have much pore space between aggregates, have more rapid permeability, and are more productive than soils of comparable fertility that are massive or even coarsely blocky or prismatic. In other parts of the world, some soils are overgranulated. Some Latosols have such well-developed spheroidal peds that the moisture-holding capacity is low, too few contacts exist between roots and soil, and the soils are relatively unproductive.

Field descriptions of soil structure note (1) the shape and arrangement, (2) the size, and (3) the distinctness and durability of the visible aggregates or peds. Field terminology for structure consists of separate sets of terms designating each of these three qualities, which by combination form the names for structure. Shape and arrangement of peds is designated as *type* of soil structure; size of peds, as *class;* and degree of distinctness, as *grades*.[1] The structural pattern of a soil horizon also includes the shapes and sizes of pore spaces as well as those of the peds themselves.

There are four primary types of structure: (1) Platy, with particles arranged around a plane, generally horizontal; (2) prismlike, with particles arranged around a vertical line and bounded by relatively flat vertical surfaces; (3) blocklike or polyhedral, with particles arranged around a point and bounded by flat or rounded surfaces which are casts of the molds formed

[1] For a useful background discussion of these concepts, see NIKIFOROFF, C. C. MORPHOLOGICAL CLASSIFICATION OF SOIL STRUCTURE. Soil Sci. 52: 193–212, illus. 1941.

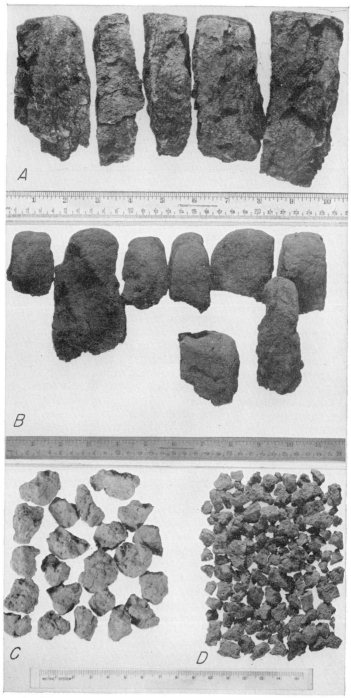

FIGURE 43.—Photographs of characteristic structural aggregates: *A*, prismatic; *B*, columnar; *C*, angular blocky; and *D*, subangular blocky.

by the faces of surrounding peds; and (4) spheroidal or poly-hedral, with particles arranged around a point and bounded by curved or very irregular surfaces that are not accommodated to the adjoining aggregates. Each of the last three have two sub-types. Under prismlike the subtypes are *prismatic*, without rounded upper ends, and *columnar*, with rounded caps. The sub-types of blocklike are *angular blocky*, bounded by planes inter-secting at relatively sharp angles, and *subangular blocky*, having mixed rounded and plane faces with vertices mostly rounded. If the term "blocky" is used alone, angular blocky is understood. Spheroidal is subdivided into *granular*, relatively nonporous, and *crumb*, very porous. Each type of structure includes peds that vary in shape, and detailed soil descriptions may require supple-mental statements about the shape of the individual peds (figs. 43 and 44).

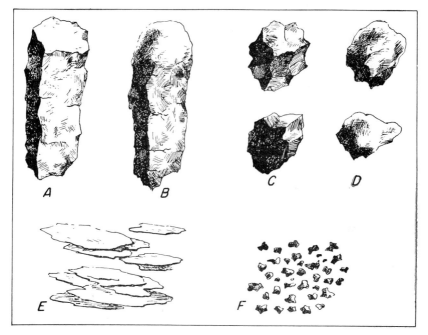

FIGURE 44.—Drawings illustrating some of the types of soil structure: *A*, prismatic; *B*, columnar; *C*, angular blocky; *D*, subangular blocky; *E*, platy; and F, granular.

The names in the preceding paragraph placed in italics are the terms most used in descriptions of soil horizons. *Nut* has been used for blocklike peds, but is not recommended; *nuciform* has been an optional alternative for subangular blocky, but *sub-angular blocky* is recommended. It is difficult for many to dis-associate a size connotation from terms like *nut* and *nuciform*. For this reason some confuse very fine blocky with granular. Terms

TABLE 6.—*Types and classes of soil structure*

Class	TYPE (Shape and arrangement of peds)						
	Platelike with one dimension (the vertical) limited and greatly less than the other two; arranged around a horizontal plane; faces mostly horizontal.	Prismlike with two dimensions (the horizontal) limited and considerably less than the vertical; arranged around a vertical line; vertical faces well defined; vertices angular.		Blocklike; polyhedronlike, or spheroidal, with three dimensions of the same order of magnitude, arranged around a point.			
				Blocklike; blocks or polyhedrons having plane or curved surfaces that are casts of the molds formed by the faces of the surrounding peds.		Spheroids or polyhedrons having plane or curved surfaces which have slight or no accommodation to the faces of surrounding peds.	
		Without rounded caps.	With rounded caps.	Faces flattened; most vertices sharply angular.	Mixed rounded and flattened faces with many rounded vertices.	Relatively non-porous peds.	Porous peds.
	Platy	Prismatic	Columnar	(Angular) Blocky [1]	Subangular blocky [2]	Granular	Crumb
Very fine or very thin.	Very thin platy; <1 mm.	Very fine prismatic; <10 mm.	Very fine columnar; <10 mm.	Very fine angular blocky; <5 mm.	Very fine subangular blocky; <5 mm.	Very fine granular; <1 mm.	Very fine crumb; <1 mm.
Fine or thin	Thin platy; 1 to 2 mm.	Fine prismatic; 10 to 20 mm.	Fine columnar; 10 to 20 mm.	Fine angular blocky; 5 to 10 mm.	Fine subangular blocky; 5 to 10 mm.	Fine granular; 1 to 2 mm.	Fine crumb; 1 to 2 mm.
Medium	Medium platy; 2 to 5 mm.	Medium prismatic; 20 to 50 mm.	Medium columnar; 20 to 50 mm.	Medium angular blocky; 10 to 20 mm.	Medium subangular blocky; 10 to 20 mm.	Medium granular; 2 to 5 mm.	Medium crumb; 2 to 5 mm.
Coarse or thick.	Thick platy; 5 to 10 mm.	Coarse prismatic; 50 to 100 mm.	Coarse columnar; 50 to 100 mm.	Coarse angular blocky; 20 to 50 mm.	Coarse subangular blocky; 20 to 50 mm.	Coarse granular; 5 to 10 mm.	
Very coarse or very thick.	Very thick platy; >10 mm.	Very coarse prismatic; >100 mm.	Very coarse columnar; >100 mm.	Very coarse angular blocky; >50 mm.	Very coarse subangular blocky; >50 mm.	Very coarse granular; >10 mm.	

[1] (a) Sometimes called *nut*. (b) The word "angular" in the name can ordinarily be omitted.
[2] Sometimes called *nuciform*, *nut*, or *subangular nut*. Since the size connotation of these terms is a source of great confusion to many, they are not recommended.

used to designate types of soil structure refer *only* to shape and arrangement and do not specify size.

Five size classes are recognized in each of the primary types. The names of these and their size limits, which vary with the four primary types for shape and arrangement, are given in table 6.

Grade of structure is the degree of aggregation and expresses the differential between cohesion within aggregates and adhesion between aggregates. In field practice, grade of structure is determined mainly by noting the durability of the aggregates and the proportions between aggregated and unaggregated material that result when the aggregates are displaced or gently crushed. Grade of structure varies with the moistening of the soil and should be described at the most important moisture contents of the soil horizon. The principal description of the structure of a soil horizon should refer to its normal moisture content, although attention should be called to any striking contrasts in structure under other moisture conditions to which the soil is subject. If grade is designated at an unstated moisture content, it is assumed that the soil is nearly dry or only very slightly moist, which is commonly that part of the range in soil moisture in which soil structure is most strongly expressed.

With exposure, structure may become much altered, often much stronger. Old road cuts are not suitable places to determine the grade of structure, but they often afford a clue to the type of structure present where the grade is so weak that it cannot be identified in the undisturbed soil.

Terms for grade of structure are as follows:

0. *Structureless.*—That condition in which there is no observable aggregation or no definite orderly arrangement of natural lines of weakness. *Massive* if coherent; *single grain* if noncoherent.

1. *Weak.*—That degree of aggregation characterized by poorly formed indistinct peds that are barely observable in place. When disturbed, soil material that has this grade of structure breaks into a mixture of few entire peds, many broken peds, and much unaggregated material. If necessary for comparison, this grade may be subdivided into *very weak* and *moderately weak.*

2. *Moderate.*—That grade of structure characterized by well-formed distinct peds that are moderately durable and evident but not distinct in undisturbed soil. Soil material of this grade, when disturbed, breaks down into a mixture of many distinct entire peds, some broken peds, and little unaggregated material. Examples are the loam A horizons of typical Chestnut soils in the granular type, and clayey B horizons of such Red-Yellow Podzolic soils as the Boswell in the blocky type.

3. *Strong.*—That grade of structure characterized by durable peds that are quite evident in undisplaced soil, that adhere weakly to one another, and that withstand displacement and become separated when the soil is disturbed. When removed from the profile, soil material of this grade of structure consists very largely of entire peds and includes few broken peds and little or no unaggregated material. If necessary for comparison, this grade may be subdivided into *moderately strong* and *very strong.* Examples of strong grade of structure are in the granular-type A horizons of the typical Chernozem and in the columnar-type B horizons of the typical solodized-Solonetz.

The sequence followed in combining the three terms to form the compound name of the structure is (1) grade (distinctness), (2) class (size), and (3) type (shape). For example, the designation for the soil structure in which the peds are loosely packed and roundish but not extremely porous, dominantly between 1 and 2 mm. in diameter, and quite distinct is *strong fine granular.* The designation of structure by grade, class, and type can be modified with any other appropriate terms wherever necessary to describe other characteristics of the peds.

Many soil horizons have compound structure consisting of one or more sets of smaller peds held together as larger peds. Compound structures are so described: for example, *compound moderate very coarse prismatic and moderate medium granular.* Soil that has one structural form when in place may assume some other form when disturbed. When removed, the larger peds may fall into smaller peds, such as large prisms into medium blocks.

With increasing disturbance or pressure any aggregate breaks into smaller particles. These finer particles may or may not be peds, depending on whether their form and size are determined by surfaces of weakness between natural aggregates or by the place and direction of the pressures applied. Mere breakage into fragments larger than the soil grains without some orderly shape and size should not be confused with soil structure. Massive soil horizons, without structure, can be shattered into fragments—so can glass. Such fragments are not peds.

SOIL CONSISTENCE

Soil consistence comprises the attributes of soil material that are expressed by the degree and kind of cohesion and adhesion or by the resistance to deformation or rupture. Every soil material has consistence irrespective of whether the mass be large or small, in a natural condition or greatly disturbed, aggregated or structureless, moist or dry. Although consistence and structure are interrelated, structure deals with the shape, size, and definition of natural aggregates that result from variations in the forces of attraction within a soil mass, whereas consistence deals with the strength and nature of such forces themselves.

The terminology for consistence includes separate terms for description at three standard moisture contents (dry, moist, and wet). If moisture conditions are not stated in using any consistence term, the moisture condition is that under which the particular term is defined. Thus *friable* used without statement of the moisture content specifies *friable when moist;* likewise, *hard* used alone means *hard when dry,* and *plastic* means *plastic when wet.* If a term is used to describe consistence at some moisture content *other* than the standard condition under which the term is defined, *a statement of the moisture condition is essential.* Usually it is unnecessary to describe consistence at all three standard moisture conditions. The consistence when moist is commonly the most significant, and a soil description with this omitted can hardly be regarded as complete; the consistence when dry is generally useful but may be irrelevant in descriptions of soil materials that are never dry; and the consistence when wet is unessential in the description of many soils but extremely important in some.

Although evaluation of consistence involves some disturbance, unless otherwise stated, descriptions of consistence customarily refer to that of soil from undisturbed horizons. In addition, descriptions of consistence under moist or wet conditions carry an implication that disturbance causes little modification of consistence or that the original consistence can be almost restored by pressing the material together. Where such an implication is misleading, as in compacted layers, the consistence both before and after disturbance may require separate description. Then, too, compound consistences occur, as in a loose mass of hard granules. In a detailed description of soils having compound structure, the consistence of the mass as a whole and of its parts should be stated.

A number of terms, including *brittle, crumbly, dense, elastic, fluffy,*[1] *mealy, mellow, soft, spongy, stiff, tight, tough,* and some

---

[1] As used in describing soils, *fluffy* denotes a combination of loose to very friable consistence and low bulk density.

others, which have often been used in descriptions of consistence, are not here defined. These are all common words of well-known meanings. Some are indispensable for describing unusual conditions not covered by other terms. They are useful in nontechnical descriptions where a little accuracy may be sacrificed to use a term familiar to lay readers. Whenever needed, these or other terms for consistence not defined in this *Manual* should be employed with meanings as given in standard dictionaries.

The terms used in soil descriptions for consistence follow:

I. CONSISTENCE WHEN WET

Consistence when wet is determined at or slightly above field capacity.

A. **Stickiness.**—Stickiness is the quality of adhesion to other objects. For field evaluation of stickiness, soil material is pressed between thumb and finger and its adherence noted. Degrees of stickiness are described as follows:

0. *Nonsticky:* After release of pressure, practically no soil material adheres to thumb or finger.

1. *Slightly sticky:* After pressure, soil material adheres to both thumb and finger but comes off one or the other rather cleanly. It is not appreciably stretched when the digits are separated.

2. *Sticky:* After pressure, soil material adheres to both thumb and finger and tends to stretch somewhat and pull apart rather than pulling free from either digit.

3. *Very sticky:* After pressure, soil material adheres strongly to both thumb and forefinger and is decidedly stretched when they are separated.

B. **Plasticity.**—Plasticity is the ability to change shape continuously under the influence of an applied stress and to retain the impressed shape on removal of the stress. For field determination of plasticity, roll the soil material between thumb and finger and observe whether or not a wire or thin rod of soil can be formed. If helpful to the reader of particular descriptions, state the range of moisture content within which plasticity continues, as plastic when slightly moist or wetter, plastic when moderately moist or wetter, and plastic only when wet, or as plastic within a wide, medium, or narrow range of moisture content. Express degree of resistance to deformation at or slightly above field capacity as follows:

0. *Nonplastic:* No wire is formable.

1. *Slightly plastic:* Wire formable but soil mass easily deformable.

2. *Plastic:* Wire formable and moderate pressure required for deformation of the soil mass.

3. *Very plastic:* Wire formable and much pressure required for deformation of the soil mass.

II. CONSISTENCE WHEN MOIST

Consistence when moist is determined at a moisture content approximately midway between air dry and field capacity. At this moisture content most soil materials exhibit a form of consistence characterized by (a) tendency to break into smaller masses rather than into powder, (b) some deformation prior to rupture, (c) absence of brittleness, and (d) ability of the material after disturbance to cohere again when pressed together. The resistance decreases with moisture content, and accuracy of field descriptions of this consistence is limited by the accuracy of estimating moisture content. To evaluate this consistence, select and attempt to crush in the hand a mass that appears slightly moist.

0. *Loose:* Noncoherent.
1. *Very friable:* Soil material crushes under very gentle pressure but coheres when pressed together.
2. *Friable:* Soil material crushes easily under gentle to moderate pressure between thumb and forefinger, and coheres when pressed together.
3. *Firm:* Soil material crushes under moderate pressure between thumb and forefinger but resistance is distinctly noticeable.
4. *Very firm:* Soil material crushes under strong pressure; barely crushable between thumb and forefinger.
5. *Extremely firm:* Soil material crushes only under very strong pressure; cannot be crushed between thumb and forefinger and must be broken apart bit by bit.

The term *compact* denotes a combination of firm consistence and close packing or arrangement of particles and should be used only in this sense. It can be given degrees by use of "very" and "extremely."

III. CONSISTENCE WHEN DRY

The consistence of soil materials when dry is characterized by rigidity, brittleness, maximum resistance to pressure, more or less tendency to crush to a powder or to fragments with rather sharp edges, and inability of crushed material to cohere again when pressed together. To evaluate, select an air-dry mass and break in the hand.

0. *Loose:* Noncoherent.
1. *Soft:* Soil mass is very weakly coherent and fragile; breaks to powder or individual grains under very slight pressure.
2. *Slightly hard:* Weakly resistant to pressure; easily broken between thumb and forefinger.
3. *Hard:* Moderately resistant to pressure; can be broken in the hands without difficulty but is barely breakable between thumb and forefinger.
4. *Very hard:* Very resistant to pressure; can be broken in the hands only with difficulty; not breakable between thumb and forefinger.

5. *Extremely hard:* Extremely resistant to pressure; cannot be broken in the hands.

IV. CEMENTATION

Cementation of soil material refers to a brittle hard consistence caused by some cementing substance other than clay minerals, such as calcium carbonate, silica, or oxides or salts of iron and aluminum. Typically the cementation is altered little if any by moistening; the hardness and brittleness persist in the wet condition. Semireversible cements, which generally resist moistening but soften under prolonged wetting, occur in some soils and give rise to soil layers having a cementation that is pronounced when dry but very weak when wet. Some layers cemented with calcium carbonate soften somewhat with wetting. Unless stated to the contrary, descriptions of cementation imply that the condition is altered little if any by wetting. If the cementation is greatly altered by moistening, it should be so stated. Cementation may be either continuous or discontinuous within a given horizon.

1. *Weakly cemented:* Cemented mass is brittle and hard but can be broken in the hands.
2. *Strongly cemented:* Cemented mass is brittle and harder than can be broken in the hand but is easily broken with a hammer.
3. *Indurated:* Very strongly cemented; brittle, does not soften under prolonged wetting, and is so extremely hard that for breakage a sharp blow with a hammer is required; hammer generally rings as a result of the blow.

SOIL REACTION

Soil reaction receives special emphasis in soil classification, partly because of its direct importance but mainly because of other soil qualities, less easily determined, that may be inferred from it. Early field workers distinguished roughly between acid soils and alkaline soils by testing for carbonates with dilute acid and by the use of litmus paper and phenolphthalein. Since then, better field methods, based upon laboratory methods, have become available.

pH

The intensity of soil acidity or alkalinity is expressed in pH— the logarithm of the reciprocal of the H-ion concentration. With this notation, pH 7 is neutral; lower values indicate acidity; and higher values show alkalinity. Soil horizons vary in pH from a little below 3.5 to a little above 9.5.

The corresponding terms to use for ranges in pH are as follows:

	pH		*pH*
Extremely acid......	Below 4.5	Neutral[1]	6.6–7.3
Very strongly acid...	4.5–5.0	Mildly alkaline......	7.4–7.8
Strongly acid	5.1–5.5	Moderately alkaline..	7.9–8.4
Medium acid	5.6–6.0	Strongly alkaline....	8.5–9.0
Slightly acid	6.1–6.5	Very strongly alkaline	9.1 and higher

[1] Strict neutrality is pH 7.0, but in field work those soils between pH 6.6 and 7.3 are called neutral. In the rare cases where significant, the terms very slightly acid and very mildly alkaline may be used for soils of pH 6.6 to 6.9 and 7.1 to 7.3, respectively.

Values for pH of the soil horizons are important in soil classification and in the identification of soils in the field.

Generally, pH reflects the base status of the soil. Acid soils are high in exchangeable hydrogen, and alkaline soils, high in exchangeable bases. The base status of the several horizons, taken with their other characteristics, tells a lot about the kind and degree of weathering, the composition of the parent material, the amount of leaching, and the influence of the vegetation. Since other factors, like the kind of clay, kind and amount of organic matter, the particular exchangeable bases present, and the soluble salts in the soil, influence pH, the relationship between pH and base status is not the same for all kinds of soil.

Then, too, pH is a measure of the intensity of acidity or alkalinity, not the capacity or total amount. Other things being equal, soils rich in clay or in organic matter have greater reserves of acidity or alkalinity than sandy soils or those low in organic matter. The reserves are very high in peat and muck. With the same clay content, Latosols or latosolic soils have less reserve than Podzols or podzolic soils. A soil with a high capacity or reserve is said to be well buffered.

A pH value much above 7 usually indicates the presence of some free carbonates of calcium, magnesium, or both, but not necessarily so. Some Solonetz soils of pH 8.5 show no test for carbonates in the field. On the other hand, a long-cropped chernozemic Wiesenboden may show tiny particles of carbonate that react to acid, although the soil horizon (A_p) as a whole has pH 5.5.

Soils having pH values higher than 8.5 nearly always contain significant amounts of exchangeable sodium; so do some soils below that pH, for example, those relatively high in exchangeable sodium and hydrogen but low in exchangeable calcium.

Plants are partly responsible for differences in soil pH. Some feed very heavily on sodium, which they return to the surface. The reaction of soil under such shrubs may be more than one whole pH unit more alkaline to a depth of 2 feet than that of soil only 2 feet away. Other plants feed very heavily on calcium, and the decomposition of their remains tends to keep the soil neutral. Still other plants feed very lightly on bases. The decomposition of their remains tends to produce acidity in the surface of the soil.

This relationship is mutual: Plants that leave acid-forming litter usually grow better where the soil is acid. Those requiring lots of lime fail to thrive on very acid soils. Yet, as with all other soil characteristics, the relationship between soil pH and plant growth varies with other soil characteristics. Some beech trees, for example, usually grow on soils well supplied with lime, yet if all of the other growth factors are favorable, they grow well and produce an acid litter where lime is scarce.

Plant nutritionists have investigated the ranges in pH for optimum growth of nearly all common plants. Such values are useful but are not specific for contrasting soils. That is, the soil pH range for optimum growth of red clover, for example, appears to be lower in Podzols than in Gray-Brown Podzolic soils. We must recall that soil pH is a sort of average, or statistical, value for many separate points within the soil horizon. The same pH value, say 6.5, for two soil samples, may represent the average of two quite different ranges in pH within the soil masses examined.

Besides its great importance in soil classification, soil pH is considered with other soil characteristics as a basis for predicting the lime needs of acid soils. For most crop plants, pH 6.5 is within the optimum soil pH range. Generally, the plant nutrients needed by crop plants are most likely to be available at around pH 6.5.

The party chief needs to gather the best available information about crop and soil requirements for liming in his soil survey area in order to make interpretations for the soil survey report. These should be reviewed in cooperating agricultural experiment stations. Table 7 suggests some general guides[1], although in most developed areas better local guides may be had. Better recommendations can be made with values for both pH and for exchangeable calcium than with those for pH alone.

[1] From EFFICIENT USE OF FERTILIZERS, Ignatieff, V., ed., as cited in the General Bibliography.

MEASUREMENTS OF SOIL pH

Methods for determining soil pH are either electrometric or colorimetric.[2]

Electrometric methods are usually used in the laboratory. The pH meter with a glass electrode is the common instrument. If precise determinations are required in the field, especially where salts are likely to interfere, a field pH meter is available. A soil-water ratio of 1 to 1 is recommended for routine work. The suspension is stirred vigorously, allowed to stand for 30 minutes, and again well stirred immediately before making the measurement. For organic soils, a soil-water ratio of 1 to 5 is generally best, with a standing period of 2 hours.

Indicators or dyes that have different colors at different pH values are commonly used in the field. Only simple equipment is required.

TABLE 7.—*Approximate amounts of finely ground limestone needed to raise the pH of a 7-inch layer of soil as indicated*[1]

Soil regions and textural classes	Limestone requirements—		
	From pH 3.5 to pH 4.5	from pH 4.5 to pH 5.5	From pH 5.5 to pH 6.5
Soils of warm-temperate and tropical regions:[2]	*Tons per acre*	*Tons per acre*	*Tons per acre*
Sand and loamy sand	0.3	0.3	0.4
Sandy loam	....	.5	.7
Loam	....	.8	1.0
Silt loam	....	1.2	1.4
Clay loam	....	1.5	2.0
Muck	[3]2.5	3.3	3.8
Soils of cool-temperate and temperate regions:[4]			
Sand and loamy sand	.4	.5	.6
Sandy loam	....	.8	1.3
Loam	....	1.2	1.7
Silt loam	....	1.5	2.0
Clay loam	....	1.9	2.3
Muck	[3]2.9	3.8	4.3

[1] All limestone goes through a 2 mm. mesh screen and at least ½ through a 0.15 mm. mesh screen. With coarser materials, applications need to be greater. For burned lime about ½ the amounts given are used; for hydrated lime about ¾.

[2] Red-Yellow Podzolic, Red Latosol, etc.

[3] The suggestions for muck soils are for those essentially free of sand and clay. For those containing much sand or clay the amounts should be reduced to values midway between those given for muck and the corresponding class of mineral soil. If the mineral soils are unusually low in organic matter, the recommendations should be reduced about 25 percent; if unusually high, increased by about 25 percent, or even more.

[4] Podzol, Gray-Brown Podzolic, Brown Forest, Brown Podzolic, etc.

A number of satisfactory kits for field use can be obtained from firms handling scientific supplies.

[2] REED, G. F., and CUMMINGS, R. W. SOIL REACTION: GLASS ELECTRODE AND COLORIMETRIC METHODS FOR DETERMINING PH VALUES OF SOILS. Soil Sci. 59(1): 97–104. 1945.

Methods using indicator dyes can give satisfactory results with mineral soils between about pH 4.5 and pH 7.5. That is, an experienced operator should expect results within 0.2 to 0.4 units of the pH values determined electrometrically. Such results require care in getting representative samples and the avoidance of contaminations from perspiration, dust, chemicals, and the like.

Common specific indicators used in the field and their pH ranges are as follows:

Indicator	pH range
Bromcresol green	3.8–5.6
Chlorphenol red	5.2–6.8
Bromthymol blue	6.0–7.6
Phenol red	6.8–8.4
Cresol red	7.2–8.8
Thymol blue	8.0–9.6

Some field kits contain mixtures of the indicators.

In many soil survey areas numerous pH measurements are required. A few mapping units are separated mainly on the basis of pH determinations in some part of the soil. A few duplicate samples should be collected from time to time for immediate determination in the laboratory as a check on the reliability of the field-determined value, especially of soils having low or high pH value, excess salts, or abundant amounts of organic matter.

For an accurate estimation of soil reaction, samples for test are needed from different parts of the soil horizon, especially in one having well-developed blocky or prismatic structure. In a columnar B_2 horizon, for example, the soil may have a pH of 7 or less between the columns to a depth of 20 or 24 inches, and a pH over 7.5 just under the caps in the interior of the columns.

FREE CARBONATES

The presence of free carbonates in the soil and parent material may be tested for with 10-percent hydrochloric acid. In testing very dry soils, the emission of air bubbles should not be confused with slight effervescence. The reaction is indicated as slight, strong, or violent effervescence.

Dolomite is more resistant to the acid than calcite. Some time needs to be allowed for the acid to react, or the presence of dolomite may be overlooked. In some rock materials, a test of the powdered rock or the use of hot hydrochloric acid is necessary for the reaction.

It may be useful to note whether the effervescence is due primarily to fragments of limestone, to accretions or concretions of lime, or to the fine earth itself. The exact boundaries of effervescing material in relationship to structural aggregates and to depth are important. The pattern of free carbonates in the soil profile and in the parent material is a useful criterion for deciding between soil series. Where the presence of carbonates is doubtful or where quantitative results are required, soil samples may be sent to the laboratory for carbonate determinations.

SPECIAL FORMATIONS IN SOIL PROFILES

Special formations include such features as concretions, pans, efflorescences, and krotovinas. These features are important because of their influence on alternative uses of soils or especially because they often indicate soil qualities that are not directly observable in the field.

CONCRETIONS

Concretions are hardened local concentrations of certain chemical compounds that form indurated grains or nodules of various sizes, shapes, and colors. They are commonly formed from local accumulation of calcite (calcium carbonate), iron, and manganese oxides. Other minerals, such as bauxite, will readily form concretions but are not common in soils.

Lime concretions.—Lime concretions usually consist of calcite along with other included soil constituents. Many are irregularly rounded (fig. 45, right) and vary in diameter from a millimeter

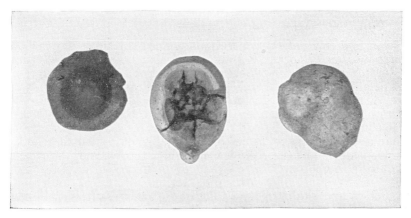

FIGURE 45.—The concretion on the left has been fractured to show concentric lamination. The center concretion has been broken to show its cavernous nature. The right concretion shows the irregularly rounded shape of the typical lime concretion.

or two up to as much as 2 feet. Some have more or less concentric laminations (fig. 45, left) ; others are cavernous (fig. 45, center). Yet lime concretions take many forms as spheres, ellipsoids, rounded shapes with pointed protuberances, rough and irregular forms, tubular or branched tubular forms, and rough plates.

The formation of lime concretions in soil is not perfectly understood, and care must be used in drawing conclusions from their presence. Since they presumably form when ground waters become supersaturated, they have often been considered **charac-** teristic of soils developed from calcareous parent materials under a subhumid or arid climate. Yet, they are not uncommon in soils of humid regions that have formed in postglacial times. Many Humic-Gley soils (Wiesenboden) in central and northern Illinois, for example, have horizons with abundant lime concretions of the cavernous type. Further, in drawing conclusions from the presence of lime concretions, it must be recalled that they may be forming now, under the present processes of weathering and soil forma- tion, or they may simply be inherited from the parent material formed under other conditions. Loess is a parent material which frequently contains lime concretions.

Often lime concretions are found near or even on the surface. Commonly this indicates truncation through erosion or soil blow- ing, but not always. Burrowing animals may have brought con- cretions to the surface from considerable depths. Many soils, especially heavy clays in regions of alternating wet and dry seasons, are "self-swallowing." During the dry season great cracks open up; then, with the coming of the rains, any dry, loose soil in the immediate surface is washed down into the cracks before they close. As the soil moistens and the cracks close, the lower soil between them is pushed up. Finally soil from the lower layers, possibly including concretions, appears at the surface.

Iron and manganese concretions.—Accumulations of iron and manganese oxides occur in a great many soils. Those in the form of indurated and irregularly spherical pellets are called concretions, or pisolites. They also take nonspherical forms. In the solum they may vary in size from less than 0.05 millimeter to 10 milli- meters or more. In deep layers they are occasionally much larger. The concretions usually show more or less concentric laminations. They are generally mixtures of soil materials cemented together by iron and manganese oxides. Roughly, the blacker the concre- tion, the higher is the content of manganese oxides. These concretions appear to develop under conditions of alternating reduction and oxidation; yet they are often present even in well- drained soils. Concretions are easily overlooked in field examina- tions of dark-colored soils, since they may be no larger than sand grains. The soil in clean-cultivated fields or on terraces may appear to have a higher concentration of small concretions than other similar soil simply because the beating rain has washed away the fine particles, exposing the concretions more clearly.

PANS IN SOILS

Horizons or layers in soils that are strongly compacted, indurated, or very high in clay content are often called "pans." They may be genetic, in the sense of having formed during and as a part of the present cycle of soil formation and weathering; or they may be relics of earlier cycles of weathering and are thus essentially a part of the parent material of the present soil. Other types of pans, accidental in relation to the present environment, may occur as noted below. The presence of a pan is of great significance to the use of many soils. The possibility of eliminating an adverse influence on root and water penetration through management practices depends upon its characteristics. Then, like other prominent horizons, pans are important indicators of genetic processes.

Indurated or cemented pans.—Massive, indurated or cemented pans are characteristic of many soils. Indeed, pans are essential horizons of soils placed in certain great soil groups, like Ground-Water Podzol, for example. Yet relict pans may occur at random, in relation to the existing combination of genetic factors. Layers of hardened laterite thought to be of Cretaceous age, for example, underlie some soils in Kansas, Nebraska, and northern Iowa at shallow depths. The common cementing agents of pans are iron, iron and organic matter, iron and silica, silica, silica and lime, and lime. Several instances of podzolic soils developing from Ground-Water Laterites formed in earlier geological periods have been reported.[1] Some of the laterite pans still show the original structure of the rock, even though its physical and chemical properties have been altered drastically. Such pans may even weather into flattened concretions suggesting the original shape of unaltered rock fragments.

Cementation by iron.—Cementation by iron is characteristic of layers of hardened laterite formed by the lowering of the water table in Ground-Water Laterite soils. Roots and water may penetrate soft laterite without serious difficulty. Indeed many of the hardened layers of laterite are permeable to water, and roots can often find their way through cracks and other openings. Hardened laterite layers may be present in a very wide variety of soils in tropical regions as an accidental feature in relation to the present environment.

Cementation with iron and organic matter.—The formation of pans cemented with iron and organic matter, called "ortstein," is characteristic of the Ground-Water Podzols and some Podzols. (Horizons of accumulation of iron and organic matter not accompanied by cementation are called "orterde.") The formation of these horizons is thought to be due to the mutual flocculation of the negative organic colloids with the positive iron colloids. Although ortstein forms within the zone of a fluctuating high water table, evidence exists that it also forms in soils of good drainage. Hilly Podzols with well-developed ortsteins, for example, are found on dunes and sandy moraines in the northern Lake States.

Cementation with iron, silica, or both.—Large areas exist having soils underlain with pans cemented with iron, silica, or both together. These pans are massive and structureless, and usually underlie a horizon of accumulated clay that is neutral to mod-

---

[1] See, for example, STEPHENS, C. G. PEDOGENESIS FOLLOWING THE DISSECTION OF LATERITIC REGIONS IN SOUTHERN AUSTRALIA. Australia Council Sci. and Indus. Res. Bul. No. 206, 21 pp., illus. Melbourne. 1946.

erately acid in reaction. Pans cemented with iron and silica are common on the gently sloping alluvial fans formed from acid alluvium in California. Pans cemented with silica are found on nearly level areas in the semiarid parts of Australia and may occur in the United States as well. The pans inhibit water and root penetration unless broken by blasting or other means. Adequate explanations of the development of these pans are lacking.

Cementation with silica and lime.—In depressional areas of arid and semiarid regions some soils have pans that are cemented with a mixture of silica and lime. The pan frequently underlies an alkaline horizon of clay accumulation. The genesis of these pans has received little attention. Extensive and continuous pans of this sort are important because they must be broken before irrigation can be successful. They must be looked for in arid regions because the natural soil may show little evidence of impeded drainage that may become serious with irrigation. Some of the deep ones, however, are not so impervious to water as they may appear to be.

Cementation with lime.—In regions where the rainfall is too low to remove all the soluble minerals from the soil, lime usually accumulates in the lower part of the soil. In some soils, lime accumulates as a soft powdery mass; in others it accumulates in concretions; and in some it accumulates as a pan. The formation of the pan is often associated with an intermittent high water table; although after a pan is once formed it may persist indefinitely even though the water table is lowered. These pans vary widely in their effects on soil drainage. Some hard ones seem not to cause much reduction in water movement; others do, especially if deep in the soil. The indurated accumulations of lime are known as *croûte calcaire* or, more commonly in the Americas, as *hardened caliche* or simply *caliche*. Where the accumulations are prominent and thick, and not hardened, they are known as *soft caliche*. Calichelike layers are present in some glacial gravels in regions as humid as Illinois and Indiana. Where the caliche layers are extensive and continuous they may inhibit the penetration of water and roots. Such caliche in soils of humid regions is not always continuous, but may be interrupted at intervals of several inches or a few feet.

Commonly, in the United States, the soft layers of accumulated lime carbonate, characteristic of most Chernozem, Chestnut, and Brown soils, are called lime horizons rather than caliche. The latter term is most commonly applied to the generally deeper and thicker accumulations that occur in soils of hot regions or warm-temperate regions like the southern Great Plains.

Nonindurated pans.—In gently sloping or nearly level soils of humid regions pans occur which are not indurated. Many such pans are sufficiently compact and slowly permeable to interfere seriously with root and moisture penetration. The presence of a slowly permeable pan near the surface greatly increases the erosion hazard of a soil under cultivation. After rain has saturated the soil above the pan, more rain causes the soil to become viscous and to flow, even on gentle slopes.

The pans high in clay content have customarily been referred to as claypans, while those low in clay and high in silt have been referred to by some as "siltpans." Many of these so-called "siltpans" are, in fact, sandy. Some regard them as primarily compact rather than cemented; yet they are no more compact than the upper part of the C in some soils from glacial till. Redeposited silica may contribute to their density and brittleness. Thus the name *fragipan* (approximately equals "brittle pan") has been given to them.

Claypans.—Claypans are compact horizons or layers rich in clay and separated more or less abruptly from the overlying horizon. Horizons that are high in clay content, either because of illuviation or by inheritance from clay-rich parent material, but that are not separated abruptly from the overlying horizon, are not universally considered to be claypans, although some authors refer to them as claypans.

The origin of a genetic claypan is often suggested by the presence in the bleached A_2 horizon of small nodular remnants of an old B_1 horizon. Generally, the minerals in genetic claypans have been strongly weathered. Commonly soils with such claypans are low in one or more essential plant nutrients, and many claypans have a relatively narrow ratio of exchangeable calcium to exchangeable magnesium.

Soils developed in alluvial materials, however, may have horizons very rich in clay or even claypans that are inherited from a stratified parent material. While such pans may be as effective as genetic claypans in retarding root and water penetration, the associated soils are quite variable in their supply of plant nutrients. Soils having inherited claypans vary in their nutrient supply with differences in the parent material.

While blasting has proved effective in ameliorating most indurated pans, it has had little lasting effect on the claypans.

Fragipans.—Fragipans are found in many gently sloping or nearly level soils in humid warm-temperate climates. These are very compact horizons, rich in silt, sand, or both, and usually relatively low in clay. Fragipans may or may not underlie or overlie a horizon of clay accumulation. They commonly interfere with water and root penetration. When dry, the compact material appears to be indurated, but the apparent induration disappears upon moistening. It has not yet been generally agreed whether fragipans are merely an expression of extreme compaction or are reversibly indurated. Fragipans are found in soils developed from both residual and transported parent materials.

EFFLORESCENCE

Efflorescence of salts refers to the occurrence of various salts in crystalline forms, as crusts, coatings, or pockets. The efflorescences of carbonates, chlorides, and sulfates of calcium, magnesium, and sodium are common. The efflorescence may occur on the surface of the soil and on vegetative remnants on the surface; as films on the walls of cracks or structural particles; as pseudomycelium, or thin, irregular veins thoroughly penetrating the soil mass; or as nodules or nests. Efflorescences are most easily seen following long dry periods. The deposits of the soluble salts occur at places where water evaporates and are proportional to the salt in the soil water and the length of time evaporation is active. Often salts appear on the margins of cracks in very heavy soils during drought and are washed down with the first rains. This accounts for the low salt content of the upper sola of some heavy soils in arid regions and the concentrations beneath.

KROTOVINAS

Krotovinas are irregular tubular streaks within one horizon of material transported from another horizon. They are caused by the filling of tunnels made by burrowing animals in one horizon with material from outside the horizon. In the soil profile they appear as rounded or elliptical spots of various sizes. They may have a light color in dark horizons, or a dark color in light horizons, and their other qualities of texture and structure may be unlike those of the main body of soil in the horizon of their occurrence. Common animals responsible for the presence of krotovinas are rodents and crayfish (Astacidae). The burrows of rodents are usually found in well-drained situations, and the burrows of crayfish in poorly drained sites. Krotovinas are a common feature of Chernozem and other dark-colored soils developed under grasses.

ORGANIC MATTER AND ROOTS

Organic matter and roots are noted in descriptions of the soil profile. Exact amounts of organic matter can be learned only by analyses of samples in the laboratory.

ORGANIC MATTER

The nature and content of organic matter are important characteristics of soils. Organic matter and its formation influence soil properties in many ways. The magnitude of the influence is usually far out of proportion to the quantity of organic carbon in the soil. Products of the decomposition of plant and animal materials hasten the weathering of minerals in the soil; and the vertical distribution of different kinds of organic matter in the soil often has a marked influence upon horizon differentiation.

Amount and distribution of organic matter in soils.—The total amount of organic matter in soils varies widely. Gray Desert soils contain only a fraction of 1 percent of organic matter in the surface layers, while Bog soils (peat and muck) consist largely of organic materials. The quantity and distribution of organic matter in the several soil horizons is a major criterion in classification. Commonly, soils have the maximum amount in the surface layer and decreasing amounts beneath; but most Podzols and many soils with claypans show two maxima of organic matter accumulation, one in the surface and a second in the B horizon or claypan.

The plant residues from which most soil organic matter is formed by decomposition consist of (1) litter, or those plant materials deposited upon the surface of the soil, and (2) roots that are formed and decay beneath the surface of the soil.

Estimates of the quantity of litter deposited annually vary from a few pounds to a few hundred pounds of dry matter per acre on the soils of arid regions, 1 to 2 tons under grass or deciduous and coniferous forests in temperate-humid or subhumid climates, and 10 to 20 tons in soils under tropical rain forests.

Litter from grass and tropical rain forests is rapidly decomposed and mixed with the surface mineral soil. In spite of the great amount of litter from the tropical rain forests, there is seldom an accumulation of more than an inch or two. Forested soils of cool humid climates usually have a rather prominent surface layer of only partly decomposed organic matter. This is particularly prominent in Podzols. The classification of these organic surface layers is based largely on the amount of mixing of the organic matter and mineral soil and the degree of decomposition. The names suggested by Heiberg and Chandler are generally accepted by foresters and soil scientists. Forest humus layers are classified in two main groups: *mull,* which is a humus-rich layer consisting of mixed organic and mineral matter, generally with a gradational boundary to the underlying mineral horizon; and *mor*, which consists of unincorporated organic matter that rests with little mixing on the underlying horizon.

Mulls are subdivided principally on the basis of structure into coarse, medium, fine, firm, and twin mulls. Mors are subdivided on the basis of decomposition and structure into matted, laminated, granular, greasy, and fibrous mors. In general, mull is common in many Gray-Brown Podzolic and Brown Forest soils, and mor in most Podzols and Gray-Wooded soils.

Various schemes have been used to designate the layers of organic matter that lie on the surface of the soil. Some use L for the freshly fallen litter, F (fermentation layer) for partially decomposed litter still recognizable as to origin and age, and H (humus layer) for rather completely decomposed litter unrecognizable as to origin.[1]

In the standard system of horizon nomenclature, the freshly fallen litter is noted as the A_{00} horizon, and the partly decomposed litter as the A_0 horizon. In detailed work the latter may be subdivided into A_{01} and A_{02} according to decomposition. Other letters, like L, F, and H, already referred to, and the words "mor," "mull," and the like are for use in the descriptions of horizons, as appropriate.

The quantities of roots that die in the soil each year are also variable. Accurate estimates of root production in the soil are wanting, partly because of the transient nature of some roots. Studies at various seasons of the year indicate that grasses have large root systems. Total roots (dry) of mature prairie grasses in temperate subhumid areas run as high as 5 tons per acre in the plow layer of soil. The roots of cultivated grasses are somewhat less, 2 to 3 tons per acre for bluegrass and 1 to 2 tons per acre for alfalfa and sweetclover. Such crops as tomatoes and peas rarely yield more than 500 pounds of roots per acre.

The distribution of roots in the soil profile bears some relationship to the distribution of organic carbon, although the relationship is not always linear.

Kinds of organic matter in soils.—Most mature plant residues are composed of a number of rather well known chemical complexes for which the loci in the plant cell and chemical and physical properties have been extensively studied. These compounds have been grouped into the following broad classes: (1) Sugars, starches, and simple carbohydrates, most of which are soluble in water; (2) hemicelluloses, pectins, and the like; (3) celluloses; (4) lignins and tannins; (5) fats, waxes, oils, sterols, and fatty acids; and (6) proteins and their derivatives. The chemical and physical nature of the complex products formed by partial decomposition or by synthesis in the cells of the decomposing microflora is not well understood, but there are many similarities and differences between these latter products and those from mature plant materials.

[1] Heiberg and Chandler, and Lunt, as cited in footnote 2, p. 178.

Some mature plant materials decompose more rapidly than others. This results from (1) differences in proportions in the various organic constituents, (2) differences in quantity of mineral nutrients, and (3) variations in the physical properties of the plant residues. These differences influence their palatability to the soil fauna as well as the manner and extent of direct attack by microfauna, bacteria, and fungi. In general, litter from broadleafed plants decomposes more rapidly than coniferous litter. The slower decomposition of coniferous needles results in part from the high resin content and the low water-absorbing capacity. Also, coniferous litter remains in a loose, well-aerated mass for a much longer period of time and does not pack with wetting. This makes the litter more susceptible to drying and results in frequent and extensive periods when decomposition is slow.

Some chemical constituents of plant materials are more susceptible to microbiological decomposition than others. In general, the water soluble constituents decompose most rapidly. The hemicellulose fraction, or those substances soluble in dilute acid or dilute alkali, also decomposes rather rapidly. The lignin fractions tend to be the most slowly decomposed of the major plant constituents.

The well-decomposed complex mixture of organic materials in soil is referred to as humus. This mixture represents the current point of equilibrium attained in a dynamic system in which decomposition is more or less continuous and in which periodic additions of fresh plant residues are made. It is quite unlikely that much of the original plant material exists in humus in an unchanged form except for a short period of time following the addition of fresh material. Most of the plant materials such as simple sugars, cellulose, hemicellulose, pectin, fats, waxes, and proteins completely disappear. Formed in the process of decomposition are numerous microbial cells and some other extraneous synthesis products, the chemical nature of which is in many ways different from the plant tissue. By far the greater part of the decomposed plant tissue is converted to carbon dioxide, water, and ash.

The decomposition process is strongly influenced by climatic factors. Optimum temperatures for mesophilic micro-organisms range from about 28 to 40 degrees centigrade. In general, plant residues decompose only one-sixth to one-third as rapidly at 12 as at 25 degrees centigrade.

The influence of moisture is likewise important. Dry plant residues will absorb 250 to 300 percent moisture. Decomposition is most rapid at these high moisture contents, provided the supply of air is optimum. Often under conditions of high moisture in the soil, air interchange is reduced and anaerobic conditions result. Under these conditions the rate of decomposition is slow.

Micro-organisms are not limited in activity at the same levels of moisture that limit plant growth. Reducing moisture to the wilting point for plants reduces the decomposition rate to only about one-third that prevailing under optimum conditions.

In studying the soil it is relatively easy to distinguish and to estimate the relative amounts of undecomposed and partially decomposed plant residues, particularly at the surface of the soil. It is much more difficult to estimate the total soil humus. Organic matter tends to impart characteristic colors to soils, but very serious errors may result if the amount of organic matter is estimated from the color of the soil alone. Within a small area where the kinds of organic and mineral matter are relatively uniform, color intensity may be used as a rough indication of the quantity of organic matter present. Between widely different climatic regions, however, color is not a useful criterion of organic-matter content.

The nature of the soil organic matter varies among the great soil groups. For example, the dark-colored organic matter of the Chernozem soils is high in lignin and protein and low in acid-extractable carbohydrates. The organic matter of these soils has a C–N ratio of roughly 10 to 12 and a high base-exchange capacity. In contrast, soils that may be equally high in organic matter but which have developed under forest vegetation in a humid or subhumid cool climate appear to have organic matter lower in lignin and proteins but higher in acid-soluble carbohydrates. (In plant analysis, the acid-soluble fractions include the celluloses and hemicelluloses.) The organic matter of these soils often has a light color and, in some soils, a strong chroma. Available evidence indicates a low base-exchange capacity. Variations in quality result partly from differences in the extent of decomposition. Generally, soils developed under forest vegetation in humid temperate climates have less organic matter than comparable soils developed under grass, although there are many exceptions; and the organic matter present usually has a wider C–N ratio.

Some important differences in degree of soil development seem to be related only to differences in vegetation. A Kauri Podzol of New Zealand, for example, with an unusually thick A_0, a very thick white A_2 horizon, and a dark reddish-brown ortstein, may be found only a few feet from a Brown Forest soil with no differences in genetic factors except the contrast between the kauri trees over the first and the broad-leafed trees over the second. Differences in the ash content of the litters hardly explain the effects; perhaps some powerful reducing compound is produced during decomposition of the kauri litter.

Relatively little is known about the composition of the organic matter in the soils of the humid tropics. They range in total organic matter from very high to very low. Some of the light-colored soils of the humid tropics are as rich in organic matter as many of the dark-colored Chernozem or Prairie soils of temperate regions, or even richer.

Organic matter and cultivation.—Many studies have been made of the influence of fresh organic matter on soil properties and crop yields. In general it is believed that the addition of fresh organic materials tends to increase aggregation and infiltration and to reduce erosion. The influence on crop yields depends on the crop, the kind of fresh organic matter added, and the amount of available moisture. Where materials high in available carbohydrate and low in nitrogen decompose, the nitrogen is temporarily immobilized by the soil microflora and crop yields may be reduced.

Systems of soil management have a strong influence upon the rate at which soil organic matter is depleted or accumulated. Plowing or other methods of distributing and mixing the soil to appreciable depths tend to hasten the decomposition of the organic constituents. The use of summer fallowing or other means of maintaining the soil at optimum aeration throughout the warm season provides optimum conditions for organic matter depletion. The culture of corn or other intertilled crops is nearly as destructive of organic matter as fallowing. On the other hand the growing of grass and deep-rooted legumes provides conditions which result in a higher stable level of organic matter. The favorable influence of grasses and legumes results chiefly because these plants provide large annual additions of fresh organic matter to the soil, which improves structure and nutrient balance, and because they permit leaving the soil relatively undisturbed for extended periods.

Exposure of the soil to the sun hastens the loss of organic matter, especially in the tropics.

ROOT DISTRIBUTION

Although a considerable body of knowledge exists about the distribution of plant roots in soils, it is inadequate for predictions about the needs of most cultivated crops. Certainly much more information is needed concerning the relation that the roots of many cultivated plants have to aeration, structure, compaction, and water- and nutrient-supplying capacity of the various soil horizons. Careful studies of plant roots in relation to detailed soil morphology are urgently needed as a basis for making better predictions concerning the adaptability of crop varieties to soil types.

To carry on their principal functions effectively, roots require soil horizons that are able to supply adequate water, air, and nutrients. Plant roots grow little in horizons lacking available moisture, or in horizons lacking nutrients, even if moisture is available elsewhere. The failure of plant roots to penetrate some soil horizons may be due to deficiencies of moisture, nutrients, or oxygen, or to extremely unfavorable physical conditions.

There are few soil horizons which some roots cannot penetrate. Ordinarily roots cannot penetrate the cemented pans, unless fractured, or the strongly developed fragipans. Although penetrated with difficulty by the roots of many plants, claypans do not prevent root development. Roots found in claypans usually follow cleavage faces and are often flattened by the pressures exerted by those faces. The failure of many roots to penetrate claypans is complicated by nutrient deficiencies and unfavorable pH.

A high proportion of the roots of most plants is in the upper soil horizons. With most grasses, from 65 to 80 percent of the roots live in the surface 6 inches, or plow layer. Some grasses are shallow rooted, and the roots are almost entirely in the upper part of the soil. Other grasses, although with a large proportion of their roots in the surface layer, have roots to depths of 6 to 10 feet, and in places, deeper. In general, the number of grass roots decreases with depth.[2]

The roots of many forest trees are also concentrated in the upper soil horizons. Some tree roots penetrate deeply, but with depth there is a gradual decrease in total root volume. The depth varies with species and soil. Some species, like oak for example, can penetrate deeply into soil that other species might find impenetrable. Generally the conifers have a higher percentage of roots in the very surface than hardwoods. In fact, in the Podzol region where the A_0 layer is thick, the roots of spruce and fir are concentrated largely in this layer and immediately under it. In cool moist regions these trees may be found growing on litter-covered hard rock.

The roots of plants have an important relation to soil structure. As the roots die, they leave food for bacteria and other microorganisms that are important to the maintenance of granular structure. This is, of course, true of deep roots as well as shallow ones. Oak roots, for example, can penetrate very heavy B horizons, even in soils where they grow poorly. Their direct effects, plus the slight movements during heavy winds, help maintain a blocky, or mixed blocky and granular, structure. When such deeply rooted plants are removed and replaced with shallow-rooted plants, the soil may lose its structure and become massive. A few years after the beginning of cultivation such soils may gradually become imperfectly or poorly drained during moist seasons.

Given favorable conditions, some plant roots penetrate to much greater depths than commonly believed. Grass roots penetrate to depths of 6 to 10 feet or more. Even corn plants have been known to remove available moisture to depths of 5 feet or more. Alfalfa roots can penetrate to much greater depths and remove available moisture to depths of 25 feet or more.

ANIMALS IN THE SOIL[3]

Notes may need to be made of insects, worms, and even larger animals in the soil that have important influences in mixing, changing, or moving the soil material. Animals contribute greatly to the decomposition of plant remains. In some soils worms and insects are chiefly responsible for the mixing of material between soil horizons, say A_0 with A_1, or A with B. In extreme instances huge termite mounds occupy over one-quarter of the surface area. Rodents sometimes cause a great deal of mixing of the soil. Colonies of prairie dogs, for example, even cause the formation of a characteristic microrelief.

[2] SHIVELY, S. B., and WEAVER, J. E. AMOUNT OF UNDERGROUND PLANT MATERIALS IN DIFFERENT GRASSLAND CLIMATES. Nebr. Conserv. Bul. 21, 68 pp. 1939.

[3] For several interesting examples, see EFFECTS OF CERTAIN ANIMALS THAT LIVE IN SOILS, by James Thorp, Sci. Monthly 67: 180–191. 1949.

ACCELERATED SOIL EROSION

In a broad geologic sense, erosion means the wearing away of the earth's surface by the forces of water and wind. The Dakota Badlands, the Grand Canyon of the Colorado River, the dunes of the Nubian Desert, and the flood plains and deltas of streams are striking results of such erosion.

Erosion is constructive as well as destructive. Through erosion and redeposition, unconsolidated mineral parent materials of soils are accumulated. Perhaps one-third of the population of the world gets its food supply from Alluvial soils and from young soils developing on alluvium. Geologically, erosion is the chief agent responsible for the natural topographic cycles, as it wears down the higher points of elevation and constructs alluvial plains in the valleys. In these valleys are a large part of the world's most productive soil. Gradually, erosion cuts drainage systems into wet level areas, making it possible meanwhile for arable soils to develop. Under the natural vegetation, especially in humid forested regions, natural erosion serves to maintain a degree of youthfulness and fertility in many soils by removing leached materials from the soil surface while new materials are added to the soil profile from beneath. On steep slopes, especially where the rock material is impervious or vegetation scanty, this removal is so rapid that little true soil forms—not until the slope has worn down to or below its angle of repose. On nearly level soils and some sloping ones natural erosion may be so slow that the older leached materials accumulate in the surface, hardpans or claypans develop, and the soils become and remain unproductive.

Natural erosion in the natural landscape may be either a gradual process, with a soil cover on the land continuously, or a catastrophic one. Once started in a new cycle of erosion—initiated by uplift, changes in climate, showers of hot volcanic ash that kill the vegetation, or other causes—a large part of the solum, or even the whole of it, may be removed rapidly. Reconstruction and the formation of a new soil then follows the stabilization of the landscape again. One may find buried soils characteristic of a set of soil-forming processes unlike those responsible for the present soil. Often only patches of truncated remnants are found that suggest catastrophic removal of an old soil prior to the formation of the present one. Thus some soil landscapes have had significant gradual erosion over a very long period; others have had relatively stable periods with little natural erosion, separated by periods of catastrophic erosion.

Commonly, in applied soil science and agriculture generally, erosion is used in a restricted sense. The terms "erosion" and "soil erosion" are often used for accelerated soil erosion, or that erosion of soil resulting from disturbance of the natural landscape, usually by man, in contrast to the natural, or normal, erosion that takes place in the undisturbed landscape. Accelerated erosion can result from exposure of the soil to runoff through burning, excessive grazing, forest cutting, and tillage, any of which destroy or weaken the vegetation. Exposed soil may erode very rapidly if it is not managed according to its limitations and requirements.

The distinction between natural erosion and accelerated erosion is an important one in soil survey work. Natural erosion is an important process in soil development. Its effects are reflected in the units of the natural system of soil classification. On the other hand, accelerated erosion truncates the soil profiles formed in the natural landscape. Significant differences in soil caused by accelerated erosion are shown on soil maps by means of erosion phases—subdivisions within the natural units of the system of soil classification. The criteria must be found in the soil. These are selected to indicate differences of importance to soil use and management. Accelerated erosion may also have altered soils enough to require a change in their classification as natural units. By removal of the moderate textured A horizon, a Cecil sandy loam may be changed to Cecil clay loam, eroded phase. With plowing, a new surface soil (A_p) is developed partly from the B horizon, rich in clay. To avoid confusion, a clay loam type of this sort may need to be separated from a normal clay loam type in the same series, should it exist.

Natural erosion and accelerated erosion are so combined in some cultural landscapes that it is difficult to sort them out, especially where the accelerated erosion is only slight. In long-cultivated areas, special short steep escarpments, called *taluds* (from old French), are gradually formed at down-slope field margins against hedges or stone walls. As the talud forms with the slow accumulation of soil wash from above, the soil slope of course decreases. A talud can scarcely be regarded as strictly man-made, since the stone wall or hedge was usually built as a field line and only incidentally gave rise to the talud because of the natural and accelerated erosion above it. In areas having fairly erodible soils, with a pattern of small fields, erosion may now be reasonably well stabilized with taluds that act as terraces to reduce the slope gradient and hence reduce runoff and accelerated erosion.

Occasionally accelerated erosion may shift a soil from one series to another. Usually, the differences between any such series in their original state were confined to the upper parts of the sola, so that with deep truncation the original differences disappear. The Monona series differs from the Ida, for example, in having a thicker and darker colored noncalcareous surface soil and a weak B horizon. With deep accelerated erosion that removes both A and B and mixes the remaining horizons, the Monona may become indistinguishable from the Ida. In such situations, the soil should be classed with the series that best describes it.

With very severe erosion, soil may have become so truncated that its distinguishing characteristics have disappeared. Such areas are classified and named with the appropriate miscellaneous land type, say Gullied land or Rock outcrop, rather than with phases of a supposed original soil type. Rough land with only a thin soil may suffer accelerated erosion. Even where the results are dramatic in appearance, the actual loss of soil may not have been great nor the productivity of the soil much if any changed.

The soil scientist must guard fully as much against exaggeration of accelerated erosion as against failure to recognize it where it is significant. Some have assumed, for example, that all the rocky, thin, sloping soils of the Mediterranean region were once deep and highly productive of crops, whereas actually only an undetermined part of them have suffered severe erosion; probably many of them have always been rocky, thin, and stony.

Erosion[1] processes can be divided into two classes, water erosion and wind erosion, according to the moving agent. Wind erosion is important primarily, but not exclusively, in subhumid, semiarid, and desert regions. Although in such common use that it can scarcely be avoided, the term "wind erosion" is not a good one for soil removal alone. Either "soil blowing" or "soil drifting" can often be used as appropriately and with less chance of confusion.

WATER EROSION

Water erosion results from the forces of flowing water and abrasion when runoff passes over soil surfaces on which the vegetation is not adequate to prevent detachment of soil particles. A part of the process is due to beating raindrops that detach soil particles from the soil mass and suspend them in the runoff. Besides that, soil particles splashed upward by raindrops beating on a sloping soil do not fall back evenly; instead, they fall a bit down slope. Then too, frost helps push particles down slope. Very wet soils can creep down the slope without going into suspension, sometimes even without great disturbance of the surface horizons. Descriptions of slips, slip scars, and other evidences of soil creep are essential to the descriptions of soil types and phases where they occur. Predictions of their formation under alternative uses are included as well.

Sheet, rill, and gully erosion are three forms of water erosion, distinguished by the relative depth and stability of the channels cut by the runoff.

Sheet erosion.—Sheet erosion is the more or less uniform removal of soil from an area without the development of conspicuous water channels. The channels are tiny or tortuous, exceedingly numerous, and unstable; they enlarge and straighten with an increasing volume of runoff. Rill erosion of short duration, obliterated by tillage, is usually included with sheet erosion in soil classification and mapping.

---

[1] For brevity, the word "erosion" is used in the sense of "accelerated water erosion" in the remainder of this section, unless otherwise specified.

To untrained observers, sheet erosion is less apparent, particularly in its earlier stages, than other types; actually, it is the most widespread. Although the evidence varies among soil types, sheet erosion can be recognized by the thinning of the surface soil layers, appearance of "galled spots" from which all the surface soil has gone, or the mixing of the B horizon into the plow layer, and by the accumulation of freshly eroded materials at the foot of slopes, along field boundaries and in drainageways, and in the lower parts of fields.

Sheet erosion may be serious on unprotected soils of only 1 or 2 percent slope, as on some highly granular Rendzinas or on Planosols with nearly impermeable claypans. Usually, however, it affects more sloping soils. On the other hand, cultivated well-developed Latosols may have little such erosion on slopes of less than 25- to 50-percent gradient.

Rill erosion.—Rill erosion refers to the removal of soil through the cutting of numerous small but conspicuous water channels or tiny rivulets that are minor concentrations of runoff. Although rill erosion is intermediate between sheet erosion and gully erosion, it is included with sheet erosion in soil classification and mapping. The shallow channels are easily obliterated by tillage; yet in the process the solum is gradually truncated, or shortened.

Gully erosion.—Gully erosion is the most conspicuous form of water erosion, often dramatic and picturesque. The removal of soil results from the formation of relatively large channels or gullies cut into the soil by concentrations of the runoff. The gullies develop in exposed natural drainageways or other depressed irregularities in the soil slope pattern, in plow furrows, animal trails, wagon ruts, below broken terraces, and between rows of crop plants that run up and down the slope. In contrast to rills, they are not obliterated by ordinary tillage. Deep gullies are not even crossable with the common types of farm machinery and form barriers that subdivide fields into small units, frequently too small for efficient farming. Although gullies are conspicuous, frequently for long distances and especially from aircraft, and locally destructive, gully erosion affects a much smaller total area of arable soil and does less damage on most farms than sheet and rill erosion.

Although the gully patterns vary widely on different soil types, individual gullies are of two general shapes: (1) Perhaps most common are the V-shaped gullies that cut down in the soil more or less uniformly throughout their courses. These develop in soils having coherent materials throughout, like the Westmoreland, Wellston, Miami, and Cincinnati series. Maximum gully depth is governed mainly by the depth to bedrock or other relatively unerosive material. In lithosolic soils, like the Muskingum and Porters series for example, gullies are generally shallower than in the associated zonal soils. (2) Also common are the U-shaped gullies that develop in materials of relatively low coherence, especially by undercutting of soft substrata at the gully head. The undercut, or cavernous U-shaped gully, results from surface water first cutting through coherent soil material into loose incoherent substrata that erode very easily. As the substrata undercut, the material above falls into the gully channel in great chunks that readily disintegrate and wash away. Soils underlain by thick deposits of loess, water-laid sands, deeply weathered granite (saprolite), or similar incoherent materials are subject to this type of gullying. Some of the soils in the Cecil, Memphis, Ruston, and Orangeburg series are examples. Some U-shaped gullies reach tremendous size, such as ones developed in Ruston and Orangeburg soils near Lumpkin in Stewart County, Ga.

Gully patterns in a soil series are often distinctive. The gully pattern of the Grenada soils (an intergrade between Planosol and Gray-Brown Podzolic from moderately deep loess) can be cited: In their early stages the gullies are V-shaped. If uncontrolled, they branch and grow laterally rather rapidly. Numerous small columns or "spires" form along their sides at or near the contact of the fragipan with the horizon above it. Eventually the columns wear away, and the individual gullies merge to form a nearly smooth eroded area separated from the ungullied soil above by a kind of bench or nearly vertical bank that may still have numerous small columns along its face.

WATER DEPOSITS

Deposits of water-eroded materials on soils are a direct result of water erosion of other soils. The deposits vary widely in character and significance. Some deposition is apt to occur at any place that the velocity of the water is reduced—at the mouths of gullies, at the bases of slopes, along stream banks, on alluvial plains, in stream reservoirs, and at the mouths of streams. The most rapidly moving water, when reduced in velocity, drops stones, then cobbles, gravel, sand, and finally silt and clay. Fine clay settles out of still water. Deposits of coarse fragments or sand on productive lower lying soils injure them for crop production. Uniform layers of fine-textured materials, rich in plant nutrients, are beneficial; they maintain the high fertility of many Alluvial soils in stream bottoms and deltas.

WIND EROSION

With a few exceptions, wind erosion in humid areas is not important, except locally in unprotected very sandy soils and in large tracts of drained and cultivated organic soils. Yet even in fairly humid regions with strong winds during dry periods, the soil scientist may need to deal with wind erosion in exposed places, not simply as a factor in soil classification and mapping but especially as a hazard to be described in his reports.

In regions of low rainfall, however, wind erosion is widespread and serious on cultivated soils, especially during drought. Unlike water erosion, wind erosion is commonly greater on level soils than on sloping ones. The hazard is increased by destruction of the vegetation through overgrazing or clean tillage that exposes dry loose soil.

During high winds the finer, and commonly more fertile, particles are swept high in the air and are sometimes carried for great distances as dust storms; while coarser particles are rolled or swept along on or very near the soil surface to be piled into ditches, along fences, or behind obstructions. Once an area is blowing badly during drought, the sand may drift back and forth locally with changes in wind direction, while most of the silt and clay goes far away. After the serious drought of the thirties, soils in barren fields in the south-central Great Plains had loamy sand or light sandy loam surface layers, in contrast to sandy loam or loam before the drought.

Blowouts, or spots from which the surface soil has blown away, may be associated with spots of deposition in such an intricate pattern that the two conditions can be shown only as a complex or by symbols. Commonly the wind blows out the surface soil in some areas and piles it up in others.

ESTIMATING EROSION AND MAPPING ERODED SOILS

Standards, or norms, for each soil can be established for reference in the estimation of erosion losses. In the natural environment the individual horizons and the solum of each soil have characteristic ranges in thickness. These values should be determined as accurately as possible. If the standards are to be useful and reliable guides to erosion losses, several precautions must be taken.

First of all, cultivation causes great differences in the thickness of solum of many soils where no erosion has taken place or is even possible. The upper part of many forested soils has a very high content of roots, even to one-half the soil volume. When these decay, the soil shrinks. Then too, upper horizons of many forested soils have a low bulk density, which increases with tillage. Emphasis has already been given to the importance of measuring the horizon boundaries and solum depth from the top of the A_1 horizon. It is especially important in setting standards for classes of eroded soils. The A_{00} and A_0 horizons should not be counted in such standards.

The difference between solum depth in virgin and cultivated areas of the same soil type can be illustrated with a Subarctic Brown Forest soil. The A_{00} may be 4 or 5 inches thick, and the A_0 some 3 or 4 inches. The upper 10 inches of solum contain abundant roots and have an exceedingly low bulk density. A superficial examination of the virgin soil might indicate a total depth from the surface of the A_{00} down to a gravel substratum of, say, 24 inches. Yet where the soil had been cultivated normally under good management without erosion, the depth to the gravel would be about 12 inches. This latter figure should be the standard against which to measure erosion classes within the soil type.

Similar changes can be expected in heavily forested Podzols. Smaller but significant differences are found in many forested soils. Removal of many stones lowers the surface. In other soils, of course, cultivation may not cause much, if any, difference in solum depth.

The depth of surface soil (A_p) cannot be used as a yardstick, because as a soil erodes, the plow cuts progressively deeper into the profile and the depth of the plowed layer (A_p) maintains a relatively uniform thickness. Nor can the thickness of the A horizon be used as a yardstick on all soils, since the A is not equally significant in all arable soils. Among Prairie soils, for example, the A_1 horizon is commonly more than a foot thick. In Brown Podzolic soils, the whole A—A_1 and A_2 together—is commonly not more than 2 inches thick. To base erosion classes on differences in the thickness of the A horizon in such soils would lead to absurdities. Thus the thickness of neither A_1 nor A can be used generally in all soils.

Comparisons also need to be made on comparable soil slopes. Near the upper limits of the slope range of a soil type, and especially on convex slopes, the depth of solum is normally thinner than near the lower part of the range of concave slopes. Thus the standards of solum thickness for different slope classes within the permissible range of a soil type are slightly different. It is an error to call that part of a soil type having slopes in the C class as "eroded" if the difference in thickness between the soil with C slopes and that with B slopes is characteristic for the soil type.

In many well-settled areas it is not possible to find satisfactory examples of virgin areas of all soil types, especially of the most productive ones. The standards are established by examining areas of cultivated soils of known management history that have no evidences of significant accelerated erosion or deposition.

Roadsides, cemeteries, fence rows, and similar small, uncultivated acres need to be avoided. By using them, some classifiers have made serious errors, generally in the direction of setting the standards for surface soil thickness far too high, thus seriously overestimating the erosion in the whole area. In naturally treeless areas, or in those nearly cleared of trees, dust blowing from cultivated fields collects in the fence rows, roadsides, and other small uncultivated areas that are covered with grass or other stabilizing plants. Such dust is often fine and productive. In a relatively short time the A_1 may become thickened by several inches.

Especially on Lithosols and lithosolic soils, the soil scientist may have difficulty distinguishing between accelerated erosion and normal erosion. Deep gullies, landslides, and slips are normal features of many natural landscapes. Yet such features may also be increased or even initiated by overgrazing, fire, or clean cutting of trees. Climatic changes have initiated new erosion cycles by weakening the vegetation in formerly stabilized landscapes, as in North Africa and in the southwestern part of the United States. Again, a few dry years, followed by heavy rains, may cause abnormal slipping; then during a moist period plant vigor is restored and the slip scars heal.

On many kinds of soil, including especially soils developing from relatively soft materials like mudstone or volcanic ash on moderate to steep slopes, slips are characteristic features, even in the natural undisturbed landscapes. After the scars form they are healed by the reinvasion of vegetation. Careful inspection may disclose that many soil slopes are simply a mass of such restabilized slips and scars. In assessing the influence of heavy grazing, for example, the observer needs to differentiate between an increase in the formation of slip scars in contrast to a decrease in the normal revegetation of such scars. In such soils the slips may be caused primarily by excessive moistening, perhaps aided by frost; and subsequent erosion on the unprotected scars may be caused by running water and wind. The proper description and interpretation of such conditions require the establishment of the typical situations for each kind of soil, which vary widely, as bases for estimating or predicting departures related to use and management.

In a region of rapid uplift, an acceleration of natural erosion is inevitable. The hazard of gully formation in arable soils increases. The scientist needs to recognize that areas of like soil have a different erosion hazard depending upon whether the local erosion cycle, in a geomorphical sense, is in its early stage or is approaching quiescence. Apparently a new period of erosion cutting had begun in the Piedmont area of the southeastern part of the United States, for example, just before its occupation by farmers. Thus the clearing of the soil and its use for row crops added to the natural process already started. One might say that "the gun was loaded and clearing pulled the trigger." The Atherton Tableland in Northern Queensland is a less dramatic example, among many others, of the same thing.

All sorts of complications arise with soil management. Burning the brush off sloping soils to encourage grass, for example, may stimulate several kinds of erosion—sheet and gully wash or slips. Yet if the soils are otherwise suited to grass and need only heavy dressings of phosphatic fertilizers for maintaining a vigorous cover, burning *and* fertilization may actually reduce the normal erosion. Much of the conflicting evidence about the effect of fire is due to failure to take account of natural fertility or fertilizer management. Thus, on the same kind of soil, brush firing plus fertilization (and reseeding if needed) may be an excellent practice, whereas brush firing alone may be a ruinous practice. Dressings of fertilizers on hilly pasture lands may greatly speed up the reinvasion of slip scars by grass.

Increasing the water percolating down into the soil by terraces or by irrigation can increase soil slipping and landslides on some soils.

Stream-straightening in a fairly well stabilized landscape may stimulate gully formation and induce a serious local erosion cycle. If a winding stream at a nearly stable grade is reduced in length by straightening, it may seek a new grade by cutting. If the materials are soft, the cutting pushes up the stream branches and even out into the fields.

The few examples cited in previous paragraphs illustrate the importance of making geomorphological study along with soil study. Each soil survey area presents its own problems. To evaluate the erosion conditions, to estimate the hazards of accelerated soil erosion, and to suggest appropriate uses of the soil where such hazards exist, the soil scientist needs to have a clear picture of the general erosion cycle, how it is changing, and what factors influence it. Topographic maps and standard texts are helpful. Geomorphologists or geologists have made special studies of some areas; yet in many survey areas the party chief will need to work out the relationships himself. He should strive to distinguish clearly between natural erosion and accelerated erosion, and especially between the erosion that it is not practical to control and that which can be controlled.

Erosion differences and their significance can be evaluated only in relation to individual soil types. Since soil conditions due to erosion are classified and mapped primarily because of their significance to soil use and management, no erosion class or category can have the same quantitative limits in terms of inches or percentage of solum or of A horizon for all soil types. Memphis silt loam, for example, a deep, permeable Gray-Brown Podzolic soil with a high water-supplying capacity, is injured much less by the loss of a given amount of surface soil than one of its planosolic associates, Grenada silt loam, which has a very slowly permeable fragipan at depths of 24 to 34 inches. Rarely is the number of inches of soil lost at a particular point within an area enclosed by boundaries a useful measure of the total soil lost or of the significance of the loss to the use of the area. That is, the pattern of erosion conditions in soil areas of mappable size is normally complex. In classifying and mapping erosion conditions, the pattern is nearly as important as the estimated proportion of the upper soil horizons lost. The classifier must recall that all mapping units are areas, not points. It is the area as a whole that is classified and mapped. The degree of complexity within mapped areas depends on both the irregularity of the erosion and the scale of the map.

With soils having clearly defined horizons, significant differences due to erosion are comparatively easily and accurately determined by reference to the cultivated norm; and good mapping guides for the classes or phases can be set up in terms of the pattern of exposures of B and C horizons and the number and size of gullies. Guides for soils with little or no horizon differentiation are more difficult to set up and harder to follow in the field. Lithosols derived from shales are a good example: After the thin surface soil is gone, little remains to furnish a clue for estimating original depth and the degree of erosion. For guides the classifier needs to rely on the relative amount and physical condition of the parent materials in the plow layer, the appearance of the coarse fragments on the surface, the number and shape of gullies, and like evidence.

Most soil types, although by no means all of them, within which classes according to conditions caused by erosion need to be set up and mapped, have distinguishable soil horizons. In estimating erosion the *whole* profile needs to be considered. Obviously areas cannot be classified on the basis of what is gone—not there. The mapping standards and guides must be based on characteristics that can be seen. Within many soil types, for example, it can be established that a particular kind of B horizon is associated with an average original depth of A horizon and of solum.

Erosion classes used in mapping should show present conditions and not be confused with susceptibility to erosion. This distinction is very important. The several kinds of soil mapped may be grouped, by interpretation, according to their susceptibility to erosion. But this is a different matter. The soil type, including soil slope class, where the slope of the type ranges beyond the limits of one slope class, is the unit for indicating susceptibility to erosion, except for subdivisions in those instances where the erosion that has taken place may have changed susceptibility to subsequent erosion. Erosion classes are intended to indicate only the erosion that has already taken place that is significant to management practices and yields as contrasted to management practices and yields for the uneroded soil or other erosion classes. At the same time, however, determining the susceptibility of each soil to erosion under alternative uses and management practices, on the basis of the best evidence available, including the results of experimental work on similar soils outside the survey area, is a prime responsibility of the soil survey party and is to be dealt with in detail in the soil survey report.

Study of each soil area is needed in mapping to avoid confusing actual erosion differences with the effects of differences in management. Two areas of the same soil type may be eroded comparably, for example, but one may have been smoothed, is now farmed properly without erosion, and has a plow layer (A_p) well supplied with organic matter; whereas the other is still gullied, perhaps idle, poorly suited to crops in its present condition, and gives the appearance of having lost much more soil.

EROSION CLASSES[2] AND SYMBOLS

Since classes of accelerated erosion are established and eroded phases mapped primarily because of their significance to soil use and management, and since a given amount of erosion has a different meaning on different soil types and in different regions, erosion classes cannot be defined in precise physical terms applicable to all soils. The number of erosion classes to be recognized and their definitions depend on the objectives of the survey, the significance of the erosion to present agriculture, the mapping scale, and the dominant plant cover. For some immediate objective next year, it may be possible and useful to map existing conditions resulting from erosion in great detail, whereas on a published map, only the more permanent ones should be shown.

---

[2] Although the term "erosion class" is used for brevity, reference is, of course, to classes of eroded soil, based upon the effects of the erosion.

A condition resulting from slight erosion might exist for a long time on undulating areas of many soils, say Memphis silt loam, for example; whereas it would be transient on a hilly erosive soil, like hilly Decatur silt loam, if used for row crops. A general sod cover, as in grazing and pasture areas, reduces the detail of erosion conditions that can be mapped accurately.

In evaluating the effects of erosion on a given soil type, as a basis for establishing the limits of an eroded phase of the type, the classifier needs to recall that erosion is usually accompanied by other factors of soil depletion and that the erosion may be only partly responsible for poor yields. In fact, if continuing cultivation is assumed, generally, although not always, low soil fertility can be regarded as a main cause of the erosion. Land users unable or unwilling to follow systems of management that prevent harmful accelerated erosion usually fail to follow the other practices necessary for optimum sustained production.

FIGURE 46.—Class 1 erosion. Slight erosion is obvious although the soil has been little changed. Cotton plants have just emerged.

Classes of erosion by water.—In the following the four classes commonly used to distinguish soils having had different degrees of water erosion are defined:

Class 1:[3] The soil has a few rills or places with thin A horizons that give evidence of accelerated erosion, but not to an extent to alter

---

[3] In survey legends, where many numbers and letters are used, these classes may be lettered as *m*, *n*, *p*, and *q*, for example, instead of *1, 2, 3,* and *4.*

greatly the thickness and character of the A horizon. Except for soils having very thin A horizons (less than 8 inches), the surface soil[4] (A$_p$) consists entirely of A horizon throughout nearly all of the delineated area. Up to about 25 percent of the original A horizon, or original plowed layer in soils with thin A horizons, may have been removed from most of the area.[5] In most soils, areas with this class of erosion are not significantly different in use capabilities and management requirements from the uneroded soil. In a few soils having very shallow sola over a nonconforming layer, or in a few having a shallow A horizon over a claypan or hardpan, a significant difference may exist (fig. 46).

FIGURE 47.—Class 2 erosion on Dunmore silty clay loam, Cocke County, Tenn. The surface soil in the light-colored areas is made up mainly of the original A, whereas the surface soil in the dark-colored areas is made up of a mixture of the original A and some of the B.

Class 2: The soil has been eroded to the extent that ordinary tillage implements reach through the remaining A horizon, or well below the depth of the original plowed layer in soils with thin A horizons. Generally, the plow layer consists of a mixture of the original A horizons and underlying horizons. Mapped areas of eroded soil usually have patches in which the plow layer consists wholly of the original A horizon and others in which it consists wholly of underlying horizons. Shallow gullies may be present. Approximately 25 to 75 percent of the original A horizon or surface soil may have been lost from most of the area (fig. 47).

[4] Surface soil refers to that ordinarily moved in tillage, or its equivalent in uncultivated soils, about 5 to 8 inches thick.
[5] The figures used here and for the other classes are only suggestive. Because of the great variations among soils in the thickness of their A horizons and in other characteristics influenced by erosion, somewhat different values must sometimes be used to define appropriate classes. The plowed layers of uneroded Brown Podzolic soils, for example, consist mainly of B horizon.

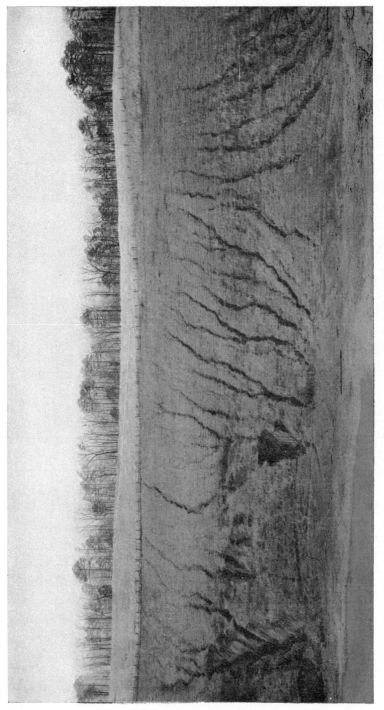

FIGURE 48.—Class 3 erosion. Gullies at the left require a gully symbol. Note the prominent rills that are obliterated in tillage. With further acceleration in erosion, these are likely to grow into gullies.

Class 3: The soil has been eroded to the extent that all or practically all of the original surface soil, or A horizon, has been removed. The plow layer consists essentially of materials from the B or other underlying horizons. Patches in which the plow layer is a mixture of the original A horizon and the B horizon or other underlying horizons may be included within mapped areas. Shallow gullies, or a few deep ones, are common on some soil types. More than about 75 percent of the original surface soil, or A horizon, and commonly part or all of the B horizon or other underlying horizons, have been lost from most of the area (figs. 48 and 49).

FIGURE 49.—Class 3 erosion. This photograph represents a soil area with very near the upper limit permitted within class 3 erosion. Knox County, Tenn.

Class 4: The land has been eroded until it has an intricate pattern of moderately deep or deep gullies. Soil profiles have been destroyed except in small areas between gullies. Such land is not useful for crops in its present condition. Reclamation for crop production or for improved pasture is difficult but may be practicable if the other characteristics of the soil are favorable and erosion can be controlled (figs. 50 and 51).

These four general classes need to be defined specifically and interpreted for each soil type. The significance of the change in soil characteristics depends upon the other soil characteristics. In ordinary basic detailed soil surveys, these classes are enough; although special needs may require subdivisions of a class. On the other hand, *individual classes should not be used as a basis for*

FIGURE 50.—Gullied land. This photograph illustrates the V-shaped gullies that develop in firm materials relatively rich in clay.

FIGURE 51.—Gullied land. This photograph illustrates the U-shaped gullies that develop in soils underlain with loose materials.

establishing phases unless the differences are significant to use and management.

In many instances, two classes are combined into one soil phase. For example, the four classes given are somewhat too narrow for defining phases of water erosion on most Regosols and Lithosols. Sheet erosion has little or no significance and is impossible to measure, even roughly, on very sandy Regosols. It is seldom practical, therefore, to map eroded phases of Regosols of this kind, but Gullied land may be defined and mapped for class 4; and elsewhere individual gullies can be indicated by symbols. For Regosols of heavier texture and for many, perhaps most, Lithosols, one eroded phase is generally adequate, since the lack of a well-defined B horizon makes it impractical to attempt to distinguish between erosion classes 2 and 3. In such soils, the eroded phase includes those areas of the soil unit from which most of the original A horizon has been lost and that have a plow layer consisting largely or entirely of material from underlying horizons.

With these and any other necessary modifications, erosion classes are used as a basis for eroded phases. For most soils, where accelerated water erosion is significant and all four classes need to be distinguished, the phase names of the first three classes are as follows:

> Class 1—Slightly eroded phase.[6]
> Class 2—Moderately[7] eroded phase.
> Class 3—Severely eroded phase.

Class 4 erosion is not normally recognized as a phase of a soil type or series but as the miscellaneous land type, Gullied land; and, where hilly, as Rough and gullied land. If significant to use, the name of the soil or rock material is added in parentheses to the name, as Gullied land (limestone material) or Gullied land (Ruston soil material).

Individual erosion symbols are used to indicate areas of eroded soils too small to enclose with boundaries on maps of the scale used but which are significant to soil use. Symbols are used also to show eroded phases of soils which are so small in total extent that named eroded phases should not be established in the legend. Each symbol is placed to show the location of the eroded spot accurately. Each is defined to represent a specific acreage, depending on the mapping scale and objectives of the survey. In a detailed survey with a mapping scale of 1:24,000, for example, each symbol ordinarily represents an area of 1 to 2 acres.

Definitions of symbols (pls. 6 and 7) used to indicate accelerated water erosion are as follows:

> The symbol *S* indicates sheet erosion significantly greater (one erosion class or more) than the average for the soil unit shown. For example, *S* in an area mapped Fullerton silt loam, hilly phase, indicates a moderately eroded inclusion.
> The symbol *SS* indicates sheet erosion greater by more than one erosion class than average for the soil unit shown. Thus, an *SS* in an area

---

[6] The word "phase" may be omitted from the name except where useful for clarity.

[7] The word "moderately" usually can be omitted.

mapped Fullerton silt loam, hilly phase, or Fullerton silt loam, slightly eroded phase, indicates a severely eroded inclusion.

The symbol *G* indicates a moderately gullied inclusion. The gullies are relatively shallow and on most soils can be obliterated with heavy tillage implements.

The symbol *GG* indicates a severely gullied inclusion too small to delineate as Gullied land. The gullies are too deep or too numerous for practical reclamation with the common heavy tillage implements.

The symbol *SG* indicates an inclusion of combined sheet and gully erosion significantly greater than average for the soil unit shown.

A wavy red line is used to indicate individual large gullies long enough to plot at the scale of mapping used, except in areas shown as Gullied land. If not crossable with farm machinery, the line is solid; if crossable a broken line is used. On detailed soil maps having a scale of 1:24,000, gullies about 300 feet long or longer are thus shown.

Water-laid deposits.—Associated with accelerated water erosion are recent deposits of local and general alluvium over other soils. Some of these soil areas are properly classified as soil types, some as miscellaneous land types, and a few as phases of soil types. As a general guide, overwash phases may be recognized in areas where the original surface soil is significantly altered but not changed enough to require the recognition of a different soil series.

Classes of erosion by wind.—The following are the definitions of three classes commonly used to distinguish eroded soils having had different degrees of wind erosion:

Class 1: Wind has removed from the soil a sufficient amount of the A horizon that ordinary tillage will bring up and mix the B horizon or other lower lying horizons with surface soil in the plow layer. Rarely is this condition uniform throughout a mappable area, however. Usually the plow layer consists mainly of the original A horizon in some patches, while in others the original A horizon is removed. Generally, about 25 to 75 percent of the original A horizon (or surface soil in soils with thin A horizons) may have been removed.

Class 2: Wind has removed all of the A horizon and a part of the B or other lower lying horizon. The plow layer consists mainly of the original horizons below the A (or below the original plowed layer in soils with thin A horizons), although some patches having much of the original A horizon remain in the area. An occasional blow-out area may be included.

Class 3 (Blown-out land): The wind has removed most of the soil profile and the land is classified as a miscellaneous land type. Use of the land for ordinary agriculture is not feasible without extensive reclamation. Blowout holes are numerous and deeply carved into the lower soil or parent material. Areas between blowouts are deeply buried by soil material from the blowouts.

Besides these classes for removal, two classes are used to define areas on which significant amounts of material have been deposited by wind:

Class 1a (Overblown).—Recent deposits of wind-drifted material cover the soil in layers thick enough to alter its characteristics significantly up to 24 inches. When the class is used as a phase, the soil type takes its texture designation from the new surface layer. For example, Baca fine sandy loam, overblown phase, consists of a Baca soil with a surface accumulation of wind-deposited fine sandy loam less than 24 inches thick. Thicker mantles usually, but not always, require series differentiations.

Class 2a (Wind hummocky).—Recent deposits of wind-drifted soil mate-rial in a fine pattern of hummocks or low dunes. The relief is less bold than that of Blown-out land. The soil materials have been drifted only locally, as contrasted to wind erosion classes 1 and 2, from which considerable soil material has been swept out of the mapped area.

As with water erosion classes, these classes serve as general guides to phases of soil types or series. Each needs to be defined and interpreted according to its local significance. With many soils these classes become phases named as follows:

Class 1.... Wind-eroded phase (or blown phase).

Class 2.... Severely wind eroded phase (or severely blown phase).

Class 1a.... Overblown phase.

Class 2a.... Wind-hummocky phase.

In class 3, wind has removed so much of the soil that the areas are included in the miscellaneous land type, Blown-out land.

Standard symbols are used for small areas of phases too small to enclose with boundaries. Each needs to be defined in terms of the area it represents (see pls. 6 and 7).

Other erosion classes.—Although the classes presented are ade-quate for most eroded soils, special classes may be needed in the definition of soil series and even for eroded phases. These in-clude slips, and combinations of slips with water erosion, or soil blowing, or both. The problem of defining such classes for de-tailed soil classification and mapping has not been studied sufficiently to suggest definitions. Yet the problem will arise in regions of grassy Tundra and elsewhere as detailed basic soil surveys are made.

EVALUATION OF EROSION EFFECTS

The soil scientist is not simply concerned to show on the map and assert in his report just what areas are eroded and how much. Erosion by itself, unrelated to the soil, means little or nothing. Tons or inches of soil lost through erosion have little general meaning in terms of soil productivity. The erosion of an otherwise productive soil shallow over bedrock, for example, seriously reduces its productivity and use capability; whereas certain deep soils may be deeply eroded without serious effects on crop production if the erosion is brought under control short of gullying. Many eroded soils were very poor for crops or pasture to begin with. The erosion of such soils does not greatly reduce their capability for use; yet the products from such erosion may contribute to stream silting, and the increased runoff may lead to local flood hazards.

Accelerated erosion has lowered the productivity of a great many soils. The effect is not necessarily permanent. Here again, the improvement of eroded soils, like uneroded ones, depends upon the soil type. Improved management not only restores the productivity in many instances but may also raise it above the level it had when first plowed. This is happening with many eroded soils in the United States and elsewhere.

It cannot be accepted that even dramatic-appearing erosion has destroyed the soil for crop production unless it has been established that the soil was suitable for crops before it was eroded. It may originally have been suited only to forest and may still be well suited to forest with proper management, even after it is eroded. Erosion is a symptom of poor soil use. Some have recognized the symptom and abandoned an impoverishing system of farming, say of row crops year after year, in favor of a system of sustained production with mixed farming and livestock. Since erosion results from poor soil use, it is usually accompanied by other factors of soil depletion that reduce productivity. Yields go down on uneroded soils, too, if they are mismanaged.

The development of tables giving predicted yields of adapted crops under an alternative, physically defined system of management is essential to a soil survey. Besides, the effects of these systems on the long-time productivity of each soil should be predicted. This matter is of special importance with soils subject to erosion.

Through farm study in the area and with the cooperation of other agriculturists, the chief of party needs to discover and explain in his report systems of farming or other uses under which accelerated erosion is avoided. Generally, the basic system of soil management—tillage, crop rotation, lime, and fertilizers—is of first importance; supplementary, where they are adapted, are strip cropping, contouring, use of terraces and small dams, and other practices for direct control of runoff and erosion. Soil erosion is treated most effectively when it is fully considered with all the other soil factors and management practices and least effectively when it is high lighted by itself or neglected.

EROSION HAZARD

It is commonly helpful to group soils according to their erodibility or the erosion hazard under defined sets of practices. Such a grouping is carried in soil survey reports in tables setting forth the principal characteristics and inferred qualities of the soils. Depending upon the information available and the detail that is significant, soils may be grouped according to erosion hazard into three classes as (1) none to slight, (2) moderate, and (3) high, or into five classes as (1) none, (2) slight, (3) moderate, (4) high, and (5) very high.

Meaningful groupings of soils according to erosion hazard are accompanied by descriptions of the sets of soil management practices and cropping systems adapted to them.

VEGETATION

Wherever possible the natural [1] vegetation should be recorded with the soil description. Correlations between vegetation and soil types or other soil classificational units have three important purposes: (1) For an understanding of soil genesis, since vegetation is one of the most important dynamic factors in soil formation; (2) for aid in recognizing soil boundaries; and (3) for making predictions about the kind and growth of natural vegetation from soil maps.

NATIVE PLANT ASSOCIATIONS

Where soil examinations are made, the dominant and associated species should be listed separately in the approximate order of their importance in the mixtures.[2] In forested areas, separate treatment is often necessary for (1) the forest trees, (2) the understory of small trees and shrubs, and (3) the ground cover of low bushes, herbaceous plants, mosses, and the like. Many soils have shrubs or low trees to be listed separately from the grasses and other ground cover. In describing forest trees an idea of the density of stand—as thin, medium, or dense—should be given. The range in size can be given in inches such as "6 to 12 inches dbh" (=diameter breast high), or "aspen 3 to 6 inches dbh with occasional seed trees of Norway pine 24 to 36 inches dbh."

In abstracting the separate descriptions into general ones for the soil type, series, or other unit, the appropriate name of the general plant association should be used, such as plains grassland, prairie grassland, desert shrub, oak-hickory forest, oak-pine forest, spruce-fir forest, tropical rain forest, and so on, together with the most important species of general occurrence. These descriptions should also include, where appropriate and useful, the descriptions of contrasting associations of successions related to cutting, fire, abandonment, and the like.

Common names of the plants may be used if such names are clear and specific. Yet many common names vary from place to place and are even used for different species in the same region. In areas of survey where the native plants are important to the use and interpretation of the soil map, lists of the plants mentioned in the soil survey report should be included that give both

[1] The term "natural" vegetation is used for wild plants in contrast to "cultural" vegetation, such as planted grains, grasses, and trees. Natural vegetation is a broad term for the associations of wild plants, and qualifying words are necessary to differentiate the "original natural vegetation" from successions following major geological changes, fire, plowing and abandonment, forest cutting, or severe grazing. Some use "native vegetation" in the same sense, and others limit this term to the indigenous species only.
[2] Emphasis is upon the important species only. In soil study, a few have a tendency to go further than necessary with the mere listing of both common and unusual plants.

271

common and scientific names. The plant identifications need to be checked by competent plant taxonomists, either in the field or from collected specimens.

Where a survey includes important areas of grazing or forest plants, the chief of party and his assistants need to learn both the common and scientific names of the principal plant species and the means of their identification. A temporary collection of identified grasses and other small plants and leaves from trees and shrubs can be maintained at field headquarters. Specimens can be placed between the leaves of large magazines and the names written on the margins of the adjacent pages.

RELATION TO SOILS

In soil survey reports and other reports of soil research, the characteristics of growth and the use of important native plants need to be described in relationship to the individual soil units and their management. The seasonal growth, rate and volume of growth, and palatability of the various species eaten by grazing animals are important. The results from research plots and the experience of ranchers are helpful in making such estimates by soil type or groups of similar soil types. The kinds and amounts of poisonous plants need special emphasis. These should be described in the soil survey report or references given to bulletins that do describe them. Present or potential invasions of weed plants on soil used for grazing should be explained.

Generally, close relationships exist between natural vegetation and soil types. Yet, there are important exceptions, especially among the azonal and intrazonal soils. Further, this relationship between vegetation and soil is complicated and confused by differences in cutting, grazing, fire, or management. *One cannot make a reliable soil map by studying vegetation alone, or even mainly.* Many are tempted to try because plants are far easier to observe than soil, especially where digging is difficult. With *both* careful soil study and plant study, excellent correlations have been established between natural vegetation associations and soil types, with adequately explained departures due to specific causes of interference, like fire and heavy grazing. But nearly worthless results have followed extensions of these correlations into other areas as a basis for making soil maps without thorough soil examinations.

Near the boundary between two plant associations, a seemingly minor factor in the environment may throw the association one way or another. Differences in exposure, wind, natural fires, and humidity are examples. Even only minor differences in soil or soil material sometimes, although rarely, account for important differences in the original plant cover.

Most important of all, the natural soil conditions under which the native plants are growing are often greatly unlike those that the farmer develops for crop plants. Differences in soils of great importance under irrigation, for example, may be little reflected in the native plants of the desert or semiarid grassland under the natural rainfall. Soil classification, and the development of predictions to go with the units, must take full account of the characteristics as they influence *response to management* as well as how they influence vegetation under natural conditions. Then, too, crop plants have different and generally greater requirements for plant nutrients than wild plants.

Natural vegetation, like the patterns on an aerial photograph, can be of great help to the soil classifier and mapper. But the use of either without complete soil examinations to the full depth of the soil profile is certain to lead him into the greatest of all difficulties for a soil scientist—a soil map without prediction value.

SEQUENCE OF VEGETATION

At the site of any one soil examination, the scientist can describe only what he can see of the current influence of the organic cycle at the particular spot. Yet by studying numerous sites on the same kind of soil under differing plant covers, he can develop important and useful principles of plant succession for each soil type. Such studies are important, as they permit some measure of the rate and direction of change in soil-forming processes. Their prediction value can be highly significant, as, for example, in areas where forest removal leads to an acceleration of gleying in soil types of impeded drainage that are otherwise suitable as arable land.

Such studies can be greatly facilitated by cooperation with forest and range ecologists, but still the soil scientist can develop the main principles himself by learning the land-use history of the sites he examines. It is often very important to be able to predict what trees follow cutting, for example, what follow cutting and fire, and what follow these, in turn, up to the climax forest. Similar principles are important in the grazing areas.

LAND USE

The land-use pattern at the site of each soil examination needs to be recorded with the soil description. Such notes are inadequate, however, for the development of a set of yield and management predictions. The additional studies required are explained in the section on Yield Predictions and Soil Management Practices. Here we shall deal briefly with the observations made in the field as the soils are examined and mapped.

As the mapping proceeds, kinds of crops and management practices on the different mapping units at representative sites need to be noted in addition to crops and management where the soil profile examinations are made. Enough observations are needed to describe the use and management of each mapping unit according to the following as relevant: (1) Common forest type and usual management of forested parts of the unit; (2) pasture and range use; (3) principal crops—kind, varieties, and rotations; (4) drainage; (5) irrigation; (6) contour cultivation and strip cropping; (7) terracing; (8) tillage practices; (9) use of lime; and (10) use of fertilizers. In addition, broad estimates of the proportion of each unit in various uses should be made.

Yields of crops and the carrying capacity of ranges can be estimated after study of measured plots or fields. Conversations with reliable land users offer opportunities for notes on yields and results of terracing, liming, fertilization, and other management practices. Such notes, however, are subject to the errors of faulty records and memories.

The detailed examination of yield records and farming systems is best made as a study separate from profile examination and soil mapping. Yet the careful observer can and does capture the essentials of the land-use pattern over which he walks while mapping soils.

LAND-USE MAPPING

In some soil surveys, where a special need exists, present land use is mapped at the same time the soils are mapped. Present land use should be mapped only where a clear need exists after weighing the greatly increased cost against the benefits. Such maps are transient at best. The land-use boundaries are very likely to be confused with the more important soil boundaries if placed on the same sheet, partly because some of them coincide and some do not. Where both soil boundaries and land-use boundaries appear on the same field sheet, the cost for cartographic assembly may be steeply increased. Further, it must be recalled that the field man can carry in his mind and remember to map accurately only a limited number of items. To increase the number of these unduly, often reduces the accuracy of all the work. Since the

275

broad classes of land use can be interpreted approximately from the aerial photographs anyway, land-use mapping often adds little of value to the standard basic soil survey.

Maps of land use in sample areas, with subclasses of cropland by crops, of pasture land by forage species, and of forest land by type, density, and size, may be helpful in developing predictions of soil-use capability, depending upon the other data available. By selecting representative sample areas, the relative acreages of crops can be related quantitatively to the individual soil types. If such data are to be most helpful, some notion of the intensity of management must be had also.

Where land-use mapping is necessary, it is almost always better to do it on a separate sheet in order to avoid confusing the boundaries and symbols on the soil map. A simple classification for the purpose follows:

L: Cropland, including rotation pasture. This class may include all inter-tilled crops, small grains, hay meadows, and apparent rotation pastures that are cleared and kept clear of brush and that receive soil amendments if required for plant growth.

O: Orchards. This class is used in fruit districts. Small plantings may be included with cropland.

P: Permanent and native pasture. This class is to include pastured areas that are plowable but not regularly used in rotation or that would require stone removal, additional clearing of brush or widely spaced trees, or other reclamation, before they could be plowed and used for tilled crops, and includes land regularly used for pasture that it would be impractical to reclaim for crops. Soil areas of brushy land pastured only intermittently may be included in this unit, or the unit may be subdivided.

X: Idle land. This unit includes land formerly used for crops and pasture, now abandoned and not yet reforested or put to other use. (In each survey area it needs to be defined in appropriate physical terms, because "idle" connotes an unmappable element—the owner's intentions.)

F: Forest. This class is to include (1) areas of land covered with a closed or nearly closed canopy of trees, at least some of which have present or potential value for lumber, pulpwood, or other economic use, and (2) areas of small trees and reproduction. Subdivisions may be required, together with estimates of stand, density, and size.

H: Urban. This class includes areas used for factories, warehouses, trading centers, houses, roads, streets, cemeteries, parks, and other public facilities.

There is a tendency among some to take present land use as something fixed in the soil, whereas it may be very far below the potential use because of economic and social factors outside of the soil. Undue concentration on present land use, including the condition of farm buildings, should never be allowed to prejudice the development of estimates on potential use and production.

UNITS OF SOIL CLASSIFICATION AND MAPPING

The examinations of the soils provide the basis for placing them into taxonomic and mapping units. Each mapping unit is identified on the map by a symbol; and each must have an identifying name within the general system of soil classification. Consistent nomenclature is essential for understanding the relationships and differences among the mapping units and for correlating the soil units with those found elsewhere in order to make use of the whole body of existing knowledge about soil genesis and behavior. Mapping units are therefore named in terms of the units in the taxonomic classification.

TAXONOMIC AND MAPPING UNITS

A taxonomic unit is a creation in the mind of man to facilitate his thought about objects in numbers so great that he cannot comprehend them individually. At a single site, the soil is examined vertically and horizontally in one place. The observer digs deeply enough to examine each horizon, including the parent material and any underlying strata that influence the genesis and behavior of the soil. The soil examination extends horizontally, in the third dimension, far enough for sampling. In relation to the whole three-dimension soil area, the places examined are little more than points. The number of such places could be almost infinite. The scientist groups the soils examined at these points into taxonomic units that have specified limits of variation. Each unit should be thought of as consisting of (1) a central core or nucleus—a single modal profile representing the most usual condition of each property of all soils in the class, and (2) many other closely related profiles that vary from this central nucleus within precisely defined limits. The same kinds of horizons are present in all of the profiles of the group and they occur in the same sequence. Such properties of these horizons as thickness, texture, structure, color, consistence, and pH vary within defined limits.

A soil mapping unit that bears the name of a taxonomic unit consists of this defined taxonomic unit and sometimes also small inclusions of other soils that must be included because of the limitations imposed by the scale of mapping and the number of points than can be examined. In other words, any single soil name stands for a specially defined unit in the taxonomic system of classification; but that *same name*, applied to a mapping unit, stands for that defined taxonomic unit plus a small proportion of other units, up to about 15 percent, that cannot be excluded in practical cartography.

Some mapping units are defined in terms of two or more taxonomic units which may or may not be associated geographically. The *soil complex* is a mapping unit, used on detailed soil surveys, which consists of two or more recognized taxonomic units. These may be similar or contrasting but occur together in a more or less regular pattern, and are so intimately associated *geographically* that they cannot be separated by boundaries at the scale used. Two or more recognized taxonomic units that are *not* regularly associated geographically may also be mapped as a single unit—an *undifferentiated group*—if the differences between them are too small to justify separate recognition for the objective of the soil survey. The steep phases of two or more soil types, for example, may be so nearly alike, because of the dominance of steep slope over the other soil characteristics, that their indication as separate mapping units would add too little to the information conveyed by the map for the objective of the survey to justify separation.

Taxonomic units at any level of generalization may be used as mapping units, provided the scale is large enough. In detailed surveys the soil type or soil phase is most commonly the unit of mapping; taxonomic units at higher levels of generalization in the scheme of classification are rarely sufficiently homogeneous for the objectives of detailed surveys. It is entirely appropriate, however, for some objectives, to use soil series, soil families, or great soil groups as mapping units, or, more commonly, as taxonomic units in complexes or associations used as mapping units. In most landscapes the use of great soil groups as mapping units reduces the detail of the map far less than it reduces the length of the mapping legend. That is, a large part of the boundaries between soil types in many areas are also boundaries between great soil groups.

In the preparation of generalized maps at smaller scales than those used in detailed mapping, limitations imposed by the scale nearly always require inclusion of two or more taxonomic units in each defined soil association. Such mapping units are defined in terms of the kinds, relative proportions, and patterns of distribution of the taxonomic units included in them. The level of generalization for these *taxonomic* units is generally the soil series or higher.

These distinctions between mapping units and taxonomic units must be clearly in mind in building a soil mapping legend. Attempts to set up each taxonomic unit as a mapping unit may lead to such great complexity, especially where the soils are used together in fields, that the final map will be less useful than one showing defined complexes. Where complexes are used, the component taxonomic units need as careful sampling and definition as if they were mapped separately.

Each mapping unit in the legend needs to be clearly mappable on the scale used. That is, each needs to be so defined that competent soil mappers can recognize the boundaries accurately on the ground, under the practical conditions of the survey, and have sufficient space on their field sheets or aerial photographs to plot them without distortion or confusion.

GENERAL GUIDE TO DETAIL OF CLASSIFICATION

The level of detail to seek in soil classification is always a difficult problem. First of all, categorical detail—the narrowness of definition and homogeneity of the individual classification and mapping units—should be clearly distinguished from cartographic detail, or the relative size of individual areas shown on the maps and the accuracy of boundaries. Categorical and cartographic detail are somewhat related. That is, areas of highly contrasting soils are separated on a map in greater detail than are areas of soils that are similar.

The classification in a detailed soil survey area must separate soils that are unlike in characteristics significant to genesis or behavior. That is, the applied purposes of the work must be served and genetically unlike soils separated. Two soils may be alike in all characteristics of the solum that reflect their genetic origin and determine their classification as genetic types and still they may vary significantly in use potentialities under a changed environment. The deep layers (D layers) may be important in irrigation or drainage, for example, or slight differences in slope or stoniness may affect the use suitability of forested soils for cultivation. On the other hand, a Brown Forest soil and a Gray-Brown Podzolic soil may appear to behave alike, in terms of present knowledge and experience, yet they should be separated.

The soil classificational units need to be sufficiently homogeneous for making whatever significant differential predictions the available principles and data of soil science, and of related sciences, permit to be made. Finer distinctions should be made only where sound scientific evidence exists for expecting that differential predictions will come with further research. This rule needs to be interpreted for each survey area in terms of the soil conditions to be dealt with, the objectives of the survey, and the information available from experience and scientific research—both within the area and on similar soils elsewhere.

The detail of classification in a survey area in the Chernozem or Chestnut soil regions, for example, is greater if the map is to be used for planning irrigation and for guiding farm practices under irrigation than if the map is to be used for guiding farm practices without irrigation. Special emphasis is given to combinations of soil characteristics that influence the movement of water on, into, and through the soil and the hazards of salinity. Units need to be defined somewhat more narrowly in relief, microrelief, depth of solum, character of underlying strata, structure and texture of horizons, permeability, exchangeable bases in horizons, salts, and drainage. The classification must set forth clearly the soil areas significantly different from one another after irrigation as well as before, and also show definitely the soil areas that need special practices for drainage, salinity control, runoff control, fertility maintenance, and the like.

In survey areas that have special problems of drainage, runoff and erosion control, or fertilizer use, certain mapping units may need to be more narrowly defined than has been customary prior to the recognition of these problems or the development of methods for dealing with them.

THE SOIL SERIES

The *soil series* is a group of soils having soil horizons similar in differentiating characteristics and arrangement in the soil profile, except for the texture of the surface soil, and developed from a particular type of parent material. The soils within a series are essentially homogeneous in all soil profile characteristics except texture, principally of the A or surface horizon, and in such features as slope, stoniness, degree of erosion, topographic position, and depth to bedrock where these features do not modify greatly the kind and arrangement of soil horizons.

The soil series by itself is seldom used as a mapping unit in any survey. It is not sufficiently homogeneous in such features as soil slope and stoniness for the objectives of most detailed soil surveys; and it rarely occurs alone in areas large enough to serve as a unit of mapping on more generalized maps. The series name, however, is the key to the majority of soil characteristics possessed by the soil types and phases used in detailed mapping. The series brings the units of mapping together in an organized manner to help us remember soil properties and the relationships among soils.

Soil series are differentiated mainly on the basis of significant variations in the morphological features of the soil profile. These features include mainly the kind, thickness, and arrangement of horizons, and their structure, color, texture (except texture of the A horizon), reaction, consistence, content of carbonates and other salts, content of humus, and mineralogical composition. A significant difference in any one of these properties in any one horizon may be the basis for recognizing a different series. Very rarely, however, does one soil series vary from another in just one of these characteristics, for the characteristics are genetically related and several usually change together.

Since relief is one important genetic factor, partly responsible for the characteristics of the profile, and since shape is a property of the soil body, each soil series has a defined range in slope. This range is very narrow in some soil series and wide in others. The width of the permissible range in a soil series depends upon the range over which no important difference is reflected in the soil profile under the native vegetation. Where variations in soil slope have practical significance but no significant effect on the behavior of the soil in its natural environment, they are recognized as *phases,* defined later.

It is not easy to make a hard-and-fast rule covering reasonable variations in properties within the range of a soil series. If every single observable characteristic in two soil profiles had to be identical to permit placing the two in the same soil series, every profile examined would be a separate series, for no two profiles are identical in all respects. Some variation in thickness of the individual soil horizons must be expected. Some variation in every property must be allowed. From the point of view of applied soil science, it might be said that mappable differences of importance to the growth of native or crop plants should be recognized. Inasmuch as soil science does not have at its disposal complete knowledge of all of the relationships between soils and plants, however, this principle cannot be accepted as the only criterion, since soils with different potentialities would be put together. As applied soil science has progressed, the enormous practical importance of soil differences, thought to be only of academic interest a few years previous, have been demonstrated again and again. Moreover, the uses of soil survey information for purposes other than those associated with the growth of plants are increasing in importance. Soil characteristics important to engineering problems, for example, are becoming increasingly recognized; and not all of the properties important in engineering are equally important to the growth of plants.

The guiding principle in separating soil series might then be revised to include all differences in the soil profile. This cannot be accepted entirely, as some characteristics can be determined only with great effort and may not be worth the time and expense involved. To illustrate: Two soils in the Gray-Brown Podzolic group may have similar profiles except that the C horizon of one has a pH of about 7.5 due to the presence of calcium carbonate, whereas the C horizon of the other has a pH of about 5.8. These soils should be separated, even though some trouble is involved. Such a difference is important to the growth of some deeply rooted crops, and it is likely that this difference is also associated with other related accessory characteristics. From a practical point of view such a separation is important to applied soil science and agronomy. On the other hand, suppose a similar difference in pH exists between two soils associated with the normal Gray-Brown Podzolic soils but developed on subnormal relief and characterized by a deep claypan or hardpan above the parent material. With these soils the agronomic importance of the difference is less than that between the first pair, because plant roots probably could not penetrate to the underlying material. Moreover, the difficulty of making the examinations necessary to separate the two soils is greater. From a practical point of view the separation would probably not be justified if no consistent external feature could be associated with this internal characteristic.

A further restriction on the mapping of different soil series is that characteristics on which the differentation is based must be mappable. Some differences may be so difficult to determine that the time and expense involved in separating two soil series based upon them cannot be justified for the objectives of the survey. As hard-to-recognize characteristics become more important to the purposes for which the soil map is to be used, a correspondingly greater expediture of time and money for separating soils according to these characteristics becomes justified. In some soil regions only very skilled and experienced soil scientists can recognize consistently the soil differences that are obscure to the layman but that have great importance to soil management systems. Physical characteristics of the lower solum from which drainage and permeability may be inferred are examples.

From what has been said, it is clear that precise rules governing exactly what characteristics are considered differentiating between series, or exactly what ranges of these characteristics may be allowed within a series, cannot be laid down for all conditions. Generally, it may be said that those observable and mappable properties which are known to have, or are likely to have, significance in soil genesis, in the growth of native or crop plants, in soil management, and in soil engineering are to be considered. With field experience and with appreciation of the findings in plant nutrition, soil management, and other relevant fields of research, the judgment of the soil scientist becomes tempered. Some special considerations are discussed in the following paragraphs, but differentiation between soil series must depend upon the experience of the scientist and the advances in soil science.

All of the profiles within a series should be developed from similar parent materials. The parent material of soil is produced from rock materials through the forces of weathering. Similar parent materials may be produced from different geological deposits and in different ways, and unlike parent materials may be produced from the same rocks because of differences in weathering. It is the character of the parent material itself which is important. Still, significant characteristics of parent materials that cannot be seen in the field can sometimes be inferred from those of the parent rock. It is not necessary that the original rocks or the manner in which unconsolidated parent material is accumulated be uniform throughout a series. The mineralogical composition of the parent material is the most important characteristic, but in addition, such features as porosity, permeability, texture, and degree of assortment must be considered.

From the definition of a soil series, it might be assumed that texture could be allowed to vary within a series only in the A horizon. Strict adherence to that concept would mean that a very large number of series could consist of only one soil type, since a close relationship commonly exists between the texture of the parent material and the textures of other horizons in the solum besides the A. With a large number of monotype series, the usefulness of the series as a tool for understanding the relationships among soils and remembering characteristics becomes small. It is necessary, therefore, to allow some range in texture of parent material, and this is commonly reflected in a range of textures in the B horizons. The very great range in texture, even from sand to clay, that was at one time permitted within a series is no longer allowed. We know now that such great differences are generally associated with important differences in the other properties of the solum. Texture is a characteristic that carries with it many accessory properties, and the range of texture allowed within a series is governed by its effects on the magnitude of variation in other important characteristics.

It is difficult to set up a general guide to govern the number of series to be established mainly on the basis of texture of the parent material. Soil texture does not have the same significance in all soils. Differences of significance in well-drained soils may not be significant in poorly drained soils. Then too, differences in drainage, mineralogy, and other qualities are often associated with variations in texture. Three subdivisions within the range from sand to clay could be sufficient if the drainage is essentially the same and if the sands, silts, and clays are of similar mineralogical composition. These would be soils on very sandy parent materials, soils on medium-textured parent materials, and soils on very clayey parent materials. Yet such comparable conditions in the separates are rarely met over a wide range of texture.

The exact limits of textural classes included in any one series must be determined by the way in which the soils occur and the importance of texture and its co-varying accessory characteristics for the objective of the natural classification of soils.

Separate series have been established on the basis of land form alone. This has been done, for example, in glaciated regions as a means of differentiating between kames and outwash terraces that consist of similar materials. If the morphology of the solum is different in the two situations, recognition of two series is justified. If the sola and the properties of the parent material are similar, however, the soils should be recognized as members of the same series and differentiated as phases. That is, land form alone is not sufficient to separate soils into different series. Usually, however, other soil characteristics are associated with differences in land form.

The soil series names are place names taken from the area where the soil is first defined, such as Miami, Hagerstown, Mohave, and Houston. In the early days of soil surveying many soil series were given very broad definitions; in fact, so broad that after the soils had been more thoroughly studied and understood, it became necessary to split some series into two, or even several, series. For example, several soil series are now recognized for soils included with the Miami and Marshall series as first defined. Although the Marshall soils were first mapped in the Marshall area (Lyon County, Minn.), subsequent investigations have shown those soils to be significantly different in many ways from those given the same name elsewhere. Since the name had been used most widely in Iowa, Missouri, and Nebraska, it was retained for the soils in that region, and some of those in Minnesota were renamed Barnes. Similar situations have developed throughout the United States as our knowledge about soils has increased. This development has caused a certain amount of unavoidable confusion, as soils shown on the older maps do not comform to the later, more precise definitions.

In the American system, these proper names have been used rather than purely genetic terms, like "weakly podzolized loams from glacial drift," since no connotative name could be long enough to define the differentiating characteristics accurately enough for detailed classification and mapping without being hopelessly unwieldy. Then, too, changes in theories of soil genesis —and these have been substantial over the last 30 years—would cause confusion. The standards for series must be written in terms of the morphology of the profile and the landscape. These standards are implied in the series name. Genetic names in addition to the series names, subject to revision, are appropriate and helpful to supplement, but not to replace, the series name.

As the same place names frequently occur in several parts of the country, care must be taken in correlation to prevent the use of the same name for unlike soils. In the field-mapping legend, each proposed series is given a place name and the soil is defined. If a doubt exists about the identity of any of the series previously defined, local names are used during the progress of the work. In the final correlation soils belonging to previously established series are given their proper names.

As the number of series has increased, there has been a certain amount of resistance to the establishment of new ones. Where this reluctance has been based on consideration of sheer numbers alone, it has led to delay in recognition of new series where significant differences occur. Failure to recognize a new series on this basis alone only causes confusion. The variation in nature is fixed; failure to recognize it in no way reduces its magnitude, and the resultant units are rendered less useful by reason of their heterogeneity. There should be no hesitation in the establishment of a new series when needed. Every effort should be made, however, to differentiate at the level of the soil type or soil phase, rather than the soil series, provided such differentiation is based on sound principles of classification. It is only by making the fullest use of the type and phase that the soil series can serve its most useful purpose as a means of remembering characteristics and understanding relationships among soils.

ALLUVIAL SOILS[1]

Special problems arise in the definition of series of Alluvial soils, which do not have sequences of genetically related horizons. Materials laid down by water commonly have layers that differ greatly in such characteristics as texture, but the occurrence of those layers is governed by geological processes and is accidental insofar as genetic relationships of the soils to the present environment are concerned. If every difference in the occurrence of such layers were used as a basis for separating series, an almost infinite number of series could be recognized among Alluvial soils alone. This would defeat the purpose of the soil series. As

---

[1] Admittedly this is a poor term since it refers *not* to "soils from alluvium" but only to the young soils in flood plains and deltas actively in process of construction and which have no developed characteristics beyond those inherited from the alluvium itself. Perhaps it would be better to reserve the term for those people who wish to speak loosely of "soils from alluvium" and coin a new word for the soils referred to here.

a general rule, the differentiation of series on the basis of texture in Alluvial soils should be based on the texture of the material of the subsoil but not of the plowed layer or of the deep substratum. From three to five series are generally needed on otherwise similar materials to cover the entire range of textures of the subsoil. Where five series are required on the basis of the texture of the profile or permeability of the subsoil, the following classes may be used:

(1) Very gravelly or stony subsoil, generally nonarable.
(2) Gravelly and very rapidly permeable subsoils but with some fine materials.
(3) Coarse-textured rapidly permeable subsoils.
(4) Medium-textured moderately permeable subsoils.
(5) Fine-textured slowly permeable subsoils.

Where three series are adequate to cover the range, the following classes may be used:

(1) Light sandy loam and coarser subsoils.
(2) Heavy sandy loam to light clay loam subsoils.
(3) Heavy clay loam and clay subsoils.

Where significant among Alluvial soils, a soil in which the subsoil rests unconformably on material of different texture should be designated as a phase of the appropriate soil type of the recognized series, i.e., Huntington silt loam, moderately deep over sand. A soil in which an unconformable layer different in texture from that of the subsoil makes up the plowed layer should be designated as a type of the series.

Depth classes.—The upper limit and the lower limit of a depth class, applied to any one soil, are fixed in definite figures. These limits need to vary somewhat among soils depending on the other soil characteristics. Still, the words "shallow" and "deep" should have approximately the same meaning everywhere.

The following outline of depth classes, applicable to all soils, not simply Alluvial soils, gives the ranges within which the upper and lower limits of depth classes may be set:

	Ranges in limits	
	Upper (inches)	*Lower (inches)*
1. *Very shallow*	0	5–10
2. *Shallow*	5–10	20–30
3. *Moderately deep* (or moderately shallow[1])	20–30	30–50
4. *Deep*[2]	$\begin{cases} 30\text{–}50 \\ \text{or} \\ 30\text{–}50 \end{cases}$	$\begin{matrix} 50\text{–}60 \\ \\ 60+ \end{matrix}$
5. *Very deep*[2]	50–60	60+

[1] "Moderately shallow" is used where the contrasting layer is nearer the surface than typical for the kind of soil.
[2] The very deep class is rarely required. Where it is needed, the deep class has a lower limit somewhere between 50 and 60 inches.

Specific limits within these ranges are established for individual taxonomic units as required. In the description of a *mapping* unit, any necessary inclusions of soils ranging in depths beyond the established limits are described.

In the classification of Alluvial soils in arid and semiarid regions, absolute values in common use are *shallow*, less than 20 inches; *moderately deep,* 20 to 36 inches; and *deep,* more than 36 inches. In a few situations *very shallow,* 0 to 10 inches; or *very deep,* below 60 inches, are used.

Other characteristics.—Significant variations in mineralogical composition and reaction of the subsoil material are suitable criteria for differentiation among soil series in the Alluvial group. Differences in color and origin of soil material may be used as indications of such differences in composition if laboratory research confirms such correlations.

Differences in drainage that lead to distinct differences in morphology of the soil should be bases for differentiation of series. If they are not reflected in soil morphology but are important from the standpoint of land use and crop adaptation, they should be differentiated as drainage phases.

Concentrations of soluble salts may be used to differentiate among series where those concentrations have greatly affected the morphology of the soil and its consequent adaptation to reclamation or irrigation. If the physical morphology is not appreciably affected, such conditions may be differentiated as phases.[2]

Physiographic position, in itself, is not a satisfactory criterion for differentiation among series. Such features of the landscape may be important from the standpoint of frequency of flooding but they should be differentiated as phases. Even Alluvial soils commonly have some characteristics that reflect the climatic zone in which they occur, even though a well-defined sequence of genetic horizons has not developed. Where such distinct morphological characteristics as reaction or content of organic matter are reflections of differences in climatic zones, separate series should be recognized. Separate series should be set up only where distinct morphological differences occur.

SHALLOW SOILS AND LITHOSOLS

Shallow soils and Lithosols also pose special problems in the differentiation among series, partly because the thinness of their sola dominates over other characteristics. Where bedrock occurs near the surface, the entire sequence of horizons may be affected. Genetic horizons may be weakly expressed. Different series are recognized for the shallow and deep soils from similar kinds of parent material. In some soils, however, bedrock at shallow depth merely cuts off the profile at the bottom. The horizons characteristic of the upper part of deeper soils may be present and as well expressed in the shallow soils as in the soils on deep materials. In such series, the shallow soil should be recognized as a phase of the deeper soil, even though the horizon at the bottom of the typical solum is absent or partly lacking. Classes of soil depth are set forth in the preceding discussion of Alluvial soils, and the phase names to use are given on pages 297-8.

---

[2] See section on Estimation and Mapping of Salts and Alkali in the Soil.

THE SOIL TYPE

The soil type is a subdivision of the soil series based on the texture of the surface soil. The soil-type name consists of the series name plus the textural class name, determined primarily by the texture of the upper part of the soil. In soils with well-developed profiles the texture of the A horizon determines the class name. Where the A horizon is thin or poorly developed, the average texture of the upper 6 inches (or approximately equivalent to the cultivated surface layer of arable soils) is the basis for determining the textural class name.[3]

The class name of a type should not be determined by the texture of a horizon deep in the profile. Such a practice leads eventually to identical names for two soils that are quite different. For example, a soil on glaciolacustrine clays may be characterized by silty clay loam texture throughout the profile, but within the area, due to unconformable layers in the parent materials, a soil with a silty clay loam plowed layer and a silt loam subsoil may occur. The soil with silty clay loam texture throughout the profile would be named a silty clay loam on the basis of the texture of the plowed layer. To differentiate between this soil and the one with the silt loam subsoil, the second might be named incorrectly a silt loam. Then, should a third soil, with a silt loam plowed layer and a silty clay loam subsoil, be found, it would also be named a silt loam of the same series; but there would be significant differences between the two in use and management. The soil with the silt loam subsoil should be recognized as a separate series, or, if it is of small extent, as a *variant*, and named appropriately.

It is not suggested that no difference whatever other than the texture of the upper part of the solum exists between soil types within a series. The textural class names of two types in the same series are determined from the upper part of the solum, but at the same time the texture may vary somewhat elsewhere in the soil. To illustrate: the surface soils of Plainfield sand and Plainfield fine sand have sand and fine sand textures. The same textural differences commonly carry down through the sola, thus giving the Plainfield fine sand a slightly higher moisture-holding capacity than Plainfield sand. Except on stratified materials—and there are many of these—it is normal to expect that small differences in texture of the B and C horizons will be associated with differences in the texture of the A horizon. Such differences must not go beyond the allowable range for the series, except for variants.

Formerly, and perhaps even to some extent now, soils were placed in the same series and differentiated on the basis of texture, when actually the soils belonged in separate series. Miami silt loam and Miami loam, for example, have a silt loam and a loam texture, respectively, in the upper part of the sola. The B and C horizons of Miami loam have, on the average, a

---

[3] In some countries, New Zealand for example, the texture of the A horizon determines the textural class name of the type, even though thin.

lower percentage of the fine separates than comparable horizons of Miami silt loam. For many years it has been assumed that the other characteristics of the soils are similar, except for differences in consistence commonly associated with the differences of texture indicated by the class names of the types. It seems now that the differences in structure and consistence, as well as in permeability and drainage, may be more important to soil use than formerly suspected. Not only that, the original parent material of the Miami soils, although mainly calcareous glacial drift, was partly calcareous glacial drift overlain by wind-blown silts. Thus, part of the Miami silt loam, according to the older definition, has the characteristic lower solum and parent material, and part of it has the lower solum and parent material characteristic of Miami loam developed from till without any covering of wind-blown silt. This example illustrates the great difficulties that will often arise in future soil correlations if series differences are designated as type differences within a broadly defined series.

In the early work, textural class names, or types, were used to separate soils that really belong in different series. This can be illustrated by the Norfolk series. This series, named from Norfolk, Va., was established about 1900. During the next 30 years it was mapped in all the states along the Atlantic and Gulf coastal plains from New Jersey to east Texas. It included deep sands with little or no horizon differentiation, shallow sands resting on sediments with some clay in them, and zonal soils with well-defined horizons. An effort to restrict the Norfolk series to yellow and gray sandy soils led to the redefinition of the Sassafras series in the late twenties.

Later, the Norfolk series was further restricted to well-drained Yellow Podzolic soils and Lithosols (Regosols) with yellow substrata. In the forties, the Norfolk was redefined and split into three series, since the range of soils included within it extended far beyond a series as then and now defined.

The Norfolk is now retained for soils of the Red-Yellow Podzolic group with sand to fine sandy loam upper sola and finer material at around 18 inches (or at 24 inches for thick surface-soil phases). Lakeland includes soils with sand to sandy loam textures down to fine material at 30 inches or deeper. Kershaw includes sands without underlying fine material of influence on the solum. Previously all of these were included in Norfolk, using both type and phase names to indicate conditions that are more properly series criteria.

Among soils developed from stratified parent materials, questions frequently arise as to what differences should be expressed by type or phase and what by series. For example, suppose a soil has developed mainly from lacustrine clay and, in places, is overlain by varying thicknesses of unconformable sand. Where the sand layer on top is about the thickness of the plowed layer, the soil should be indicated as a sandy type of the series that includes the soil that is clayey throughout. As the sand layer on top becomes thicker, however, the question arises as to how much of the soil must be developed from the sand before it is placed in a different series. In this example, since the outstanding characteristic of the series is the heavy clay, at least a significant part of the solum must be developed from the clay for the soil to be included as a type within the series.

With Bog soils, the textural class names used with other soils are not applicable, and there are no type designations in a strict sense. In Bog soils having well-decomposed surface soils, the designation *muck* is used after the series name; and those which do not have well-decomposed surface soils are called *peat*. This muck surface soil may be developed by soil-building forces from peat or may be inherited from parent material. Thus, the complete soil name of a Bog soil consists of the series name plus the word "peat" or "muck." Intermediate types are called *peaty muck* or *mucky peat*.

The soil type is the lowest and most nearly homogenous unit in the natural system of classification. A soil type may include defined variations in such characteristics as slope, stoniness, degree of erosion, or depth to bedrock or layers of unconformable material. To be allowed within the soil type, soils cannot vary in these features beyond the range of significance to the genesis of the natural soil under the native vegetation in the natural landscape. Yet within the permissible ranges in these characteristics of the soil type are variations of great importance to the use and management of soils. Consequently, the soils included within a soil type may range widely in their suitability for use or in their management requirements. One phase of a soil type may be suitable for intertilled crops, though a steep phase of the same type may be suited only to pasture. The soil type is a most useful unit in the classification of soils, for in it all of the important properties of genetic horizons are held to a minimum of variation; yet for making predictions to use in farm planning and for similar objectives, only those types that have no significant ranges in characteristics affecting use and management are satisfactory units for use in detailed mapping.

The importance in defining the ranges of *all* relevant characteristics permitted within both soil type and soil series can scarcely be overemphasized. Certain variations within soil types are shown by phase, but this should not cause the soil scientist to overlook these characteristics in the definition of series and types. The classes for slope, erosion, stoniness, depth, and the like apply in the definitions of series and types as well as in those of phase.

THE SOIL PHASE

The *soil phase* has been most commonly used as a segment of a soil type. Recently, the concept of phase has been broadened so that it may be defined as a subdivision of any class in the natural system of soil classification, but it is not itself a category of that system. Any class of any category, such as type, series, family, great soil group, suborder, or order, may be subdivided into phases. The basis of subdivision may be any characteristic or combination of characteristics potentially significant to man's use or management of soils. When used as a subdivision of a soil type, which is by far the common use, the phase is defined and shown on the soil map on the basis of all of the characteristics of the soil type, of which it is a part, but with a narrower definition in certain features of importance to soil use than are differentiating for the genetic soil type. Any subdivision of a soil type based on such features is the equivalent of a soil phase, whether or not it is recognized as such in the name, or whether the word "phase" is used in the name. Except for monophase soil types, the phase of a soil type on detailed maps is the unit about which the greatest number of precise statements and predictions can be made concerning soil use, management, and productivity.

Differences in the texture in the upper part of the soil sufficiently important to be recognized in mapping are indicated by textural class designations in the name of the soil type. Similarly, important differences in structure and other characteristics of the solum, including texture of the subsoil or parent material, are recognized by series definitions. The most common bases for differentiating among phases within soil types include variations in soil slope, degree of erosion, physiographic position, contrasting layers in the substratum, depth to bedrock, stoniness, and salinity that have not influenced soil morphology significantly.

The authors should like to give the reader the opportunity to consider other current suggestions about the relationships among soil series, soil type, and soil phase, even at the risk of introducing some confusion. Some have tentatively proposed that the units now called soil phases in currently published detailed soil surveys and in this *Manual* be called soil types. Thus a soil type could be any significant subdivision within a soil series, whether differentiated by texture of the surface soil, slope, stoniness, or any of the other features used to define phases as explained in the following pages.

In some ways this would simplify the nomenclature, as illustrated in the discussion of stoniness. It would be a great break in custom. Most people are accustomed to associate soil type with only the texture of the surface soil within a series. Much research is already reported on that basis.

The interested reader can study the question himself. Such a change would have little or no effect on the classification or mapping. It would change the nomenclature slightly and require redefinition of the traditional categories used in detailed soil classification.

SOIL SLOPE PHASES

Each soil type has its own characteristic range in slope. Any marked departures are associated with other characteristics that determine soil series. With some soil types or series, the permissible range in slope is narrow—within one slope class; with others, it is wide enough to include differences that are important to soil use and management. In these, the slope range of the type either extends beyond that of one slope class or the class itself may need to be subdivided in highly detailed mapping. Phases of soil slope are established to separate such parts of soil types or other classificational units.

The characteristics of soil slope are discussed in the section on Land Form, Relief, and Drainage. The classes, by soil slope gradient, are defined and named on pages 162-4, together with the limits of each class. These classes are used in describing all classification units, and the names are used as phase names when needed. In increasing order of slope gradient, the phase names are repeated here; names in parentheses are those to use where needed in very detailed mapping that requires subdivisions of the major classes.

		Names
A class:		
	Single slopes	*Level* (or *Level* and *Nearly level*).
	Complex slopes	*Level* (or *Level* and *Nearly level*).
B class:		
	Single slopes	*Gently sloping* (or *Very gently sloping and Gently sloping*).
	Complex slopes	*Undulating* (or *Gently undulating* and *Undulating*).
C class:		
	Single slopes	*Sloping*[1] or (*Sloping*[1] and *Strongly sloping*).
	Complex slopes	*Rolling* (or *Gently rolling* and *Rolling*).
D class:		
	Single slopes	*Moderately steep*.
	Complex slopes	*Hilly*.
E class:		
	Single slopes	*Steep*.
	Complex slopes	*Steep*.
F class:		
	Single slopes	*Very steep*.
	Complex slopes	*Very steep*.

[1] "Moderately sloping" may need to be substituted for "sloping" for clarity.

With soil types and series that have differences in soil slope significant to soil use and management, phases are separated at the *significant* gradient or percentage of slope for each unit. These definitions of specific slope phases vary widely among soil types, depending upon the other soil characteristics. That is, the sloping phase of one soil type may have soil slopes between 5 and 10 percent; another, slopes between 8 and 16 percent; and still others, slopes somewhere between. The phase names need to fall within the definition of the soil slope classes outlined on pages 162 to 164. Mapping units, including phases, may include two soil slope classes. Such soil slope phases carry compound names, as "level and gently sloping."

Soils vary widely, for example, in their erodibility on different slopes. The division lines among the slope classes, especially in relation to erodibility may not have the same values in terms of percentage of slope for different soils in the same region. Usually, however, it is not advisable to adjust the slope limitations to individual phases on the basis of any single quality, such as erodibility, alone. That is, the sloping phases of some soil types may be erodible under intertilled crops, whereas sloping phases of other soil types are not. The Decatur soils of Tennessee and Alabama, for example, are highly responsive to management but quite erodible—more so than the Clarksville soils, which are low in productivity. Thus for the phase names to be uniformly associated with the practices required for erosion control, the definitions of soil slope classes could be broader on the Clarksville than on the Decatur soils. On the other hand, and with nearly equal justification, soil slope classes might be more narrowly defined on the Clarksville than on the Decatur if the boundaries were chosen on the basis of the intensity, or inputs, of management needed for the optimum production that would return the costs for runoff and erosion control.

Although the soil classifier can make some adjustments of his phase definitions within the general classes of soil slope, he cannot hope to make all his slope phases bearing the same name similar in erodibility, in erosion hazard, or in management recommendations for the control of erosion. The erodibility of some soils increases as the degree of erosion increases. Thus the eroded phase of a soil type may be more subject to additional erosion than the uneroded phases. It simply is not possible to lay down any general rules for defining slope phases in general, beyond those given in the definitions of the major classes of soil slope already referred to. The soil classifier needs to weigh all of the characteristics of a soil type and all the available information about its response to management and make the definition so that mapping units will carry the most specific information and predictions.

Then too, he must consider the practical limitations of carrying on the soil survey work. It simply is not practicable in ordinary mapping to attempt accuracy within 1 or 2 percent of slope in rolling or forested country; nor is it practicable to have minor differences in definition of slope phases for similar soils. The party chief cannot count upon his assistants remembering an enormous number of such distinctions and mapping them accurately.

It is important that slope distinction among series, types, and phases be consistent with the natural conditions of soil slope. In the northeastern part of the United States, for example, the line between B and C slope classes comes at 8 percent in many soils. The major portion of the soil areas of a few soil types in this region falls below 3 percent in slope gradient, and the rest has a range from about 6 to 10 percent. With such soils, the 8-percent dividing line would result in a large number of soil areas with gradients only a little below 8 percent being placed in the B class and an equally large number of similar areas a little above 8 percent being placed in the C class. The differences in interpretation of the phases thus defined would not be consistently significant, partly because of the impracticability of measuring the slopes that closely. Thus the boundaries of the soil slope phases should be placed at 3 and 6 percent, with (1) areas below 3 percent of slope, (2) areas with 3 to 6 percent of slope, and (3) areas above 6 percent of slope to the permissible upper limit for the soil type.

In setting up all units, and perhaps more especially phases, the classifier must always remember the ultimate objective is producing a soil map that can be clearly interpreted for predicting crop adaptations and soil management practices. In humid regions, soils are used in three principal use groups: Cropping, grazing, and forestry, in the order of their decreasing intensity. Certainly the boundaries among soil areas having different potentialities for these uses need to be interpreted from a soil map. Soil slope is an important factor in defining these boundaries.

Some study of soil slope is required in advance of defining the soil types and phases accurately in terms of gradient. The definition of the classes must first meet the requirements of significance to the objectives of the survey. They must be defined so that boundary lines are readily recognized in the field. With the units definitely established, soil slope in percentage should be determined by means of a hand level (fig. 24) or other suitable instrument. When the range of slope of the unit has been determined, the slope limits in percentage are added to the definitions of each mapping unit and are used as criteria for differentiation during the progress of the survey.

In the final correlation of detailed soil surveys, slope phases are named as subdivisions of soil types. In addition to the phase names already outlined, it is usually helpful to add the actual limits of slope in percentage. Formerly, one slope phase of a soil type that extended over two or more classes of soil slope, generally the most extensive one, was selected as typical for the soil type and the fixed designation was omitted in the name of that unit. This makes it difficult for some to interpret the soil map from the legend alone, unless the figures for slope are given too, since the typical in some instances would have the least slope and in some the most. Further, the type name stands on the map for two units (1) the whole soil type with all its phases and (2) a slope phase within the type. On the map and in the report, the soil type name should stand for the entire type with all its phases. This does not mean, however, that the word "phase" needs always to be added. The word "phase" may be omitted from the name of the unit wherever that can be done without loss of clarity.

The classification of soil slopes provides for naming both complex and single slopes. Usually the distinction between these is inherent in the definition of the soil series. In only the most highly detailed soil maps for special purposes should attempts be made to separate phases within the same soil type and having the same slope class on the basis of one having complex slopes and one having single slopes.

ERODED SOIL PHASES

Significant differences within the natural soil classificational units—types, series, families, and great soil groups—brought about by accelerated erosion are recognized by phases of eroded soil. Where such erosion has destroyed the essential profile features of the soil, the area is, of course, classified in some other unit—some miscellaneous land type.

Conditions caused by normal or natural erosion, characteristic of the soil unit, are not shown in phases but are a part of the definition of the natural unit. Nor are eroded phases used to indicate erodibility or erosion hazard—a quality that depends on the whole set of soil characteristics that define soil series.

The determination of erosion in the field and the definition of the classes of eroded soil are explained in the section on Accelerated Soil Erosion. The translation of these classes, described on pages 261 to 268, into taxonomic and mapping units depends upon their significance to the use and management of each individual soil type. Most soils with class 1 erosion, for example, are not significantly different in use capability and management requirements from the uneroded parts of the soil types. Yet with a few soil types having thin sola over strongly contrasting material or thin A horizons over a claypan or hardpan, class 1 erosion may be significant, if all factors were favorable to intensive use and some of them have been changed by erosion.

The important guiding principle to the number of eroded phases and their definitions is the need to recognize mappable differences in soil use capability caused by the erosion that has already taken place, and not to make more phases than necessary to bring out these differences. If a tentatively established eroded phase turns out to have the same recommendations for use and the same estimated yields for the same crops as another phase or as the uneroded soil, it should be eliminated and the definitions redrawn to include it with a similar mapping unit. The principle is the same as it is with the translation of classes of stoniness or of soil slope into phases. Definitions of the phases need to be adjusted so that the boundaries on the maps will separate (1) soil areas of unlike use capabilities and (2) soil areas of unlike management response and requirements.

The classes described on pages 261 to 268 have been developed after long experience with widely different soil types. Within the general definitions, specific definitions of phases should be developed for each soil type. In any one soil survey area, of course, several soil types will turn out to have similarly defined eroded phases.

Symbols to use in the mapping legend for significant areas of eroded phases too small to be enclosed with boundaries are shown in the plates of standard symbols and explained in the section on Accelerated Soil Erosion. Each symbol needs to be defined in terms of both the conditions it represents and the area one symbol represents.

For a large part of the arable soils, the eroded phases are defined in terms of the classes of eroded soil. For very detailed soil surveys these phases may be subdivided if the need exists. Sometimes they need to be combined into complexes for the establishment of mapping units.

Water erosion.—Water-erosion phases of eroded soil are as follows:

Slightly eroded phase[4]: Used only for a few soils where the erosion has changed the soil enough to require a little but significantly different set of management practices for sustained production than that used for the uneroded soil. This is usually class 1 erosion.

Moderately[5] eroded phase: Used where erosion has changed a soil to such an extent that it requires a set of management practices different from the set used for the uneroded soils (or slightly eroded phase, if established) but where erosion has not changed the use-group capability of the soil for crops, pasture, or forestry. The distinction is made by comparing the management practices made necessary by the effects of the erosion with the practices needed to prevent erosion on the uneroded soil. Usually this is class 2 erosion, but sometimes, especially with lithosolic soils, classes 2 and 3 are combined.

Severely eroded phase: Used where erosion has so altered the soil that (1) it has a different use capability, say pasture instead of crops, or forestry instead of pasture or crops, or (2) it needs drastic treatment, such as improvement of tilth and substantial fertilization, and perhaps terracing or contouring, with or without the need of filling small gullies, to be maintained in the same use group as the uneroded soil. The distinction is guided by comparing the management practices made necessary by the effects of the erosion with the practices required to prevent erosion on the uneroded soil. This is commonly class 3 erosion, rarely class 2 erosion, rarely class 4 erosion, and sometimes classes 2 and 3 erosion combined.

Gullied land: Used for land on which the soil profile has been destroyed except for small patches between the deep gullies and which is not useful for crops and pasture without extensive reclamation. This land type may be subdivided by slope and by kinds of soil or parent material where significant. Gullied land, Decatur soil material, or Sloping gullied land, limestone material, are examples.

Wind erosion or soil blowing.—Phases of wind-eroded soils are as follows:

Wind-eroded (or blown) phase: The wind has removed soil to such extent that a set of management practices significantly different from the set used on the uneroded soil is required. Its use-group capabilities have not been substantially changed. If originally capable of use for crops, it can still be so used with proper management. Usually this is rated class 1 wind erosion.

Severely wind-eroded (or severely blown) phase: The wind has removed material to such extent that the soil can be used for crops only if it is extensively reworked and a set of management practices unlike that for the uneroded soil is used. It may be useful for permanent grasses or trees, depending upon the climate and the other soil characteristics. Usually this is class 2 wind erosion.

Blown-out land: The wind has removed nearly all of the solum. The land is barren or nearly so. It usually cannot be used for crops without extensive levelling and special management, but stabilizing trees or grasses, depending upon the other soil characteristics and the climate, may be established. Usually this is class 3 wind erosion. (See under the heading Miscellaneous Land Types.)

Depositions.—Phases for depositions are as follows:

Overblown phase: The deposit of wind-removed material lying on the soil is great enough to influence management but not great enough

---

[4] The word "phase" may be omitted from the name unless needed for clarity.
[5] The word "moderately" is omitted unless needed to differentiate between this phase and other eroded phases.

to destroy the essential characteristics of the soil series. Such a soil takes its textural class name from that of the overlying material. (See class 1a, p. 267.)

Wind-hummocky phase: Recent wind deposits lie on the soil in a fine pattern of hummocks that markedly alter management requirements of the soil but do not obliterate the essential characteristics of the soil series. (See class 2a, p. 268.)

Overwash phase: Deposits from water erosion lie thick enough on the soil to influence management requirements significantly but are not deep enough to destroy the essential characteristics of the soil series. Such a soil takes its textural class name from that of the overlying materials. These may be named *overwash phases, sanded phases,* or *rock-wash phases.* Ordinarily they are not needed on very young Alluvial soils.

PHASES OF STONINESS AND ROCKINESS

Stoniness and rockiness are discussed in detail in the section on Soil Texture, Coarse Fragments, Stoniness, and Rockiness. Coarse fragments are recognized as a part of the soil class names. Classes of stoniness and rockiness are phase distinctions. In order to reduce the length of the name, the terms indicating these phases are added to the textural class names as modifiers. The relationships among the classes of stoniness and rockiness, and between them and some phases are set forth in table 5, page 222.

For soil types with characteristics such that they are otherwise suitable for intensive use, except for stoniness and rockiness, the phases are listed in the following paragraphs. Some stony phases also include classes of rockiness and of coarse fragments 3 to 10 inches in diameter where the separation according to individual classes serves no useful purpose.

Stony phase: Sufficient stones to interfere with tillage but not enough to make intertilled crops impracticable. Usually this is class 1 stoniness on detailed surveys. In soils having coarse fragments, stoniness, and rockiness, if the distinctions among them are unimportant, the stony phase may have some of all three conditions.

Very stony phase: Sufficient stones to make tillage of intertilled crops impracticable, but not the tillage required for hay crops or improved pasture if other soil characteristics are favorable. Usually this is class 2 stoniness. In soils having coarse fragments, stoniness, and rockiness, if the distinctions among them are unimportant, the very stony phase may have some of all three conditions.

Extremely stony phase: Sufficient stones to make all use of machinery impracticable except for light machinery where other soil characteristics are especially favorable for improved pasture. In soils having coarse fragments, stoniness, and rockiness, if the distinctions among them are unimportant, the extremely stony phase may have some of all three conditions. If the other soil characteristics are not especially favorable for improved pasture, land of class 3 stoniness is included with Stony land—a miscellaneous land type—rather than in a phase of a soil type.

If the soil characteristics are such that the soil is not suited to intertilled crops anyway, the distinction between classes 0, 1, and 2 stoniness may be omitted and the range in stoniness described in the soil type definition. With such soil types it usually will not be necessary to establish stony phases; the soil conditions can be expressed adequately by allowing the soil type as the mapping unit to include classes 1 and 2 stoniness and Stony land to include classes 3 and 4 stoniness.

The same principles apply in translating classes of rockiness into rocky phases. These are as follows:

Rocky phase: Sufficient bedrock exposure to interfere with tillage but not enough to make intertilled crops impractical. With soil suitable for crops, this is class 1 rockiness.

Very rocky phase: Sufficient bedrock exposures to make tillage of intertilled crops impractical, but not the tillage required for hay crops or improved pasture, if the other soil characteristics are favorable. With soils otherwise suited to hay crops, this is usually class 2 rockiness.

Extremely rocky phase: Sufficient rock outcrop to make all use of machinery impractical, except for light machinery where other soil characteristics are especially favorable for improved pasture. Such a phase is used only for highly responsive soil having class 3 rockiness. If the other soil characteristics are not favorable for improved pasture, the land is included as Rock land and not as a phase of a soil type.

As with stoniness, the use suitability of the soil must be considered in using the above phases. If characteristics of a soil other than rockiness are not favorable to use for crops or improved pasture, phases are not used to show distinctions between classes 0, 1, and 2 rockiness, and class 3 rockiness is included along with class 4 in Rock land. Small rock outcrops are shown by the standard symbol. The area of land represented by one symbol on the map needs to be defined in each survey.

SOIL DEPTH PHASES

Soil depth phases are distinguished for variations in the total depth of the soil profile, including the C if present, which are significant to soil use and management, over bedrock or other strongly contrasting nonconforming rock material. The standard depth classes used are the same as those used in separating soil series, as set forth in the early part of this section on page 285.

Formerly, names were wholly relative to individual soil types. Thus shallow phases of soil types normally deep turned out to be deeper in inches than deep phases of soil types normally shallow. To avoid confusion for the map reader, broad classes of soil depth are recognized, within which there is sufficient flexibility to set depth limits at the significant places and still give the terms their usual significance when considered generally without reference to the detailed soil descriptions. The specific significance of soil depth phases in terms of soil use and management can be interpreted, however, only within the soil type definition.

The establishment and definition of each soil depth phase needs to be made in specific terms within the soil series definition and within the general guides set forth on page 285. No one soil series or type could be expected to cover the whole range. Depth phases should not be used to represent differences among natural units that are significant to their definitions as types or series. The phase names and their definitions are as follows:

Very shallow phase: The shallowest part of a shallow soil unit,[a] from 5 to 10 inches deep.

---

[a] In the category type, series, family, or great soil group.

Shallow phase: That part of a soil unit, typically deeper (or shallower), that is more than 5 to 10 inches deep but less than 20 to 30 inches deep.

Moderately shallow phase: That part of a soil unit, typically deeper, that is more than 20 to 30 inches deep and less than 30 to 50 inches deep.

Moderately deep phase: That part of a soil unit, typically shallower, that is more than 20 to 30 inches deep and less than 30 to 50 inches deep.

Deep phase: That part of a soil unit, typically shallower, that is (1) more than 30 to 50 inches deep but less than 50 to 60 inches deep or (2) more than 30 to 50 inches deep.

Very deep phase: That part of a soil unit, typically shallower, that is more than 60 inches deep. Ordinarily, this phase is unnecessary.

Besides definitions of the ranges in depth of the taxonomic unit, any necessary inclusions are mentioned in the description of a mapping unit. That is, as a mapping unit, *(series name)* silt loam, deep phase, may contain small percentages of moderately deep and shallow soil.

SOIL THICKNESS PHASES

Besides any variations in soil depth to nonconforming materials and differences due to accelerated erosion, some areas of a few soil units have thinner or thicker A horizons or sola than the typical. Where such differences within any soil type or other unit are significant to soil use and management, they are indicated as phases. No general class ranges are given. Each phase needs to be defined specifically in relation to the typical part of the soil unit. The thickness of the specific horizons or groups of horizons needs to be defined. Here again, the classifier is cautioned not to use thickness phases for insignificant differences or for soils that should be classified as separate series or as variants. Soil thickness phases are defined as follows:

Thick-surface phase: That part of the soil unit that has an A_1 or A horizon significantly thicker than the typical.

Thin-surface phase: That part of the soil unit that has an A_1 or A horizon significantly thinner than the typical.

Thick-solum phase: That part of a soil unit that has a solum significantly thicker than the typical.

Thin-solum phase: That part of a soil unit that has a solum significantly thinner than the typical.

OTHER PHASES

A few other phases are used but less commonly than the ones already described. The old published soil surveys cannot be used as guides, since formerly many soils were indicated by phases, some with nearly bizarre names, that are now indicated as separate soil series or as soil variants.

Drainage phases.—These may be used for other subdivisions within those soil units that extend over two or more classes of soil drainage as set forth in the section on Land Form, Relief, and Drainage, pages 109-72. The soil-drainage classes are guides to the establishment of all units, and any drainage phases should conform to these definitions and be given the same names as the specific soil-drainage classes. The use of drainage phases is confined to those relatively young soils, especially Alluvial soils, in which the differences in drainage classes are not reflected in the other differentiating soil characteristics.

Drained phases.—These are used for those areas of a taxonomic unit having improved drainage, usually by two or more drainage classes, brought about by recent natural processes or by drainage structures, and accompanied by little or no change in the other differentiating soil characteristics.

Physiographic phases.—These are sometimes needed to distinguish between soils within a taxonomic unit that are otherwise similar but have unlike relationships to the ground water or to flooding not already expressed by soil slope. On a deep covering of loess over a gravelly terrace, soils may be developed like those formed on a deep covering of loess over a till plain. If the former have a much better water supply in the deep underlying gravel, it may be necessary to separate them as a *terrace phase*.

More commonly, distinctions are made among Alluvial soils to separate out parts that may be less or more susceptible to flooding than the typical soil, as *low-bottom phase* or *high-bottom phase*. A *fan phase* of soils typically developed on terraces or in bottom lands is sometimes needed to indicate the important differences in water problems or potentialities.

Burned phases.—These phases are used for areas of organic soils that have had enough of the surface burned to alter their characteristics of importance to use capability.

Silted phases.—Silted phases are used for irrigated areas of soil units that have had sufficient amounts of silt added more or less uniformly to the surface through deposition from muddy irrigation water to alter their use capability but not enough to require the recognition of a different soil series.

THE SOIL VARIANT

A soil variant is a taxonomic soil unit closely related to another taxonomic unit, say a soil series, but departing from it in at least one differentiating characteristic at the series level, from which it derives its name as modified by the principal distinguishing feature. Many so-called phases of old soil surveys are now regarded as variants as herein defined. Variants are really separate soil series but of too small known extent to justify establishment as new series. Thus a soil may be recognized and defined as a variant in one survey area and later be designated as a separate series if found to be of important extent.

The variant is a convenient unit that permits the classifier to avoid establishing separate soil series for soils of minor extent and still keep his soil series definition as narrow as required. It makes it possible for him to hold strictly to the rule that each series description comprehends all types and phases within it. Unfortunately, this rule was not observed in some soil surveys, especially in setting up soil phases that did include soils outside the series definition. Serious confusion was inevitable, especially in using the soil series as a basis for grouping into families or other higher categories.

In older soil surveys, for example, the name Hayden loam, dark-colored phase, was used for what should be called Hayden loam, dark-colored variant. The Hayden loam is a Gray-Brown Podzolic soil developed on calcareous glacial till like that from which the Clarion of the Prairie group is developed. This variant is a transitional soil between the two, since found to be important enough for separate recognition as Lester loam.

Other examples of variants are as follows: Chastain silt loam, phosphatic variant; Angie sandy clay loam, calcareous-substratum variant; Flom silty clay loam, calcareous variant; and Bosket very fine sandy loam, gently sloping shallow variant.

These variants are not soils within the soil type named, but are specific departures from them. Some of the variants may be recognized as soil series later.

THE SOIL FAMILY

As this *Manual* is being prepared, the category "soil family" is still in process of definition and development. It is not possible to define the category precisely now, but tentative principles and criteria developed to date are presented for the guidance of those needing to use this unit.

The purpose of the category is to make the similarities and differences among the soils apparent at a level between that of the great soil group and that of the soil series. The category is more urgently needed now because the number of soil series is becoming too great to permit remembering all of them individually; and the great soil group is too heterogeneous to be used for very many objectives. The soil family should consist of similar soil series, and all soil series within one soil family should be members of the same great soil group.

The criteria used to differentiate among soil families must be chosen from among those characteristics that become homogeneous between the great soil groups and the soil series. Since differentiating characteristics accumulate from the higher to the lower categories, the criteria used to differentiate among soil series must include the distinguishing criteria of the soil family and all other categories above the series. The differentiating criteria of the family therefore, must be drawn from those characteristics which accumulate between these two levels—the great soil group and the series.

Soil series are described in terms of characteristics of single horizons, but no one of these can be used systematically to define the series, or a class of any category, because the significance of each one depends upon its combination with the other. The entire soil, with all of its horizons, must be defined as a unit. Neither the A or B horizon, by itself, defines a Podzol. Generally, the great soil groups can be defined in terms of kind and sequence of the master horizons—A and B—including all subdivisions as part of the whole. The Podzol, for example, is defined in terms of the acid, strongly leached, light-colored A and the underlying B with its characteristic form of iron and humus accumulation. Below the great soil group, characteristics such as the degree of expression of these master horizons, kind and arrangement of their subdivisions, and mineralogy of the solum accumulate as differentiating characteristics at the series level. It is from among characteristics such as these that the differentiating criteria of the category of families must be drawn.

First approximations of family groupings have been made for soils of Iowa, New York, California, Hawaii, and the Tennessee Valley. In these diverse soil regions, a combination of three or more of the following criteria has given tentatively satisfactory subdivisions of the great soil groups involved:

1. Kind and sequence of horizons within the master horizons that define the great soil groups. These identify the central concepts of great soil groups, and of intergrades between them, such as the modal horizons of intergrades between Gray-Brown Podzolic and Low-Humic Gley soils.
2. Relative degree of horizon differentiation—the degree of expression of master horizons that are characteristic of a specific great soil group.
3. Mineralogy of the solum—major mineralogical differences associated with strongly contrasting parent materials, particle-size distribution, or kind of clay, but within the limits of the great soil group.
4. Relative "size" of the solum—such as difference in thickness of solum not associated with degree of expression of the master horizons.

Criteria 1 and 2 provide homogeneity of kind, sequence, and degree of expression of the horizons. Criteria 3 and 4 may appear to belong below them in level of abstraction. In the trial groupings made, many of the characteristics dropped between the series and the family levels were primarily functions of parent material not reflected in the criteria listed above.

Although the primary function of the family is to help us remember characteristics and see relationships among soil series, other uses of soil families are important. Families should be so constituted that they can be used as primary classes for subdivisions in technical groupings for the objectives of applied soil science. It would be helpful, for example, if each family could be subdivided into phases on the basis of such characteristics as slope, stoniness, and degree of erosion, to provide groups sufficiently homogeneous for useful generalizations about soil use and management requirements. If properties such as slope or stoniness range widely, one cannot be precise about soil use and management of a family or a series, or even of a type, as a unit. To be precise, one must subdivide the type into phases on the basis of slope and similar criteria; one should also be able to achieve a moderately high degree of precision for applied objectives by

subdividing groups of soil series in like manner. An effort to
define the category of soil families at a level of generalization
that will permit the use of the family for this purpose has been
made in the Tennessee Valley and in Hawaii.

Two alternative systems for nomenclature of the soil family
are possible. In one, the soil family could be given a geographic
name, as with the soil series. The family might carry the name
of a prominent constituent soil series. Such names are not
connotative and may become confused with the constituent series
name within the family. As a second alternative, coined names,
preferably connotative ones, may be used. Combined syllables that
are connotative of the suggested criteria may be thrown together
into coined names. This has been done tentatively for some soils,
but the suitability of the scheme and its clarity to users of soil
maps are still uncertain.

COMBINED TAXONOMIC UNITS

The individual taxonomic unit cannot always be shown separately on detailed soil maps and usually not at all on reconnaissance, exploratory, generalized, or schematic soil maps of small
scale. In the largest scale reconnaissance survey some of the
taxonomic units can be shown separately. Depending on the scale
of the map and its purpose, the soil map is often easier to read
with understanding if well-defined groups of soils are shown on
them rather than a very intricate pattern of taxonomic units.
Rarely does grouping according to *taxonomic* similarity greatly
reduce the complexity of the soil boundaries. The mapping unit
needs to be defined in terms of a mappable pattern of geographically associated taxonomic units, defined in terms of the properties of the individually defined and named taxonomic units and
their patterns.

Such groups are called, generally, *soil associations*. In detailed
soil surveys the separate taxonomic members of soil associations
are mapped individually if the scale permits. Otherwise they are
mapped as *soil complexes*. To avoid confusion, the term soil complex is confined to units in legends of detailed soil surveys for
soil associations of which the individual members are not mappable. The separate taxonomic units of most soil associations are
unmappable in soil surveys of small scale. Since both soil associations and soil complexes are named by joining the names of two
or three of the principal taxonomic units by hyphens, in detail-
reconnaissance surveys having both units, the word "complex"
or "association" needs to be added to all soil mapping units that
contain two or more taxonomic units to avoid confusion.

Besides these mapping units, occasional need arises for mapping
units of taxonomically similar soils that are not regularly geographically associated. Such a unit is called an *undifferentiated
group* and is named by combining the names of the units with
"and."

THE SOIL ASSOCIATION

The soil association is a group of defined and named taxonomic soil units, regularly geographically associated in a defined proportional pattern. It is the principal soil mapping unit shown on all small-scale maps, including original surveys and compiled maps. On relatively large-scale reconnaissance soil maps made in fairly well-known areas, the associations are defined in terms of the same kinds of taxonomic soil units as the ones mapped individually or in soil complexes in a detailed soil survey—series, types, phases, and variants. In broader scale mapping only the names, proportions, and definitions of soil series may be given. On maps of small scale, great soil groups, or soil families, or subdivisions of great soil groups according to parent material, with phases for relief and stoniness, may be the lowest units defined within the individual soil association.

The levels of grouping and the limits of homogeneity used in defining soil associations vary widely with the purpose of the map. These are outlined broadly in the following numbered paragraphs.

1. *Level of farm unit.*—The soil associations are defined in terms of combinations of soil types and phases that permit predictions of the potentialities of whole farm units, either existing or prospective ones that might be created by land subdivision or by consolidation of existing parcels. Such predictions include the adapted systems of farming, the principal problems of soil use and management, and the productivity of various sizes of farms.

This is the level of abstraction of soil association maps ordinarily required of the soil survey party chief. Soil association maps at higher levels of abstraction are sometimes useful.

2. *Level of rural neighborhood.*—The soil associations are defined in terms of combinations of soil series, and of phases where significant, that permit predictions concerning small groups of farms or potential farms, including systems of farming or forestry, potential density of the individual farms, and the broad problems of soil use and management in the area.

3. *Level of rural community and trading center.*—The soil associations are defined in terms of combinations of soil families or subdivisions of great soil groups, and of phases where significant, that permit predictions about the potentialities of existing or proposed rural communities and trading centers as to soil use potentialities for cropping, grazing, and forestry; the potentialities for rural community organization and development; and the broad problems of soil use and management.

The definition of a specific soil association consists of the definitions of its constituent taxonomic units, their proportions and patterns. In reconnaissance soil surveys, tentative soil associations and descriptions need to be tested and defined by detailed mapping of representative sample areas.

Examples of names of soil associations are as follows:

1. Great soil groups:
    Podzol-Bog
    Podzol-Half Bog (Calcareous till)
    Chernozem (loess)-Solonetz-Alluvial
2. Series:
    Miami-Crosby-Brookston
    Iron River-Adolph
3. Series and miscellaneous land types:
    Iron River-Rock land-Peat
4. Soil types:
    Kennan-Freer silt loams
5. Phases:
    Keenan-Freer stony silt loams
    Kennan stony silt loam, rolling-Adolph stony silt loam.

Associations of soils developed from one kind of parent material but differing in characteristics due to differences in relief and drainage are called *catenary*. That is, the Miami *catena* is an association of soils of which the soil series in the normal position is Miami, belonging to the Gray-Brown Podzolic group, along with others belonging to different great soil groups, and intergrades between them, and derived from similar parent material.

THE SOIL COMPLEX

The soil complex is a soil association, the taxonomic members of which cannot be separated individually in a detailed soil survey. Complexes are mapping units, not classes in the system of classification. Complexes should not be given separate series names; they are mixtures of soils and cannot be defined in terms of a modal profile and variations from it. Many of the Solonetz and Solonchak soils occur as spots within other soils and the two associates are so intimately mixed that the areas can be shown only as complexes, even on highly detailed soil maps. Intricate patterns of Bog or Half Bog soils with associated upland soil must be mapped as complexes.

The constituent taxonomic unit may be soil phases of different types, soil types of the same series, soil types of different series, or even two or more soil series.

The name of the complex should be the combined names of the principal constituents joined by a hyphen. If the textural class names in the type name, or the phase names, are the same for both constituents, the combined name may be shortened by using the plural. For example, a complex of Odessa silt loam and Schoharie silt loam may be designated as Odessa-Schoharie silt loams. This is a unit in which the entire range of both soil types is involved. If only one of their phases is involved, such as the gently sloping phases of each, the name is Odessa-Schoharie silt loams, gently sloping phases.

In parts of the northern Lake States, intricate patterns of Rubicon sand, Saugatuck sand, Newton sand, and Rifle peat are mapped as the Rubicon-Rifle complex. The naming of the two end members in this complex suggests clearly the presence of the two intergrades. In the Chestnut soil region, the solodized-Solonetz soil, Rhoades, so dominates the complex in association with several other soils that the unit is named simply Rhoades complex.

For the definition of a complex in the soil survey report, the same definitions of the taxonomic units are needed as if they were mapped individually, in addition to a description of the proportional pattern that they make in the complex. Such descriptions of complexes are enhanced by one highly detailed soil map of a representative area of a few acres.

The chemical and physical data obtained in the laboratory can be interpreted only in relation to the taxonomic unit; but the results from experimental plots and from farm fields can be interpreted in terms of the complex as a whole. Yield estimates, productivity ratings, and management requirements are given for the complex as a whole.

THE UNDIFFERENTIATED SOIL GROUP

Occasionally, it may be better to show two or more similar taxonomic units, which do not occur in regular geographic association, as one mapping unit. Such groups are called *undifferentiated soil groups*. Such mapping units are named in terms of their constituent taxonomic units and connected by "and." In some soil surveys the differences between the steep phases of two soil types of the same or of similar series, for example, may not be significant because slope is so important that it outweighs the other soil characteristics in terms of the objective of the survey. As a specific example, the Howard and Palmyra series are both Gray-Brown Podzolic soils on glacial outwash material. Both have calcareous substrata, but the calcareous material occurs about 20 inches deeper in the Howard soil than in the Palmyra. On the nearly level terraces this difference in depth of material is significant, but on slopes greater than 30 percent gradient, soil slope so outweighs the depth to calcareous material that a separation between the two soils has little significance. Similarly, the separation between the loam and silt loam types of the two series has little significance on such steep slopes. Thus the steep phases of Palmyra loam, Howard silt loam, and Howard loam can be included in an undifferentiated soil group as Howard and Palmyra loam and silt loam, steep phases. Other examples are Spaulding and Greenwood peats; Cloquet and Gogebic sandy loams; Clarion silt loam and Nicollet silty clay loam; Clarksville and Fullerton cherty loams, steep phases; and Clarksville stony loam, rolling, and Fullerton cherty loam, steep.

Such combinations may be set up in survey legends, but ordinarily it is better to make the separation in a detailed soil survey, especially if their use capabilities are uncertain. Since the individual types do not ordinarily occur together, combining them saves little time or no time in mapping. They may be combined later on a published map, however, if their differences are found to be insignificant. The prospect of such combinations on the published map should not encourage the party chief to set up many mapping units with a view to their later combination. If early in the work, any symbol or separation is found to be unnecessary, it should be eliminated, and any mapped areas given the proper symbols. If the mapping is far along, the symbol should remain in the legend, but its further use should be discontinued. The making of a large number of combinations in map compilation greatly increases the cost.

Although the use of undifferentiated soil groups reduces the length of the legend and of the soil survey report, it may not significantly reduce the number of lines on the map or the amount of time required in mapping. The use of soil complexes and soil associations as mapping units in place of individual taxonomic units does reduce the number of boundaries to be drawn.

MISCELLANEOUS LAND TYPES

Miscellaneous land types are used in soil classification and mapping for areas of land that have little or no natural soil or that are too nearly inaccessible for orderly examination, or where, for other reasons, it is not feasible to classify the soil. In practical mapping work, their recognition and definition depends partly upon the detailed required for the objective of the survey. They are named primarily in terms of land form and secondarily in terms of material. A miscellaneous land type may be part of a complex that includes one or more other miscellaneous land types or part of a complex that has one or more soil types in it. Small areas of some miscellaneous land types, as rock outcrop, for example, may be shown by defined symbols. Phases of miscellaneous land types should be avoided. Some classifiers are inclined to make unnecessary separations among miscellaneous land types, partly because the differences, although insignificant to the purposes of a soil survey, are obvious without digging.

Definitions of accepted classes and subclasses of miscellaneous land types are given in the following:

Alluvial land consists of areas of unconsolidated alluvium, generally stratified and varying widely in texture, recently deposited by streams, and subject to frequent changes through stream overflow. Subclasses include: *Sandy alluvial land, Gravelly alluvial land, Cobbly alluvial land, Stony alluvial land,* and *Bouldery alluvial land.* Several of these types may be included in one mapping unit as *Mixed alluvial land. Riverwash* is essentially barren *Alluvial land,* commonly sandy, exposed along streams at low water and subject to shifting during normal high water.

Although subject to change through periodic overflow, *Alluvial land,* except for *Riverwash,* has remained long enough for plants to become established. The deposits are too recent for soil profile development, although the material may be mottled. Drainage is variable, and shallow pools are common. *Alluvial land* has little agricultural value unless leveled and protected from overflow, although forests may grow on it. *Riverwash* has little or no vegetation. If necessary, subclasses can be recognized as *Riverwash (sandy)* and *Riverwash (cobbly).* Riverwash has no agricultural value.

Areas formerly classified as "Alluvial soils, undifferentiated" should be classified as named complexes of defined Alluvial soil series or types, such as "Eel-Sloan silt loams" for example, or as *Alluvial land.*

Badland is steep or very steep nearly barren land, ordinarily not stony, broken by numerous intermittent drainage channels. *Badland* is most common in semiarid and arid regions, where streams have entrenched themselves in soft geologic materials. Local relief generally falls between 25 and 500 feet. Runoff is very high, and geological erosion active. *Badland* has practically no agricultural value, except for small areas of soil with some value for grazing that may be included in the mapping unit. The relief is similar to that of *Rough broken land*, which has a cover of vegetation.

Beaches are sandy, gravelly, or cobbly shores washed and rewashed by waves. The land may be partly covered with water during high tides or stormy periods. *Coastal beaches* occur along the coasts of oceans and seas; *Lake beaches* occur along the shores of lakes or large ponds. *Old beaches* are no longer being washed and reworked by waves but retain their original form. Subclasses include *Coastal beaches (sandy)* and *Coastal beaches (cobbly)*. *Beaches* support little or no vegetation and have no agricultural value, although they may be sources of sand and gravel.

Blown-out land consists of areas from which all or most of the soil material has been removed by wind—a condition resulting from an extreme degree of soil blowing or wind erosion. The areas are shallow depressions that have flat or irregular floors formed by some more resistant layers, by an accumulation of pebbles or cobbles, or by exposure of the water table. Some areas have a small proportion of hummocks or small dunes. The land is barren, or nearly so, and generally useless for crops. Transient areas of *Blown-out land*, developed in loose deep sand, are included along with adjacent dunes in *Sand-dune land*. Small areas of *Blown-out land* are often called "blowouts" and are shown with symbols.

Colluvial land includes areas of unconsolidated recent colluvium—a heterogeneous deposit of soil material, rock fragments, or mixtures of the two—accumulated at the base of slopes primarily by gravity. Subclasses of *Colluvial land* are named according to the dominant textural class or kinds of rock material: for example, *Stony colluvial land* and *Cherty colluvial land*. Mapping units of *Colluvial land* commonly include small areas of soil creep and local alluvium.

Coquina land consists of shell fragments, mainly from the coquina clam but with lesser amounts from the conch, oyster, and other shell-bearing mollusks. This land is not useful for crops but commonly supports a few trees. The material has been used for building.

Ditches and spoil banks include areas of land occupied by ditches and by the rock-waste banks and dumps from their excavation. Often this type of land can be shown only with symbols.

Dumps are areas of uneven accumulations, or piles, of waste rock. Subclasses include (1) *Mine dumps*—areas of waste rock, with little or no segregation that came from ore and coal mines, quarries, and smelters; (2) *Placer diggings*—areas in which the original soil has been disturbed, overturned, or removed in placer mining, leaving an uneven or rough, eroded, and scarred surface; and (3) *Tailings*—areas of coarse debris from which finer material has been removed during mining operations.

Commonly dumps are so closely associated with pits that complexes of *Pits and dumps* or *Mine pits and dumps* are needed. *Dumps* is a miscellaneous land type having little or no agricultural value. Where smoothed, the areas are classed as *Made land*. Areas too small to be delineated on the map are shown by symbols.

Dune land consists of hills or ridges of sand-sized particles drifted and piled up by the wind and either actively shifting or so recently fixed or stabilized that no soil horizons have developed. *Active dune land* is still drifting, and *Stabilized dune land* is fixed by vegetation. Some areas mapped in the past as *Stabilized dune land* should be classed as a named soil. In places *Blown-out land* is associated with *Dune* *land;* although in mapping practice, transient areas of *Blown-out land,* developed in loose deep sand, are included in *Sand-dune land,* as are the areas of shifting sand that occur between dunes or on the slopes.

Gullied land is land so cut by recent gullies that it is nonarable, and the soil profiles have been largely destroyed. Where necessary, separations based on dominant slope of the original land surface may be made, as *Sloping gullied land.* It may or may not be feasible to convert gullied land to arable land by leveling, depending upon the kind and depth of the soil material. It is often useful to indicate the kind of soil material involved as in: *Gullied land (Ruston soil material)* or *Gullied land (deep acid sandy materials).*

Kitchen middens are sites of aboriginal human homes. They consist of mixtures of soil material, mollusk shells or fragments, ashes, charcoal, artifacts, and a few stones and bones. They are generally slightly higher than adjacent land and in some places form distinct mounds. Many are so small that they can be shown on the map only by symbols.

Landslides are masses of rock fragments, soil, or other unconsolidated materials that have slid down slopes in recent times, together with the scarred surfaces resulting from such movement. A common form of landslide is soil slump—the slow downward slipping of a mass of soil, or of several subsidiary masses, usually with some degree of backward rotation, on a more or less horizontal axis parallel to the slope. Such landslides of soil material commonly have an uneven concave-convex, or sigmoid, cross section with wide cracks. The surface may have the appearance of steps or small benches on a slope. Materials of the lower solum or substrata are exposed as scars where the soil mass broke away from its original position. Slumps are common in some clay soils of the uplands, particularly on steep slopes in the vicinity of recent faulting, or along contacts of differing geologic formations. The slippage takes place during or after long rains or near irrigation ditches, and may be accompanied by earth flow. Rapidly moving landslides—debris-slides or wet debris-avalanches—may be dangerous and damaging.

Lava flows include areas covered with lava rock, commonly basalt. These flows are geologically recent, especially those in humid regions. Most lava flows have sharp jagged surfaces, crevices, and angular blocks, although a few have relatively smooth surfaces. A little soil material may have blown into a few cracks and sheltered pockets. Vegetation is limited to lichens, occasional bunches of grass, and scattered shrubs and trees. With slightly more soil material this type merges into *Lava rock land. Lava flows* has no agricultural value, and, because of the commonly rough surface and sparse vegetation, it is avoided by livestock.

Made land consists of areas filled artificially with earth, trash, or both, and smoothed. It occurs most commonly in and around urban areas.
   Stabilized land areas with clearly developed soil characteristics or even those with young soils if definable and uniform enough to map, and especially if arable, should be classified as soils even though originally made or reworked by man.

Marl beds include areas where marl (an earthy crumbling deposit consisting chiefly of calcium carbonate mixed with clay or other impurities) is exposed or lies a few inches below the surface. Marl is usually formed in lakes or ponds. The calcium carbonate may have originated from the calcareous remains of the chara plant (chara marl), from mollusk shells (shell marl), or from simple precipitation from solution. These beds are commonly a good source of agricultural lime.

Marsh consists of wet periodically flooded areas covered dominantly with grasses, cattails, rushes, or other herbaceous plants. Subclasses include *Tidal marsh,* periodically inundated because of the tide; *Fresh water marsh,* which is influenced by fresh water and not by the tide;

and *Salt water marsh,* which is influenced by salty water but not by the tide. *Tidal marsh* may be subdivided into *Tidal marsh (salty)* and *Tidal marsh (fresh). Tidal marsh* may be associated with *Tidal flats. Salt water marsh* generally occurs in wet salty flats along stream valleys. *Marsh* is mainly covered with grasses and grasslike plants, while *Swamp* is covered with trees.

Mine wash consists of accumulations of sandy, silty, or clayey material recently eroded in mining operations. *Mine wash* commonly originates in areas of *Strip mines.* It is distinct from *Slickens,* which consists of fine-textured material separated in placer-mine or ore-mill operations. *Mine wash* may clog stream channels and damage the land on which it is deposited.

Oil-waste land includes areas where liquid oily wastes have accumulated. This miscellaneous land type includes slush pits and adjacent uplands and bottoms affected by the liquid wastes, principally salt water and oil. The land is unsuited to agricultural purposes, although some of it can be reclaimed.

Pits are open excavations from which soil and underlying material have been removed. Several kinds of pits are recognized, including: *Borrow pits, Clay pits, Gravel pits, Mine pits, Quarries, Sand pits,* and *Strip mines.* Commonly *Pits* are closely associated with *Dumps,* making it necessary to map complexes, such as *Pits and Dumps* or *Mine pits and dumps.* Pits too small to be delineated on the map are shown by symbols.

Playas are essentially barren, flat, generally dry, undrained basins in arid and semiarid regions. They may contain water of shallow depth for short periods at infrequent intervals. Many of them are salty.

Rock land consists of areas having enough rock outcrop and very shallow soil to submerge other soil characteristics. The upper limit of rock outcrop is 90 percent of the mapped area and, unless the other features place the land in some other miscellaneous land type anyway, the lower limit is ordinarily 25 percent. The word "rock" may appear in the land type names if only 3 percent of the area is rock outcrop: for example, *Stony rock land* or *Rough broken land and rock land.* Where a mappable area contains more than 90 percent rock outcrop, the whole is classed as *Rock outcrop.* Several kinds of *Rock land* are named according to the kind of rock material, including: *Limestone rock land, Sandstone rock land, Lava rock land, Quartzite rock land,* and *Granite rock land.* Usually such distinctions are not necessary.

Rock land may offer some light grazing. Tree growth is usually sparse and scrubby even where the climatic and other conditions are favorable. If a soil type has prominent soil features despite more than 25 percent rock outcrop, a very rocky phase of the soil type may be defined with 25 to 50 percent rock outcrop.

Rock outcrop consists of exposures of bare bedrock. Although very rarely needed, subclasses can be named according to the kind of rock materials, including: *Chalk outcrop, Limestone outcrop, Sandstone outcrop,* and *Shale outcrop.* Commonly, areas of *Rock outcrop* are too small to be delineated on the map and are shown by symbols.

Rough broken land consists of very steep land, ordinarily not stony, broken by numerous intermittent drainage channels. It is used for grazing and for timber. It has a cover of vegetation, as opposed to *Badland,* which has sparse vegetation or complete lack of cover. Stony areas are classed as *Rough broken and stony land. Rough broken land* is deeply dissected by narrow V-shaped valleys and sharp torturous divides. Local relief is generally between 25 and 500 feet. Soil slipping is often common, and the steep slopes have a succession of short vertical exposures or "cat steps." Runoff is high and geologic erosion is active.

Rough mountainous land refers to mountainous areas, dominantly stony, that include small areas of land suitable for cropping, and, in places, considerable land suitable for grazing. *Rough mountainous land* is essentially a complex of *Rough broken and stony land*, shallow phases of unidentified soils, and small areas of unidentified soils suitable for crops or pastures. Local relief is generally more than 500 feet. This unit is included in mapping legends only in reconnaissance surveys.

Rubble land includes areas with 90 percent or more of stones and boulders. It is the extreme of *Stony land*, as *Rock outcrop* is of *Rock land*. Practically no soil is exposed. If some purpose will be served, *Rubble land* may be modified by the name of the principal rocks from which the stones are derived, as *Granite rubble land*.

Scoria land consists of areas of slaglike clinkers and burned shale and fine-grained sandstone characteristic of burned-out coal beds. Although it commonly supports a sparse cover of grasses, this land is of low value for grazing and of no value for crops.

Slickens are accumulations of fine-textured materials separated in placer-mine and ore-mill operations. Slickens from ore mills consist largely of freshly ground rock that generally has undergone chemical treatment during the milling process. Such materials may be detrimental to plant growth but are usually confined in specially constructed basins.

Stony land includes areas having enough stones and boulders to submerge other soil characteristics. At the upper limit 90 percent of the exposed surface is stones; the lower limit is ordinarily 15 percent unless other features place the land in some other miscellaneous land type anyway. The word "stony" may appear in land type names if over 3 percent of the area is covered with stones, as for example, *Rough broken and stony land*. Areas having over 90 percent stones are called *Rubble*. Where significant to forestry or grazing, areas having more than 50 percent stones and boulders are called *Very stony land*. If a soil type has prominent soil features, despite more than 15 percent of stones, a very stony phase of the soil type may be defined with 15 to 50 percent of the area occupied by stones.

Stony land may be combined with other miscellaneous land types to give, for example, *Stony alluvial land*, *Stony colluvial land*, or *Rough broken and stony land*. If significant to land use, the type may be subdivided to *Stony smooth land* (A and B soil-slope classes), *Stony rolling land* (C and D soil-slope classes), and *Stony rough land* and *Stony steep land* (E and F soil-slope classes). *Stony land* may form a complex with *Rock land*, as *Stony rock land*. Significant differences can be indicated by modifying the type name to indicate the source of material, as for example, *Stony smooth land* (*Hagerstown soil material*) and *Stony rough land* (*Muskingum soil material*).

Areas of *Stony land* or *Very stony land* too small to enclose with boundaries are indicated by symbols and defined as to the area represented by one symbol. If areas of both *Stony land* and *Very stony land* are recognized in detailed surveys, a separate symbol is needed for each.

Swamp consists of naturally wooded areas, all or most of which are covered with water much of the time. *Tidal swamp* is influenced by salty tidal water, and *Fresh water swamp* is influenced by nontidal fresh water. Some *tidal swamp* has a characteristic growth of mangrove, as along the coast of southern Florida. In places it is associated with *Tidal marsh*. Occasionally it is significant to indicate the dominant kind of trees, as *Tidal swamp (mangrove)* or *Fresh water swamp (cypress)*. *Swamp* is not suitable for agriculture without extensive reclamation by drainage and dikes. (These designations are used sparingly. Most swamps and marshes have some kind of soil.)

Terrace escarpments include sloping or steep relatively even fronts of terraces. Where the terrace face is broken by numerous intermittent drainage channels and the differences in elevation exceed 25 feet, the areas should be classified as *Rough broken land* or *Badland*, rather than *Terrace escarpments*. Where gullying has been active, the areas should be classified as *Gullied land*. Where the terrace escarpments are especially stony they may be named *Terrace escarpments (stony)*. Of course, many terrace escarpments have well-developed soil types on them that should be mapped as such.

Tidal flats include essentially barren, nearly flat areas of mud, periodically covered by tidal water. The lower parts of these areas are covered by water daily; the higher parts may be covered only at unusually high tides. The flats consist of silty and clayey material that in places contains considerable very fine sand. Normally the material has an excess of soluble salts. When the surface dries, it cracks and may become hard enough to support a man.

Urban land is land so altered or obscured by urban works and structures that identification of soils is not feasible. Soil boundaries should be extended into urban areas wherever it is possible to do so with reasonable accuracy, and the use of this miscellaneous land type is restricted to the closely built-up parts of cities.

Very stony land includes areas having from 50 to 90 percent of the surface covered with stones and boulders. The same qualifying adjectives apply as to *Stony land*.

Volcanic-ash land consists of areas of nearly unmodified deposits of volcanic ash. This land type should be reserved for those few deposits of volcanic ash that are so recent as to have little or no evidence of soil development and little or no vegetation.

THE SOIL MAPPING LEGEND

After the soils have been examined, identified, and described, a mapping legend is prepared. Every soil survey needs two legends, usually developed together: (1) The identification legend and (2) the descriptive legend. Although serving different and overlapping purposes, both legends are essential and must be kept up to date by frequent revision for good results.

The task of developing and maintaining proper legends is, perhaps, the most important duty of the soil survey party chief. The quality of these legends, especially of the descriptive legend, reflects the completeness and accuracy of his study and understanding of his mapping units. If he is alert to his technical and administrative responsibilities, the legends are clear and up to date. Lack of clarity in the legend indicates poor classification and is bound to be reflected in inconsistent mapping. The larger the soil survey party the greater the hazard. The legends need to be clear to each mapper so that all draw the boundaries accurately in comparable places and so that the mapping units are consistent throughout the map.

The soil correlator or other supervisory scientist should give special attention to the survey legend. He should help the party chief to correct any inadequacies or ambiguities. A minor error, simple to correct in the early stages of the work, can grow into a major problem in requiring extensive field revision or greatly increased cost in map compilation. Administrative arrangements should provide first priority for typing soil survey legends and revised legends for use by the field party.

No mapping should be done by any member of the party until he has been furnished a legend of *all soil symbols as complete as it is possible to make*. Rarely, however, can the legend be made fully complete at the start. As each mapper finds a new soil or feature not provided for in the legend, or if he is uncertain about the application of any symbol, a note should be made on the map and the matter drawn to the attention of the party chief immediately. Any additions or corrections should be given to all mappers so that all legends within the party are alike.

Complete standardization of mapping symbols on a national or regional basis is impracticable. If enough symbols and combinations of symbols are developed to take care of every need on the most detailed surveys, symbols are bound to be far too long and unwieldy for clarity on the field sheets.

CONVENTIONAL SYMBOLS

The standard symbols for natural and cultural features are illustrated in plates 1 to 5. Nearly all of these are standard for all accurate maps. In the United States, the topographic map of

935034°—51——21

the United States Geologic Survey sets the standards for the general symbolization of base data on maps of the scale used in soil cartography. Yet some alternatives are provided, and some additional symbols are needed on soil maps. Thus, even within the general system of notation, differences are made for different areas, depending upon the scale of the maps, the nature of the country, and the objectives of the survey. Trails are shown when they offer the only means of entry into an undeveloped region, but not in well-settled country. For some objectives, roads are classified in more detail than for others. In areas where recreation is very important to local land use, cottages ought to be clearly set off from permanent residences.

A proper legend for any soil survey includes all mapping symbols of every kind that go on the map, as selected from the standards given. No area will require all of them; and in some areas one or more special symbols may have to be added to show a locally important feature not provided for among the standards.

The special symbols (pls. 6 and 7) for sinkholes, gullies, wet spots, eroded phases, stony phases, and the like fall between the general conventional symbols and the symbols used to identify soil areas. They are used for small areas, too small to enclose within a boundary, yet significant to soil use and management. In the soil survey legend for any area, these need to be defined specifically for that area in terms of both *area* and *quality,* depending upon the scale and significance.

A stone symbol, for example, may be used for small areas of a stony phase not isolated by a boundary. Depending upon the detail required, the symbol may be defined in area as (1) $\frac{1}{4}$ to $\frac{1}{2}$ acre, (2) $\frac{1}{2}$ to $1\frac{3}{4}$ acres, or (3) 1 to $3\frac{1}{2}$ acres. The same applies to all similar symbols. Small spots of eroded phases of soil types, too small to enclose with boundaries, may be defined similarly with different symbols, say S and $SS,$ for moderate and severe sheet erosion, respectively.

Such symbols for phases or miscellaneous land types that contrast sharply with the adjacent soils are especially useful if the total acreage is very small or if the separate areas are too small to enclose in boundaries without exaggeration. But *none* should be used without accurate definition. On the finished map each symbol should tell the reader the nature of the land represented by the symbol and its area.

THE IDENTIFICATION SOIL LEGEND

Each mapping unit—type, phase, variant, complex, association, or miscellaneous land type—has a symbol that is placed in areas on the map to identify it. Although letters are commonly used on published soil maps, the basic symbols for field sheets are mostly numbers with letters for phases.

The identification legend is a list of all these symbols and their names, arranged alphabetically and numerically so that one may see the symbol for each kind of soil and the kind of soil for each symbol.

Each permissible symbol—*each combination of figures and letters*—used to identify areas on the soil map needs to be listed and named. If extra subdivisions, say of phases, are made for a special use of photographic copies of the field sheets but are not for inclusion on the final compiled soil map, they may be listed under one name, provided the differences between the symbols are clear from specific notations or from a general one that applies to several soils. For example, 14A and 14A$_2$ may both indicate Huntington silt loam with slope class A, the first *level*, with slopes of 0 to 1 percent, and the second *nearly level*, with slopes of 1 to 2 percent.

Commonly figures are used for soil types, with letters for soil-slope phases and either letters or figures for eroded phases added to the symbol for the soil type. A standard local convention can be very helpful to those who must remember the symbols accurately. Some use a convention in the soil-type number symbol so that the last digit indicates the textural class as follows: (1) Clay, (2) clay loam, (3) silty clay loam, (4) silt loam, (5) loam, (6) fine sandy loam, (7) sandy loam, (8) loamy fine sand, (9) loamy sand, and (10) sand. This scheme will not work in many areas, because more than ten textural class names need to be recognized. Further, its use may result in the mapping of insignificant differences in soil texture. The biggest difficulty with this kind of scheme is the need for three figures in the soil-map symbol. If all mapping units can be conveniently symbolized between figure 1 and figure 99, significantly less space is required on the map for the symbols.

Where needed, the soil-slope symbol—A, B, C, D, E, or F—directly follows the soil-type number or is the first letter in the denominator of a fractional symbol. If photographic copies of the field sheets are to be used by laymen, it may be helpful to add the soil-slope symbols to all soil-type symbols, including those falling wholly within one slope class. This makes it possible to read soil slope approximately without consulting a legend for the numbers. But if the field sheets are not to be used directly, the soil-slope symbol may be omitted from any symbol if all the areas of a soil type fall within one slope class.

The symbol for an eroded phase, if needed, usually follows the soil-slope symbol in the numerator, or is put as the second symbol in the denominator of a fractional symbol. Either letters or numbers may be used, whichever are more convenient. Thus, Dexter silt loam, eroded sloping phase, could be shown as 24Cn, $\frac{24C}{3}$, or $\frac{24}{C-3}$. The first of the three is easiest to place and takes the least space.

Symbols for stony phases may be added to the above as needed, say 24CnS, or $\frac{24S}{C-3}$, although stony phases and eroded phases are not usually needed within the same soil type. Commonly, however, stony phases are indicated with a separate numeral for this phase of the soil type.

Less common phases, like drained phases and depth phases, can often be handled most conveniently by a separate number, such as 84 Brookston clay loam and 814 Brookston clay loam, drained phase.

Where land use must be mapped, the symbols should be used separately, not as a part of the soil legend. Generally, it is better to map land use on a separate photograph or overlay, especially in detailed work. It can be mapped on the same photograph if colored ink is used both for symbols and boundaries or if dotted lines are used for the boundaries; yet with much detail such maps become exceedingly difficult to read accurately and very costly to compile for publication.

To the field mapper it is most helpful if the legend is arranged alphabetically by soil names, or first by major groups according to physiographic position or on some other broad basis, and then alphabetically within each group. To the map user, it is most convenient to have the legend arranged, progressively, by symbols, from the smallest figure to the largest, with subdivisions by soil slope classes and eroded phases or other phases under these numbered symbols. A small section from such a list reads as follows:

40Cp	Tippah silty clay loam, severely eroded rolling phase
41Dl	Susquehanna very fine sandy loam
41Dp	Susquehanna clay, severely eroded phase
42Bl	Dulac silt loam
42Bm	Dulac silt loam, slightly eroded phase
42Bn	Dulac silt loam, eroded phase
42Cl	Dulac silt loam, rolling phase
42Cm	Dulac silt loam, slightly eroded rolling phase
42Cn	Dulac silt loam, eroded rolling phase
42Cp	Dulac silty clay loam, severely eroded rolling phase
42Al	Dulac silt loam, level phase
42Am	Dulac silt loam, slightly eroded level phase
43Dl	Cuthbert fine sandy loam
43Dn	Cuthbert clay loam, eroded phase

The conventions used in the soil legend should be worked out individually for each area, bearing in mind the following principles:

1. The primary purpose of the identification soil legend is to key the kinds of soil areas to the names in the legend. The symbols should be as brief as possible and still be legible to the user after photography. Long involved fractional symbols should be avoided since they are difficult to place properly without being made too small for legibility. The more symbols that must be placed outside of small areas and keyed into them with an arrow, the greater the chances for confusion and error and for obscuring other symbols. Recent experience has shown that agricultural advisers and farmers have great difficulty in reading accurately photographic copies of field sheets with symbols placed outside of the areas to which they apply and keyed into them with a short arrow. Since so many soil features are relevant, if one tries to

go far beyond the main purpose of identification in order to develop connotative symbols, his legend may fail in its primary function. No connotative symbol can be more than an oversimplification at best and its small value can be many times offset by decreased legibility of the map.

2. The symbols should all be defined and named in the legend. Wherever the party chief and soil correlator are doubtful of the name, a local name (not already used in correlation) should be given the soil. Separations or subdivisions of major soil types, phases, or other units *need names*. Symbols should not be left dangling by themselves, especially complicated ones that only the members of the immediate soil survey party can read with understanding. This is highly important if photographs of the field sheets are to be used by agricultural advisers or other technicians in farm planning.

3. The legend needs to be revised from time to time and retyped so that all additions are arranged in their proper places. It is equally important to drop out any symbol for kinds of areas that were expected but that were not found, or for subdivisions, further study of which has revealed to be insignificant. If any symbols have been used, they need to be retained in the complete legend but marked "discontinue" to avoid the possibility of having unnamed symbols on the field sheet. (As an extreme example, one tentative legend provided for over 100 separate symbols each meaning exactly the same thing—*Rough gullied land from limestone material!*)

UNCONTROLLED SOIL LEGENDS

The most costly experiments in soil mapping have been with the uncontrolled soil legend. The errors have been so large, avoidable delays in publication so long, and the resulting avoidable extra cost so great, that this kind of legend deserves special emphasis.

The uncontrolled legend is really a means for avoiding the problem of classification. It postpones the problem but does not solve it. If a useful report and map are to result, a classification will be needed. Any generally useful soil map must have clearly defined, named, and classified units. The time to make the classification is before and during mapping, not afterward.

By an uncontrolled legend is meant a scheme of symbolization in which classes of certain selected soil features, or combinations of selected features, are set up independently of one another and used in any combination. Such a scheme might provide for 25 to 100 "soil types," let us say, defined *only* in terms of profile (or some arbitrary combinations of soil features and qualities), 6 classes of slope, 3, 4, or 5 classes of erosion, perhaps subdivided for gully and sheet erosion, and other classes as needed for stoniness, effects of soil blowing, and the like.

If the soil mapper is free to map any combination of these, many hundreds, even thousands, of mapping units may result, and errors and inconsistencies are inevitable. As pointed out repeatedly in this *Manual,* the significance of soil slope, effects of erosion, stoniness, and the like, depend upon the other factors involved in the combination. A difference in slope that is critically important on one soil type may not be so on another. Differences in stoniness critical to otherwise potentially arable soils have no significance on nonarable soils. Thus, with such a scheme, the mapper may use several symbols for areas that should be shown with one symbol and given one name. Then too, he is bound to get some of the boundaries in the wrong places; the divisions between soil-slope phases among different soil types, for example, may come at different percentages of slope.

Besides that, mappers, especially the less experienced ones, are likely to map erroneous combinations—combinations that cannot exist—either through error in writing the symbol or from ignorance of the relationships among the factors. Suppose, for example, that through failure to observe properly or to remember the correct symbol, the mapper uses the symbol for Brookston silt loam—a nearly level poorly drained soil—but adds the symbol for class C soil slope and the one for moderate erosion. A skilled map reader will, of course, recognize this as an impossible situation. With so many kinds of symbols on the map—perhaps thousands of them—the chief of party may not find such errors. If all combinations are checked and listed, many hundreds of them may be found to apply to only a few acres each, primarily because of such errors as the example above.

The greatest source of error with the uncontrolled legend, however, is excessive categorical detail—the separation of all soils on the basis of small differences in one or more features—differences that are really significant in only a very few soils.

Only a soil scientist familiar with the particular area can tell from a complicated symbol what the conditions really are—can, in other words, evaluate the combination into an integrated soil unit. The compilation of a soil map from such field sheets is an enormous undertaking, since a vast group of symbols need to be combined and arranged into classificational units. A draftsman, untrained in soil science, simply cannot do it consistently. A soil scientist familiar with the area needs to go over the whole mass of field sheets and to prepare a new manuscript map for use in compiling the published map. Even with all of this extra work, time, and expense, the results are bound to be poor, since many of the boundaries will not have been drawn in the appropriate places. Yet, the field party will have drawn more lines with such a legend than with a proper soil legend. As the number of lines and symbols per square mile increases, the chances for error greatly increase. The aim should be to place only the really significant lines on the map and to place them accurately.

Obviously, uncontrolled legends greatly increase the problem of accurate soil correlation, since the units may not be properly synthesized soil units in the first place. The elimination of insignificant units *en masse,* by a rule for the map draftsman to follow, is rarely satisfactory. Where such generalization is needed, it can only be done satisfactorily in the field before the field survey is completed.

All legends for soil surveys need to be controlled. Every symbol —every combination of letters and figures used to identify areas— needs to stand for a specific, named (or nameable) unit in the classification. It is the *combination* of letters and figures that is the mapping symbol, not the individual parts of it. Any new combination of letters and figures must be regarded by the mapper and the party chief as an entirely new symbol—just as much a new symbol as if a different letter or figure had been introduced into the legend. Any new symbols proposed by field mappers in the party should be considered immediately by the party chief. Any added to the legend need to be described in relation to the other units, and all legends appropriately revised. Where the proposed new symbol is not needed, the party chief should explain how the area is to be classified and why.

THE DESCRIPTIVE SOIL LEGEND

Besides the identification soil legend, the party chief needs to prepare a descriptive soil legend. The *first duty* of the soil correlator or other supervisory scientist is to help the party chief with the first draft of this legend and help him keep it revised from time to time as the work progresses.

A descriptive legend serves as:

1. A guide to each soil mapper in the party for all symbols and for descriptions of all mapping units in ways that show their relationships to each other, how they are differentiated from one another, their relationships to physiography, geology, and vegetation, and a tentative assessment of their use capabilities and management requirements.

2. A current summary of the research and mapping work that can be made available to cooperators, agricultural advisers, farm planning technicians, and others needing to use the field work that has already been completed.

3. A guide and record of research that can be turned over to a new party chief, if necessary, so that he may go ahead with the work without interruption.

4. The skeleton of the soil survey report under which field notes, photographs, literature reviews, and other materials may be sought and collected as the field work progresses.

It would not be possible to overemphasize the importance of the descriptive soil legend. Through it the soil correlator and other scientists can give the maximum help to the party chief. It gives the other members of the party a uniform guide and, at the same time, an excellent medium for making suggestions and additions of great value to the total effort. Around it and its revision, staff conferences of the party can be organized. The quality of final soil maps and reports bears an amazingly close correlation with the quality and up-to-dateness of the descriptive soil legend. A

good descriptive legend is, perhaps, the most important evidence
of an efficient party chief. Failures to develop and keep up to date
a proper legend have led to great additional cost and delay,
especially where party chiefs have changed during the progress
of the survey.

The form of the legend can vary, although the major items of
the soil survey report outline should be provided for, especially
in drafts following completion of about one-half of the field
mapping. The following items should be included:

1. The identification soil legend—a list of all soil mapping
   symbols and their names—preferably in order of numbers
   so one can find quickly the proper soil name to go with
   any symbol identified on the map.
2. Brief local definitions of slope classes, by groups of soils,
   erosion classes, and the like.
3. Descriptions of all soil series, either alphabetically, or
   alphabetically under broad soil or physiographic groups.
   The series descriptions do not necessarily need to be so
   complete as the official series descriptions used in correlation, *except for new ones.* Yet the description of each
   soil series should set it off clearly from any other soil
   series. Under each soil series, the *names* and symbols of
   each type, phase, or variant should be included with
   whatever descriptions are necessary to distinguish them
   from one another. Complexes and miscellaneous land
   types should be included in the proper place alphabetically,
   or at the end after the soil series descriptions.
4. A genetic key to the soil series.
5. A schematic soil association map, which can be very
   useful to the mappers in areas of contrasting soil regions.
6. Summaries of geology, relief, vegetation, and the like,
   as required in a soil survey report; these should be prepared as it becomes possible to do so.

Besides these main points, the party chief may add references
to books and papers of special significance to an understanding
of the nature and use of the soils in the area being surveyed.

PLOTTING SOIL BOUNDARIES IN THE FIELD

After a suitable base map has been selected, the soil mapping units identified, and the legends prepared, soil mapping can begin. In those few areas where the field party needs to prepare its own base map, it is best to lay out the primary traverse or grid in advance of soil mapping. The plotting of detailed base features and the soil mapping can be done together afterward.

Most of the important operations and requirements of soil mapping have already been discussed under specific topics. Here we are concerned with only a few general principles.

Soil mapping is a technical art. Men lacking sound training in soil science should not be expected to do well, especially those unfamiliar with the principles of the earth sciences. Yet some well-trained men, even men well above the average in competence in soil classification, lack the ability to plot soil boundaries accurately. Some can learn slowly, whereas others are unable to develop good skills. A competent soil mapper is able to abstract the essentials of the pattern of soil landscapes before him and sketch this pattern on the map; then, in reverse, from the lines and symbols on the map, he visualizes the soil pattern they collectively represent. His lines and symbols are drawn carefully. They are clear and neat.

Above all, the successful soil mapper is accurate. He maintains uniform standards of accuracy in his work, in open country and through the bush. He realizes that soil maps without accurate boundaries—guessed at rather than determined—are poor soil maps, regardless of the classification. No man of questionable honesty in research should ever be retained in a soil survey party. It is too difficult to check his results in the critical places; and the damage from using a poor soil map may be very serious.

LOCATION OF BOUNDARIES

Soil boundaries are located on the mapper's route or line of traverse and are sketched accurately on the base. Foot traverses need to be near enough together for accurate plotting between locations. In detailed basic soil surveys, the minimum distance between routes or traverse lines is about ⅛ to ¼ mile, say about 800 to 1,600 feet, depending upon the scale of the map and the complexity of the soil pattern. Even with traverses at around 800 to 1,000 feet, some side traverses are needed to locate boundaries and to identify soils. Although soil boundaries are not actually traversed, *they must be plotted from observations made throughout their course* in detailed soil mapping.

Once identified, the boundaries between most soil types, phases, and other mapping units, coincide with observable features on the surface, such as the foot of a slope, the crest of a ridge, the margin of a swamp forest, a change in color of surface soil, and so on. Such correlations between surface features and soil boundaries require continual testing.

The experienced soil mapper lays out his traverses in order to cross as many soil boundaries as possible. Commonly, he walks roughly at right angles to the drainage. As he proceeds, he plots *tentatively* the soil boundaries apparent from surface features a short distance ahead of himself. As he crosses these boundaries he verifies them. Not until then does he plot them in final form and place the symbol in the area that he has crossed. Good mappers commonly turn and reappraise the landscape they have just crossed before plotting the boundaries finally.

Not all soil boundaries are correlated with external features. Many have to be "dug for." For example, unlike soils varying widely in use capabilities may be developed from interbedded lacustrine or alluvial deposits and have no reliable external features to guide the sketching of boundaries. They need to be located with the spade and auger. In desert and semidesert areas especially, many soil boundaries must be sketched primarily from excavations or borings. Characteristics of the lower horizons and layers of little significance to the native vegetation are often very important to potentialities for irrigation and to hazards of waterlogging and salinity under irrigation. Yet even in the desert, the skilled mapper, able to recognize land forms and plant species accurately, uses external features a great deal, although he continually checks the soil boundaries with test holes.

Some soil boundaries are sharply defined; others are midway lines in transition zones within which one soil gradually merges with another. The establishment of transitional units between the original mapping units often worsens the problem by requiring two boundaries in place of one, each of which is even more difficult to sketch satisfactorily.

On detailed soil maps to be published at about 2 inches to the mile (1:31,680), boundaries should be accurate within at least 100 feet. Even more important is the relative positional accuracy of boundaries in relation to roads, streams, and other local reference points. Even though a soil boundary were in error by only 50 feet, if it were placed on the wrong side of a stream or road, the error would be so conspicuous that map users would lose confidence in the work. Soil maps are commonly read by reference to base features. A farmer, for example, is concerned with the soils in his fields, say in one between a stream or gully and the road, in another between the stream and a steep hill, and so on. The engineer may be vitally interested in the soil just where a road crosses a railroad. Correct relative position is more important to the accuracy of a soil map for most of its uses than absolute or geodetic accuracy.

Only the most experienced mappers can estimate distances accurately beyond one-eighth mile or 660 feet, even under the best conditions. Most mappers need checks on estimates beyond 300 feet in detailed mapping. Variations in land form introduce many illusions of distance that mislead the beginner. Equal distances, for example, when viewed over water, cleared land, or brush land or through trees, do not appear equal to the beginner. The distance across a smooth valley appears to be less than a similar distance across a valley with low hills in it.

In reconnaissance soil mapping, the boundaries are not necessarily observed throughout their course. They are plotted where the lines of traverse cross them; but between these points of observation, many boundaries are sketched from the appearance of patterns on aerial photographs and the general appearance of the landscape. Exceptional skill is required in the interpretation of external features.

In soil mapping it is recognized that some soil boundaries are more important than others. Boundaries between highly contrasting soils need emphasis, like those, for example, that separate wet soil from dry soil, very clayey soil from very sandy soil, level soil from hilly soil, and stony soil from nonstony soil. The boundaries that carry a color distinction on the published map are especially critical because they commonly separate soils of different, broad use potentialities as well as those of different management requirements.

The sketching of soil boundaries is a continual check on the soil classification. Theoretically, it may be possible to develop a good system of soil classification without mapping; yet few, if any, such systems have been developed. Soils are areas, and in this sense the boundaries are a part of their definitions. If boundaries cannot be clearly and similarly identified by competent men, the classification obviously needs revision. If the mapper needs many supplemental symbols and notes to describe the mapped areas, beyond those provided for in the mapping legend, the classification is inadequate or the units are inadequately described in the descriptive legend. Without the test of drawing soil boundaries, classifiers may set up mapping units that are really points, not areas. Poor mapping units may be established on the basis of characteristics in the lower part of the solum that cannot be regularly observed or that vary erratically. Then too, the early drafts of a mapping legend may suggest the use of taxonomic units as mapping units but later experience shows the taxonomic units should be recognized as parts of defined complexes.

Perhaps the ability to conceive the soil pattern, in contrast to a group of individual mapping units, is the most difficult skill for a beginning soil mapper to acquire. No skill is more important. Put simply, he must learn that all the soil must be "called something." It is far easier to pick out well-established and easily identified areas, enclose them with boundaries, and ignore the rest. But in making a soil map, one is not simply mapping out individual units; rather, he is sketching a pattern of units. The boundary of one soil unit is also that of another or parts of several others. In legends and instructions, party chiefs and supervisory scientists always need to emphasize relationships among the units—not simply individual, detached descriptions of each unit. To do this job effectively, the mapper must learn what kinds of units go together in geographic patterns.

SIZE OF AREAS AND DETAIL

Attention has already been drawn to the difference between categorical and cartographic detail. Here we are concerned with the latter. The problem is most frequently posed in terms of the minimum size of areas of one mapping unit to separate from another. The party chief should study this problem and issue instructions that will insure uniformity throughout the map.

As a general rule, all areas need to be shown that are significant to differential predictions of soil use and management requirements. If a separate field boundary is required by the farmer for effective and economical use of the soil area, certainly the boundary needs to be shown. In regions of very intensive soil use, areas of as little as ½, 1, or 2 acres may need to be shown. In areas of extensive soil use for crops, areas smaller than 5 acres may be ignored unless they are strongly contrasting.

Spots of wet soil, steep soil, rocky soil, or of other soil unsuited for crops should be indicated on the map if they occur within areas otherwise potentially useful for crops. Depending on the mapping scale, they may be enclosed by boundaries or indicated by symbols shown in the standard legends and defined as to the kind of area represented and its size. Thus, the more important the boundary, the smaller is the minimum size of area to be enclosed by it. Yet the size of such small areas should not be exaggerated on the map. For the really small ones, defined symbols should be used.

Where the pattern of small areas becomes too complex for accurate mapping and symbolization, the soil mapping legend needs to be reexamined with a view of using soil complexes as mapping units.

The following rule should be a strict guide: *No boundaries should be placed on the detailed soil map unless they can be sketched accurately.* Between soils that gradually grade from one to another, the soil boundary may be placed within a broad transitional belt. Such occasional soil boundaries are not precise; they cannot be; but they are placed after detailed examination of the soils and their associated features.

SECONDARY SHEETS

Secondary sheets are used for secondary traverses or side routes where it is impractical to carry the master map, as in heavily wooded areas. The data from the secondary sheets are transferred to the master field sheet as soon as convenient. These sheets should be filed as a part of the original manuscript material.

Secondary sheets are also used for the entire area, or some part of it, to show data or fine distinctions beyond those included on the master map. Their use should be limited to clearly established needs, because they increase the time and cost of the survey. Data not intended for the final published map, such as land cover or subphases of soil slope, stoniness, or eroded soil, may be mapped on secondary sheets for some special objective. The extra time and cost of handling the secondary sheets are less than in the assembly of a soil map from highly detailed field sheets, from which the boundaries and symbols to be published have to be sorted out from many that are not to be published. Transparent, oil-treated paper is preferable for such use.

Field notes to accompany the soil map should be made for any special conditions not adequately expressed by the map itself. These are especially helpful during the early stages of a survey, before the legend has been worked into final form. Any suggested departures from the legend should be noted by the mapper on the spot and brought to the attention of the party chief immediately. The party chief should help beginners learn to keep such notes of their mapping, as a part of their essential training and in order to assist him in checking their work, both in the office and in the field. Still it must be recalled that greater accuracy and uniformity can be had by the use of well-defined standard symbols than by written notes. When copious field notes are necessary to explain the boundaries and departures from the symbols, it is evident that the legend is not correct or that it is improperly understood by the mappers.

CHECKING FIELD SHEETS

Every field sheet needs to be checked with all adjoining sheets to be sure that boundaries and other lines properly join and that symbols are alike. The separate sheets should also be examined for any open boundaries, areas without symbols, and other omissions. Each mapper should check his own sheets; and besides, they should be rechecked by some other worker to be sure that each part of the map is complete and clearly legible. The chief of party should check the sheets of each mapper in several places in the field. The field sheets of beginners will need much field checking. The party chief can assign the work in such a way that he gets daily comparisons among men at the borders of their sheets. The soil correlator or supervisory soil scientist responsible for the technical standards should check boundaries and symbols on several sheets selected at random.

Finally all the field sheets are given a careful final checking, including checks for corrections and remapping required by the soil correlator, by the chief of party just before they are sent forward to the correlator for review. Omissions on the map or in the legend, or inconsistencies between them, greatly increase the costs of map construction and delay publication.

COLLECTION AND EXAMINATION OF SOIL SAMPLES

Besides the soil characteristics observed and measured in the field, other measurements need to be made in the laboratory. A complete soil, of course, cannot be moved into a laboratory; only parts of it. Items of great importance to soil classification and behavior, such as temperature and living organisms, cannot be preserved in samples, nor can slope, stoniness, or the thickness and arrangement of horizons in the profile.

The value of laboratory work depends upon care in sampling and upon a synthesis of the results with field morphology in making interpretations. No matter how carefully laboratory work is done, firm predictions cannot be expected from such data alone.

The selection of sample areas has been discussed in the section on Examination and Description of Soils in the Field. Each soil sample needs to be a fair sample of a specific genetic horizon or other layer of a kind of soil worth sampling. Samples collected by arbitrary depths, unrelated to the genetic horizons, are generally useless—even worse than useless and downright misleading if they contain unknown mixtures of two or more contrasting horizons. It is wasteful to use laboratory facilities and time on poorly collected soil samples or those without adequate descriptions and names.

Then too, the purpose of the samples needs to be clearly in the mind of those collecting them. For measurements of constituents present in only tiny amounts, for example, unusual care to prevent contamination is required. Also it needs to be recalled that soil samples must be fumigated when passing through some quarantine stations. This can be done without injuring them for all ordinary uses, at least, and is a necessary precaution against the spread of harmful insects and diseases.

COLLECTION OF SAMPLES

Depending on how well the soils in a survey area are known, soil samples may be required at the start, during the course of the survey, and after the field mapping is completed. In areas having new or doubtful taxonomic units, analyses may be needed to establish the appropriate limits or ranges to be allowed. Many decisions on soil correlation cannot be made accurately without considerable mapping, but the more that can be made at the start of the survey the better. After the map is well along it makes extra work in the cartographic office to combine several units into one. In entirely new areas, samples of many tentative soil units are needed at the very start, before the legend for a detailed survey is well established.

Samples are collected from soil survey areas for laboratory measurements for (1) determining the fundamental properties

327

of soils in relation to their classification as specific types, series, families, and great soil groups; (2) suggesting their genesis and relationships to their environment; (3) checking field measurements and observations of textural class, pH, soluble salts, carbonates, permeability, and the like; (4) help in suggesting their responses to management practices; and (5) help in assessing their physical properties that influence trafficability, highway and airport design, and similar engineering uses. Although some measurements are common to two or more of these objectives, different sets are needed. Besides these uses in the laboratory, samples are taken for comparing the color and structure of soils and for exhibits used as visual aids in soil recognition.

FRAGMENTAL SAMPLES

As Cline[1] has emphasized, soil volumes, not areas, are sampled. Each sample needs to represent a homogeneous volume insofar as that can be determined by field observations. Where possible, samples should be collected to represent the volume and appraise its parameter. By statistical tests, the range in variability and accuracy of results may be determined. Nevertheless, the use of statistical methods in no way reduces the need for careful selection in the field.

It is not possible to make separate determinations on a large number of representative samples of the same horizons, except in a few selected and important soils. The cost is usually too great. For precise studies of soil genesis, however, several samples of each representative horizon lead to more accurate results than single samples.

Selection of sampling site.—Since one, two, or three sites within a mapping unit ordinarily can be sampled in detailed soil surveys, these are located to represent the unit. (Even where many samples can be taken the sites should be randomized only *within* a narrowly defined taxonomic unit.) Within the soil type or phase the scientist should be careful to avoid bias. The sites chosen should represent the taxonomic unit as it occurs. In view of the large amount of time needed to handle the samples, and their importance for correlation and analyses, adequate time needs to be allowed for the location of representative sites. The soil scientist should be ever mindful that much time and expense on the part of other workers in the laboratory, in the greenhouse, and on the field experimental plot may be nullified if he neglects to collect representative samples from well-described profiles.

Where conveniently available, virgin soils are sampled for correlation and analyses unless the samples are specifically taken for a study of cultivated soils. In selecting sites for virgin soils those showing evidence of disturbance, even of the very upper part, are avoided.

---

[1] For an excellent discussion of sampling, see Cline, M. G. PRINCIPLES OF SOIL SAMPLING. Soil Sci. 58: 275–288. 1944. For a shorter discussion, with special reference to sampling for chemical analysis, see Cline, M. G. METHODS OF COLLECTING AND PREPARING SOIL SAMPLES. Soil Sci. 59: 3–5. 1945.

For studies of soil genesis, the very upper layers, A_0 and A_1 are especially important. Rarely can adequate samples be taken from roadsides. Where representative virgin sites are not to be found, samples need to be taken of soils in cultivation or in pasture. It is best to go out into a field and avoid the very margin. Where possible the management history should be obtained. Before choosing the exact point of sampling the soil should be examined at several points to help in choosing one with typical horizon depths and other observable features.

Care in sampling depends partly on the purpose. Samples taken for more or less routine analyses and for correlation alone require less care and detail of description than those to be used for intensive morphological or genetic studies.

Samples should be taken from a fresh excavation, especially for chemical work. No soil samples for any purpose other than visual examination in immediate field identification or for exhibit should be taken from road cuts unless those cuts are unusually recent. Samples of rock and occasionally of parent material can be taken from road cuts, but not soil samples. Soil samples from road cuts may be unsatisfactory for several reasons. Dust from roads, especially those surfaced with gravel, quickly contaminates the exposed soil, and the surface soil perhaps for several hundred feet to the side. The native vegetation has usually been so disturbed along roadbeds that the soil is markedly altered, even though the soil has not been plowed or otherwise mechanically disturbed. For example, A_1 horizons of Podzols are thickened under the more luxuriant mesophytic vegetation made possible by the greater light intensity along the roadway as compared to conditions within the forest. In open areas, dust and other foreign matter accumulate along fences and roadways. An exposed soil profile is soon altered. Alternate wetting-and-drying and freezing-and-thawing change the structure. The soil becomes more thoroughly oxidized. In the natural soil, water movement, both by capillary action and from differences in vapor pressure, is largely vertical; but in the exposed road cut water moves laterally to the face, leaving an increased concentration of soluble salts on the exposed surface. Many soil horizons that are soft under natural conditions may become hard or indurated with exposure. Some caliche and laterite are extreme examples.

Kinds of samples.—Most soil samples taken in the soil survey are (1) fragmental or loose samples from individual horizons, but a few are (2) undisturbed core samples taken from individual horizons, and some are (3) undisturbed monoliths for study and exhibit.

Fragmental samples are taken from the individual horizons by loosening the materials and storing them in paper or cloth bags. These samples are those most generally used for soil correlation and for mechanical and chemical analyses. Undisturbed core samples are taken from the individual horizon by careful cutting, and stored in a way to preserve soil structure. Such samples are useful for determinations of porosity, bulk density, petrographic examination, and similar physical measurements. Undisturbed monoliths are used mainly for exhibit.

Preparation of soil for sampling.—The tools used in sampling have already been described in the section on Preparation for Field Work. A pit is necessary to collect adequate samples for most purposes. Samples taken by augers, tubes, or core machines are always suspect of contamination or unrepresentativeness from unseen rodent holes or other unconformities. No easy way has been found to get the pits. Pits must be dug with shovel, pick, and crowbar. They should be large enough to permit careful observation of the entire profile. A pit about 2 feet wide and 5 or 6 feet long is usually necessary. Really a pit of this size can often be dug faster than a smaller one because of greater ease in handling the digging tools. Good light should fall on one of the long sides. When dug, the best lighted wall should be cleaned with a knife or trowel to expose the structure. The surface just above this wall should be kept free of disturbance if possible. The horizons can be marked off, designated, and the profile then described in detail as already explained. In forested regions one frequently must sacrifice good lighting for representativeness.

Sampling.—After the profile has been exposed and described, representative samples are collected from each individual horizon. For purposes of correlation it is usually adequate to sample each recognizable horizon. For laboratory analyses, particularly if a study of genesis is to be made, the thicker horizons may need to be separated arbitrarily into thinner subhorizons. Nothing is gained by subdividing recognizable horizons into layers less than 3 inches thick.

Fragmented samples of about 1 quart or liter provide adequate amounts for most analyses. Generally, samples should be taken in a vertical section, one directly beneath the other from the side of the pit. Margins or gradations between horizons need to be avoided in taking samples; otherwise soil is taken uniformly from the entire horizon. Normally, the sample can be removed readily by holding a large trowel or shovel at the bottom limit of the horizon while the soil above is loosened by a knife or trowel. The material is collected on the shovel blade and then transferred to a container. Obviously care must be used to avoid material from the horizons above that would contaminate the sample. When very thin horizons are sampled, or if extremely detailed morphological studies are to be made along with the sampling, it may be helpful to remove the horizons above the one being sampled so that only one horizon is dealt with at a time. The pit may be dug as a series of steps, each step representing a horizon or subhorizon. This kind of pit is especially useful if vertical undisturbed cores of individual horizons are to be taken. In detailed morphological studies the step method of preparing the pit gives the additional advantage of exposing each horizon in three dimensions.

In the straight-walled pits, after the profile is described, many find it most convenient to sample the very upper horizons

—A_{00}, A_0, and A_1—first, then to clean the wall, and next to sample the remaining horizons from the lowest upward. It is often a major problem to avoid contamination of the top horizon.

Coarse fragments larger than an inch or so in diameter are picked out from the soil material on the shovel and discarded. It is helpful to make an estimate of the volume occupied by these discarded coarse fragments. Studies of soil volume and some of soil texture require sieving and weighing in the field to obtain measurements of the volume or weight occupied by these fragments.

Especially in reconnaissance and exploratory surveys it is often helpful to collect samples of vegetation, especially of widely occurring grasses or grasslike plants, that may be analyzed for any outstanding excesses or deficiencies in calcium, phosphorus, manganese, iron, cobalt, zinc, molybdenum, and other mineral elements.

Samples are placed in containers, labeled, and carried to a suitable place for drying.

Containers.—The containers used vary widely. Undisturbed core samples are generally collected directly in cylindrical metal containers provided with covers for top and bottom. Samples for moisture determinations are placed in moisture-tight metal or plastic boxes and sent immediately to the laboratory for weighing.

Loose fragmental samples are commonly put into clean sacks of cloth, plastic, or heavy paper. If canvas bags are used they must be heavy if the samples are to be mailed; otherwise fine material is lost. Cloth sacks are not suitable for soil samples containing large amounts of soluble salts. If samples are moist, or become moist, the salts are carried out to the surface of the cloth. Heavy cardboard containers are also used. Moist samples can be exposed in open sacks at the field headquarters for drying. For shipment, they must be packed *tightly* in strong wooden boxes. The separate boxes should not be too large, ordinarily not more than 50 pounds, or they are likely to loosen in transit. Heavy metal-sealed boxes are ideal for long shipments of dry samples, especially by ocean freight.

Recently very light-weight, translucent, waterproof, strong plastic sacks for soil samples have come on the market. These are ideal for use in exploratory surveys away from a work car or truck. Tight-fitting metal cans need to be used for soils that harden irreversibly upon drying, as some lateritic soils, especially if mechanical analyses are to be made.

Labeling.—Each sample should be labeled adequately as soon as it is taken. Since samples from the various horizons may become separated from one another, each one should be completely labeled. If time is very short, each sample may be given a profile number and subhorizon designation; but as soon as possible the complete label should be prepared and attached. It is best to do this on the spot if time allows. The label should carry the date, location, name of collector, name of soil type, and number of the soil horizon, its position in the profile, and a very brief summary of its description. The writing should be done with a hard pencil or moisture-proof ink, since the labels often become damp and the writing obscured. For safety, it is well to put labels both inside and outside the container.

The labeling of soil samples has been standardized in the Division of Soil Survey. In the system, the label indicates whether a particular sample is taken for special studies or whether for routine soil correlation. The system designates the year in which the sample is collected, its location by State and county, and both the individual soil profile and the soil horizon.

Special samples have a six-part label: *Part 1* is a capital S; *part 2* is the last two digits of the year; *part 3* is the standard letter abbreviation of the State; *part 4* is a number designating the county; *part 5* is a number identifying the soil profile within the special set of samples; and *part 6* is a number designating the particular horizon sampled. Short dashes separate parts 4 from 5 and 5 from 6 and also the State abbreviations ending in "l" from the county number. The label for the last sample of each profile is followed by an asterisk, to show that no other sample was collected from a greater depth.

Routine samples from survey areas are labeled similarly except for the omission of the prefix letter S.

The number S46Ill–11–12–9*, for example, identifies a special sample collected in 1946, from Illinois. The number 11 in the fourth part of the symbol identifies the county as Christian County, the eleventh county in the alphabetical list of Illinois counties. The sample is in the twelfth soil profile of the series of special samples, and is the ninth and last horizon sampled. This system of numbering soil samples helps all who need to deal with them. Special samples are further identified by the number of the research project, instead of the area name as used for routine samples from survey areas.

The following illustrates a tag filled out in accordance with this system. The number is written at both the top and bottom of the tag, to assist in filing. When unpacked, the top part of the tag can be cut off and put with the soil sample, and the rest of the tag is filed.

		Field No. 2
		S46Ill–11–12–9*
Area	*Line Proj. Z–1–2–8*	
Location	*SW4NW4Sec27T11NR1E; 1 mi.* *So. Pana*	
Collector	*John Doe*	
Soil Type	*Alma silt loam*	
Depth	*72 in. to 79 in.*	
Description	*Light yellowish-brown* *friable calcareous silt loam (calcareous loess)*	
S46Ill–11–12–9*		

Abbreviations of the names of the States and Territories (and full names for those not abbreviated) used in the standard soil sample labels are as follows:

State	Abbreviation	State	Abbreviation
Alabama	Ala.	New Mexico	N. Mex.
Arizona	Ariz.	New York	N. Y.
Arkansas	Ark.	North Carolina	N. C.
California	Calif.	North Dakota	N. Dak.
Colorado	Colo.	Ohio	Ohio
Connecticut	Conn.	Oklahoma	Okla.
Delaware	Del.	Oregon	Oreg.
Florida	Fla.	Pennsylvania	Pa.
Georgia	Ga.	Rhode Island	R. I.
Idaho	Idaho	South Carolina	S. C.
Illinois	Ill.	South Dakota	S. Dak.
Indiana	Ind.	Tennessee	Tenn.
Iowa	Iowa	Texas	Tex.
Kansas	Kans.	Utah	Utah
Kentucky	Ky.	Vermont	Vt.
Louisiana	La.	Virginia	Va.
Maine	Maine	Washington	Wash.
Maryland	Md.	West Virginia	W. Va.
Massachusetts	Mass.	Wisconsin	Wis.
Michigan	Mich.	Wyoming	Wyo.
Minnesota	Minn.		
Mississippi	Miss.	*Other areas*	*Abbreviation*
Missouri	Mo.	Alaska	Alaska
Montana	Mont.	Canal Zone	C. Z.
Nebraska	Nebr.	Hawaiian Islands	T. H.
Nevada	Nev.	Panama	Panama
New Hampshire	N. H.	Puerto Rico	P. R.
New Jersey	N. J.	Virgin Islands	V. I.

For other countries use full name or standard abbreviation if it does not conflict with the others in this list.

Drying and storage of samples.—The soil samples should be dried[2] in a place where there are no gases or dust that might contaminate them. Depending on circumstances, the samples may be removed from their containers and spread out on papers. Large lumps are crushed. Small or relatively dry samples may dry well enough in the opened container. On arrival at headquarters, samples are transferred to labeled glass jars for storage. Usually small subsamples of about 100 grams are filed in glass vials for ready reference. Each horizon sample is placed in a separately labeled glass vial. The several samples of a profile may be viewed together and compared with other samples of the same and related soil types. The vial samples are useful mainly for comparisons of texture and color.

Samples placed in the large glass jars may be used for laboratory analyses. Representative portions are removed and sieved through a 2 millimeter screen. That passing through the screen is then made ready for analyses.

SOIL MONOLITHS

Monoliths of soil profiles are taken as visual aids in soil study and identification. The collection of complete undisturbed mono-

---

[2] Except, of course, samples that change irreversibly upon drying.

liths takes much time and is not commonly done in the research work itself. Monoliths are useful, however, for display and classroom work.

Both thick and thin monoliths have been used. The thick monoliths are collected by placing a box around an undisturbed section, and the soil is thereafter preserved in this open-faced box. Generally, the section is about 6 or 8 inches wide, 4 inches deep, and long enough to include a part of the C horizon. The collection is made from an excavation. The exposed wall is cut so that a vertical section of the soil just fits into a wooden or metal box. The box is placed over the monolith and held in place while the back side of the monolith is loosened from the wall. A cover is placed on the exposed side. This cover is removed when the monolith is exhibited. The disadvantages of these thick-boxed monoliths are the great care necessary in collection, the great weight of the resulting monolith, and the hazard of damage in handling. They have been collected only a little in the United States.

A better method of collecting monoliths depends on the use of an adhesive that holds a section an inch or less thick to a stiff board. In one process, the wall of the excavation is smoothed and cellulose acetate is sprayed or painted directly on the soil material. When dry the soil adheres to this tough film. The somewhat flexible monolith is cut from the bank and glued to a board. Any excess soil is removed. The monolith is treated with a vinylite resin to harden the soil material and to preserve it from damage. Details of this method of collection are given by Smith and Moodie.[3]

Another process to achieve the same kind of thin monolith has been described by Berger and Muckenhirn.[4] A thin section of soil is removed from the wall of the excavation by use of a metal form and is then treated directly with vinylite resin to preserve it.

These thin monoliths have been used a good deal in the past 5 years. They are light in weight, resistant to damage, easy to store, and exhibit soil structures and colors satisfactorily. They are hard to take in stony soils.

SOIL MICROMONOLITHS

Micromonoliths are being used increasingly in soil correlation work. Small thin sections of each horizon are taken with a metal cutter that is fitted with a wooden plunger (fig. 52). These sections are glued to a stiff narrow piece of cardboard, one above the other in natural sequence. This gives the effect of a small-scale monolith. Such a monolith can be taken in 10 to 15 minutes and is easy to file. These micromonoliths have advantages over the vial samples. They can be taken more quickly and they allow better comparisons between samples. But the vial samples are needed for comparisons of texture.

[3] SMITH, H. W., and MOODIE, C. D. COLLECTION AND PRESERVATION OF SOIL PROFILES. Soil Sci. 64: 61–69, illus. 1947.
[4] BERGER, K. C., and MUCKENHIRN, R. J. SOIL PROFILES OF NATURAL APPEARANCE MOUNTED WITH VINYLITE RESIN. Soil Sci. Soc. Amer. Proc. 10: 368–370, illus. 1946.

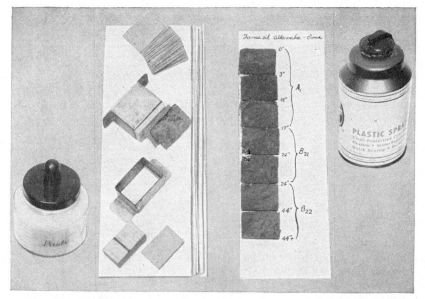

FIGURE 52.—Equipment for mounting micromonoliths, and a mounted one.

Bushnell has described the method of collection and mounting these micromonoliths.[5]

After selection of a site, the soil profile is exposed. The plunger is inserted in the cutter. A small backing card of blotting paper, about 1 inch by $1\frac{3}{8}$ inches, is fitted over the plunger and within the cutter. This is coated with liquid paste or "waterglass." The cutter is forced into the soil, either directly on the wall of the cut or into a large lump. The cutter, with an excess of soil on its face, is cut away. The excess soil on the face is carefully removed to preserve the natural structure of the sample. By pushing the plunger, the sample is pushed out; then it is pasted in its proper place on a 10- by 2-inch mounting strip of heavy blotting paper.[6] If each individual microsection is tight against the next, they will help support one another.

After all horizon samples are fixed on the mounting, the assembled strip is marked with depth figures and horizon designations. Dried specimens may be strengthened by immersing the trimmed monolith in a 10-percent solution of vinylite or by applying it as a spray or with a soft brush.

These fixed strips may be pasted onto a stiff mounting card, say 4 or 6 inches by 10 inches, on which depth figures, horizon designations, and data about the soil may be lettered.

---

[5] BUSHNELL, T. M. SOIL PROFILE SAMPLING MADE EASY. Purdue Univ. Agr. Expt. Sta. Spec. Cir. 2, 8 pp., illus. Lafayette, Ind. 1949.
[6] Many prefer to mount the samples directly on the stiff mounting card and omit the intermediate mounting on strips of blotting paper, partly to complete the whole job, notes and all, on the spot.

The individual small sections are most often made in a standard size of 1 by 1½ inches and then glued to cards 3 or 4 inches wide and 10 inches long.

The use of individual sections of the same size, regardless of horizon thickness, distorts the micromonolith in relation to the actual profile. Some avoid such distortion by using an adjustable cutter so that the widths of the micro-samples are made proportional to the thicknesses of the horizons. One long side of the cutter is movable with a thumb screw. An assortment of small backing cards of various widths may be carried. The resulting micromonoliths then reflect the true scale of the soil profile. The extra work is scarcely justified in taking micromonoliths for use by soil scientists in soil correlation, since they are not misled by the apparent distortion. Properly scaled micromonoliths are much preferred for exhibits or for use in the classroom.

USEFUL LABORATORY DATA

Generally, it may be said that all accurate physical, chemical, and mineralogical measurements on representative samples of soil horizons from well-described soils are helpful. Yet certainly not all are equally useful. Measurements that are exceedingly helpful in one soil area, or even in understanding relationships among one group of soils within an area, may not be especially revealing with another group of soils. Above all, the value of the laboratory data depends upon the associated morphological data: The two sets of data must be interpreted together. Chemical data obtained on soil samples collected with augers, unaccompanied by good profile descriptions, are usually not worth the expense, except possibly in broad exploratory surveys of totally unknown areas.

Plans for laboratory work should be laid in advance of the soil survey, with provisions made for additional studies should the need arise. These plans should be developed jointly between the field scientists and the laboratory scientists, and the results should be interpreted jointly, especially where the problems are complex. Judgment is needed in selecting the determinations to be made with the facilities available. It is easy to load a laboratory with routine measurements of such low significance that it loses its effectiveness in the research program.

Laboratory determinations made as a part of the soil survey may be roughly classed into five main groups according to their purpose.

1. Those to establish the characteristics of genetic soil types, elucidate their origin, and set each off from related soil types. Here are included mechanical analyses, pH, organic carbon, exchangeable cations, carbonates, nitrogen, bulk density, permeability, mineralogical composition, sometimes total chemical analyses, and perhaps others depending upon the problem involved.

2. Those to check identification of established soil types and field determinations. These include mechanical analyses, pH, carbonates, sometimes organic carbon, and sometimes others.

3. Those used as an aid in suggesting management practices, including determinations of permeability, available or soluble plant nutrients, exchangeable cations, pH, and the like.
4. Those needed for predicting the effects of irrigation, the drainage and management practices required if soil is placed under irrigation, and the requirements for rehabilitation of soil that has become salty through the effects of irrigation. The field methods are explained briefly in the section on Estimation and Mapping of Salts and Alkali in the Soil.
5. The determinations required for predictions of highway design, airport location and design, trafficability, and other problems in soil engineering. The results of such determinations may be used directly in a particular project and also to characterize soil types, provided that the samples are collected by defined soil horizons and types.

A full treatment of the laboratory methods and work to be done to accompany soil classification and interpretation lies beyond the scope of this *Manual*. Only a few principles need to be dealt with here.

First of all, field scientists and laboratory scientists, to work effectively, need considerable knowledge of one another's skills and problems. Only a few men can or should attempt to be highly proficient in actually doing both kinds of work. The laboratory scientist needs to have an appreciation of the problems of soil classification, soil mapping, and soil management, and of the range of variability in the universe that a soil sample represents. Often time is wasted to achieve an accuracy within the laboratory between duplicates from the same sample that is out of proportion to the error of field sampling. The field scientist must learn a good deal about the methods used in laboratories and the value and limitations of laboratory data. Field men often ask for laboratory work without realizing fully the time and cost involved or how the results may be useful to them.

Both kinds of specialists need to work together. Especially in analyzing the field problems and collecting soil samples for extensive work in fundamental soil characterization and soil genesis, the scientist responsible for the laboratory work should take part in enough of the field work to have a clear picture of the problem. Only then can the final decisions be made concerning the set of laboratory determinations most likely to be helpful. For many problems a geologist should also be a member of such study parties.

Standard methods need emphasis so that widely separated soils may be compared. New and better methods need to be adopted as they are developed, but only when clearly superior. Often it is necessary to make determinations by both old and new methods for some time so that the results of the one can be interpreted by comparison with those of the other.

Work plans for survey areas should provide for laboratory service more adequately than has generally been the practice in the past. Too often all the laboratory work follows the completion of the field work, after the soil separations have been made. Where laboratory data are needed for deciding clearly between soil units, these should be obtained in the very beginning of the survey. Once the differences are established, study of soil morphology will usually disclose accessory characteristics that may serve as criteria for identification in the field.

In developing data for use in making predictions about fertilizers, lime, and other amendments, the aim is to establish the *responsiveness* of the soil type to the various treatments. For the purpose of making predictions of management practices, the soil survey party chief should interpret the data in cooperation with specialists in soil fertility and management. Specific recommendations depend upon the previous use of amendments and the cropping history as well as upon soil type. Determinations of available plant nutrients will give different results, of course, on different areas of the same soil type that have had different treatments. Among highly responsive soils these differences may be simply enormous. In the soil descriptions and management predictions, the responsiveness of the soil, or the level of yields under a given management system, is the thing fixed in the soil type, not the specific treatment required from year to year. Cooperation with advisory soil scientists can be mutually useful. Soil classification is an essential tool in advisory work with fertilizers, since most of the "quick-test" results, used by farm advisers, have a different interpretation on different soil types.

ESTIMATION AND MAPPING OF SALTS AND ALKALI IN THE SOIL

Strongly alkaline soils and those containing harmful amounts of salts need to be separated from other soils in soil mapping. Those having sufficient quantities of soluble salts or such a high degree of alkalinity as to interfere with the growth of crop plants are largely confined to arid and semiarid regions, although they also occur in humid regions in coastal strips affected by tides and in local areas affected by seepage of salty waters. Such soils require special management practices and measures for reclamation. The amount and kind of salts in the soil, now and in the past, are commonly reflected in the morphology of the soil profile, but not with sufficient specificity to suggest the actual quantities or specific crop adaptabilities. This is especially true of young or recent soils on alluvial deposits. Many salty soils are useful for crops if the salts are removed and are not allowed to accumulate again, provided the other soil characteristics are favorable.

A considerable part of the irrigated soils in the West contain sufficient salts or are alkaline enough to depress crop yields. On some, crop production is curtailed or even prevented. Many acres of irrigated land have had to be abandoned because of salts that were originally present in the soil or especially because of salts that accumulated during irrigation.

One of the principal purposes of detailed soil surveys in such areas is to identify soils that cannot be irrigated practicably and to suggest the probable problems and methods of reclamation and use for those that can be used for crops. The amount of soluble salts in a soil or its degree of alkalinity, and the many other soil conditions that affect salt accumulation or movement, even to great depths, are observed and evaluated in the classification and its interpretation.

THE NATURE AND ORIGIN OF SALINE AND ALKALI SOILS

A *saline soil* contains enough salts so distributed in the profile that they interfere with the growth of most crop plants.

An *alkali soil* has either so high a degree of alkalinity—pH 8.5 or higher—or so high a percentage of exchangeable sodium—15 percent or higher—or both, that the growth of most crop plants is reduced. Thus, alkali soils, as a group, have a wide range of exchangeable sodium and of pH. Some soils with more than 15 percent exchangeable sodium, for example, have pH values less than 8.5 if the other exchangeable cations are mainly hydrogen.

A *saline-alkali soil* has a combination of harmful quantities of salts and either a high alkalinity or high exchangeable sodium, or both, so distributed in the profile that the growth of most crop plants is reduced.

339

Locally, the terms "alkali" and "alkali soil" have been used for all these conditions. Some have used "alkali soil" as the general term, "white alkali" as roughly equivalent to saline soils as now defined, and "black alkali" as roughly equivalent to alkali soils. The term "black" was suggested by the dark color caused by the dispersion of the organic matter at a high pH. These older terms should not be used in soil descriptions or reports, except in quotes with a footnote explanation of local usage where it exists.

The soluble salts in soils may come from the deposits left by decomposition of primary minerals in rocks, from sedimentary rocks, from invasion of the sea, or from the salt carried in winds off the sea ("cyclic" salt). Salts are readily carried by water and accumulate within the soil or at the surface when the water evaporates. Thus, salty soils commonly occur in low areas and many have periodically or permanently high water tables. Generally speaking, salty soils are formed in arid or semiarid regions in low places or on seepy slopes that would be occupied by swamps in humid regions. A high water table, or a perched water table, may exist naturally above underlying impervious strata, or a water table may be caused or elevated by excessive irrigation or by seepage from streams or water-distribution systems. Large quantities of salt may be added to the soil in salty irrigation water. Some sedimentary rocks contain large quantities of gypsum and other salts that contribute to the salt content of the soils developed from them. Water seeping through such rocks carries the salts to soils at lower elevations. Where rainfall is so light and evaporation so high that little leaching takes place, the salts released from the minerals in the soil remain in it; yet rarely do enough salts accumulate in this way alone to make a soil too salty for crops.

Many combinations of different salts occur in saline soils. The presence of normally neutral, or nearly neutral, salts, like the chlorides and sulfates of sodium, calcium, and magnesium, does not make the soil strongly alkaline; but the alkaline salts, like sodium carbonate and bicarbonate, do cause a strongly alkaline reaction.

The exchangeable cations in a soil greatly influence its properties. In pure water, acid clays are fairly easily dispersed;[1] calcium-clays are mildly to moderately alkaline and usually less easily dispersed; while sodium-clays are strongly to very strongly alkaline and are most easily dispersed. While a high salt concentration is maintained in the soil, the colloids are flocculated; but

---

[1] The degree of dispersion and other properties of clays depend also on the type of clay mineral. Even acid clays of well-developed Latosols are not easily dispersed. Flocculation and granulation in natural soils also depend upon the kinds and amounts of organic matter, root growth, and the microflora and fauna. For these reasons, some acid clays are as well aggregated as calcium-clays. The flocculation of clays by excess salts is not necessarily like the granulation developed through the effects of living organisms. Then too, simple replacement of the sodium by calcium may not be enough to induce granulation without alternate wetting-and-drying, incorporation of organic matter, or other treatments.

as drainage improves and excess salts are removed, the sodium-clays become strongly or very strongly alkaline and easily dispersed in water, and sticky when wet and hard when dry.

The proportion of the several cations absorbed by the soil colloids depends upon the soluble salts present. In the presence of a large proportion of sodium salts, sodium becomes dominant on the exchange complex. Such soils may not have a high pH (above 8.5) so long as excess neutral salts are present. With the removal of the excess salts by leaching, hydrolysis of the sodium-clay produces sodium hydroxide and a strongly alkaline reaction. The carbon dioxide of the soil air combines with the sodium hydroxide to form sodium carbonate. Thus the sodium carbonate in alkali soil originates within the soil itself, except where the leachate from an alkali soil collects in another soil at a lower elevation. More than 15 percent exchangeable sodium in the exchange complex is ordinarily harmful to the growth of crop plants.[2]

The alkalinity of alkali soils is expressed by pH, percentage of exchangeable sodium (or sodium plus potassium), or by a combination of the two. Strictly, any soil above pH 7.0 is alkaline, whether salty or not. (See section of Soil Reaction.) Soils made alkaline by calcium carbonate alone are called *calcareous* and rarely have pH values above 8.5. Soils above pH 8.5 usually contain a high percentage of exchangeable sodium and are called alkali soils, along with some with as much as 15 percent exchangeable sodium that have pH values below 8.5.

Morphological differences occur among saline and alkali soils. Saline soils are usually friable; but soils with well defined structure, for example, a typical Chestnut soil, may become saline naturally or through irrigation practices. Strongly saline soils often have salt crusts, or efflorescences, on the surface and streaks, layers, or spots ("eyes") of salts within the profile. The structure of many saline soils is favorable to the movement of water and air. Saline-alkali soils are morphologically similar to saline soils as long as excess salts are present and the clays do not swell or become dispersed. As salt concentrations are reduced, the clays may disperse as in alkali soils. In time, many natural alkali soils develop characteristic prismatic or columnar B horizons. A man-made alkali soil, developed incident to irrigation as a result of the leaching of a saline soil high in exchangeable sodium, becomes massive, hard when dry, and slowly permeable, without a distinctive structural profile other than a puddled surface soil that shrinks and cracks with drying.

Saline and alkali soils are extremely variable, both vertically and horizontally. Salts may be localized in the surface soil or in a lower horizon, or they may be more or less uniformly distributed throughout the soil profile. Slight differences in texture may result in unequal movements of salty water and large differences

---

[2] The following was drawn on considerably for this section: DIAGNOSIS AND IMPROVEMENT OF SALINE AND ALKALI SOILS. United States Regional Salinity Laboratory. L. A. Richards, Ed. 157 pp., illus., 1947. [Processed.]

in salt accumulation. Some growing shrubs take in large amounts of salts and "pump" them from the lower soil to the surface; others do not. Thus, salt content and pH, or both, may vary widely within a few feet, depending on differences in vegetation [3] as well as differences in relief and stratigraphy. Within a small area, soils of widely different characteristics may be found, and at any one spot the salt content may fluctuate with the seasons, weather conditions, and irrigation management.

Genetic groups.—In addition to the terms already given for saline and alkali soils, the soil scientist finds others used in the literature, defined primarily on the basis of morphology and genesis. Although the two sets of terms are not entirely consistent, a brief explanation of the genetic types may be helpful. If soils in this general group—saline and alkali soils—are defined primarily in chemical terms, one gets some strange morphological bedfellows; and if they are defined primarily according to morphology, one gets some strange chemical bedfellows. Then too, some nonsaline soils may appear to have profiles suggestive of Solonetz or solodized-Solonetz.

The light-colored, flocculated, salty soils are sometimes called "structureless" soils. They are not really structureless, but are softly and finely granular. Characteristically, they lack either prismatic or blocky structure. Soils dominantly of these characteristics are called *Solonchak* in genetic soil classification. If a salt crust exists at the surface, the soil is sometimes called an "external" Solonchak, or a "puff" Solonchak if the crust is immediately underlain by a fluffy layer. Where the salts have moved up part way into the solum in capillary water and are concentrated at some level beneath the surface, the soil may be called an "internal" Solonchak. Since the salts often enter the soil from beneath, Solonchaks are commonly variable and occur in intricate patterns with zonal and other soils of the region. Yet, "flooded" Solonchaks, which occupy old ponded basins, may be relatively uniform, even though exceedingly salty.

The term "Solonchak" is also modified by the name of the dominant salt present. One having dominantly calcium salts is called a calcium-Solonchak. With improved drainage and removal of the salts, it gradually changes to a normal soil. With leaching and removal of the excess salts, following improved drainage under natural conditions, the sodium-Solonchak may change to a Solonetz or solodized-Solonetz, and perhaps finally to a Soloth, before the processes responsible for the development of a zonal soil become dominant.

The development of the morphology required of the Solonchak is not always coincident with the definition of a saline soil. A saline soil may be produced simply by the addition of salts to a nonsaline soil, a process called "salinization." Thus there are many intergrades between Solonchak and other soils, as Solonchak-Chernozem, Solonchak-Sierozem, and so on. In detailed soil surveys the local soil types and phases are separated on the basis of salt conditions significant to crop growth and to reclamation and management practices. Later they may be placed in the appropriate genetic groups.

While excess salts are present, Solonchak soils with different kinds of salt look much alike; but when drainage improves during the ages and the excess salts leach out, enormous differences may develop. The calcium-clays remain flocculated, granulated; whereas the sodium-clays become easily dispersed and puddled, or "run together." The soil becomes highly alkaline—so much so that part of the organic matter is dissolved and may form a dark coating around the soil grains or aggregates. Some sodium ions of the colloid are disassociated to form sodium hydroxide and finally sodium carbonate. Since the colloids are easily dispersed, some of them start to move downward, out of the surface layers, and accumulate beneath. The puddled soil cracks on drying. The next rain causes more dispersion, and fine material moves down. After long periods, this results in an accumulation

---

[3] ROBERTS, R. C. CHEMICAL EFFECTS OF THE SALT-TOLERANT SHRUBS ON SOILS. 4th Internatl. Cong. Soil Sci. Trans. 1: 404–406. Amsterdam. 1950.

of fine material in the B horizon, with the silt and sand left in the A. Besides, continued weathering of minerals within the B horizon contributes to its high content of clay.

The B horizon has a characteristic columnar structure; the soil exists in hard vertical prisms with rounded caps. This process of change is sometimes called "solonization," and the resulting soil is called a Solonetz. Thus in contrast to Solonchak, the Solonetz has a striking structural profile.

If the leaching continues actively for a long time, the soil may finally become acid in the surface, with a deep gray layer over an acid blocky B horizon. Such soils are called Soloth, and the process of change of Solonetz to Soloth is called "solodization." Fully developed Soloth soils are relatively uncommon in the United States, and in the world for that matter. In morphological characteristics they merge with the Planosols. Far more common are the intergrades—the solodized-Solonetz soils—soils with well-developed structure and texture profiles having the leached A horizons of the Soloth and the nonacid columnar B horizon of the Solonetz.

A great many soils are transitional between Solonchak, Solonetz, and Soloth. Some have characteristics of all three. In fact, Solonetz with neither excess salts in the solum nor suggestion of solodization in the A horizon is rare. The solodized-Solonetz is especially common. These soils may have acid A horizons and very slightly acid to strongly alkaline B horizons with well-developed columnar structure. Since the formation of Solonetz usually takes place during a very gradual lowering of the water table, the upper layers change to Solonetz and the surface horizons become strongly leached, though the lower solum is still salty. Thus a soil may go from a sodium-Solonchak to a solodized-Solonetz without ever being in position of a Solonetz. Then too, after a well-developed solodized-Solonetz morphology has developed, calcium and magnesium may be released from the soil minerals by further weathering in place to be brought up by the native vegetation, and replace most of the sodium. Advanced weathering of the clays releases magnesium especially. Thus soils with the striking morphology of the solodized-Solonetz may have lost most of their exchangeable sodium. Soils developed from stratified materials—sand over clay—may develop a structural profile quite like that of solodized-Solonetz, even though the clay has little exchangeable sodium.

Frequently, the leached surface layer of the solodized-Solonetz is blown away during periods of great drought, exposing the hard clay of the B horizon in the bottoms of shallow pits. Such soils are called truncated solodized-Solonetz. Locally, the shallow pits are called "slick-spots" or "scabby-spots." Enormous areas containing many small spots of these soils exist in the Chestnut and Brown soil regions of the northern Great Plains. After truncation, the solodized-Solonetz may go through another stage of being a solodized-Solonetz. But gradually with improved drainage and the invasion of the normal native vegetation, the soil again becomes saturated mainly with calcium or calcium and magnesium and changes to the zonal soil of the region, for example, Chestnut or Brown.

Well-developed solodized-Solonetz soils are formed only after considerable time. They are not found on young alluvial flood plains. They are more common in temperate or cool-temperate regions than in warm ones, although they do exist in warm areas, even near the Equator.

Commonly all these soils, and especially the solodized-Solonetz, occur irregularly. The solodized-Solonetz nearly always occurs in intricate complexes, like "smallpox on the face of the steppe." After frequent tillage, the spots may not be easily identified. Where irrigation is being considered, the soils need to be examined with great care, since irrigation of them raises serious hazards.

THE ELECTROLYTIC BRIDGE FOR FIELD USE

Determinations of the approximate salt content or degree of salinity of soil samples are made in the field by use of a Wheatstone bridge specially designed for this purpose (fig. 53).

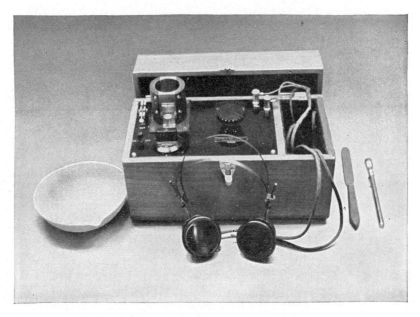

FIGURE 53.—Portable Wheatstone bridge, especially designed for field use, with "Bureau of Soils" cup in place.

The electrical conductivity of the soluble salts is determined by measuring the electrical resistance of a prepared sample of the soil in a special cup, called "Bureau of Soils" cup, inserted in the bridge circuit. The results of the resistance determinations may be expressed in terms of percentage of total salts in the air-dry soil or in terms of conductivity in millimhos of the saturation extract.

Electrical resistance is affected by the degree of dissociation of the salts, moisture content, kind of exchangeable cations, and temperature, as well as by salt concentration. In field operations, corrections for temperature and compensation for moisture content are made. The approximate salt content or degree of salinity is determined from curves or from tables compiled on the assumption of average conditions in chemical character and relative proportions of different kinds of salts.

Soil samples for salt determination are carefully selected from representative locations. Some should be chosen to represent the salt content in places of maximum concentration and others to represent the lower and intermediate degrees of accumulation. To obtain data for phase distinctions or for compiling a special map showing the distribution of salts and alkali, samples should represent average conditions and ranges of salt accumulation over areas of such extent and uniformity of character that they may be shown clearly on the map. Samples of maximum salt accumulation on the immediate surface, including crusts and efflorescence, or localized in any horizon of the soil profile may be taken for special study.

As a basis for defining mapping units, soil profile samples are obtained for the determination of the approximate salt content. Samples are taken by horizons from soils that show distinct morphological differences. Soils with weakly developed profiles are sampled at arbitrary depths, depending upon the character of the salt accumulation, stratification, and the presence of a water table or of layers of rock or gravel. Samples are preferably taken with a spade, but the lower part of the soil may be sampled with an auger where the use of a spade is impracticable. Care is needed to avoid contamination, especially where the auger is used.

Determinations of salt content may be made in the field at the time the samples are taken or later in a laboratory or other convenient place where water is available for washing equipment. For field tests, it is necessary to carry distilled water for saturating the soil and a large can of water for washing equipment. The soil samples may be mixed on small squares of oilcloth.

Frequently field testing is preferable, for the salt content of the soil can be correlated immediately on the spot with vegetation, drainage, relief, surface appearance of the soil, and other related factors. In this way the field scientist can quickly form a sound basis for estimating the salt content of soil types and can draw fairly accurate boundaries of salt-affected areas. Determination in the field is often desirable when the soil conditions in the area are not well known, as at the beginning of a survey. Where general correlations are known, however, it may be preferable to take samples and make the tests at some more convenient place and time. It often saves time not to interrupt the field mapping and to make a number of salt determinations at once. If tests are made at headquarters, the scientist may find it necessary to return to the field for checking after the results are available. Boundaries showing salt or alkali conditions can then be drawn or revised partly on the basis of the test results.

In preparing the soil sample for determination of the approximate salt content, pebbles, root fragments, and other foreign materials are removed. A portion of the sample is placed in a convenient mixing cup and distilled water is added slowly while the soil is stirred with a spatula and mixed until saturation is reached. This saturated soil is called a soil paste. Since dry samples of plastic clays adsorb water slowly, it may be necessary to crush the sample and pass it through a 2-millimeter sieve before attempting to saturate it with distilled water. The hard rubber cup, or conductivity cell, is filled with the saturated soil. The cell should be tapped gently to release air bubbles. The top of the soil is struck off with the spatula, leaving the surface smooth and the cell evenly filled. The cell is placed between the electrical contacts, the circuit closed, and the bridge pointer turned back and forth around the scale, placing the 10-, 100-, or 1,000-ohm coils into the circuit as needed, until the null point is found, as is indicated when the buzzing in the earphone is reduced

TABLE 8.—*Reduction of the electrical resistance of soils to a uniform temperature at 60° F.*

Degrees, Fahrenheit	Resistance when indicated resistance is—								
	1,000	2,000	3,000	4,000	5,000	6,000	7,000	8,000	9,000
	Ohms	*Ohms*	*Ohms*	*Ohms*	*Ohms*	*Ohms*	*Ohms*	*Ohms*	*Ohms*
32	625	1,250	1,875	2,500	3,125	3,750	4,375	5,000	5,625
32.5	632	1,264	1,896	2,528	3,150	3,792	4,424	5,056	5,688
33	639	1,278	1,917	2,556	3,195	3,834	4,473	5,112	5,751
33.5	646	1,292	1,938	2,584	3,230	3,876	4,522	5,168	5,814
34	653	1,306	1,959	2,612	3,265	3,918	4,571	5,224	5,877
34.5	660	1,320	1,980	2,640	3,300	3,960	4,620	5,280	5,940
35	667	1,334	2,001	2,668	3,335	4,002	4,669	5,336	6,003
35.5	674	1,348	2,022	2,696	3,370	4,044	4,718	5,392	6,066
36	681	1,362	2,043	2,724	3,405	4,086	4,767	5,448	6,129
36.5	688	1,376	2,064	2,752	3,440	4,128	4,816	5,504	6,192
37	695	1,390	2,085	2,780	3,475	4,170	4,865	5,560	6,255
37.5	702	1,404	2,106	2,808	3,510	4,212	4,914	5,616	6,318
38	709	1,418	2,127	2,836	3,545	4,254	4,963	5,672	6,381
38.5	716	1,432	2,148	2,864	3,580	4,296	5,012	5,728	6,444
39	722	1,444	2,166	2,888	3,610	4,332	5,054	5,776	6,498
39.5	729	1,458	2,187	2,916	3,645	4,374	5,103	5,832	6,561
40	736	1,472	2,208	2,944	3,680	4,416	5,152	5,888	6,634
40.5	743	1,486	2,229	2,972	3,715	4,458	5,201	5,944	6,687
41	750	1,500	2,250	3,000	3,750	4,500	5,250	6,000	6,750
41.5	757	1,514	2,271	3,028	3,785	4,542	5,299	6,056	6,813
42	763	1,526	2,289	3,052	3,815	4,578	5,341	6,104	6,867
42.5	770	1,540	2,310	3,080	3,850	4,620	5,390	6,160	6,930
43	776	1,552	2,328	3,104	3,880	4,656	5,432	6,208	6,984
43.5	782	1,564	2,346	3,128	3,910	4,692	5,474	6,256	7,038
44	788	1,576	2,361	3,152	3,940	4,728	5,516	6,304	7,092
44.5	794	1,588	2,382	3,176	3,970	4,764	5,558	6,352	7,146
45	800	1,600	2,400	3,200	4,000	4,800	5,600	6,400	7,200
45.5	807	1,614	2,421	3,228	4,035	4,842	5,649	6,456	7,263
46	814	1,628	2,442	3,256	4,070	4,884	5,698	6,512	7,326
46.5	821	1,642	2,463	3,284	4,105	4,926	5,747	6,568	7,389
47	828	1,656	2,484	3,312	4,140	4,968	5,796	6,624	7,452
47.5	835	1,670	2,505	3,340	4,175	5,010	5,845	6,680	7,515
48	842	1,684	2,526	3,368	4,210	5,052	5,884	6,736	7,578
48.5	849	1,698	2,547	3,396	4,245	5,094	5,933	6,792	7,641
49	856	1,712	2,568	3,424	4,280	5,136	5,992	6,848	7,704
49.5	862	1,724	2,586	3,448	4,310	5,172	6,034	6,896	7,758
50	868	1,736	2,604	3,472	4,340	5,208	6,076	6,944	7,812
50.5	875	1,750	2,625	3,500	4,375	5,250	6,125	7,000	7,875
51	881	1,762	2,643	3,524	4,405	5,286	6,167	7,048	7,929
51.5	887	1,774	2,661	3,548	4,435	5,322	6,209	7,096	7,983
52	893	1,786	2,679	3,572	4,465	5,358	6,251	7,144	8,037
52.5	900	1,800	2,700	3,600	4,500	5,400	6,300	7,200	8,100
53	906	1,812	2,718	3,624	4,530	5,436	6,342	7,248	8,154
53.5	912	1,824	2,736	3,648	4,560	5,472	6,384	7,296	8,208
54	919	1,838	2,757	3,676	4,595	5,514	6,433	7,352	8,271
54.5	926	1,852	2,778	3,704	4,630	5,556	6,482	7,408	8,334
55	933	1,866	2,799	3,732	4,665	5,598	6,531	7,464	8,397
55.5	940	1,880	2,820	3,760	4,700	5,640	6,580	7,520	8,460
56	947	1,894	2,841	3,780	4,735	5,682	6,629	7,576	8,523
56.5	954	1,908	2,862	3,816	4,770	5,724	6,678	7,632	8,586
57	961	1,922	2,883	3,844	4,805	5,766	6,727	7,688	8,649
57.5	968	1,936	2,904	3,872	4,839	5,807	6,775	7,743	8,711
58	974	1,948	2,922	3,896	4,870	5,844	6,818	7,792	8,766
58.5	981	1,962	2,943	3,924	4,905	5,886	6,867	7,848	8,829
59	987	1,974	2,962	3,949	4,936	5,923	6,910	7,898	8,885
59.5	994	1,988	2,982	3,976	4,971	5,965	6,959	7,953	8,947
60	1,000	2,000	3,000	4,000	5,000	6,000	7,000	8,000	9,000
60.5	1,006	2,012	3,018	4,024	5,030	6,036	7,042	8,048	9,054
61	1,013	2,026	3,039	4,052	5,065	6,078	7,091	8,104	9,117
61.5	1,020	2,040	3,060	4,080	5,100	6,120	7,140	8,160	9,180
62	1,027	2,054	3,081	4,108	5,135	6,162	7,189	8,216	9,243
62.5	1,033	2,066	3,099	4,132	5,165	6,198	7,231	8,264	9,297
63	1,040	2,080	3,120	4,160	5,200	6,240	7,280	8,320	9,360
63.5	1,047	2,094	3,141	4,188	5,235	6,282	7,329	8,376	9,423
64	1,054	2,108	3,162	4,216	5,270	6,324	7,378	8,432	9,486
64.5	1,061	2,122	3,183	4,244	5,305	6,366	7,427	8,488	9,549
65	1,068	2,136	3,204	4,272	5,340	6,408	7,476	8,544	9,612
65.5	1,075	2,150	3,225	4,300	5,375	6,450	7,525	8,600	9,675
66	1,082	2,164	3,246	4,328	5,410	6,492	7,574	8,656	9,738
66.5	1,089	2,178	3,267	4,356	5,445	6,534	7,623	8,712	9,801
67	1,096	2,192	3,288	4,384	5,480	6,576	7,672	8,768	9,864
67.5	1,103	2,206	3,309	4,412	5,515	6,618	7,721	8,824	9,927
68	1,110	2,220	3,330	4,440	5,550	6,660	7,770	8,880	9,990

TABLE 8.—*Reduction of the electrical resistance of soils to a uniform temperature at 60° F.—Continued*

Degrees, Fahrenheit	Resistance when indicated resistance is—								
	1,000	2,000	3,000	4,000	5,000	6,000	7,000	8,000	9,000
	Ohms	Ohms	Ohms	Ohms	Ohms	Ohms	Ohms	Ohms	Ohms
68.5	1,117	2,234	3,351	4,468	5,585	6,702	7,819	8,936	10,053
69	1,125	2,250	3,375	4,500	5,625	6,750	7,875	9,000	10,125
69.5	1,133	2,266	3,399	4,532	5,665	6,798	7,931	9,064	10,197
70	1,140	2,280	3,420	4,560	5,700	6,840	7,980	9,120	10,260
70.5	1,147	2,294	3,441	4,588	5,735	6,882	8,029	9,176	10,323
71	1,155	2,310	3,465	4,620	5,775	6,930	8,085	9,240	10,395
71.5	1,162	2,324	3,486	4,648	5,810	6,972	8,134	9,296	10,458
72	1,170	2,340	3,510	4,680	5,850	7,028	8,190	9,360	10,530
72.5	1,177	2,354	3,531	4,708	5,885	7,062	8,239	9,416	10,593
73	1,185	2,370	3,555	4,740	5,925	7,110	8,295	9,480	10,665
73.5	1,193	2,386	3,579	4,772	5,965	7,158	8,351	9,544	10,737
74	1,201	2,402	3,603	4,804	6,005	7,206	8,407	9,608	10,809
74.5	1,208	2,416	3,624	4,832	6,040	7,248	8,456	9,664	10,872
75	1,215	2,430	3,645	4,860	6,075	7,290	8,505	9,720	10,935
75.5	1,222	2,444	3,666	4,888	6,110	7,332	8,554	9,776	10,998
76	1,230	2,460	3,690	4,920	6,150	7,380	8,610	9,840	11,070
76.5	1,238	2,476	3,714	4,952	6,190	7,428	8,666	9,904	11,142
77	1,246	2,492	3,738	4,984	6,230	7,476	8,722	9,968	11,214
77.5	1,254	2,508	3,762	5,016	6,270	7,524	8,778	10,032	11,286
78	1,262	2,524	3,786	5,048	6,310	7,572	8,834	10,096	11,358
78.5	1,270	2,540	3,810	5,080	6,350	7,620	8,890	10,160	11,430
79	1,278	2,556	3,834	5,112	6,390	7,668	8,946	10,224	11,502
79.5	1,286	2,572	3,858	5,144	6,430	7,716	9,002	10,288	11,574
80	1,294	2,588	3,882	5,176	6,470	7,754	9,058	10,352	11,646
80.5	1,302	2,604	3,906	5,208	6,510	7,812	9,114	10,416	11,718
81	1,310	2,620	3,930	5,240	6,550	7,860	9,170	10,480	11,790
81.5	1,318	2,636	3,954	5,272	6,590	7,908	9,226	10,544	11,862
82	1,327	2,654	3,981	5,308	6,635	7,962	9,289	10,616	11,943
82.5	1,335	2,670	4,005	5,340	6,675	8,010	9,345	10,680	12,015
83	1,343	2,686	4,029	5,372	6,715	8,058	9,401	10,744	12,087
83.5	1,351	2,702	4,053	5,404	6,755	8,106	9,457	10,808	12,159
84	1,359	2,718	4,077	5,436	6,795	8,154	9,513	10,872	12,231
84.5	1,367	2,734	4,101	5,468	6,835	8,202	9,569	10,936	12,303
85	1,376	2,752	4,128	5,504	6,880	8,256	9,632	11,008	12,384
85.5	1,385	2,770	4,155	5,540	6,925	8,310	9,695	11,080	12,465
86	1,393	2,786	4,179	5,572	6,965	8,358	9,751	11,144	12,537
86.5	1,401	2,802	4,203	5,604	7,005	8,406	9,807	11,208	12,609
87	1,409	2,818	4,227	5,636	7,015	8,454	9,863	11,272	12,681
87.5	1,418	2,836	4,254	5,672	7,090	8,508	9,931	11,344	12,762
88	1,427	2,854	4,281	5,708	7,135	8,562	9,989	11,416	12,843
88.5	1,435	2,870	4,305	5,740	7,175	8,610	10,040	11,480	12,915
89	1,443	2,886	4,329	5,772	7,215	8,658	10,091	11,544	12,987
89.5	1,451	2,902	4,353	5,804	7,255	8,706	10,157	11,608	13,059
90	1,460	2,920	4,380	5,840	7,300	8,760	10,220	11,680	13,140
90.5	1,468	2,936	4,404	5,872	7,340	8,808	10,276	11,744	13,212
91	1,477	2,954	4,431	5,908	7,385	8,862	10,339	11,816	13,293
91.5	1,486	2,972	4,458	5,944	7,430	8,916	10,402	11,888	13,374
92	1,495	2,990	4,485	5,980	7,475	8,970	10,465	11,960	13,455
92.5	1,504	3,008	4,512	6,016	7,520	9,024	10,528	12,032	13,536
93	1,513	3,026	4,539	6,052	7,565	9,078	10,591	12,104	13,617
93.5	1,522	3,044	4,566	6,088	7,610	9,132	10,654	12,176	13,698
94	1,531	3,062	4,593	6,124	7,655	9,186	10,717	12,248	13,779
94.5	1,540	3,080	4,620	6,160	7,700	9,240	10,780	12,320	13,860
95	1,549	3,098	4,647	6,196	7,745	9,294	10,843	12,392	13,941
95.5	1,559	3,118	4,677	6,236	7,795	9,354	10,913	12,472	14,031
96	1,569	3,138	4,707	6,276	7,845	9,414	10,983	12,552	14,121
96.5	1,579	3,158	4,737	6,316	7,895	9,474	11,053	12,632	14,211
97	1,589	3,178	4,767	6,356	7,945	9,534	11,123	12,712	14,301
97.5	1,599	3,198	4,797	6,396	7,995	9,594	11,193	12,792	14,391
98	1,699	3,218	4,827	6,436	8,045	9,654	11,263	12,872	14,481
98.5	1,619	3,238	4,857	6,476	8,095	9,714	11,333	12,952	14,571
99	1,629	3,258	4,887	6,516	8,145	9,774	11,403	13,032	14,661

to a minimum. The product of the coil resistance and the scale reading is the bridge reading, or the resistance of the soil uncorrected for temperature. For example, if the 100-ohm coil is used and the scale reading is 1.25, the resistance of the soil is 125. If the null point is found to occur near the end of the scale, it is advisable to place the extra 100-ohm test coil in the circuit; then 100 ohms is subtracted from the product of the soil resistance and the scale reading to obtain the bridge reading. The temperature of the saturated soil in the cell is recorded immediately after the resistance is measured, and the reading corrected to a uniform basis. Electrical resistance of irrigation, drainage, or other waters may be determined by substituting the water sample for the saturated soil in the cell.

Temperature correction of bridge readings.—The soil resistance is corrected to a uniform temperature of 60° F. This may be done by using the values in table 8, taken from Bureau of Soils Bulletin 61,[4] or by the use of a nomogram.

In other types of Wheatstone bridges that may be used in the laboratory and which operate from batteries or from 110-volt alternating current, the null point may be determined by an electric eye rather than the earphone. A cell that corrects for temperature can be used with this type of bridge.

Interpretation of bridge readings or soil resistance.—Two methods are presented for interpreting the bridge readings. The older and more common interpretation of soil resistance readings has been in terms of the approximate salt content of the soil sample expressed in percentage on the basis of dry weight of soil. As an example; suppose the resistance at 78° F. to be 1,439 ohms: A resistance of 1,000 ohms at 78° is shown in table 8 as having a value at 60° of 1,262 ohms, one of 400 ohms (one-tenth of 4,000 ohms) an equivalent value of 505 ohms, one of 30 ohms (one one-hundredth of 3,000 ohms) a value of 38 ohms, and one of 9 ohms is equivalent to 11 ohms. The sum of these corrected values is 1,816 ohms, which is the corrected value for 60° as shown below.

Resistance at 78° F.	Resistance at 60° F.
1,000	1,262
400	505
30	38
9	11
1,439	1,816

The conversion of the soil resistance readings into approximate salt content of the soil sample is made by use of the standard values given in table 9, adapted from Bureau of Soils Bulletin 61, or by use of a standardization curve prepared for the particular area. Where unusual local conditions are suspected, samples should be sent to the laboratory for analysis. Since variations in soil texture affect the quantity of water required for saturation of the soil sample, soil class must be taken into consideration in making the conversion. Table 9 may be used for estimating the approximate content of salts. The figures represent parts per

---

[4] DAVIS, R. O. E., and BRYAN, H. THE ELECTRICAL BRIDGE FOR THE DETERMINATION OF SOLUBLE SALTS IN SOILS. U. S. Dept. Agr., Bur. Soils Bul. 61, 36 pp., illus. 1910.

100,000—equivalent to 1,000 times the percentage of total salts in the air-dry soil.

The second method relates the resistance readings to the conductivity of a saturation extract rather than to percentage of salt. Although useful when properly interpreted, percentage of salt is less directly related to crop growth than the concentration of salt in a water extract taken from the saturated soils, a value obtained through direct conductivity measurement.

TABLE 9.—*Approximate amount of salts in soils containing predominantly sulfates and chlorides with given resistances*

Resistance at 60° F.	Sand	Loam	Clay loam	Clay	Resistance at 60° F.	Sand	Loam	Clay loam	Clay
	Parts per 100,000	Parts per 100,000	Parts per 100,000	Parts per 100,000		Parts per 100,000	Parts per 100,000	Parts per 100,000	Parts per 100,000
18 ohms___	3,000	3,000	---------	--------	95 ohms___	350	370	390	420
19 ohms___	2,400	2,640	3,090	--------	100 ohms__	330	350	370	390
20 ohms___	2,200	2,420	2,800	3,000	105 ohms__	310	330	350	370
25 ohms___	1,500	1,700	1,940	2,200	110 ohms__	300	320	330	350
30 ohms___	1,240	1,340	1,460	1,580	115 ohms__	280	290	310	330
35 ohms___	1,040	1,140	1,220	1,320	120 ohms__	270	280	290	320
40 ohms___	860	940	1,040	1,140	125 ohms__	250	260	280	300
45 ohms___	750	780	880	980	130 ohms__	240	250	260	280
50 ohms___	670	710	770	860	135 ohms__	230	240	250	270
55 ohms___	600	640	690	770	140 ohms__	220	230	240	260
60 ohms___	550	580	630	700	145 ohms__	210	220	230	250
65 ohms___	510	540	570	630	150 ohms__	210	210	220	240
70 ohms___	480	500	530	590	155 ohms__	200	210	210	230
75 ohms___	450	470	500	550	160 ohms__	200	200	210	220
80 ohms___	420	440	470	510	165 ohms__	190	200	200	210
85 ohms___	390	420	440	480	170 ohms__	190	190	200	200
90 ohms___	370	390	410	450					

In recent years many determinations of saturated soil resistance and conductivity of the saturation extract from the same sample have been made at the United States Regional Salinity Laboratory. For saline soils containing mixed chloride and sulfate salts it has been found that the soil resistance readings may be used for estimating the conductivity of the saturation extract as well as for estimating the percentage of salt. This permits direct interpretation of the soil resistance reading in units more precisely related to crop growth.

Table 10 relates soil resistance readings to both percentage of salt and conductivity of the saturation extract for stated moisture percentages of the saturated soil. (Graphs or nomograms constructed from the table are more convenient in routine work.)

After determining the ohms of resistance by using the bridge and correcting that reading to a temperature of 60° F., table 10 may be used to show the approximate percentage of soluble salts by weight in the dry soil, and the conductivity in millimhos per centimeter of a corresponding saturation extract. The conductivity should then be used as a basis for estimating salinity classes rather than percentage of salt in the soil. If the soil sample under test has a loam texture it may have a saturation percentage of about 30 percent. If the resistance, after being corrected to 60°, is 160, table 10 shows that the approximate salt content is 0.14 percent on a dry-weight basis and that the electrical conductivity of a saturation extract from this soil would be 6 millimhos per centimeter. The soil represented by this sample would be classed as "containing sufficient salt to have a slight effect on most crop plants" (class 1). By a similar procedure, a soil sample of clay texture having a saturation percentage of 70 percent and a resistance of 110 ohms would contain about 0.34 percent soluble salts and a saturated extract from this soil would have a conductivity of 6 millimhos per centimeter. This clay soil, therefore, would be placed in the same salinity class as the loam described above. The limits for differentiating salinity classes are similar to those used when conductivity of the saturated extract is determined. In millimhos per centimeter suggested classes are 0 to 4, 4 to 8, 8 to 15, and above 15. (See p. 360.) The suggested limits correlate well with plant growth because conductivity of the saturation extract gives direct measurement of ion activity in a solution that apparently approaches the nature of an actual soil solution.

The saturation percentage for samples of muck, peat, or organic-rich soils must be estimated rather accurately or actually determined.

A simple method for determining saturation percentage can be used in the field with a rough balance that will weigh to 0.1 gram. The procedure is as follows[5]: Determine the volume and tare weight of the cup that is to be used. (The "Bureau of Soils" cup is suitable.) Fill the cup with saturated soil paste, jarring it during filling to exclude air, and strike off the excess soil even with the top. Weigh, and from the net weight calculate the saturation percentage from the equation

$$SP = \frac{100(2.65V - W)}{2.65(W - V)}$$

where SP = saturation percentage;

V = volume of saturated soil paste, in cubic centimeters —a constant; and

W = net weight of the volume (V) of saturated soil paste in grams.

Calculations are simplified by the use of a table or graph connecting values of W and SP for a given V. To facilitate preparation of such a table, the equation can be rearranged to the form:

$$W = \frac{V(100 + SP)}{(37.74 + SP)}$$

The principal assumptions in this equation are that the solid phase (soil grains) of the saturated soil paste has a density of 2.65 gm/cc; that the liquid phase has a density of 1.00 gm/cc; and that when the weighing is done, air or other gas is excluded.

[5] WILCOX, L. V.   A METHOD FOR CALCULATING THE SATURATION PERCENTAGE FROM THE WEIGHT OF A KNOWN VOLUME OF SATURATED SOIL PASTE.   1949. [Unpublished manuscript.]

TABLE 10.—*Saline soils containing mixed neutral salts: Conductivity of saturation extract; ohms resistance of saturated soil paste at 60° F. for stated moisture percentage; percentage salt in saturated soil paste for stated moisture percentage*[1]

[R = Resistance at 60° F. for designated moisture percentage; S = Salt at designated moisture percentage]

Conductivity of saturation extract	Moisture percentage of soil paste																	
	20		30		40		50		60		70		80		90		100	
Millimhos per cm. at 25°C. (Ec × 10³):	R	S	R	S	R	S	R	S	R	S	R	S	R	S	R	S	R	S
	Ohms	Pct.	Ohms	Pct.	Ohms	Pct.	Ohms	Pct.	Ohms	Pct.	Ohms	Pct.	Ohms	Pct.	Ohms	Pct.	Ohms	Pct.
3	380	0.05	295	0.07	255	0.09	230	0.11	210	0.14	200	0.16	190	0.18	185	0.20	180	0.23
4	295	.06	230	.09	195	.12	180	.16	165	.19	155	.22	145	.25	140	.28	140	.31
5	245	.08	190	.12	160	.16	145	.20	135	.24	125	.28	120	.32	115	.36	115	.39
6	205	.10	160	.14	140	.19	125	.24	115	.29	110	.34	105	.39	100	.43	96	.48
7	180	.11	140	.17	120	.23	110	.28	99	.34	93	.40	89	.46	86	.51	83	.57
8	160	.13	125	.20	105	.26	96	.33	88	.40	83	.46	80	.53	77	.59	74	.66
9	145	.15	110	.22	96	.30	87	.37	81	.45	76	.52	73	.60	70	.67	68	.75
10	130	.17	100	.25	88	.34	80	.42	74	.50	69	.59	66	.67	64	.76	62	.84
12	110	.20	87	.31	73	.41	67	.51	62	.61	59	.72	56	.82	54	.92	52	1.00
15	92	.26	71	.39	61	.52	55	.65	51	.78	48	.91	46	1.05	44	1.15	43	1.30
20	71	.36	55	.53	47	.71	43	.89	40	1.05	37	1.25	35	1.40	34	1.60	33	1.80
25	60	.45	45	.68	39	.91	35	1.15	32	1.35	30	1.60	29	1.80	28	2.05	27	2.25
30	50	.55	39	.83	33	1.10	30	1.40	28	1.65	26	1.95	25	2.20	24	2.50	23	2.75
35	43	.65	34	.98	29	1.30	26	1.65	24	1.95	23	2.30	22	2.60	21	2.95	20	3.25
40	39	.76	30	1.10	26	1.50	23	1.90	21	2.25	20	2.65	19.0	3.00	18.5	3.40	18.0	3.80
45	35	.86	27	1.30	23	1.70	21	2.15	20	2.55	18.5	3.00	17.5	3.45	17.0	3.85	16.5	4.30
50	32	.96	25	1.45	21	1.90	19.0	2.40	17.5	2.90	16.5	3.35	16.0	3.85	15.0	4.35	15.0	4.80

[1] Values calculated by Robert A. Gardner from mean relationships of measurements made at the U. S. Regional Salinity Laboratory on soil samples taken in the soil survey of the Grand Junction area, Colo. Ohms resistance above 100 are given to the closest 5 ohms and below 20 to the closest 0.5 ohms. Percentage salt in soil above 1.00 given to closest 0.05 percent.

Ordinarily in the field, however, the approximate saturation percentage is estimated from texture of the soil as follows:

Texture	*Saturation percentage*
Sand	15–20
Sandy loam	20–30
Loam	30–45
Silt loam	30–50
Clay loam	45–60
Silty clay loam	45–60
Silty clay	55–90
Clay	55–90

Well-decomposed organic matter increases the water-holding capacity of soil about 2 percent for each 1 percent of organic matter in it. Exchangeable sodium and type of clay mineral also have a marked effect on water-holding capacity. Most clays in soils of the southwestern part of the United States have saturation percentages ranging from 55 to 70. Clays of low specific gravity and those that swell and shrink excessively have very high saturation percentages. The saturation percentage for Bowdoin clay of Montana, for example, varies from 90 to 100 percent.[6] When working in an area where saturation percentages are likely to be unusual, the field scientist should either determine the values himself or have the determinations made in a laboratory. Many saline soils high in exchangeable sodium have higher saturation percentages than those indicated in the previous list. Strongly alkaline saline soils require tests besides conductivity for adequate classification and management predictions, including pH of the paste and of a 1 to 5 soil-water dilution, percentage exchangeable sodium, and permeability. Type of clay mineral and total exchange capacity are also helpful.

Water solutions.—The salt content of a water solution may be determined in the same manner as for saturated soil. Because water solutions are reported in terms of electrical conductivity at 25° C., in micromhos or millimhos per centimeter, this standard method should be used. If gravimetric equivalents are needed, the electrical conductivity in millimhos per centimeter times 600 gives the approximate parts per million.

Table 11 may be used for determining the electrical conductivity of natural waters in millimhos per centimeter at 25° C., with a cell constant (k) of 0.25.

Nomograms.—Although the resistance readings can be interpreted by using tables 8, 9, 10, and 11, if many determinations are being made it is faster and more convenient to use a nomogram. A very much reduced example of one of these, too small to use, is shown in figure 54. Since such nomograms are useful only to those making many of these determinations, they are not included as a part of the *Manual* itself. Upon request to the Division of Soil Survey, Plant Industry Station, Beltsville, Md.,

---

[6] FRAHM, E. E. CHEMICAL AND PHYSICAL CHARACTERISTICS OF BOWDOIN CLAY FROM THE MILK RIVER VALLEY OF MONTANA. Soil Sci. Soc. Amer. Proc. 13: 445–460, illus. 1948.

TABLE 11.—*Electrical conductivity of natural waters (in millimhos per centimeter) at 25° C.,*[1] *with a cell constant of 0.25*[2]

[k × f$_t$ to be divided by bridge resistance to obtain conductivity]

°C.	°F.	k × f$_t$	°C.	°F.	k × f$_t$	°C.	°F.	k × f$_t$
3.0	37.4	432	17.0	62.6	299	31.0	87.8	222
4.0	39.2	420	18.0	64.4	292	32.0	89.6	218
5.0	41.0	408	19.0	66.2	286	33.0	91.4	214
6.0	42.8	396	20.0	68.0	280	34.0	93.2	210
7.0	44.6	385	21.0	69.8	273	35.0	95.0	207
8.0	46.4	375	22.0	71.6	267	36.0	96.8	203
9.0	48.2	365	23.0	73.4	261	37.0	98.6	200
10.0	50.0	355	24.0	75.2	255	38.0	100.2	196
11.0	51.8	346	25.0	77.0	250	39.0	102.2	193
12.0	53.6	338	26.0	78.8	245	40.0	104.0	190
13.0	55.4	329	27.0	80.6	240	41.0	105.8	187
14.0	57.2	321	28.0	82.4	235	42.0	107.6	184
15.0	59.0	314	29.0	84.2	230	43.0	109.4	181
16.0	60.8	306	30.0	86.0	226	44.0	111.2	179

[1] Millimhos per centimeter at 25° C. multiplied by 600 gives approximate parts per million of salt in natural waters.

[2] With cell constant (k) at 0.25, f$_t$ is temperature correction.

a copy of any one of the following nomograms may be had (1) for relating resistance in ohms, temperature, and electrical conductivity in millimhos per centimeter at 25° C. of solutions in natural waters as measured in a "Bureau of Soils" cup, assuming a cell constant of 0.25; (2) for reducing soil-paste resistance in ohms at a particular temperature, as measured in the "Bureau of Soils" cup, to resistance at 60° F., assuming a cell constant of 0.25; or (3) for changing soil-paste resistance readings from "Bureau of Soils" cup to percentage salt, based upon the old methods.

Care of the electrolytic bridge.—The electrolytic bridge is a delicate instrument easily broken by unusual shock or jar. It may be carried safely in the field if placed in a container with good cushions or packing. The electrodes of the hard-rubber cell need to be bright and free from grease, and the cell and bridge parts should not be allowed to become encrusted with mud. Contacts should be kept clean. Major adjustments of the bridge and repairs should not be attempted in the field. When shipping or transporting the bridge long distances, the heavy electric battery in the lower compartment should be removed, as it might become loosened and cause serious damage.

OTHER METHODS OF DETERMINING SOIL SALINITY

The Wheatstone bridge has for many years been useful in determining the approximate salt content of soils. The salt content is measured by soil resistance, but results are only approximate. The electric current carried by a saturated soil may vary considerably with salts of different composition, even though

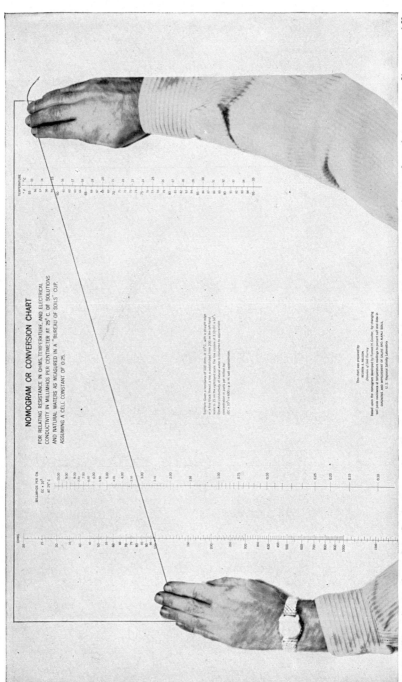

FIGURE 54.—A much reduced photograph of a nomogram used in making interpretations of resistance readings rapidly.

the total salt content is the same. A chemical analysis[7] that determines the composition of the soluble salts offers a more accurate method of determining the salt content of a soil and the concentration of salt in a soil solution. Such chemical analyses are not readily adapted to field needs and can be justified only for special studies or as checks. Variations in the conductivity of soil minerals and variations in moisture content of the soil paste are other sources of error if salt content is determined by measuring the resistance of the saturated soil.[8]

Direct conductivity measurements of a soil solution or soil extract may be used for estimating soil salinity or for appraising its relation to plant growth. Conductivity measurements of soil extracts are more precise than interpretations of paste resistances, but are less so than chemical analyses. More apparatus is required for conductivity measurements of soil extracts, and the method is slower than measurements of the resistance of saturated soil. The extract method may be adapted for field use by setting up the equipment in a convenient location within the survey area. A complete laboratory is not necessary.

The use of conductivity measurements for appraising the salinity of soil samples is explained in the manual *Diagnosis and Improvement of Saline and Alkali Soils* prepared by the United States Regional Salinity Laboratory. The use of the extract from the saturated soil—called the saturation extract—is recommended for conductivity measurements. This is the lowest feasible soil-moisture content for extracting the soil solution for routine testing. With medium-textured soils, the moisture percentage at saturation is approximately twice the field capacity. Thus measurements made on the saturation extract are related to the soil solution at field capacity; and the salt dilution effect in clay soils, due to their higher moisture-retaining capacity, is automatically taken into account. The conductivity of the saturation extract can be used directly for correlating salinity with plant growth, without conversion or reference to any other scale.

The saturation extract is obtained from the saturated soil, prepared as described for use of the electrolytic bridge, by using a suction or pressure filter. Electrical conductance is the reciprocal of resistance and is expressed in terms of mhos or reciprocal ohms. The standard unit for conductivity is mhos per centimeter at 25° C. For use with extracts from saline soils, the millimhos per centimeter (1,000 millimhos equals one mho) is a convenient conductivity unit. After the saturation extract is obtained from the saturated soil sample, its conductivity is measured by means of a suitable conductivity bridge and cell. From correlating measurements of electrical conductivity of the saturation extract

[7] MAGISTAD, O. C., REITEMEIER, R. F., and WILCOX, L. V. DETERMINATION OF SOLUBLE SALTS IN SOILS. Soil Sci. 59: 65–75. 1945.
[8] REITEMEIER, R. F., and WILCOX, L. V. A CRITIQUE OF ESTIMATING SOIL SOLUTION CONCENTRATION FROM THE ELECTRICAL CONDUCTIVITY OF SATURATED SOILS. Soil Sci. 61: 281–293, illus. 1946.

with plant growth, soil samples with conductivities greater than 4 millimhos per centimeter are now considered to be saline.

Measurements for electrical conductivity of extracts of greater dilution than the saturated soil, such as 1:1 or 1:5 soil-water suspensions, have also been used for salinity appraisal. Since the extract can be obtained by filtering without suction or pressure, such extracts are convenient for rapid determinations. The reliability of conductivity measurements made on these extracts depends upon the kinds of salts present. If only chloride salts are present, the results are little affected by the moisture content, but if calcium sulfate is present in significant quantities, the quantity brought into solution depends upon the soil-water ratio. Calcium carbonate has a much smaller effect, significant only at very low values. In evaluating the accuracy of methods, one must remember the unavoidable errors of soil sampling. Extra expense and time for accuracy of measurement, beyond the accuracy with which the samples represent the soil in the field, are not warranted.

THE MAPPING OF SOILS TO INDICATE SALT AND ALKALI

The field scientist has many problems to consider in mapping soils to indicate the salt and alkali in them, as these qualities relate to other soil characteristics and to predictions about use and management. Many of these conditions can be described adequately on the basis of the soil type. Usually, however, special phases and symbols or special maps must be used to show defined classes of salt and alkali in sufficient detail for the predictions needed. Different kinds of salts and combinations of salts have varied effects on crops. In many soils salts are transitory, whereas in others they are comparitively stationary. Alkalinity may or may not be combined with excess salts. In setting up mapping units to indicate the conditions in saline or alkali soils, account must be taken of the crops most likely to be grown.

In dry-farming areas where the removal of salts or the correction of alkali conditions is ordinarily impractical, the mapping problem differs from that in irrigated areas or areas of potential irrigation. Salts are usually fairly stable in dry-farming areas; and where they exist only in the deep subsoil or substratum, shallow-rooted crops may be grown. In dry-farming areas, soils do not ordinarily need to be sampled for salinity below the depth of moisture penetration. By studying the soils and the depth of root penetration, the field scientist can judge the depths to which he needs to take samples.

In irrigated areas, or where irrigation is anticipated, the problems are more difficult. Deep strata that are not significant in the natural environment become so with the addition of water. If a saline water table occurs within a depth of 6 feet, salt may rapidly accumulate in the solum, especially if the surface is barren and capillary rise is moderate to high.

The vegetation, especially the native cover, aids in recognizing saline or alkali soils and their boundaries. Using the land form, vegetation, and other features as guides, salt and alkali tests are made to correlate the different concentrations of salt or degrees of alkalinity with the observable features. The different concentrations can then be used in drawing boundaries on the map. Plants vary in their tolerance of salt according to species, variety, and even age, and somewhat with other growing conditions. Some plants are not good indicators, because they grow well with either fair amounts of salt in the soil or in the absence of salinity or alkalinity.

Soil morphology may also be correlated with the salinity and alkalinity as determined by the testing of soil samples. Such correlations are of primary importance among mature soils, but are less dependable among those of young flood plains.

Soil samples used in the appraisal of salinity and alkalinity should be taken with specific regard to the existing problems. In dry-farming areas, where the movement of salts in the soil is usually very slow, the samples should be taken to determine the specific portions of the soil in which salts occur or which have a high degree of alkalinity. In irrigated areas, especially those in which subirrigation is used or in which ground-water levels are high, sometimes most of the salts occur on the surface or in the uppermost few inches of the surface soil. In most irrigated Alluvial soils it is suggested that salt content be determined on composite samples of the topmost 6 inches and on composite samples taken at 6 to 18 inches, 18 to 36 inches, and 36 to 72 inches. If the soil is markedly stratified, however, the specific strata should be sampled separately. Soils with developed profiles are sampled according to horizons. If the germination of seed is of prime importance, it may be necessary to test the topmost 2 or 3 inches of soil separately. In fields with furrow irrigation, salt may accumulate rapidly on the top of the ridges. If any reason exists to suspect salt or alkali problems, sufficient samples should be tested to appraise the general condition.

SALINE AND ALKALI CLASSES

Soils with harmful quantities of soluble salts and those with a high degree of alkalinity are shown separately on detailed soil maps from nonsaline or nonalkali soils. Each subdivision of a soil type according to salinity or alkalinity needs to be defined and predictions for its use developed, together with recommendations for its treatment. The definition of mapping units varies with the character and condition of salt accumulations, the physical character of the soil, the possible utilization of the soil, and the objectives of the survey. In areas where salinity is widespread and the salt concentrations vary from one part of the area to another or where the degrees of alkalinity are varied, soils may be grouped in terms of the agronomic significance of salt and alkali, as follows:

Class 0: Soils free of excess salt or alkali. Practically no crops are inhibited by or show evidence of injury from excess of salts or alkali.

Class 1: Soils slightly affected by salt or alkali. The growth of sensitive crops is inhibited but that of salt-tolerant crops may not be.

Class 2: Soils moderatey affected by salt or alkali. Crop growth is inhibited and no crop does well.

Class 3: Soils strongly affected by salt or alkali. Only a few kinds of plants survive.

The first group (Class 0) includes those soils in which the average concentration of salts, or the degree of alkalinity to a depth of 5 or 6 feet, is such that crop plants are not affected and there is no localization of harmful salts in any one horizon within the rooting zone of plants. Mapping units are rarely, if ever, entirely homogeneous in respect to the limits of just one of these classes. If the salt or alkali pattern is especially uneven, with only spots of affected soils, a defined complex is mapped.

Boundaries separating soils free of excess salts or alkali from these slightly, moderately, or strongly affected, are usually drawn on the map after the sample locations are plotted and the analytical data are available. The boundaries are drawn by evaluating the recorded data, the apparent effects of the salt or alkali on the soil, crops, and native vegetation, and the other features of the landscape. Boundaries can be made generally reliable so that few crop plants on the soils mapped as "free" will be noticeably damaged by salt or alkali. This does not mean that the concentration of soluble salts will everywhere fall within the range set up for the typical soil of the mapping unit. Small areas having stronger concentrations or small areas of salt-free soils may be included in the area. It is not economically practicable to map out every small body that differs in salt concentration.

If saline and alkaline conditions are not common among the soils, or if it is not necessary to establish a complete range of classes, two conditions—(1) salt-free and (2) salt- or alkali-affected—may be enough. If salt accumulations are infrequent they need not be indicated by soil boundaries; the conditions may be shown satisfactorily by symbols, defined according to area and the results of field tests. Ordinarily, however, if the accumulation of salts presents a definite problem, some boundaries drawn according to differing degrees of salinity or alkali will be necessary within soil types.

Excess salts, and especially alkali, are often characteristic of individual soil types, so that field boundaries drawn between classes according to salt or alkali coincide with soil-type boundaries.

Symbols to indicate salt- and alkali-affected areas and boundaries among classes are shown on the completed map in red or blue[9] (pl. 7). They are published on the master soil map unless the boundaries and symbols are so numerous as to obscure the other symbols. Where very intricate, a separate salt or alkali map is prepared on the same scale as the soil map. If the symbols are numerous and the pattern intricate, the field mapping is done

---

[9] In blue rather than red, if there is no other reason to make a red plate.

on an overlay of acetate rather than on the aerial photograph or the soil map.

The data on individual samples are placed in a special table in the soil survey report. The site of each profile sampled can be indicated on the published map by a red dot with a reference number keyed to the data in the table. Such a table should include the depth of each horizon or layer, the percentage of soluble salts, the pH value, and where relevant, the depth of the water table.[10]

Determination of salinity classes.—The significance of the average salt content in the soil profile in determining the classes to be recognized in defining mapping units and in predicting the capabilities of the soil for use are, of course, modified by a concentration of salts in the surface soil or any other horizon in the rooting zone and by soil texture. Generally, the salt concentration of the surface soil or the average concentration of the profile, whichever is the higher, is used in determining the salinity class of the soil.

Two sets of values are presented for the limits among salinity classes: (1) The older method of using values for the percentage of salts and (2) the more recent and better method of using measurements of the conductivity of the saturation extract.

In the older method based on percentage of salt, the dividing percentage between saline and nonsaline soils, below which most crop plants are not affected, is set at 0.15 percent. At one time, this percentage had been placed at 0.2; but surface concentrations exceeding 0.15 percent may be sufficient to limit or prohibit crop production, even though the average salt content to a depth of 6 feet may fall under this percentage. Sometimes, but not always, the soil needs to be classed as at least "slightly affected" if any horizon in the profile has a salt content greater than 0.15 percent, although most crop plants are not harmed with 0.15 percent in the lower soil.

Slightly affected soils contain from 0.15 to 0.35 percent of salt, so distributed in the profile as to injure crops or decrease yields. Moderately affected soils have concentrations of 0.35 to 0.65 percent of salt, which cause serious decreases in yields and in the capabilities of soil for agricultural use. Strongly affected soils contain salts in excess of 0.65 percent. High concentrations are usually associated with barrenness and crusts. Such soils cannot be used for crops.[11] These limits are suggested guides that may

---

[10] A former method for recording salt concentrations of individual profiles tested with the conductivity bridge was to print a fraction on the map in which the numerator indicated the quantity of soluble salts in the surface soil or surface foot, and the denominator the average quantity of soluble salts of the profile to a depth of 6 feet, or to the depth of the sampling up to 6 feet. Sodium carbonate or a high pH value was indicated by the letters *C* or *B* after the fraction.

[11] The percentages of salts just suggested are usually valid where chloride salts or sodium sulfate predominate. If calcium sulfate (gypsum) is present in appreciable quantities, each limit may be raised by 0.05 or 0.1 percent, since the gypsum, even though it is not highly soluble, affects the reading obtained with the electrolytic bridge.

need to be varied somewhat locally to develop the most meaningful classes and mapping units. The precise limits for a specific soil, for example, vary with soil texture and water-holding capacity. With further research and experience, refined standards may be developed for broadly defined kinds of soil profiles.

More nearly adequate standards for converting measurements for conductivity of the saturation extract into salinity classes have been established by the United States Regional Salinity Laboratory. The interpretation is in terms of millimhos per centimeter as shown in table 12.

TABLE 12.—*Approximate limits of salinity classes*

Class	Percentage of salt[1]	Conductivity of extract in millimhos per centimeter[2]
Class 0: Free	0–0.15	0–4.
Class 1: Slightly affected	0.15–.35	4–8.
Class 2: Moderately affected	0.35–.65	8–15.
Class 3: Strongly affected	Above .65	Above 15.

[1] See text for qualification.
[2] Suggested values based on recent research.

By comparison with table 10 it will be noted that the two sets of values are approximately the same for soils with 50 percent moisture at saturation, normally clay loams.

Determination of alkali classes.—Soils may be both saline and strongly alkaline. Many are. Yet some Solonetz soils are strongly alkaline but not saline.

With saline soils of high alkalinity, salinity classes should be supplemented with values for pH, or percentage exchangeable sodium, or both. Besides these, determinations of permeability, swelling, and clay minerals may be helpful. Samples for pH tests may be collected from the same layers or horizons as those used for determining salts. It may also be necessary to sample a thin surface crust or coating in order to detect the detrimental alkali conditions. Surface crusts or specific horizons of dispersed soils should be tested.

The approximate pH of the soil may be determined in the field with indicators. Useful indicator solutions and their effective ranges are: Bromthymol blue, pH 6.0 to 7.6; phenol red, pH 7.0 to 8.6; cresol red, pH 7.2 to 8.8; thymol blue, pH 8.0 to 9.6; and phenolphthalein, above pH 8.3. The color of phenolphthalein should be strongly pink or red to indicate strong alkalinity. Color charts are available for the other indicators. Thymol blue and cresol red give a generally satisfactory range for strongly alkaline soils. Determinations made with these indicators in the field, using similar soil-water ratios, agree fairly well with glass-electrode measurements. Phenolphthalein is useful but does not give definite pH values.

Tests of pH with the indicator solutions are made in spot plates. The color readings are most nearly accurate with soil-water dilutions between 1 to 4 and 1 to 10. Some skill is required to arrive at the proper amount of soil and solution to make the test. One may count the number of drops required to fill a depression in the spot plate. Then the depression may be filled with soil and divided into as many portions as there were drops. Five drops of indicator solution added to one portion of the soil would then give a dilution of about 1 to 5.

Readings near the upper or lower limit of the indicator range are less reliable than those more nearly midway on the color chart. Those near the limits of the range can be checked with another indicator. The indicator solution itself must have the correct pH; its color should match that of the color chip midway in its range. If the indicator fails to match the proper color chip, it may be corrected by use of dilute solutions of acid or base. Concentrations of indicator solutions of about 0.01 percent have been satisfactory. This dilution avoids too much indicator color, which may give an erroneous value.

The glass electrode is generally regarded as a more reliable means of measuring the pH of a soil. In areas where alkalinity is a major problem, it may be helpful to have a pH meter of this type in the field.

Although pH alone is not a positive diagnosis for all alkali soils, most soils that have pH values above 8.5 have significant quantities of exchangeable sodium. A very few may also contain abundant exchangeable potassium. Generally, pH values of a paste between 8.5 and 9.0 indicate soils with alkalinity problems; and values above 9.0 indicate serious alkalinity problems. Some soils with significantly harmful quantities of exchangeable sodium have pH values below 8.5. An alkali soil may contain small quantities of soluble salts, sufficient to depress hydrolysis, with the result that the soil may not have a pH above 8.5 when the soil paste is tested. Since pH values and values for exchangeable sodium are not always correlative, a strongly alkaline soil, as defined in terms of exchangeable sodium, may not have a pH above 8.5. Yet a soil paste having a value of 8.5 may have a pH above 8.5, even as high as 10.5, on dilution to 1:5, 1:10, or more.

In predicting the feasibility of irrigating a saline soil, it is important to know the pH that will develop after the soil has been leached of excess salts. This is suggested by determining soil pH at dilutions of 1:5 or greater and comparing these results with the pH of the soil paste.[12] Most soils having a pH above 9.0 with a dilution of 1:5 are high in exchangeable sodium and are apt to swell and puddle when the excess salts are leached out.

---

[12] The methods for determining pH, including indicators and dilution used, should be recorded in the field notes. It is not satisfactory to measure pH by using ordinary indicator solutions on a soil paste placed in spot plates. Indicator solutions are generally used at a soil-water dilution of 1:5, but they can be used with greater dilutions. The Hellige Triplex indicator and the soil reaction powder for the Truog soil reaction test can be used to an upper limit of pH 8.5 in the field for determining the pH of a paste sample.

Some soils having a pH between 8.5 and 9.0 contain sufficient gypsum so that after dilution the pH will be reduced below what it would be if gypsum were not present. Such soils may or may not have clearly visible crystals of gypsum.

The percentage of exchangeable sodium is required in defining alkali soils that do not have high pH values. The dividing point between alkali and nonalkali soils, on the basis of exchangeable sodium, has been set, tentatively, at about 15 percent exchangeable sodium in the exchange complex. Determinations of exchangeable sodium are made in the laboratory. A quick test has been described for determining the total soluble sodium. From a knowledge of the salt concentration and the percentage of soluble sodium, exchangeable sodium may be estimated with the Gapon equation.[13] The adequacy of the method is yet to be determined by correlation with field experience.

Like salinity, the pH of soils varies within the profile and within very short horizontal distances. Some areas have many spots of alkali soils where the pH ranges from 8.5 to about 8.8. In others, the pH of the alkali-affected spots ranges from 9.0 to 10.0. If the spots in two such areas were about equally distributed and the growth of most crop plants is prevented in the spots, both areas should be classed similarly, as far as alkalinity is concerned. (Of course, the soils might have other mappable differences.) In a discussion of the soils it should be brought out that the spots with the lower pH probably could be reclaimed more easily or with less expense than those of higher pH.

If spots of alkali soils with pH values of 8.5 or above are intermingled with alkali-free soils, the mapping units for (1) *slightly affected,* (2) *moderately affected,* and (3) *strongly affected* areas are defined by the percentage of the area occupied by the alkali soils. If the spots are comparatively few, they may be shown by defined symbols.

The following values are intended to serve as guides for mapping units:

(0) *Alkali free:* Excepting those conveniently shown by defined symbols, spots of alkali are too few to be significant.
(1) *Slightly affected:* From very little to 5 percent of the area has alkali soil unsuited to most crops.
(2) *Moderately affected:* From 5 to 35 percent of the area has alkali soil unsuited to most crops.
(3) *Strongly affected:* More than 35 percent of the area has alkali soil unsuited to most crops. Such areas are unproductive.

For some survey areas mapping units defined in terms of combinations of salinity and alkalinity classes are needed. These classes may become mapping units within one or more soil types, or parts of defined complexes that include other taxonomic units.

---

[13] See footnote, p. 341. See also, RICHARDS, L. A. CHEMICAL AND PHYSICAL CHARACTERISTICS OF SALINE AND ALKALI SOILS OF WESTERN UNITED STATES. 4th Internatl. Cong. Soil Sci. Trans. 1: 378–383. 1950.

As with slope, stoniness, and similar features, the classes according to salinity and alkalinity need to be evaluated in relation to the other characteristics of the soil in defining mapping units. If for some other reason, a soil is not suitable for crops or pasture, no useful purpose will be served by making fine distinctions in salinity.

Perhaps a final warning is needed. Field scientists must guard against such exclusive attention to the salt concentration and alkalinity of saline and alkali soils that they neglect their many other important characteristics. No one can either classify or map these soils properly on the basis of values for salt content, pH, and exchangeable sodium alone. Such data on soil samples are exceedingly valuable, but only when properly synthesized with all the other characteristics that combine to make a soil area of a certain kind.

YIELD PREDICTIONS AND SOIL MANAGEMENT PRACTICES

Most soil surveys are made for practical purposes, several of which have been outlined in the section on Purpose of Soil Maps and Reports. For many of the most important of these purposes, the agricultural capabilities of each mapping unit need to be predicted in terms of expected average yields of adapted crops under alternative uses and sets of management practices.

A table giving the predicted yields of soils mapped, under defined sets of management practices, is a key to interpretation and use of soil map. The basic purposes of such a table may be summarized as follows:

(1) It is the simplest and most concise summary of the available information about the management of the soils shown on the map.

(2) It provides the connecting link between agricultural research and specific tracts of land.

(3) The yield predictions under defined sets of management practices provide the basis for using the soil map and report for farm planning, including farm production budgets.

(4) It provides a basis for a wide variety of important soil groupings.

(5) With it land values can be related to productivity for using the soil map in land evaluation.

Such predictions are not, of course, hard-and-fast recommendations. Even for different areas of the same kind of soil different uses are selected by the farmer among the alternatives according to the size of the farm, its location in relation to markets and its other economic characteristics, and the capabilities of the other soils in the farm unit, and according to the desires, skills, and resources of the farm manager and his family. The soil survey report does not aim to tell the farm manager precisely what to do, but it should tell him what he may expect from the use of certain practices and combinations of practices, both in yields of adapted crops and in the effects they have on the long-time productivity of the soil.

By means of predictions of average yields and of the effects of management practices on the soil itself, the results of the research can be synthesized in specific terms for the user. In times past, soil scientists left the job of interpretation largely to others. This did not work. Too few other people could study the soils closely enough to consider all their characteristics collectively and to make accurate predictions of their performance. In old soil survey reports, interpretations were given largely as general discussions of soil use and management. Although useful, these were not specific enough. This was partly due to broad definitions of the mapping units and to significant inclusions of contrasting soils in the mapping units. That is, the more homogeneous the mapping units, the better they can be defined and interpreted in specific terms.

Two technical developments in soil survey made more satisfactory yield predictions possible: (1) The use of aerial photographs as the base for mapping, which led to more accurately plotted soil boundaries; and (2) more sharply defined series, types, phases, and complexes. Equally important has been recent progress in the integration of soil classification with research in soil management, crop production, and the economics of farm management. Increasingly, experimental results and records of farm experience are being sorted by kinds of soil as defined and named in the standard system of soil classification.

Yield predictions and soil productivity ratings are arrived at in two principal ways: (1) Through judgments based upon evidence afforded by actual yield data from sample areas of the soil mapping units, and (2) through judgments based on comparisons of the characteristics of soils and basic knowledge of plant requirements. In some survey areas, few, if any, precise yield data by soil units are available. Yet the mapping units can be arrayed from the highest to the lowest in yield potentiality under each assumed management class on the basis of field observations during the survey, interviews with farmers, and a knowledge of fundamental soil-plant relationships. To translate such an array into yield predictions requires a few "bench marks," or absolute yield values, for some of the soils in terms of tons, bushels, or pounds, which may be had from farm records, experimental data, sample harvests, or carefully analyzed oral reports of yield experience. Some useful data may be had from outside the survey area.

In practice, the scientist "never has enough data." Sound judgment will always be a primary basis for predicting yield expectancy of soils or for rating them according to their productivity. In most soil survey areas, the scientist will need to predict yields for many soil types for which he has no "hard data," much as he wants them. Still, no one else is likely to be in so good a position to interpret the soil survey data as he is. He must make the most of what evidence he can find. The final result —the predictions of yields and of the results of management practices—should be reasonable when tested against the reliable data that are available and when tested against the known principles of soil-crop relationships.

Summarizing briefly, the main characteristics of a good table of predicted average crop yields by kinds of soil are as follows:

(1) The predictions are as reliable as it is possible to make them with the available data and as tested against the judgment of competent agriculturists familiar with the soils and farming of the area.

(2) The set of management practices associated with each yield prediction is described in as much detail (but no

more) as is consistent with the accuracy of the prediction. For example, the quantities and kinds of fertilizer need to be defined as parts of the sets of management practices if yield predictions with and without fertilizer are to be meaningful.

(3) Yield predictions should not simply reflect history, but the potentialities of the new, tried combinations of practices resulting from the agricultural science of today.

CONCEPT OF SOIL PRODUCTIVITY

Besides their direct use by farmers and others, predicted yields give a measure of soil productivity. The combined effect of all growth factors is reflected in the crop even though the scientist is unable to explain all the interrelationships. Clearly, any precise statement about soil productivity must be in terms of a specific kind of soil, a specific kind of crop or combination of crops, and a specific set of management practices.

Soil productivity is perhaps more an economic concept than it is one of soil science. It is the capacity of a soil for producing a specified plant or sequence of plants under a physically defined set of management practices. It is measured in terms of inputs of production factors in relation to outputs or harvest. Thus, soil productivity is not itself an inherent quality of the soil. All the chemical, physical, and biological properties of a soil, together with the associated climate, determine its response to management—response to inputs of labor and materials. Two soils may each give low yields with a set of simple practices—mere tillage, seeding, and harvesting. The soil productivity of both is low. Yet one may respond far more to inputs of fertilizer and lime, and to the use of rotations with deeply rooted legumes, than the other. One soil has, with this class of management, high productivity, while the other remains low. Thus, one cannot define "natural soil productivity." Such an expression is, in fact, meaningless. It is only in a cultural setting that soil productivity exists or can be measured. When people use "natural soil productivity" in loose speaking, they have already an unconscious assumption of management—usually that common to the area. Certain tropical soils, for example, in one cultural setting are said to be unproductive, while in another setting they are highly productive. Neither is more appropriately "natural" than the other.

In the United States, a "productive" soil is generally regarded as one that will give good yields, in relation to inputs of materials and labor per acre, when used for a combination of the principal grains and grasses—corn, oats, wheat, clover, and other common crops. In some areas, sugar beets, soybeans, or cotton are an accepted part of the general crop combination. Some crops, however, have such special requirements that relative yields of them are obviously unlike those of "general farm crops." Flue-cured tobacco is an example. Cranberries is a crop still further removed from the usual. As work with yield predictions goes forward, it will be found increasingly necessary to treat each crop, and even different varieties of crops, separately, although general productivity ratings will continue to be somewhat useful too, *if properly qualified.*

YIELD PREDICTIONS

Estimates of the average crop yields that may be expected from the soil types and phases shown on the map are an essential part of soil survey reports. These predicted yields and the definitions of management that may be expected to produce them are essential for the interpretive grouping of soils according to soil-use capability, crop adaptability, management requirements, and the like. These estimates are the basic stuff for agricultural and economic interpretations. Some systematic procedure needs to be developed as each soil survey is initiated and followed during the continuation of the work to insure getting the yield data under defined classes of management.

The party chief is responsible for collecting data on yields and management practices by soil types and phases. By arrangement, part of the task may be delegated to a representative of a cooperating State agricultural experiment station in the party. Other members of the party may be given specific assignments, especially those trained in the principles of statistics and who show aptitude for interviewing farmers. The work cannot be slighted, nor left to casual questioning of farmers and others. Sufficient time must be allowed for a thorough job of exploring, collecting, and analyzing relevant yield data and estimates by mapping units.

Where possible, the soil survey work plan should provide for detailing a qualified staff member of the cooperating experiment station the task of bringing together the relevant data on soil and crop management and of collaborating with the soil survey party in developing the table of yield predictions. The help of specialists at nearby State and Federal experiment stations, or substations, should be sought during the course of the survey and for reviewing the results. Then the final review of the whole table may be made jointly by the party chief, the soil correlator, representatives in soil management research and in soil survey of the cooperating experiment station, and the supervisory scientist. In the Soil Survey final review of this work is done in much the same manner as the final review of soil correlation and nomenclature.

YIELD AND MANAGEMENT PRACTICES

Yield predictions for a soil type or a phase depend upon management definitions; and the requirements or suggestions for management need to be set against resulting yields. They are intimately related.

Ideally at least, one should like to have yield predictions for each kind of soil under all significantly different sets of management practices that are likely to be used by farmers. As research in soil classification and on the performance of crops on different kinds of soil progresses, we shall be able to go much further than we can now. The prediction tables being made today are vastly improved over the beginning tables of some 20 years ago. As yet, data and techniques for analyzing them do not permit us to distinguish the yield differences that might result from every small difference between sets of management practices, even though significant differences can be seen on some farms where records are kept. Further, the management of a farm involves a very large number of practices that influence yield. Even with the best record books, only a few of the major practices are noted. These major practices are defined, but we cannot conclude that the yields obtained resulted from these recorded practices alone. A farmer who follows several good practices is likely to do the other things necessary for good results, and on time. It is the whole collection of practices that gives the yield.

At least for the present, in soil survey interpretation only fairly broad definitions of management can be dealt with, broader in some survey areas than in others. As much specificity and subdivision of management classes should be made as the available data will permit and as will be useful, but no more.

Management classes are commonly defined in terms of levels and sets.

Levels of management.—Under comparable conditions, the farm operators in a county, say, ordinarily group themselves into a small "poor" class, a large "average," or modal, class, and a small "superior" class, according to the efficiency of their production, or yields in relation to inputs of materials and labor. The management practices followed by such groups are sometimes called "levels" of management.[1]

In the early work with yield estimates and soil productivity ratings, the "average," or modal, level was chosen for definition in physical terms. Perhaps "most common" practice is a better expression, since the yields are usually above the county average.

---

[1] Farms may be also stratified according to types or systems of farming. Such stratification is not essential to the development of the classes of management used in yield predictions. In areas, however, with strongly contrasting types of farming, it may be helpful to block out areas according to general systems of farming within which the classes of management are chosen.

These differences among farming systems arise partly out of management decisions, partly out of the capabilities of the soil pattern on the farm, and partly out of size and location. The potentialities for various systems of farming are related more appropriately to soil associations than to the individual mapping units of a detailed soil map. Yet areas of the same kind of soil may be found as important parts of a grain farm, a dairy farm, a beef-cattle farm, a mixed, or general, farm, and a fruit farm. Even though one may return more income than another, no one system can necessarily be judged "best" without considering the varying skills, labor force, and desires of the operator and his family. The crops grown on the soil and the practices to produce them may be different in the different systems. On one farm, for example, a sloping soil may be used for permanent pasture, while on another it may be terraced and used for a rotation with corn and small grains.

A few estimates have also been made for the low or "poor" level, but ordinarily these are less useful. Few who go to the trouble to read and use the soil survey, or to seek advice based upon it, are interested in estimates at the low level.

Far more important are the yields and management practices at the superior level (not counting "play" farms or other uneconomic units). Generally, these are practices that other farmers can follow under comparable conditions.

Yields and practices can occasionally be estimated at a still higher or "ceiling" level, above superior, where the best combination of all known practices is followed. Where established and functioning, such are the sets of management practices finally developed on a pilot-research farm.

Summarizing, definitions of management practices may be sought at three primary levels—always at one, usually at one and two, and occasionally at all three—as listed below. Since the actual sets of practices may vary within any one level, most importance must be attached to their definition.

> *Level 1.*—The most common combinations of management practices followed by the majority of successful farmers using the soil being dealt with.
>
> *Level 2.*—The superior combinations of management practices followed by the leading farmers using the soil, perhaps 1 percent or perhaps over 10 percent.
>
> *Level 3.*—The optimum combinations of management practices developed on pilot-research farms, if any, or on other farms that represent the best (or "ceiling") that can be done in the present state of the agricultural arts.

As progress is made in the development of methods for making yield predictions, this admittedly loose concept of levels of management according to poor, average, and superior managers is being replaced by defined sets of management practices at different levels of intensity (inputs).

Sets of management practices.—Sets of management practices are the combinations of tillage practices, crop rotations, fertilizer practices, and so on that are combined to produce the crop or a group of crops. The table of predicted yields should include one or more sets near the minimum intensity, and possible intermediate ones. Sets of management practices that should have separate predictions may vary by only a single factor, such as continuous wheat and alternate wheat and fallow, for example, on a Chestnut soil. Other sets of management practices selected for the table may vary by several factors, such as the rotation, the tillage practices, and the fertilizers used. Since farmers use sets of practices, the predictions are valid even though it may not be possible to isolate the individual effect of any one practice on yield.

Ideally, it would be useful to have yield predictions for each significantly different set of management practices, physically defined, under three levels of intensity. These levels might be further stratified by important systems of farming. Usually such refinements of distinction are beyond the available data and resources for the soil survey project. How far the soil survey party can and should go in making distinctions among sets of management practices depends a great deal upon the research and interest of the other agriculturists at the cooperating experiment stations.

Classes of management.—The important sets of management practices selected from among those that represent each important level of management and used in the table of yield predictions are often referred to as classes of management. These need to be described in considerable detail and as definitely as possible. It is not enough to indicate merely the level. It is only when the sets of management practices are physically defined in terms of crop rotations, kinds and amounts of fertilizer and lime, drainage, irrigation, contour cultivation, and so on, that the estimates can be used in predicting the farm returns for existing or reorganized farms by the ordinary process of budgeting.

For many survey areas, the same management classes at each level are not appropriate for all soils, especially where the soils vary widely in major use capabilities—crops, pasture, and forestry, in adapted crops, or in responses to management. In footnotes to the tables, in an accompanying explanatory legend, or in the text, each management class should be clearly explained and keyed to the soils to which it applies.

Bench marks.—If the number of separate figures for yields in a single season under each class of management, however developed, are plotted for each soil in the usual frequency distribution curves, some curves are flatter than others. Let us say that 40 bushels of corn, for example, is the average yield. It may represent a median between 35 and 45 for 90 percent of the values, or for 80 percent of them, or even for only 50 percent. Individual yields reported from a soil in a given management class may depart widely from the average over a period of years. With the average yield of corn at 40 bushels, for one soil one-half the yields may fall between 30 and 50 bushels, while for another soil perhaps only one-third may fall within that range.

Several factors cause departures from the average yield figure: (1) Certain hidden factors of management are not included even in a detailed description of the principal items that define the management class. (2) Crops are subject to many variations in weather and to destruction by animals, insects, and diseases. (3) Even with unusual care in soil classification and mapping, no soil mapping unit is entirely homogeneous; and some fields are near one extreme of the definition and others near the other extreme. (4) Depending upon the responsiveness of the soil to fertilizers, lime, and similar management practices that change its fertility or tilth, past management is reflected in current crop yield in ways often difficult to allow for accurately. (5) Yields taken from fields often reflect some inclusions of other soils shown on the map. (6) Since seasonal variations in weather produce good years and poor years, yield records collected over a short term of years may not provide reliable predictions of average expectancy.

The length of time in years required to represent the normal climatic variation is not the same for all soil regions. Among the podzolic soils generally, for example, about 10 years can be expected to give a fair sample of seasons; while among Chestnut soils, 10 years is too short a period.

Bench-mark average yields, in tons, bushels, or pounds, predicted for the principal soils, and used as a basis for giving expected yield values for all soils in an array from highest to lowest, should have added to them, where possible, an indication of expected variations. For example, both a Gray-Brown Podzolic soil in Maryland and a Chestnut soil in western North Dakota may have valid yield expectancies for wheat of 20 bushels per acre. Varieties and class of management practices are, of course, different. The expected variation in yield from year to year is also different. Over a 20-year period, it may turn out to be 20 ± 20 in North Dakota and 20 ± 7 in Maryland, for say 90 percent of the values.

Party chiefs are not required to give such ranges in variability everywhere, only where sound data are available for doing so. The aim should be to give the best yield estimates possible with the data at hand, using such statistical analyses as may be helpful. Both the setting of impossibly high standards for yield estimates in areas having few data and the failure to make full use of the available data in areas having a great many need to be avoided.

Reliability of yield predictions.—After the task is completed, the party chief and supervisory scientists should explain the sources of data and suggest the general reliability of the table of yield expectancies and management classes by one of the following notations:

1. *Fair:* Developed mainly from estimates based upon observations and interviews supplemented by a few records and experimental data.

2. *Fairly good:* Developed from estimates based upon observations, interviews, farm records, and experimental data

3. *Good:* Developed from farm records and experimental data, supplemented by observations and interviews.

In addition, it is helpful to underscore the "bench mark" values included in the table.

SOURCES OF DATA FOR ESTIMATES[2]

Information on the productivity of soils and their responses to management has its origin in measurements or estimates of crop yields. Some estimates can be had in terms of tons, bushels, and pounds; others can be had only in relative terms—one soil higher than another and a third one lower. Such values are related to the combinations of soil characteristics that define soils as mapping units and the management practices applied to them.

Field observations.—Observations of crop growth on different soils and under different sets of management practices made during the course of the survey are an important source of information. Such observations are not precise yield estimates, of course, but can be of aid in arraying the soils from highest to lowest in productivity for a crop. Valuable observations of relative crop growth can be made on two or more soils within the same field. This kind of information is very useful in making an array of the soils. Most soil scientists make many such observations every day. Their usefulness increases with their number and with orderly notation and assembly.

Of course, if two or more soils that normally respond to quite different management practices occur in one field, all of which is managed in the same way, an evaluation of yields from these different soils cannot lead to valid comparisons of their productivity. One soil may produce low yields simply because the management practiced in the field is poor for it, whereas those practices may be near optimum for another soil in the field.

Experimental results.—Data on crop yields from experimental plots have an accessory value for yield predictions, besides the primary objectives of the experiments, provided the plots are fair representatives of the mapping units. Where experimental stations, substations, farms, or fields are on any of the soils mapped in the county, arrangements should be made for study of data on crop yields. If a proper soil map has not already been made, one may be needed of the plots. The experimental sites need not necessarily be within the survey area so long as the soils and other growing conditions are similar.

Many experimental stations arrange with farmers for trials of new crop varieties or of new practices. Sometimes accurate yields

[2] On this subject, as well as on other phases of the problem of developing yield predictions, see the following:

ABLEITER, J. K. PRODUCTIVITY RATINGS OF SOIL TYPES. *In* The Classification of Land. Mo. Agr. Expt. Sta. Bul. 421, pp. 13–24. 1940.

ODELL, R. T. MEASUREMENT OF THE PRODUCTIVITY OF SOILS UNDER VARIOUS ENVIRONMENTAL CONDITIONS. Jour. Amer. Soc. Agron. 42 (6): 282–292, illus. 1950.

——— and SMITH, GUY D. A STUDY OF CROP YIELD RECORDS BY SOIL TYPES. Soil Sci. Soc. Amer. Proc. 5: 316–321, illus. 1940.

———. A STUDY OF SAMPLING METHODS USED IN DETERMINING THE PRODUCTIVITY OF ILLINOIS SOILS. Jour. Amer. Soc. Agron. 42 (7): 328–335. 1950.

SIMONSON, R. W., and ENGLEHORN, A. J. METHODS OF ESTIMATING THE PRODUCTIVE CAPACITIES OF SOILS. Soil Sci. Soc. Amer. Proc. 3: 247–252. 1938.

SMITH, GUY D., and SMITH, R. S. A STUDY OF CROP-YIELD RECORDS BY SOIL TYPES AND SOIL RATINGS. Soil Sci. Soc. Amer. Proc. 4: 375–377. 1939.

are reported from such trials. Either the county agricultural agent or workers in the State experiment station may be expected to have records of the results.

Yields obtained in experiments or field trials may be recorded on Form No. 1 (pp. 375 and 376). Since the production practices used in experimental work are usually recorded, the set of practices for each yield value should be entered on Form No. 1.

Yield measurements on experimental plots are more accurate as a rule than those obtained from other sources. The management conditions, however, are not generally similar to those on most farms. Experiments usually include a considerable range of soil management practices. The data from plot experiments can be very useful, nevertheless, especially in estimating the effects of different soil management practices on yields and on long-time soil productivity, even though the yields are apt to be higher than yields on farms.

At the same time the experimental data are being analyzed for yield estimates, they should also be analyzed for use in making predictions in the report on such soil management practices as liming, use of fertilizers, terracing, crop rotations, tillage practices, varieties of adapted crops, weed control, irrigation practices, pasture management, time of seeding, rates of seeding, and information of this kind.

Data from experimental plots need to be used cautiously in the establishment of bench marks to be sure that the management practices used represent management classes for which predictions are to be made. The party chief can generally use the analyses and summaries of the experiments already made by experiment station workers. It is his responsibility, however, to be sure that the soils are comparable.

Data from pilot-research farms are also useful but there are not yet many of these. The large and growing number of unit-test demonstration farms on which records are kept are very useful. Data from these are obtained chiefly from farm record books.

Field samples.—Useful data may be obtained where sample areas of the crops have been harvested from different soils within the same field. Such data are especially useful in arranging the soils relative to one another and can be used to establish bench-mark yields. The method also makes possible more efficient use of farm records where fields lack homogeneity of soil types and phases. Unfortunately, not many data are yet available from the use of this method.

Farm experience.—The experience of farmers managing different soils under the different management practices is potentially, by far, the most important source of data on soil productivity. Unfortunately, however, only a few farmers keep accurate records of their yields and practices by individual fields that can be related to soil types or soil associations.

Even those who record their receipts and expenditures often do not record crop yields and management practices. These farmers can only furnish their experience out of their memories.

Form No. 1—Sheet 1

CROP YIELD RECORD SHEET

County_____ Farm operator_____ Legal description of farm_____ Year_____

Field No.	Crop	Acres	Production	Name of variety (or hybrid)	Soil mapping units

In using this form to record data from farm record books, circle the number of fields where the soil pattern is too complex to be used in relating yields to soils. The proportion of different soils making up such fields need not be estimated.

Data from: Farm account books_____
Experiments_____
Farmer's memory_____
Other source[1]_____
Other source_____

[1] Indicate source.

Form No. 1—Sheet 2

Field No.	Lime		Fertilizer		Manure (tons)	Cover crop plowed under (kind)	Other treatment (specify)	Is this field—			Management class[2]
	Kind	Quantity	Kind (formula)	Quantity				Planted on contour	Drained	Terraced	

[2] The management class will be entered after the crop history and treatment of the field previous to the year of record have been studied and after the management classes for the soils of the county have been determined.

Farm record books.—Well-kept farm record books that include an annual record of yields and management practices by fields are perhaps the best source of data. Although shorter records are of value and should by all means be explored, records long enough to represent the normal cycle of weather adequately are best. A 10-year record is satisfactory in most humid areas, but longer records are better in semiarid regions with marked fluctuations in weather.

The party chief should explore all possibilities for record books. Even if only two or three usable records are found, the data from them may be very useful in establishing bench marks and giving quantitative values for the soils arrayed relatively on the basis of other observations and estimates. Those farmers who have kept some records, even though not by fields, are more likely to recapture their past experience out of their memories than farmers who have kept no records at all. Therefore, when selecting farmers for questioning, those having record books should be given priority, provided that the locations of the farms and their soil patterns give promise of fields uniform enough to warrant getting yield data from them. A single visit with such a farmer may suffice to examine his record books, to appraise their usefulness, and to leave with him a questionnaire on yields and practices. In selecting the farmers, one must recall that the selection of those with record books may introduce some bias that needs to be taken into account. That is, farmers keeping record books are apt to follow a higher level of management practices than those who do not. They may follow practices not listed in the record books or may use more skill in following the listed practices, especially in timing them.

The usefulness of records, especially those not broken down by fields, depends a lot on the soil pattern. If the entire farm consists of one kind of soil, total production figures and soil management information are nearly as useful as field data. Rarely, however, are farms that simple. Where yield estimates are made for individual soils, the presence of only one soil in a field is desired. Even this situation does not exist generally, and judgment will need to be exercised about which fields to use and which to reject. It must also be kept in mind that yields from one soil in a field may be influenced by the presence of other soils in the same field, if they delay the timing of operations. Where yields depend on timely planting, for example, the presence of a soil that dries out slowly may delay planting beyond the ideal time for other soils. Yields may sometimes need to be measured or estimated by soil associations.

The most satisfactory farm record book contains a diagram of the farm showing the individual fields and giving annual records of management and production. Where such records are promising, even outside the survey area, a soil map can be made. Even though only one field has uniform soil, the yield and treatment record should be summarized by fields for the whole farm. Comparison of the soil map with the farm map will permit sorting out the fields that can be used. Ordinarily, this can be done more conveniently in the office after the records are taken than at the farm. Fields may need to be rejected if 10 percent or more of the soil is markedly different from the predominant soil. Yields from associations of two soils occurring in a field may be valuable, however, if this is a common association on many fields.

A form similar to the one illustrated as Form No. 1 may be used to record yields and practices by fields as well as to record yield figures and estimates from other sources. Where data are obtained from a farm record book, a tracing of the farm map showing the boundaries and identification numbers of the fields for which yields are recorded on Form No. 1 should be saved and clipped to the form. The date needs to be written on the tracing so that it can be placed with the form for that year. If the field layout remains unchanged for two or more years, the tracings can be so dated.

If field boundaries change a great deal, it may be better to make, as a basis for later tabulation on Form No. 1, an outline sketch of the farm for each year and to show directly on these sketches the crops grown, the management practices, and the yields.

Some farmers have kept records as a part of the soil productivity research program of the cooperating experiment station. These records should be treated in a way similar to those from experimental plots. The party chief can usually work with the analyses and summaries already developed.

The first step in analyzing the data of farm records is to study the soils of the individual farm, including the soil pattern in relation to the field pattern. Having classified the fields by soil mapping units and chosen the ones to use, the next step is to define the soil management classes for which yield predictions will be made and to classify the important sets of practices that may be permitted in each class. Perhaps this grouping is the most difficult part of the procedure. The analyst must decide on a relatively small number of management classes that can be handled practicably and that will permit a display of the significant variations. It may be helpful to array the yields of key crops in tabular form, giving individual yields and associated descriptions of soil management. From the study of such a summary of all available records, whether from record books or questionnaires, appropriate classes of soil management practices may be established and defined.

Questionnaires.—Since the actual yield records that can be related to kinds of soil and to classes of management are so few in most survey areas, yield experience drawn from the memories of farmers will usually need to be used. Representative fields of the important soils can be selected and the operators asked to cooperate in the work by estimating the production from one or more fields along with crop varieties and practices used. Ordinarily this information may be expected to go back only 2 or 3 years, although some may have notes that will allow them to go back farther than that.

The most reliable estimates usually can be had by visiting the farm, explaining what is wanted and why, and asking the farmer to report his estimates on a questionnaire left for him to fill out later and to mail. He may not do a good job if he is asked to recall yields and practices on the spur of the moment, especially if he is busy at the time of the visit. It is helpful to select in advance fields that seem from the soil map to be ones that would be useful. The field or fields can be identified to the farmer at the time of the visit and also in the questionnaire left with him. There follows a sample questionnaire of a type that has been used, together with a covering letter explaining its purpose to the farmer.

Covering letter for suggested field questionnaire

Office of the County Agent
....

Mr. ....

....

....

Dear Sir:

For the past few months the .... State Agricultural Experiment Station and the United States Department of Agriculture have been conducting a detailed study of the soils of .... County. The purpose of this research and survey is to make a detailed basic soil map and gather as much information as possible about the soils of your county.

You are one of the ten farmers in your township asked to cooperate with us in obtaining this information. Your help will be greatly appreciated.

We are trying to classify the soils on their physical and chemical properties and how and from what they are formed or developed. We need information concerning the best adapted crop rotation, methods of handling the soils for the different crops, and average crop yields under the different management practices. All of this information we will use in making recommendations for rotations and farm and soil management practices for the different soils, which we will incorporate in the report accompanying the soil map. We realize the farmer can furnish part of this information out of his experience and are taking this method to obtain it. The more aid you can give us in determining these matters, the more reliable the report will be.

The questions asked apply to your own farm. We have tried to prepare the questions so that they will require only a little time to answer. Most of the questions can be answered with one word or figures; others require short statements, as brief as possible. It is realized that it is not always possible to give exact yields; and where exact yields are not known, your best estimate will be sufficiently accurate.

The questions refer to one particular field on your farm. It is identified in the first paragraph and on the attached farm outline. This particular field has been selected because specific information about the cropping and farm management practices on the soil in that field is needed.

Your answers will be treated confidentially and will not be quoted individually, but will be used in assembling facts for use in the soil survey report of .... County, ...

Your cooperation is sincerely desired and will be appreciated.

Sincerely,

....

(County Agricultural Agent)

Suggested Field Questionnaire[3]

.... Farm

Section .... Township .... County, ...

All questions in this form refer to the particular field of your farm consisting of approximately .... acres in the .... Section .... Township ...., and lying .... of your farm buildings. Also see attached outline map for location of field.

1. What crop rotation have you found best adapted to this field? (Give one complete rotation, as, for example, wheat 2 years, corn 1 year, alfalfa 2 years.)

   ....
   ....
   ....

2. Give yield for each crop in the above rotation and year it was obtained. (For example, wheat yield in 1942 .... bushels, and 1943 .... bushels; corn yield 1944 .... bushels; alfalfa yield 1945 .... tons, and 1946 .... tons.)

   ....
   ....
   ....

3. If you do not use a fixed crop rotation for this field, list the crops grown, year grown, and yield per acre, for the last 5 years the field was in crop.

Crop	Year	Bushels or tons per acre
....	19	....
....	19	....
....	19	....
....	19	....
....	19	....

4. Have you used commercial fertilizers: Yes ...... No ......; barnyard manure: Yes ...... No ......; or green manure: Yes ...... No ...... on this field? (Check yes or no following type of fertilizer used, if any.)

5. If fertilizers were used, please fill out the following table. (If the use of fertilizer gave no increased yield, be sure to put a check mark in column under "No increase observed." It is as important to find out if no increased yields were obtained as it is to find out if there were increases. In the last column, if check strips were used to estimate increases, write "yes;" if not, write "no.")

Kind and analysis of fertilizer used	On what crop	Year used	Amount per acre (lb.)	No. of applications	How was fertilizer used	Approximate date of seeding	Estimated increase due to fertilizer	No increase observed	Check strips (yes or no)

6. If your rotation does not contain a legume, what year did you last grow a legume on this field? ....

---

[3] An actual questionnaire of this kind needs to be approved by the Budget Bureau Committee on Statistical Standards before it can be used by workers in the U. S. Department of Agriculture.

7. Have you noticed any parts of this field that consistently yield differently than the rest of the field? . . . . If so, what parts, and how did they differ in yield? Roughly sketch areas with different yield on enclosed map.

. . . .
. . . .
. . . .
. . . .

8. Have you had difficulty in getting certain crops to grow in this field? . . . . If so, what crops and how did they act? . . . .
. . . .

9. Have you noticed any crops or varieties that seem particularly well adapted to this field? . . . . . . If so, what crops or varieties? . . . .
. . . .
. . . .

10. Do you have engineering structures such as terraces or artificial drainage systems on this field? . . . . . . If so, are they successful? . . . . . .
11. Do you till this field on the contour? . . . . . .
12. List other crops not already mentioned that you have grown in the field and state whether you feel they are well adapted or not well adapted to it. Give the yield you obtained. . . . .
. . . .
. . . .

13. How many years has this field been in cultivation? . . . .
14. How many years have you farmed your present farm? . . . .

In the particular survey area where this sample questionnaire would be appropriate, lime and fertilizers would not be generally used. In areas where they are generally used, additional questions need to be added to bring out the amounts and kinds used. In other areas, questions will be needed on drainage and irrigation methods. Questions on crop varieties are frequently needed. Sometimes more reliable estimates of yields can be had if the farmer is asked to estimate the total production from a field of known size rather than if he is asked for yields per acre; others are accustomed to think more in terms of acre yields.

Farmers should not be asked to estimate their normal, or average, yields from a field until they have estimated the yields for individual years. Different farmers are apt to have different concepts of such terms as "normal" or "average." The tendency is widespread to think of normal, or average, yields as those obtained in the relatively good years, neglecting to include the poor years in the averaging process. Years of crop failure are sometimes omitted; yet predicted yields should be on the basis of planted acres, not simply harvested acres. It is better, therefore, to help the operator estimate the yields year by year, beginning with the latest crop year, then going back to the year before that, and so on as far as reliable estimates can be recalled.

The date should be given for each specific crop year. This makes it possible to use weather data as a check to detect cases in which a serious error might have been made. If years of severe drought, for example, are not reflected in a farmer's estimated yield, his yield figures may need to be rejected if the evidence indicates that he is confused regarding the years in which particular yields were obtained. Especially in regions of fluctuating weather, the omission of 1 year of near crop failure from a series of 3 to 5 years can result in a serious error for the average figure.

Interviews.—Members of the soil survey party encounter farmers regularly during their work. Conversations with them are a normal part of the daily work, since farmers are interested in what the soil mapper is doing and why. In these conversations, the soil mapper can get a farmer's general observations on crops and soils. He can also estimate the possible value of the records and estimates the farmer gives. Besides that, he may get some useful points for supplementing his own observations on soil response.

Usually, however, not a great deal of value for making yield estimates comes from these more or less casual conversations. Farmers cannot quickly recall out of their memories sufficiently accurate estimates. It is much better to give them some sort of questionnaire of the type already illustrated so that they may have more time to think about the matter.

Other yield estimates.—Adjacent to many soil survey areas are other areas covered by soil survey reports made at an earlier date. Tables of yield predictions in these older reports may be helpful, but the party chief must be careful that they do not prejudice him. It is best that he withhold analysis of them until he has made the first draft of his own tables of estimates. These old estimates may vary from his because of differences in agricultural practices. Ordinarily he may expect to have additional data because of the rapidly growing interest in this research. There may be slight differences in the homogeneity of the mapping units between the two areas. Small but significant differences in climate may be reflected in yields. Yet after the completion of his own work, the party chief may find them a useful check.

Other sources.—Various public agencies have obtained estimated yields of crops on individual farms. All such sources should be investigated.

Census data.[4]—The United States Census Bureau provides estimates of acres and yields for the principal crops on a county basis every 5 years. These reports give some general suggestions of management, for the acres of different crops grown, the number of livestock, and the amount of lime and fertilizer used are included. These data are of limited use because they cover only every fifth year, are compiled on a county basis, and generalize management practices too broadly.

In addition, some States have an annual farm census made every year by the local assessors. This census gives data on acres of crops and yields by counties and sometimes by townships. This

---

[4] For a good discussion of the use and limitations of census data see BLACK, JOHN D. THE RURAL ECONOMY OF NEW ENGLAND. 796 pp., illus. Cambridge. 1950.

information is of considerable value, as it discloses something of the important fluctuations in climate. Where the township is the reporting unit, the data help in estimating the farming systems and their productivity in relationship to soil associations.

Other county offices of agricultural agencies.—As a part of the agricultural conservation program, 10-year average yields of wheat are kept for many individual farms in some States. The county office of the Production and Marketing Administration should be visited for records of this sort. In States where the land is sectionized, the yield records are associated with the regular description of the land so that the farm can be located on the soil map. In most other places farms can also be located from the records. Farms having soil patterns uniform enough to enable the arraying of yields by soil mapping units can be sorted out and the yields tabulated. Records of this kind, however, rarely give an adequate statement of the management practices, including rotations, use of lime and fertilizer, tillage, contour cultivation, use of winter cover crops, and the like. Before they can be used it may be necessary to visit some of the farms to obtain additional information on management practices. After information on management practices has been obtained, sorting can begin. For sorting, it is usually helpful to have a separate sheet for tabulating the yields of each crop on each soil as provided for in Form No. 2 (pp. 384 and 385). That is, one would have a single sheet for corn on Tama silt loam, rolling phase, another for corn on Tama silt loam, undulating phase, and so on. The data may be arranged in vertical columns under the two, three, or more classes of management set up for each soil mapping unit in Form No. 2. These classes are established after a study of the data from all sources. The analyst needs to exercise judgment in defining a few major classes in order to display the important relationships. In arriving at this judgment, it is often helpful to discuss the classes and their definitions with other agriculturists in the county or in the cooperating experiment station.

Having sorted the yield data from various sources according to the several management classes for each soil, the average yield and the variation among the yields reported for each management class may be shown somewhat as indicated on Form No. 2.

The variation should be shown by arraying the individual yield figures; that is, by placing them in descending or ascending order of magnitude, as 31, 29, 25, 19 bushels. If a given yield occurs in more than one case, the number of times it occurs can be put in parentheses directly after the yield figure, thus: 51 (4), 49 (3). Where the number of cases is so large that they cannot conveniently to be arrayed on Form No. 2, an additional sheet can be attached to Form No. 2 to show the array or frequency distribution of the yields for each management class. Giving merely the range between the high and low yields, say 20 to 55 bushels, is not enough, since this would give no indication of how many times yields occur high or low in the range.

Form No. 2

SOIL...

CROP...

Management class:

	I (Define)	II (Define)	III (Define)
For yields reported by years: No. of cases[1]			
Array of cases[2]			
Average yield[3]			
No. of years for which yield record was obtained[4]			
For yields reported as average over a period of years: Average yield			

[1] Each yield reported for 1 year on a field constitutes a case.

[2] Arrange cases of yield in descending order of magnitude, e.g., 85, 83, 80(2), 79(3), 75, 70, 66, 63 bu. Figures in parentheses following a yield figure indicate number of cases of that yield, where it is more than 1. Letter "(e)" following a yield figure indicates a yield from an experiment.

[3] Mean of all cases.

[4] For example, if yield records on this soil under management class I were obtained in 1941, 1943, and 1945, the number of years would be 3.

Supplement to Form No. 2
ARRAY OF CORN YIELDS UNDER MANAGEMENT CLASS II
Tama silt loam, undulating phase

75	70(4)	66	62
73	69(3)	65(2)	61
72(2)	68(5)	64(2)	60
71(4)	67(4)	63	58

Because of the possibility that changes in the management classes might be made after discussion of them with other agriculturists, computation of average yields and recording of yield arrays or frequency distributions should be delayed until the management classes to be used have been finally determined.

Cases of average yields reported from farms should be tabulated on a separate copy of Form No. 2 from that used to report cases of yields for individual years. The mean of these averages can be checked against the mean of the yields from individual years to help gain an estimate of the reliability of the figures.

The Bureau of Reclamation has collected crop-yield data from irrigated farms on many of its projects. Such data may also be related to soil mapping units on some of the fields. These data are treated like those from other sources.

ESTIMATES OF YIELD EXPECTANCY

From studies and comparisons of the yield data from several sources, tentative estimates of average expected yields are set up for each soil mapping unit under each defined class of management. If the observations for a given soil and management class are limited to a short period, say 3 or 4 years, averages of these observations alone may not represent the yields that could be expected over a longer period, because of the great effect on the average value of just 1 year of unusual weather. To avoid errors through use of data from short periods, it may be necessary to study the weather data for the years covered by the observations. Comparison of weather data for the short period covered with those of a longer period may help in making yield adjustments. If average county-yield figures are available for the period covered by the observations, these may be compared with long-time yield averages to discover any effects of weather. In making such comparisons, however, the effects that better varieties, improved management practices, and major shifts in total acreage have on yield trends need to be kept in mind so that differences in yield due to these factors are separated from those due to differences in weather.

Because of unmeasured variations in management, several observations in any one year are needed to give reliable yield estimates. The proper evaluation of the data from the many sources is important. On the one hand the analyst needs to guard against subjective selection that may lead to unconscious bias, and on the other, against statistical averages of uncomparable data. Rough statistical tests sometimes can be devised to determine which estimates from different sources can usefully be combined.

SAMPLE PRODUCTIVITY TABLE No. 1

[From table 5, page 71, in the Soil Survey of Tama County, Iowa, by A. R. Aandahl et al. Data for many of the soils and estimates of probable erosion hazard omitted to save space; hence, headings and numbering of footnotes in this sample table do not conform exactly with those of the original table.]

Estimated average yields per acre of important crops on each soil of Tama County, Iowa, under different systems of soil management

Soil (type, phase, or land type)	System of soil management[1]		Applications of—				Estimated average yields per acre					
	Symbol	Crop rotation[2]	Lime[3]	Fertilizer[4]	Manure[5]	Other practices[6]	Corn	Soybeans[7]	Oats	Clover and timothy	Alfalfa	Pasture[8]
				Pounds	Tons		Bushels	Bushels	Bushels	Tons	Tons	Cow-acre days
Bremer silt loam	A	CCO	No	0	0	Tile drained if necessary	55	24	40	(9)	(10)	150
	B	CCOM	No	0	4	do	60	26	45	1.4	(10)	190
	C	CCOM	Yes	0	8	do	70	28	50	2.0	(11)3.8	----
Bremer silty clay loam	A	CCO	No	0	0	do	40	18	30	(9)	(10)	140
	B	CCOM	No	0	4	do	50	20	35	.8	(10)	170
	C	CCOM	Yes	0	8	do	60	22	40	1.2	(11)2.0	----
Buckner sandy loam	A	CCO	No	0	0	None	10	4	15	.2	(10)	20
	B	CCOM	No	0	4	do	15	8	20	.4	(10)	40
	C	CCOMM	Yes	200	8	do	30	14	35	.6	.8	----
Carrington loam	A	CCO	No	0	0	do	30	10	27	(9)	(10)	100
	B	CCOM	No	0	4	do	45	14	40	1.2	(10)	170
	C	CCOMM	Yes	200	8	Contour cultivation	55	22	52	2.0	3.4	----
Eroded gently rolling phase	A	CCO	No	0	0	None	25	4	17	(9)	(9)	70
	B	CCOM	No	0	4	do	35	8	27	1.0	(10)	140
	C	CCOMM	Yes	200	8	Contour strip cropping	50	16	40	1.7	3.0	----
Carrington silt loam	A	CCO	No	0	0	None	35	12	30	(9)	(10)	105
	B	CCOM	No	0	4	do	45	16	40	1.4	(10)	180
	C	CCOMM	Yes	200	8	Contour cultivation	55	24	52	2.0	3.6	----
Eroded gently rolling phase	A	CCO	No	0	0	None	25	6	20	(9)	(9)	80
	B	CCOM	No	0	4	do	35	10	30	1.2	(10)	150
	C	CCOMM	Yes	200	8	Contour strip cropping	50	18	45	1.8	3.2	----

Soil / phase[1]	System	Rotation[2]	Lime[3]	Manure	Erosion control[6]	Corn	Soybeans[7]	Oats	Clover and timothy	Alfalfa	Pasture
Eroded rolling phase	A	CCO	No	0	None	20	2	15	(9).8	(10)	60
	B	CCOM	No	0	..do..	30	6	25	(12)1.6	(10)	110
	C	CCOMMM	Yes	200	Contour strip cropping	45	12	40	2.8	(11)2.8	---
Chariton silt loam	A	CCO	No	0	Drained if necessary	30	18	30	(9)1.0	(10)	140
	B	CCOM		0	..do..	40	20	35	1.4	(10)	180
	C	CCOM	Yes	200	..do..	50	24	40	(12)2.2	(11)2.2	---

¹ 3 systems of soil management defined for most of the soils and indicated by the letters A, B, and C are used as the basis for estimating the average acre yields of most of the crops. Pasture management is defined separately.

² Crops included in the rotations are indicated by the following letters: C, O, and M. The letter "C" means corn, with one exception. When the average acre yield of soybeans is estimated, 1 crop of corn in the rotation, except for continuous corn when it is considered that soybeans are raised every third year. The letter "O" indicates oats. Meadow, "M", is meant to include a mixture of timothy with red, white, and alsike clovers, except when the yield of alfalfa is estimated or when there are 3 or more years of meadow in the rotation. For these two exceptions, meadow is meant to be alfalfa.

³ When lime applications are included in the management system, they are made once during the rotation in quantities sufficient to neutralize the soil acidity. It is applied prior to the planting of the legumes.

⁴ The fertilizer application is 20-percent superphosphate (P_2O_5), and it is applied on the oat crop. This application is not to be considered the recommended one.

⁵ The manure applications are made once during the rotation on the first or second corn crop.

⁶ Grassed waterways are included with contour cultivation and contour strip cropping.

⁷ Soybeans are a relatively new crop in Tama County, and data on yields and soil adaptations are limited; consequently, the estimated average yields per acre are less accurate than for other crops.

⁸ Only 2 systems of pasture management are defined for estimating the productivity of the soils for pasture:

System A:
(1) No application of lime or fertilizer is made.
(2) Vegetation consists principally of grasses, although no effort is made to improve the species or to add legumes.
(3) Weeds are not eradicated.
(4) Pastures are not overgrazed.

System B:
(1) Enough lime is applied every 6 to 10 years to maintain neutrality of the soil.
(2) A good stand of grasses and legumes is maintained.
(3) Phosphate fertilizer (400 pounds of 20-percent superphosphate) is applied at the time of seeding the legumes and every 5 years thereafter.
(4) Weeds are eradicated.
(5) Pastures are not overgrazed.

The term "cow-acre days," used to express the carrying capacity of pasture land, is the product of the number of animal units carried per acre multiplied by number of days the animals can be grazed without injury to the pasture; for example, a soil that supports 1 animal unit per acre for 360 days rates 360; a soil supporting 1 animal unit on 2 acres for 180 days rates 90; and a soil supporting 1 animal unit on 4 acres for 100 days rates 25.

⁹ System of management does not include this crop in the rotation.
¹⁰ Because alfalfa is very sensitive to acid conditions, no estimate of yield is given unless an application of lime is included.
¹¹ Rotation is COMMM for estimating the average acre yield of alfalfa.
¹² Rotation is COMM for estimating the average acre yield of clover and timothy.

In some areas it may be best to start with the bench-mark yields for the important soils by management classes established under the levels used. Ideally, these bench marks should be developed for soils of high and low productivity and for all of those between for which good data can be had. At this stage, reviews by other agriculturists may be helpful. Following this, the other soils may be arrayed between the bench marks in accordance with estimates of their relative productivity.

In other areas it may be best to start by making arrays of the soils by crops under each class of management according to productivity for individual crops, and then translate these into absolute values in terms of pounds, bushels, and tons from the bench-mark figures that can be had.

Yield estimates for a crop are given only for those soils to which the crop is well enough adapted that farmers use them for it. No yield estimates are given in the tables for many of the miscellaneous land types and some of the other mapping units not used for crops or pasture. Where needed for clarity, figures for a yield estimate may be replaced with the word "unsuited." Some mapping units are given estimates for pasture and hay, but not for other crops if they are unsuited.

The tentative yield estimates set up after an analysis of all the recorded data and estimates should be discussed with other well-informed agriculturists. Depending upon interest and competence, these should include the county agricultural agent, the staff members of the agronomy, soils, and farm economics departments at the cooperating State agricultural experiment station, and perhaps also PMA committeemen, local farm loan supervisors, soil conservation technicians, and crop reporters. Especially useful will be those soil scientists, agronomists, and horticulturists familiar with the performance of improved varieties.

Final yield estimates prepared for the soil survey report should be reasonable when viewed in the light of the available data and the judgment of informed agricultural scientists and advisers familiar with the crops and soils in the survey area.

Methods of presentation.—Forms of yield tables can be seen in most of the recent soil survey reports published by the United States Department of Agriculture. Two sample tables from this source are included here. The one for Tama County, Iowa, has the advantage of showing the principal features of the management classes directly in the table. Variations in this county are not so great as in many other counties. Usually it is necessary to describe the management classes for which predicted yields are estimated more fully than is possible within the table. This is done by describing the management classes for each of the soil mapping units under the subhead *Use and management* in the soil survey report or in one of the tables. The general features of the management classes can be used as a basis for grouping soils having common management requirements, as discussed in the section The Soil Survey Report.

The table for Calloway County, Ky., is less readily used because it depends entirely on the accompanying text to explain the management classes under which the yields are estimated. These descriptions in the text are difficult to associate with particular estimates.

SOIL PRODUCTIVITY RATINGS

The most useful expression of soil productivity is average crop yield under defined management classes. For making comparisons among soils, it is convenient, although less precise, to have a productivity rating or index under defined management classes in terms of National standards. This is calculated as follows:

$$\text{Productivity rating index} = \frac{\text{Expected yield per acre}}{\text{Standard yield per acre}} \times 100.$$

Such productivity ratings allow rough comparisons among soils, especially by people who do not have in mind the standard yields of various crops. That is, a person unacquainted with the production of sweetpotatoes might not know whether a yield of 100 bushels per acre is high or low. They also permit some brcad comparisons of the productivity of soils that are normally used for widely different crops.

The table of yield estimates is directly translatable into productivity ratings from standard yields of the individual crops. Examples of such standard yields for a few crops are given in table 13. These are by no means the highest yields. Under superior or ceiling management, many soils have ratings greater than 100. If included in the soil survey report, the productivity rating table can be prepared by clerical assistants from the yield estimates and standard yields.

In addition to productivity ratings for individual crops, there is some usefulness for a general productivity rating, considering all the adapted crops. No entirely satisfactory method has yet been developed for giving statistically satisfactory summaries. Where such general ratings are developed, full account is taken of the ratings for individual crops and the relative importance of those in the farming system. But no satisfactory formula has been developed for doing it mathematically. For example, soils that may be highly productive for crops like rye and buckwheat are often not used at all for those crops because of their more economic use for some more intensive crops, as sugar beets, for example. On the other hand, a soil that has low productivity for most crops grown on it may have a very high productivity for one particular crop, such as flue-cured tobacco, or, to take more extreme examples, blueberries or cranberries.

This general rating can serve to sum up the combined effects of all the soil qualities, including fertility, frequency with which a high-value crop can be grown, ease of tillage, moisture relationships, erosion hazard, and flood hazard, as they may be expected to influence the ratio of inputs to outputs. These general ratings are made relatively within large regions rather than for the United States as a whole. Party chiefs should make them relatively within their areas. Where presented, the soils may be arrayed by groups in 5, 10, or some other number of classes according to general productivity.

TABLE 13.—*Standard yields of selected crops used in calculating productivity ratings from predicted yields*

Crop	Yield per acre	Crop	Yield per acre
Alfalfa seed ......bushels..	10	Timothy and	
Apples ....do....	200	clover ....ton..	2
Barley ....do....	40	Velvet bean .....do....	1
Beans, navy ....do....	25	Lespedeza seed...pounds..	450
Broomcorn ....pounds..	600	Oats ....bushels..	50
Buckwheat ......bushels..	25	Peaches ....do....	200
Clover, red, seed.....do....	7	Peanuts ....pounds..	1,200
Cabbage ....ton..	12	Peas ....bushels..	25
Corn ....bushels..	50	Permanent	
Corn silage ....ton..	12	pasture .....cow days..	100
Cotton, lint ......pounds..	400	Potatoes ....bushels..	200
Flax ....bushels..	15	Sorghum:	
Green beans (truck).do....	120	Forage ....ton..	4
Hay:		Grain .....bushels..	40
Alfalfa ....ton..	4	Sorghum (sorgo)	
Alsike clover ....do....	2	syrup ....gallons..	100
Cowpea ....do....	1	Strawberries .....quarts..	2,000
Lespedeza ......do....	1½	Sugar beets ....ton..	12
Millet ....do....	3½	Sweetpotatoes ...bushels..	150
Native ....do....	1	Tobacco:	
Oat ....do....	2	Bright leaf ..pounds..	1,000
Red clover ......do....	2	Burley .....do....	1,500
Soybean ....do....	2½	Western	
Sweetclover ....do....	2	fire-cured ....do....	1,000
Timothy ....do....	2	Wheat ....bushels..	25

SOIL USES AND MANAGEMENT PRACTICES

A soil survey report should give adequate and reliable information on suitable uses and management practices for each soil. The more complete and specific this information, the more valuable the soil map to farmers and farm advisers. These interpretations can never be substituted for full descriptions of the soils. In fact, the more specific the interpretations, the more quickly they become out of date.

For the convenience of readers, much of the information should be explained in easy-to-read tables and outlines. A large part of the basic stuff for such tables and outlines has already been developed in making the yield estimates. Without a sound table of yield estimates by management classes, it is not possible to make good interpretive groupings.

It is very important that the report contain clear statements of the major uses for which the soils are capable, such as crops requiring tillage, permanent pasture, and forestry. Usually, some soils are marginal and hard to place. Under some economic conditions or in some farms, they should be used in one way; whereas, under other economic conditions or in other farms, they should be used in another way. Thus, the soil scientist should avoid categorical recommendations on the one hand, and lack of clarity and specificity of the results of alternative sets of practices on the other.

In an earlier section on Purpose of Soil Maps and Reports, the requirements for farm planning have been broadly outlined. The party chief should go as far as possible in assembling facts to serve that purpose. The following items are especially important for each soil potentially suitable for crops:

1. Suitable crop rotations, including cover crops.
2. Suitable crop varieties, where these are reasonably well fixed and different for different soils in the survey area. Specific varieties of some of the common field crops are almost too subject to change to emphasize by name in so permanent a document as the soil survey report. But principles of choice may be discussed, broad groups suggested, and specific varieties that are reasonably stable, like those of tree fruits, mentioned. The soil type preference of varieties of field crops are more appropriately emphasized in special leaflets and notices to farmers.
3. Lime requirements.
4. Fertilizer requirements.
5. Suitable tillage practices, including time of tillage, where important.
6. Suitable special practices for runoff and erosion control where needed, including terraces, contour cultivation, and strip cropping.
7. Suitable drainage systems and practices, if required.
8. Suitable irrigation practices, including methods of salinity control, if important.
9. Special practices for the establishment and maintenance of improved pastures.
10. Special practices for controlling soil blowing, if important.

For soils unsuited to crops but suited to permanent pasture, the practices to use are to be explained. Where forestry is important and differences in management are related to soil types, these practices should be discussed, if authentic information can be found about them.

To insure that each item is covered for each soil to which it applies, the party chief will find it helpful to provide himself with blank forms listing each item. This complete record for each mapping unit helps him to avoid missing any item and helps him throughout the preparation of his report in the development of statements on use and management and summary tables.

The sources of information on suitable uses and practices are about the same as those already outlined in detail for developing yield estimates. Reports and summaries of experimental results are especially useful. Most State agricultural experiment stations attempt to keep their summaries of experimental data, revelant to different purposes, up to date. In areas with well-developed unit-test demonstration farms, useful data can be had from the summaries of the county agricultural agent, other extension specialists, and through interviews. As with yield estimates, the most valuable data are those from good farm record books.

SOIL GROUPINGS

Much of the material needed to characterize the soils in terms of use and practice can be presented in various sorts of tables and groupings. These need to vary widely because of the differences in conditions and problems in different areas. After the table of predicted yields itself, of first importance are groupings of the soils according to their broad use capabilities or use suitabilities and groupings according to management classes or management requirements for optimum production. Various kinds of useful groupings are mentioned elsewhere in the *Manual*. Many can be seen in recent soil survey reports published by the United States Department of Agriculture. A special bibliography of reports is included near the end of this *Manual*. A few important examples may be summarized briefly as follows:

Soil-use capability.—In areas where the soil mapping units vary widely in their broad use capabilities, it is necessary to group them under three main headings according to their suitability for (1) crops requiring tillage, (2) permanent pasture or grazing, and (3) forestry. Besides these, a few mapping units may be essentially wasteland. As a first major grouping, it is usually helpful to divide the first group—the soils suitable for crops requiring tillage—into three subgroups that may be called (1) excellent for crops and pasture, (2) good for crops and pasture, and (3) fair for crops and pasture. For many uses to which soil maps are put, this broad grouping into five major classes is exceedingly helpful; but, of course, the major problems and the necessary management practices for the individual soils within the same group vary widely. In some soil survey areas, this grouping is less useful than in others because only a few of the major groups are represented. If all the soils are at least reasonably well suited to crops, for example, the important distinctions to be made are within the first major group. Nevertheless such a simple grouping is so easily grasped by many people wanting some sort of general "land inventory" and unlikely to study the detailed classes and ratings that it should be made in most, if not all, surveys.

Management requirements.—The most important grouping is the one by management requirements. The management groups are subclasses of the major use groups. These management groups are related as nearly as possible to the classes of management used in developing the yield estimates, although it may be useful to have more management requirement groups than management classes for yield estimates.

The number of management groups required depends upon the range of soil conditions within the area, intensity of use, and adequacy of detailed information. The broader the groups, the less specific can be their definitions and the descriptions of management requirements. *It cannot be expected that all mapping units within a group have identical management requirements.* The specific variations within the groups need to be dealt with under individual names of the soil mapping units. This is very important to the use of the soil survey. The benefit from management groupings can be wholly offset by ignoring the specific requirements of individual soil types, phases, and complexes, on the one hand, or by making a very large number of separate groupings, varying only slightly from one another, on the other. On some very complex areas the number of groups required to provide homogeneity that will permit specific statements about management is so great that little is gained by the grouping. In such areas tables which list management needs of individual mapping units should be used.

Fertilizer and lime requirements.—In some areas the requirements for lime and fertilizer can be described adequately under the management groups, although sometimes they can be handled properly only by individual kinds of soil or by a slightly different grouping. These needs can be made clear by supplemental groups indicating requirements for lime, phosphatic fertilizers, potash fertilizers, nitrogen fertilizers, and perhaps others, individually. Even though most farmers in an area now use mixed fertilizers mainly because of habit or trade practices, the "straight goods" may be more economical. Many farmers forfeit income by using low-analysis fertilizers.

Actual recommendations for lime and fertilizer applications to a specific field depend upon the cropping system and previous use, including any former additions of these materials. The soil survey report needs to make this clear. In areas where good recommendations can be made through a proper soil-testing service, this should be made clear. At the same time, the needs for fertilizers should be indicated as specifically as possible.

Irrigation.—In areas proposed for irrigation, the soils can usefully be grouped in about five classes according to arability under irrigation. Under some situations, fewer classes may be required; and under others, more. The individual mapping units may be grouped under five headings as follows:

1. Soils very well suited to irrigation.
2. Soils moderately well suited to irrigation.
3. Soils poorly suited to irrigation.
4. Soils very poorly suited to irrigation.
5. Soils unsuited to irrigation.

The irrigation practices suited to the soils should be explained, usually by subgroups under the main classes. Such practices include length of runs, rate of application of water and amounts of water applied, dimensions of borders, relations between slope gradients and ditch layout, and the like.

Drainage.—In survey areas where drainage works are under consideration, the soils may be grouped into five classes according to their suitability for use with drainage, as suggested for irrigation. Usually, however, they may be grouped in three classes according to (1) drainage necessary, (2) drainage helpful, and (3) drainage not needed. In some areas the first group needs to be subdivided according to type of drainage—tile, ditches, or bedding.

Individual crops.—Usually it is not necessary to make separate groupings of soils according to their suitability for individual crops. Yet there are places where such groupings are highly useful. Where the agriculture of an area is largely built around a single crop, as is often the case with corn, wheat, cotton, or fruit, suitability for the major crop largely determines land values. For people concerned with land values, a suitability grouping for the major crop, with ten classes, might be more valuable than the general productivity rating. While it might appear that suitability can be readily interpreted from the table of yield estimates under management classes, this is not always so.

If the management requirements of the soils vary widely, two soils with about the same predicted yield for a crop might vary in their suitability for the crop. In the Middle West, for example, the Humic-Gley soils (Wiesenboden) are commonly planted to corn 2 years out of 3 or 4, while associated Gray-Brown Podzolic soils are planted to corn only 1 year out of 3 or 4. Yet yields per acre may be similar.

Even though farmers generally in an area are concentrating on one main crop, it does not necessarily mean that other more economic alternative systems should not be used. Where they are known, such alternatives need emphasis in the report.

For clarity and ease of reading of the report, it is often helpful to make groupings of soils by individual crops, especially for pasture and specialty crops. Usually four classes are adequate, as (1) excellent, (2) good, (3) fair, and (4) poor; sometimes finer distinctions are possible and helpful.

Erosion hazard.—The erosion hazard is normally dealt with adequately in the discussion of groups according to management requirements. Yet, if the erosion hazard is especially important, it may be useful to group the mapping units into three classes, as (1) slight to none, (2) moderate, and (3) high. In a few instances, it may be helpful to use five classes, as (1) none, (2) slight, (3) moderate, (4) high, and (5) very high. For such classes to be meaningful, the soil management assumptions must be stated.

These distinctions in erosion hazard are usually most conveniently displayed in the table of the report setting forth the characteristics and behavior of the individual soils.

General productivity.—The groupings according to general productivity, as discussed under soil productivity ratings, follow from the table of soil productivity ratings if one is prepared. Ordinarily, ten classes are used from the highest to the lowest. Of course, within any such class, soil management requirements may vary widely. That is, two soils may be highly productive, in class 1 or 2, and still have great differences in adapted crops and in the practices required to reach a high ratio of output to input. If a productivity rating table is not included, these general ratings may be included as a separate column in the table of yield predictions.

Although groupings according to general productivity are not especially helpful in presenting material needed in farm planning, they are useful for purposes of land appraisal for tax assessment and the like.

SINGLE-FACTOR GROUPINGS

Soils may also be grouped according to single soil factors, like slope, depth, color of one horizon, and so on, and maps showing these groupings may be prepared. These are not generally useful, however, because it is rarely possible to make dependable interpretations from any single factor. If other characteristics vary only within narrow limits and the general setting is known, single-value maps have some practical uses. The soil scientist must recall, however, that his primary task in making the soil map and classification useful is one of synthesis rather than analysis. Even though single-factor groupings and maps are relatively easy to prepare, usually they do not help the reader, since the guidance he seeks from a soil survey requires the syntheses of many factors, no one of which has a simple direct relationship to the combined result.

SOIL CORRELATION AND INSPECTION

The ultimate usefulness of soil classification and soil mapping depends upon accurate soil correlation. This process involves (1) comparing local classificational units—soil types and phases—with those already defined and named in the general system of classification; (2) recognizing, establishing, and naming new units consistent with the system; (3) grouping taxonomic units into series, families, great soil groups, suborders, and orders; (4) grouping geographic units into named and defined soil associations; and (5) arranging the units into keys or groups, as needed to bring out principles and relationships, according to observed characteristics, inferred qualities, genetic factors, or combinations of these.

It is the responsibility of the chief of the party, with the guidance of the supervisory soil scientist or soil correlator, to define the units in his survey so that their appropriate correlation and nomenclature will be facilitated. At the same time he should avoid any possible warping of the definitions of local units in anticipation of particular correlations. The party chief's first responsibility is to see to it that the classification in his area is internally consistent and adequate. Correlation of these units with those of other regions follows.

Names of established units should not be given the local units until the party chief and supervisory scientists are reasonably certain that correlation will hold in the subsequent review; else workers in the party may get a name associated with a wrong set of soil characteristics.

INSPECTION AND CORRELATION REPORTS

Since the same supervisory scientist—the soil correlator—is usually charged with inspection of the classification, mapping, and report writing for adequacy and accuracy, as well as with correlation, the inspection and correlation reports are often combined in one document. A report of inspection is made by the supervisory soil scientist or soil correlator in charge after each visit to a survey area and is designated as *first, progress,* or *final,* as appropriate. Reports on the progress of the soil survey are made on standard forms, with attachments, providing for the following:

Report of . . . . inspection
(First, progress, or final)

Date submitted: . . . .
Name and number of area (including county and State) : . . . .

. . . .

Organizations (a) initiating and (b) cooperating in survey: . . . .

. . . .

. . . .

Size of area:................ Date survey started:....................
     Sq. miles (or) Acres
Type of survey:...
              (Detailed, reconnaissance, detailed-reconnaissance, or other)
....
                    Other (Explain)
Status of field work:..
....
Survey party (Indicate party chief and organization of each member):
....
....
....
Transportation: Cost arranged by.................................
Is it ample?............. Is character of service severe?............
....
Base map (including aerial photographs): Kind....................
Scale.............. Is scale adequate?................ Are control data
available? ....
     Are alterations or revisions being shown properly and accurately?.......
     Where used, are aerial photographs mounted on plane table when necessary
     for accurate orientation?.....................................
Legibility of maps: Boundaries clearly defined?............ Symbols in all
areas?.......... Symbols oriented?.......... Streams named?..........
Bench marks and section corners marked?..........................
Individual sheets—Do they show: Date of survey?...................
Name of area?.......... Name of surveyor?.......... Scale?........
Magnetic north?.......... On the margin of sheet, a list of soil symbols
used?.................................... Are they joined?.........
(Further remarks) ....
Legend: Submit list showing all mapping units as soil types, phases, com-
     plexes, or miscellaneous land types, classes for soil slope, erosion, stoniness,
     and excess salts where established, and classes (if any) for land use or
     other special features. (Include complete description of all new soil series
     or other classificational units and any variations in existing units as a
     part of the inspection report.)..................................
....
Indicate if complete descriptive legend, showing all mapping symbols and
     permissible combinations of symbols and soil separations, including types,
     phases, and complexes, has been given each member of field party........
     .... (If answer is "No," explain provisions for getting
     it done.)
....
....
Does each party member report new symbols or new combinations of symbols
     used each day?...
Field notes (how kept, by whom, and if full enough for a soil survey report):
....
....
....
Soil samples: Have they been collected?........ Does party chief understand
     collection of soil samples and their importance?.....................
What provision is being made for an extra copy of the map for cooperating
     agencies? ....
....

Give the name and address of the county agricultural agent, and mention any local organizations especially interested in the survey and results:

....

....

....

What provisions are being made to obtain relevant agronomic data and other data regarding the responsiveness to management of individual soil types (and phases) from farmers, extension agents, planning technicians, and experiment stations?..

....

....

What progress is being made toward developing a table of expected average yields of the adapted crops for each soil type (and phase) under alternative, physically defined classes of management?.............................

....

....

....

What provisions are being made for soil groupings according to adaptability for specific crops, general productivity, erosion hazard, management requirements, or other?...

....

....

....

Report: Who is to prepare?.............................. Expected date of completion?......................... What progress has been made?

....

....

Remarks (recommendations given to field men, changes and departures from preliminary field working agreements, etc.) :......................

....

....

....

....

....

....
Signature of Soil Correlator

Date reached area............................ Time...........
Date left area.............................. Time...........

Date	*Approved by*	*Agency*
....	....	....
....	....	....
....	....	....

....

The field legend is prepared jointly by the party chief and the soil correlator, often with the help of representatives of cooperating agencies, at the time of the first visit of the soil correlator and is attached to the first inspection report. It is made as nearly complete as practicable and includes a list of all soil types, phases, and other soil mapping units and related features to be mapped in the survey, together with the map symbols. Provision must be made for the inclusion of additional soil types, phases, and other features not recognized during this first inspection visit. Great care needs to be taken with the first inspection report, since it serves as the mapping guide to the field party. As soon as it is finished the party chief should proceed with preparation of the descriptive legend.

Progress inspections are made during the course of the work in order to check the adequacy and accuracy of the mapping, to review the descriptive field legend with the chief of the party, and to help him plan the supplemental studies for yield estimates, soil groupings, and the soil survey report. Besides actual visits to the field, the supervisory scientist needs to make frequent checks by letter and especially through the descriptive legend. The completeness and adequacy of this legend is the best single evidence of how well the party chief is doing his job, his competence, and his potential suitability for increased responsibility.

The final inspection is made at the close of the survey work in an area. Field mapping is thoroughly checked for adequacy and accuracy and discussed in the field with the chief of party and with representatives of cooperating agencies. The soil correlator also checks the suitability of the field maps for cartographic compilation and drafting for publication, the detailed outline and progress of the survey report, and the collection of soil samples. During this same visit a field correlation memorandum is prepared and attached to the final inspection report. It includes a list of all mapping units and symbols shown on the map, together with recommendations for nomenclature.

PURPOSE OF SOIL CORRELATION

The immediate purpose of soil correlation is to assign names to the mapping units to be shown on the published maps that are consistent with the general system of classification and nomenclature. In correlation, decisions are reached to identify the soils in the new survey with similar soils already established and named and to name new soils that need to be recognized by new names. Each mapping unit is properly designated as a soil type, phase, variant, complex, undifferentiated unit, miscellaneous land type, or soil association.

The results of soil and other agricultural research and of farm experience are related to specific kinds of soil through the use of the standard soil names. Purely descriptive names like "permeable brown loam" or "gray sandy soils with hardpans" are wholly inadequate for detailed predictions. Such a large number of characteristics are combined to make a soil of a certain kind that any adequate descriptive name would be unwieldy beyond words, just as would be such names for individual plants, animals, or people. Many broad interpretative groupings of soils may usefully employ descriptive names.

Good soil correlation is essential to the usefulness of the soil map and to the many interpretative groupings and land classifications derived from it.

PROCEDURE

Field.—Even though the preparation of the inspection and correlation report is the responsibility of the soil correlator, it is desirable that representatives of cooperating agencies accompany him on his visits to the area and review the work with him and with the party chief. This is most important for the initial visit when the legend is being established and for the final inspection and field correlation. Copies of the report are signed by the soil correlator and representatives of cooperating agencies, forwarded to the principal soil correlator for his review, and finally sent to the chief soil correlator.

The field correlation memorandum includes the recommended nomenclature of all units shown on the map, descriptions of all new soil series, and suggested modifications of established series. In its preparation full recognition is given to the established classification, nomenclature, and definition of both taxonomic and mapping units (great soil groups, families, series, types, phases, associations, and complexes) ; to any local peculiarities of the soil units in the soil survey area; and to available data on the soils from field and laboratory study. This memorandum is prepared by the soil correlator working with the party chief and representatives of cooperating agencies. If practicable, it is prepared along with the inspection report and attached to it; but if considerable time is necessary for additional study to prepare it, the inspection report should be forwarded at once and a date set for the later submission of the field correlation memorandum.

Regional.—After receiving the field correlation memorandum from the soil correlator, the soil samples, map, relevant laboratory data, and soil survey report or descriptive field legend, the principal soil correlator reviews the field correlation memorandum carefully and thoroughly. The proposed definitions and suggested nomenclature of all mapping units are carefully checked against the standard definitions. He or his delegated representative may set a date for a correlation conference to which all interested representatives of cooperating agencies are invited. Such a conference needs be scheduled only if important differences in judgment seem to exist between soil correlators or between the soil correlator and the representatives of cooperating agencies. Additional laboratory work or joint field studies may be required to resolve such differences. Only differences of interpretation of data may be reconciled in the office.

After acceptance or modification of the individual recommendations in the field correlation, copies of a suggested correlation memorandum are forwarded for comment to the chief of the soil survey party and representatives of the cooperating agencies, including those who may have failed to attend the correlation meeting. After considering all the evidence and suggestions, the principal soil correlator sends his approved regional correlation memorandum to the chief correlator, who is responsible for nomenclature throughout the country, together with copies of the field correlation memorandum, statements of approval or objections from all cooperating agencies, and reasons for any differences between the field and regional correlation memoranda. Descriptions of any new soil series and suggestions for modifications of existing definitions of any soil units are forwarded, along with samples of all new or redefined soil series.

Final.—The chief soil correlator reviews the regional correlation memorandum in relation to the whole system of soil classification for the country. He approves it or makes such changes as are necessary to maintain uniformity of standards in the system. Copies of the approved correlation memorandum are sent to the principal soil correlator for his use and for transmittal to representatives of the cooperating agencies. Even after a final correlation memorandum has been approved, amendments may be proposed to the principal soil correlator or to the chief soil correlator, on the basis of new evidence. These are handled like an original correlation.

Throughout the progress of the soil survey, up to the time of the release of the manuscript map and report for publication, the laboratory data may be requested on selected soil samples. Since these data are expensive to get, they should be requested only as needed for proper definition, nomenclature, classification, or interpretation. Blanket requests for "chemical, physical, and mineralogical data on the soils of the area" should not be approved. But when an important decision depends upon particular determinations, the request should be made promptly. If these data are to be useful to the field party, the proper samples should be taken immediately when the problem is recognized and given high priority in the laboratory, so the results may be sent back to the field party as soon as possible. Where the chief of the party and the soil correlator are faced with a serious problem requiring extensive morphological and laboratory study, special research projects need to be established cooperatively with the laboratory for joint study and joint interpretation of the results.

SOIL GROUPING ON THE MAP

Since 75 to 200 different kinds of soil—types, phases, complexes, and variants—may need to be recognized in a modern detailed soil map of an area to show the significantly different conditions, the soils need to be grouped in various ways to bring out their similarities, different potentialities for use, and management requirements.

Soil groupings are made for many purposes. Those relating to soil use and management are discussed in the section on Yield Predictions and Soil Management Practices, and examples of the groupings are included in the section on The Soil Survey Report. Taxonomic units are discussed in the section on Units of Soil Classification and Mapping. It would not be practicable to describe in this *Manual* the host of useful soil groupings used in the many scientific, educational, and service programs.

In this section we are concerned primarily with color groupings for the soil map. By using color groupings, one is able to establish two orders of soil boundaries—(1) a line alone and (2) a line marking a color change—and to present a map with major color patterns as well as with all the details of boundary lines and symbols. Further, it would be unwise to show, or attempt to show, each mapping unit in a different color, because of the mechanical problems and the enormous costs.

Not all soil maps are printed with color, partly because of the cost. With clear lines and symbols in black, of course, all the information can be read from the map. Color helps in map reading, in differentiating one soil area from another, and especially in reading the map broadly—in seeing the patterns of the major groups of soils in relationship to other physical and cultural features. Uncolored soil maps can be colored by the map users rather easily, according to the grouping on the map legend, or in other ways that are most useful to them. In fact, so many useful groupings can be made that many users of soil maps find it convenient to have several soil maps of the same area colored in different ways, in order to bring out different sets of relationships and interpretations. In printing soil maps, some copies are obtained without color for this purpose.

Soil groupings according to color on the map are designed, first of all, to give the maximum help to the map reader. In reaching that objective their forms vary from area to area.

A soil grouping based upon those soil characteristics that determine management requirements is commonly the most useful one. In surveys where more than 15 of these groups are necessary, some broader grouping, consistent with that used in the text of the soil survey report, may be necessary. Ordinarily, 10 to 15 individual colors or color patterns may be used on a soil map. Even more can be printed at additional cost if the value of the soil map will be greatly increased.

In some soil surveys, color groupings based upon characteristics determining management requirements may also carry interpretations of soil-use capability or suitability, with subgroups that can be interpreted in terms of soil management. The advantages of such groupings, however, are partly offset by the likelihood that they may become outdated in the future. Individual crops and cropping systems vary widely in their adaptability to a soil type or soil phase. That is, there are great contrasts even among the kinds of soil placed in one class called "highly productive" or "class 1." For these reasons color groupings should be based on the more or less fixed features. Yet if color groups based upon soil characteristics are quite unlike the interpretative groupings put forward in the report, the map loses some in readability for the layman.

Many relationships among soils need to be developed. In some areas other color groups based on soil characteristics may give maximum readability of the map even though they are not directly interpretable in terms of soil-use capability or soil management requirements. In some of these areas, the grouping of soils by management requirements, and especially by soil-use capabilities, might give misleading results.

Since many agricultural advisers and farmers use the soil maps, color groups that can be given reliable interpretations in terms of soil management are preferred so long as there is no undue risk of the groupings misleading the reader either when the map is published, or shortly thereafter. Since conditions vary so widely, no hard-and-fast rule can be laid down beyond the basic one of helping people to read and understand the map as clearly as possible.

As a general guide, it may be said that soils similar in common characteristics that influence their use in management should be placed in one group that is shown on the published map in a single color. Where practicable, the grouping of soils under a single color on the map should be avoided if differences in their characteristics are likely to make them (1) suitable for different major uses—forest, pasture, or crops requiring tillage; (2) suitable for very different crops; or (3) require very different management practices. For example, poorly drained soils should generally not be shown with the same color as well-drained soils, or steeply sloping soils in the same color as gently sloping soils, or shallow soils in the same color as deep soils. Exceptions should be made, however, for a group of soils having some one or more characteristics so extremely unfavorable to agriculture as to make them essentially nonarable. Several miscellaneous land types, for example, may be combined and shown with one color on the map. Each unit, of course, will have its individual symbol for specific identification.

A useful grouping can be made by placing the soils into five broad soil-use capability classes, such as first-, second-, and third-class land for crops requiring tillage, fourth-class land for pasture, and fifth-class land for forest. These may then be subdivided into groups according to the characteristics that determine their management requirements. It must be recalled that no groupings can be established that are homogeneous in respect to all the factors of importance to soil use and management. Only the individual soil type or phase can carry all the available information. Coloring the map according to such groupings has two distinct disadvantages. (1) Some users are inclined to accept the color groups as a homogeneous unit and ignore the important differences among the soils shown in the same color; and (2) any grouping, though making it easy to see the relationships for which it is designed, commonly makes it difficult to see other relationships that may be equally important.

The groupings used on the soil map need to be consistent with but not necessarily identical to the groupings used in the soil survey report. Often several groupings need to be used in the report, many of which are more detailed than can be handled in the map legend. For this reason, among others, it is important that the soil survey report be outlined in considerable detail at the close of field work and before soil correlation and the preparation of the soil map. The use and management groups in the report should be so devised that they do not straddle or overlap two or more of the color groups shown on the map. That is, where color groups by management classes are shown on the map, each should consist of one or more whole management groups and not parts of several.

Each group of soils shown with one color on the soil map should be given a *local* descriptive name, which will explain to the map user the basis on which several soils were grouped under one color. Names of groups, for example, might be, "Deep, well-drained, gently sloping, medium-textured soils from limy till" or "Deep, loose sands." It is not practicable to attempt standardization of such connotative names for a large region or State. Attempts to do so lead to long unwieldy names, to serious oversimplification, or to an incorrect use of soil terms. Within an area, suitable names can usually be developed, since the number of soils to be dealt with is relatively small and the characteristics that they have in common can be omitted from names while bringing out the local contrasts.

The names of the groups should show what distinguishes each group from the others, but do not necessarily need to show all the important characteristics of each group. No connotative name could. In a local area, for example, a group of "Steeply sloping soils" may be distinguished from all other groups by the steep slopes. If so, it is not necessary to name this group, say, "Steep, medium-textured, well to excessively drained, shallow to moderately deep soils from sandstone or shale materials."

It is important that the name should indicate mutual exclusiveness of the soils in the different groups. For example, two groups named "Poorly to imperfectly drained soils with slowly permeable subsoils" and "Dark-colored poorly drained soils with slowly permeable subsoils" are not mutually exclusive. Either could contain poorly drained soils with slowly permeable subsoils. Further, all soils having the characteristics expressed in the name of a group should be included in that group. For example, if a group is named "Dark-colored poorly drained soils with slowly permeable subsoils," no soil having the characteristics indicated in the name of this group should be placed in some other group.

Having the full descriptions of each mapping unit in outline form on an individual card or sheet facilitates the development of the groupings. Several alternative schemes may easily be tested. It is important above all that a consistent basis be used, so that each soil can fall easily into some one group. "Sandy soils," "Poorly drained soils," and "Nearly level soils" could not be used as major headings, for these would leave no clear group for a level poorly drained sandy soil.[1]

Three sample outlines for placing the mapping units into color groups for the map follow:

Soil Survey of Roane County, Tennessee:
First-class soils:
    Uplands.
    Bottom lands.
Second-class soils:
    Uplands.
    Terraces.
    Colluvial slopes.
    Bottom lands.
Third-class soils:
    Uplands (on sandstone and shale).
    Uplands (on limestone).
    Colluvial slopes.
    Bottom lands.
    Terraces.
Fourth-class soils:
    Terraces.
    Uplands.
    Bottom lands.
Fifth-class soils:
    Uplands (on limestone)
    Uplands (on sandstone and shale).

Soil Survey of Grainger County, Tennessee:
Soils of the undulating and rolling uplands derived from relatively pure limestone.
Soils of the undulating and rolling uplands derived from cherty or siliceous limestone.
Soils of the undulating and rolling uplands derived from highly argillaceous limestone.
Soils of the undulating and rolling uplands derived from interbedded limestone and shale.
Soils of the undulating and rolling uplands derived from acid shale.
Soils of the hilly uplands derived from cherty limestone.
Soils of the hilly uplands derived from relatively pure limestone.
Soils of the hilly, steep, and very steep uplands derived from interbedded limestone and shale.

---

[1] The late Dr. C. F. Marbut often referred to all such inconsistent groupings with an example for the grouping of houses: "Little houses, red houses, and brick houses."

Soils of the hilly and steep uplands derived from acid shale.
Soils of the hilly and steep uplands derived from interbedded sandstone and shale.
Soils of the steep uplands derived from cherty limestone.
Soils of the relatively gently sloping colluvial slopes.
Soils of the steeper colluvial slopes.
Undulating to sloping soils of the terraces.
Sloping and strongly sloping soils of the terraces.
Well-drained soils of the first bottoms or depressions.
Imperfectly drained soils of the first bottoms or depressions.
Poorly drained soils of the first bottoms, depressions, or terraces.
Stony, rough or gullied land types.

Soil Survey of the Casa Grande Area, Arizona:
Soils well suited to irrigation:
Heavy but friable; no lime accumulation.
Heavy but friable; no lime accumulation (over tough subsoil).
Medium to light texture; no lime accumulation.
Soils moderately well suited to irrigation:
Slight lime accumulation.
Moderate lime accumulation.
Tough nodular lime layer of fragmental hardpan.
Soils requiring special management under irrigation:
Heavy, tight, more or less salty.
Heavy texture, compact limy subsoil.
Fragmental lime hardpan.
Sandy and porous.
Loose and sandy.
Frequently overflowed.
Lime hardpan.
Solonetzlike (alkali).
Solonetzlike with lime hardpan.
Soils definitely unsuited to irrigation:
Severely eroded.
Miscellaneous land types.
Concentrations of salts and alkali.

THE SOIL SURVEY REPORT

A complete soil survey includes a soil map and a report or text that describes the kinds of soils shown on the map and summarizes what is known about them. The report interprets the results of agricultural research in terms of kinds of soil. In a sense, it links the laboratory, the experimental plot, and the research farm to the individual tracts of land in the survey area. The characteristics, responses to management, and capabilities for use of each mapping unit are given to enable farmers, farm advisers, and other users to make full use of the soil map. At best, it is not possible to include more than a very tiny fraction of the relevant information with the map legend.

Most soil survey reports are designed primarily for agricultural users of the map. With a basic scientific soil classification, many other useful interpretations can also be made; but nonagricultural interpretations can usually be handled better in another special report than in the one intended for agricultural users.

The principal purposes of the report are (1) to make all the specific information about each kind of soil that is significant to its use and behavior available to those who must decide how to manage it and (2) to provide such descriptions of the mapping units that the survey can be interpreted for those purposes requiring the fundamental facts about the soil. This first purpose can be accomplished most adequately by presenting predictions of expected yields for each kind of soil under specific sets of management practices, together with predictions of adapted crops and management requirements for optimum sustained production. It must be recalled that the descriptions of the mapping units need to be in objective terms so that the survey may be interpreted for a number of purposes, some of which may be unforeseen by the writers at the time the survey is completed. In addition, the relevant facts about climate, physiography, geology, land use, agriculture, and public facilities need to be included to the extent that they influence soil use and management. Discussions of land use, agricultural systems, forestry, grazing, erosion control, drainage, irrigation, salinity control, fertilization, and the like, should bring out specific relationships to individual soils or special groups of soils. General discussions of such subjects, however, unrelated to the units shown on the map, are out of place. Since the basic soil survey serves many purposes, those of importance in any specific survey area need to be reviewed in advance of preparing the report so they may be given proper emphasis.

Three basic sets of values are needed for each mapping unit: (1) The observable characteristics of the soil as a natural body; (2) the inferred qualities—productivity, fertility, erodibility,

935034°—51——27

409

drainage, and so on; and (3) yield predictions of adapted crops under alternative defined sets of management practices.

The data necessary to develop these sets of values come from three main sources: (1) Observations of soils in the field and of samples in the laboratory in relation to vegetation, relief, geological formations, and present use; (2) synthesis of the data obtained in other soil and plant research on the same or similar soils, including adaptability of various crops and varieties of crops, responses to lime and fertilizer, the amount of runoff and erosion under different treatments, response to drainage and irrigation, and the like; and (3) analysis of farm experience to find out what yields practical operators have received under different systems of management and the effects that these systems have had on soil productivity.

Many of the data and predictions should be assembled in tables for convenience of the rapid reader and to bring out relationships and contrasts among the soils. Such tables are best completed before the final descriptions of the individual soils for the report are written, since they serve as a helpful check list to avoid omissions from the text of important things to be said about the individual soils. It is a good practice to systematize the preparation of soil descriptions and tables by using a set of cards, one card for each soil, on which all the standard items are listed. These cards can be sorted into groups according to soil management requirements, use capability, response to lime, or to any one of many bases that may be useful. From them, it is easy to abstract general descriptions of the groups.

The text should be prepared for the convenience of the readers, most of whom are not soil specialists. The writing ought to be direct and simple. Concrete terms are better than abstractions, and positive statements usually better than negative ones. Where clarity of statement requires the use of technical terms, these should be defined.

Some otherwise excellent soil surveys have lost effectiveness because of clumsy writing.[1] The writer needs to have his material clearly in mind and then write it as simply as possible. Long,

---

[1] Nearly all writers need some writing aids, including a dictionary and one or more handbooks of grammar, punctuation, and composition. The authors hesitate to make specific recommendations, since the needs of individuals vary widely. The following are suggestive of ones that may be useful to many soil scientists:

GOWERS, ERNEST. PLAIN WORDS: A GUIDE TO THE USE OF ENGLISH. 94 pp. London. 1948.

HALL, MILTON. GETTING YOUR IDEAS ACROSS THROUGH WRITING. U. S. Fed. Sec. Agency Training Manual No. 7. 44 pp. Washington. 1950.

ROBERTS, C. W., HARRIS, J. W., and JOHNSON, W. G. A HANDBOOK OF ENGLISH. 292 pp. New York. 1944.

UNIVERSITY OF CHICAGO PRESS. A MANUAL OF STYLE. Ed. 11, 497 pp., illus. 1949.

WOOD, G. W. SUGGESTIONS TO AUTHORS OF PAPERS SUBMITTED FOR PUBLICATION BY THE UNITED STATES GEOLOGICAL SURVEY, WITH DIRECTIONS TO TYPISTS. U. S. Dept. Int. Ed. 4. (Rev. by B. H. Lane), 126 pp. Washington. 1935.

WOOLLEY, E. C., SCOTT, F. W., and BERDAHL, E. T. COLLEGE HANDBOOK OF COMPOSITION. Ed. 4, 452 pp. Boston. 1944.

qualified sentences, with the subjects deeply buried, bore the reader or even confuse him. Unfamiliar technical terms should be avoided where clarity can be had without them, and so should other long words not commonly used in everyday speech. In technical writing more trouble stems from the use of long or unusual nontechnical words that the writer does not understand well than from the technical words that he does understand.

Good writing requires a lot of work and reworking. It sounds well when read aloud. The writer should recall that many of his potential readers will cast his work aside after a few long, involved sentences—the kind one needs to fight through, inch by inch. No scientist ever got a good name from "erudite" writing (although a very few have in spite of it!).

FORM OF THE REPORT

The form of the report depends upon the anticipated use and users of it and what information is available.

The amount and kind of available information, besides that gathered by the soil survey party itself, varies widely from area to area. At least some supplemental information about soils is available in all counties. Then too, the basic principles of soil-plant-management relationships explained in the scientific literature of the world can be interpreted by qualified scientists in relation to specific kinds of soil. In some survey areas, a large potential body of information is available from the results of agricultural research and of farmer experience. Thus, even though similar items are discussed in reports for different areas, the best form of presentation varies among them.

The form of the report depends also upon its intended use and those expected to use it. In some areas, few land users may be expected to read it, and it may be assumed that professional agriculturists will interpret it for them. Ordinarily, few trained soil scientists are available for such advisory work and the soil survey reports are interpreted by people with little or no formal training in soil science. Especially for areas with a highly educated rural population, a great deal of direct use by farmers may be expected, besides indirect use through agricultural advisers and technicians. For such areas, at least the greater part of the report should be clear to anyone with general training in agriculture without further interpretation by soil scientists. The parts of the report essential to an understanding of the use of the soil map should be clear to those who can read agricultural literature. The utility of the report to professional soil scientists need not be diminished by meeting this requirement. The basic data soil scientists need for comparing the soils of the area with those of other areas may be included in a separate section or in an appendix.

Occasionally it may be practicable to publish a technical bulletin devoted mainly to soil classification and genesis, in addition to the primary one concerned chiefly with interpretations for soil use and management. Such technical bulletins, however, are usually best organized for larger areas than for the ones covered in detailed soil surveys.[2]

CONTENTS OF THE REPORT

Practically every report of a detailed basic soil survey should include the following:

(1) An explanation of how to use the soil map and report.
(2) A table of contents.
(3) A general description of the area.
(4) Descriptions of the individual soil mapping units shown on the map, supplemented with tables showing their characteristics and their relationships.
(5) Predictions of the yields of the common crops of the area under different specifically defined sets of management practices for all of the soils mapped. These should supply the basic information necessary to make farm production budgets under the principal sets of management practices likely to be used.
(6) Explanations of the management problems of each soil, with special emphasis on how the characteristics of the soil influence the problems and their solutions.

This list is not an outline for a report; it represents only the minimum requirements. Additional information should be included in specific areas according to local conditions.

The essentials to be included under the topics listed are as follows:

An explanation of how to use the soil map and report.—In this section the reader is told how to locate a farm or field on the map. The map scale and use of symbols for landmarks are explained. The use of townships and sections or other land grids is explained as an aid to location. The reader is told how to find what soils are on the located farm or other land tract and how to get the specific information about them from the report. Finally, the other topics covered in the report are mentioned in relation to the interests of various classes of readers.

Many detailed soil surveys could include to advantage an explanation of how to use the soil map and the tables of estimated crop yields and management requirements for making farm plans, including production budgets.[3]

Table of contents.—Besides serving as an outline, the primary purpose of the table of contents is to help the reader find specific items in the report. It should be detailed enough that the name of each soil mapping unit appears in it.

The general description of the area.—This section should give briefly the relevant facts about climate, physiography, geography,

---

[2] For an excellent example of such a technical discussion see SMITH, GUY D., ALLAWAY, W. H., and RIECKEN, F. F. PRAIRIE SOILS OF THE UPPER MISSISSIPPI VALLEY. Advances in Agronomy 2: 157–205. 1950.
[4] See Black, John D., *et al.* as cited in the General Bibliography.

geology, land use, agriculture, public facilities, population, and history as related to the soils and their use and management. Nonresident readers find this section of great use. For many areas, much of the information can be summarized in tables. Schematic drawings may help to present the information on geology and geomorphology. Part of the material suggested here may be included in other related sections and part in an appendix. The following outline suggests how this material may be presented:

Geography and agriculture of Blank County (major head).
A. *Physiography and drainage* (second-grade head).
 1. Brief description of the physiography, geology, relief, elevation, and drainage. If the area has two or more distinct physiographic divisions, describe these, giving the principal soils in each. A simple map or cross-section drawing of these may be useful.
B. *Climate* (second-grade head).
 1. A few paragraphs giving salient features of the climate, including mention of how climate has affected soil formation and agriculture.
 2. Standard tables of climatic data from the United States Weather Bureau, showing temperature, precipitation, and frost-free season. Supplement these with only enough discussion to bring out important facts not shown by the tables. Such facts might include:
    a. Frequency and severity of droughts, detrimental wet periods, and floods.
    b. Form and intensity of precipitation—rain, snow, hail, and cloudbursts.
    c. Length of grazing period.
    d. Local variations of climate due to such factors as elevation, air drainage, exposure, and proximity to lakes.
    e. Wind, tornadoes, sunshine, and humidity.
  When any of these climatic conditions have some special effect on the agriculture of the county, bring this out when discussing them.
C. *Water supply* (second-grade head).
  Describe the principal sources of water for domestic use, livestock, and irrigation.
D. *Vegetation* (second-grade head).
  Brief discussion of the vegetation, mentioning vegetation types in relation to soils. Give main facts about the distribution of forest, grassland, and desert shrub before settlement and at present. If wildlife is important, discuss it here and head the section "Vegetation and Wildlife."
E. *Settlement and population* (second-grade head).
  Give some of the outstanding facts about the settlement of the county, its agricultural and industrial development, and its population. Give the present (last census) population, important facts about its geographic distribution, and its distribution among farm, rural nonfarm, and urban groups. Gives names of important towns and their population.
F. *Industries* (second-grade head).
 1. Kinds of industries, including extractive industries.
 2. Location.
 3. Effect of industries on agricultural and rural population.
G. *Transportation and markets* (second-grade head).
 1. Railroad, truck, bus, air, and steamship lines.
 2. Highways, character and condition.

3. Service of transportation facilities in relation to agriculture, particularly with respect to geography of soils.
4. Markets for county products—auctions, factories, condenseries, packing plants—and where shipped.

H. *Community facilities* (second-grade head).
Discuss by natural regions if possible: Schools, churches, hospitals, clinics, libraries, telephones, electrification, recreational facilities, and other features related to rural living.

I. *Agriculture* (second-grade head).
1. *Land use* (third-grade head).
   a. Total land area in farms, number of farms, improved land per farm, according to last census.
   b. Farms classified by size of farm according to last census, and percentage of land in all farms of each size group, where possible.
   c. Important recent trends in land use, if any, such as from forestry to crops or pasture, from crops to pasture, or vice versa, or from intertilled to close-growing crops.
   d. Present use of farm land according to last census: Cropland, pasture, woodland, and other.
2. *Crops* (third-grade head).
   a. Table from the last census, giving acreage and production of principal crops.
   b. For each principal crop, including hay crops and rotation pasture:
      (1) Important recent trends in acreage, and reasons for changes, if known.
      (2) Distribution in relation to soils.
      (3) Cultural practices; tillage dates and methods of planting and harvesting; storage practices.
      (4) Disposal of crop—fed on farm, sold, or consumed by family.
3. *Permanent pastures* (third-grade head).
   a. General distribution as related to soils, briefly.
   b. Principal pasture plants.
   c. Significant trends in total acreage and reasons for these.
4. *Livestock and livestock products* (third-grade head).
   a. Table from last census, giving number of principal kinds of livestock, except work stock, and quantities of livestock products sold.
   b. For each principal kind of livestock.
      (1) Distribution in relation to soils.
      (2) Principal breeds.
      (3) Feed, grown or purchased.
      (4) Disposal of livestock and livestock products.
5. *Farm power and mechanical equipment* (third-grade head).
   a. Work stock.
      (1) Total number, according to class (census); significant trends.
      (2) Average per farm.
   b. Tractors and trucks.
   c. Tillage implements.
   d. Other mechanical equipment.
6. *Types of farms* (third-grade head).
   a. Number of each type as classified by the census.
   b. Relate distribution of main types of farms to soils.
7. *Farm tenure* (third-grade head).
   a. Percentage of farms operated by owners, managers, and tenants (census).

b. Systems of tenure.
(1) Percentage of farms rented for cash; for share of crops (census).
(2) Briefly but clearly state prevailing systems of renting farms where other than for cash.
(3) Any relation to soils?
8. *Farm buildings and farm home conveniences* (third-grade head). Show relation to soils if possible.

Descriptions of the individual soil mapping units shown on the map.—The description of the individual soil units shown on the map is a basic feature of any report. The legend on the map itself can include little besides an identification symbol or "tag" for the various kinds of soil. Depending partly on the classes of users for whom the report is intended, narrative descriptions, block descriptions, tables, schematic drawings, and photographs are used, or some combination of these devices.

In many reports this section begins with an explanation of how the soils differ and a general description of the soils and their occurrences. It helps if the report is keyed to the map by using the symbol for each unit with the name of the unit in tables and description headings.

In the organization of the report a part of the material on management problems is often combined with the description of the mapping unit. This arrangement minimizes the amount of searching necessary to find information on any particular soil, and facilitates the use of the report by those interested only in a very few of the soils on the map. The following suggests how these descriptions may be introduced:

The soils of Blank County, their use and management
(major head):

Three tables are normally inserted at the beginning of this section. The first shows acreages of the soils in the county [Sample table not given in this *Manual*]; the second, some important characteristics of soils [See Sample Table A, p. 416.]; and the third, position, parent material, and profile characteristics [See Sample Table B, p. 417]. One or more illustrations, as block diagrams showing the relation of soils to parent material and topography, are added as further aids to seeing the relationships among the principal kinds of soils (fig. 55).

Following this introductory material, the individual soils mapped in the county are described in alphabetic order by *series* name. In the text, the most extensive or important *type* in the series may be described first, followed by less important types in turn. The first type or the first phase of a type should be described in detail, but the less important types and phases may not need to be described fully by themselves if their nature is made clear by cross reference to the others. Miscellaneous land types should be described in alphabetic sequence along with the series and types. For example, Rough broken land will fall among the series beginning with "R."

Sample Table A

TABLE [Insert No.].—*Blank County soils: Some important characteristics*

Map symbol	Soil	Dominant slope range	Drainage through the soil[1]	Occurrence of high water table[2]	Moisture supplying capacity[3]	Layer limiting root penetration (if any)[4]	Depth above layer limiting root penetration[5]	Erosion hazard[6]	Natural fertility[7]	Special soil management problems[8]
[To be entered by editor.]	Lakeland sand.	*Percent* 3-8	Rapid	None	Low	None		Slight	Low	Fertility maintenance.

[1] In absence of high water table, report as: none, very slow, slow, medium, rapid, or very rapid.

[2] Report in appropriate terms as: none, intermittent, in winter, etc.

[3] Refers to relative capacity of the soil to *take in* and *hold supply* of moisture in amounts favorable to most crop plants. It reflects slope, infiltration capacity, moisture retentiveness, and depth of the soil. Report as very high, high, good, fair, low, or very low.

[4] Layer that hinders penetration of roots of many crop plants, even if free of high water table, or if kept moist, as by irrigation. Report as: bedrock, hardpan, gravel, caliche, etc.

[5] Report as: very shallow, shallow, moderately deep, deep, or very deep, with depth figures in inches as appropriate (see p. 285).

[6] Report as: none, slight, moderate, high, or very high; or none to slight, moderate, or high.

[7] Report as: low, moderately low, moderate, moderately high, high.

[8] Includes presence of salts or alkali, flood hazard, need for artificial drainage, maintenance of good tilth, etc.

Sample Table B

TABLE [Insert No.].—*Physiographic position, parent material, and profile characteristics of the soil series of Blank County*

Physiographic position	Series	Map symbol[1]	Parent material	Relief	Internal drainage	Surface soil Color	Surface soil Consistence	Surface soil Approximate thickness	Subsoil Color	Subsoil Consistence	Subsoil Texture	Subsoil Approximate thickness
SOILS OF THE UPLANDS												
Highland Rim plateau.	Dickson		Material residual from cherty limestone.	Undulating	Slow	Brownish gray	Friable	Inches 6-8	Brownish yellow	Friable	Silty clay loam.	Inches 12-18
Ridge tops of Highland Rim escarpment.	Baxter		...do...	Rolling	Medium	Brown to light brown.	...do...	5-8	Brownish red	Firm, friable.	Cherty clay loam to cherty silty clay loam.	20-30
	Frankstown		...do...	...do...	...do...	Dark gray	...do...	8-12	Brownish yellow	...do...	Cherty silty clay loam.	18-36
SOILS OF THE COLLUVIAL LANDS												
Foot slopes	Greendale		Mimosa and Dellrose soils, mainly.	Gently sloping.	Medium	Grayish brown to dark brown.	Friable	12-18	Yellowish brown	Firm, friable.	Silty clay loam.	10-20
	Burgin		Soils developed from limestone residuum.	Nearly level to gently sloping.	Very slow	Dark gray to black	...do...	8-12	Medium gray mottled with yellow and brown.	Tough, plastic.	Silty clay	12-24
SOILS OF THE TERRACES												
Low terraces or second bottoms.	Etowah		Alluvial, chiefly from soils developed from limestone residuum.	Gently sloping to sloping.	Medium	Grayish brown to brown.	Friable	8-12	Yellowish brown to reddish brown.	Firm, friable.	Clay loam to silty clay loam.	18-40
	Wolftever		...do...	Nearly level to gently sloping.	Slow	Light grayish brown.	...do...	6-12	Yellowish brown	Compact	Silty clay loam.	12-18
	Taft		...do...	...do...	...do...	Brownish gray	...do...	6-10	Brownish yellow	Firm, friable.	...do...	10-24
	Robertsville		...do...	Nearly level	Very slow	Gray or light brownish gray.	...do...	6-10	Mottled yellow and gray.	Compact	Silty clay	12-20

[1] Map symbols to be entered by editor.

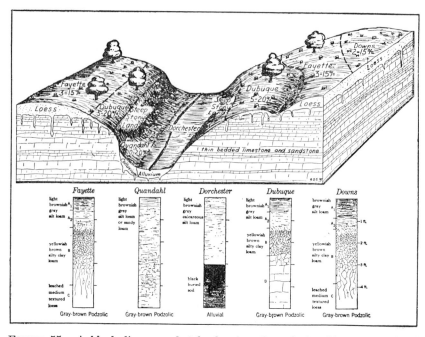

FIGURE 55.—A block-diagram sketch showing the relationships among local soil types and phases within a soil association. (Fayette-Dubuque stony land in the northeastern part of Iowa.) Such diagrams are helpful to the reader in visualizing the relationships between kinds of soil areas and such factors as relief, parent material, and vegetation.

Soil phases are commonly subdivisions of a soil type. A soil type, therefore, includes all its phases. When a soil type is divided into phases on the basis of slope, each of the subdivisions should bear its slope class designation. For example, Tama silt loam, as found in Tama County, Iowa, is divided into the following phases, which may be described in the order of increasing gradient (percent):

Tama silt loam, 1–3 percent slopes.
Tama silt loam, 3–8 percent slopes.
Tama silt loam, 3–8 percent slopes, eroded.
Tama silt loam, 8–12 percent slopes.
Tama silt loam, 8–12 percent slopes, eroded.

Note that the soil type, Tama silt loam, consists of a total of its five phases. This is a departure from a former practice of designating one of the phases of a type as the type itself and only the others as phases. When a soil type is not divided into phases on the basis of slope, but *is* divided into phases on the basis of some other characteristic, such as stoniness, the phase or phases that are characterized by the condition of stoniness should be designated; for example, stony or very stony; and the phase that is not characterized by the condition, if such a phase is mapped, should be designated by the name of the type alone without phase designation and may then be referred to in the text as the typical phase of the type. This convention keeps the names of the individual units as short as possible and avoids the use of terms like "noneroded" and "nonstony" in the names. Commonly two or more features used to differentiate phases are coexistent and appear in the name of the mapping unit, as in Hayter stony loam, eroded steep phase, for example. Many soil types, of course, are not divided into phases.

An outline for soil descriptions follows:[4]

1. **Name of mapping unit** (boldface side head):
   a. Use one or two sentences to point out the *outstanding features or important facts* about the soil, that will help the reader to identify it.
   (1) Relief and physiographic position, association with other soils, and the kind of landscape in which it exists. These may include one or more of the following:
   (2) Parent material.
   (3) Drainage.
   (4) Native vegetation.
   (5) General location in the county and extent. Highly detailed descriptions of the location of areas of the soil, such as "2 miles northwest of St. Andrews Church and south of Blackhawk School," should not be given. The great majority of users do not need to know where all the bodies of a particular soil are located. Those who do can find them from a study of the map.
   b. Profile description (without head):
   Either block or running description of the soil profile may be used, but the block description is usually best. It should cover only the main horizons, rather than all the subdivisions that need to be dealt with in a genetic study of the profile.
   The following characteristics of each main horizon should be kept in mind and satisfactorily covered in the profile descriptions:
   (1) Color.
   (2) Texture.
   (3) Structure.
   (4) Consistence.
   (5) Thickness.
   (6) Reaction and content of lime.
   (7) Organic matter.
   (8) Permeability to roots, moisture, and air.
   (9) Salts or alkali.
   (10) Stone, gravel, or chert.
   (11) Water-holding capacity.
   (12) Known deficiencies in plant nutrients.
   The description should be simple, concise, and nontechnical. Following is a description of Muscatine silt loam, taken from Soil Report No. 71 of the Illinois Agricultural Experiment Station, that meets this requirement:

   > Soil Profile.—The surface is a brown or dark-brown heavy silt loam 8 to 10 inches thick and only weakly granular. The subsurface layer is a silt loam varying from a yellowish brown to brown. The subsoil begins at a depth of 16 to 20 inches. It is a grayish-yellow silty clay loam or silty clay with brown coatings. The entire profile absorbs water readily. Carbonates (free lime) usually occur below 40 to 50 inches. In some small areas which are entirely surrounded by Hartsburg silty clay (244) the free lime begins at 20 to 35 inches and the soil is somewhat lighter colored throughout.

---

[4] An alternative arrangement for soil descriptions of soil types not divided into phases is given later.

This description is perhaps not so complete as might be desirable, for some soils at least. It does not mention consistence, for example, nor the usual reaction of the surface layer. It is, however, clear and concise.

It is not necessary or desirable to describe soil profiles in this section of the report in all the detail that might be needed by soil scientists for accurate definition of a soil series. More detailed descriptions of profiles of important representative soils can be given in the section How the Soils of Blank County Were Formed and How They Are Classified. For other soils, the very detailed descriptions are needed only in the correlation work.

In a separate paragraph mention principal inclusions in the mapping unit of soils other than the one named.

c. Soil qualities (without head):

Follow the objective description with a paragraph dealing with significant inferred qualities such as fertility, productivity, erodibility, and the like, as important. Although helpful, such statements are more subject to change with further research than the basic soil descriptions.

d. Use and management (italic side head):

(1) Present use. Include estimated proportion cleared; estimated percentage in crops, pasture, forest, and idle; and mention the more important crops. Indicate differences in use among different parts of the area, if significant.

(2) Prevailing systems of management. This should define the sets of management practices for the appropriate column in the table of predicted yields. If other sets of management practices are important, each should be described. Yields reported or predicted should be tied to the appropriate set of management practices. If the prevailing practices are closely similar on two or more soils, a complete description can be given for one of these, and reference made to this one when the other soils are described. Mention for each set of management practices:

(a) Rotations.

(b) Fertilization of crops in the rotation, kind, and frequency; also use of lime and manure.

(c) Engineering methods of water control, including those for control of runoff and erosion and for drainage and irrigation.

(d) Methods of preventing salt accumulation or removing excess salts or alkali (where applicable).

(e) Tillage practices, kind, and timing.

(f) Pasture management.

(3) Suitable uses and management practices. This discussion should be developed in cooperation with the State agricultural experiment station and have its approval. Some management practices apply generally to a good many of the soils. This might be true of the choice of varieties of some of the crops. To avoid continually repeating descriptions of the same management practices, those that apply to many soils may be given in the subsection Use and Management of Important Groups of Soils for a whole group of soils. The discussion here could then be used primarily to emphasize those practices that are especially appropriate on this soil in view of its characteristics. Also, where two or more soils receive very similar discussions of suitable uses and management practices, a complete discussion can be given for one and reference made to this one when the second soil is described. Mention:

(a) Suitable crops and crop varieties; other uses.

(b) Good management practices. This discussion should include the definition of management for the appropriate column in the table of expectable yields. It should cover the items listed above under (2).

(c) In the management discussion, emphasis needs to be given to the influence of acidity, claypans, or other features so that the reader may be able to estimate the responses of the soil to other sets of practices besides those described in detail—sets of practices that may become practicable in the future after the report is published, due to advancements in the agricultural arts.

An alternative arrangement for the description of soil types, when these are not divided into phases, is as follows:

Tama silt loam (boldface side head):
Outstanding features (of type as a whole).
Profile description (of type as a whole).
1–3 percent slopes (italic side head).
Use and management.
3–8 percent slopes (italic side head).
Use and management.
3–8 percent slopes, eroded (italic side head).
Difference in profile from the rest of the type.
Use and management.

An alternative arrangement for describing the soil mapping units is illustrated by the following, adapted from the manuscript of the soil survey report of Cherokee County, Tex.:

Caddo fine sandy loam, level (0–1 percent slopes) (side head).—This is a light-gray poorly drained soil that occurs in nearly level streamhead positions in association with higher lying better drained soils, mainly of the Bowie, Lakeland, and Ruston series. It stays wet during the cool season, is of very low natural fertility, and is unsuitable for crop use unless artificially drained.

A. Representative profile: (Virgin area, 2½ miles southeast of Alto along State Highway 21.)
  1. 0 to 4 inches. Gray fine sandy loam; very friable; strongly acid.
  2. 4 to 15 inches. Light-gray very fine sandy loam slightly mottled with yellowish brown; very friable; hard when dry; contains a few rounded concretions of iron oxide; grades to horizon below; strongly acid.
  3. 15 to 40 inches. Mottled yellow and light-gray sandy clay loam; massive; porous; friable; strongly acid.
  4. 40 to 60 inches or more. Light-gray strongly acid sandy clay loam, mottled with yellow and containing a few spots of reddish yellow or strong brown.
B. Variations: In disturbed areas, the surface layer is light gray or white; texture of horizons 1 and 2 ranges from loamy sand to fine sandy loam.
C. Parent material: Light-gray or mottled light-gray and yellow acid sandy loam and clay loam, more or less thin-bedded and stratified.
D. Relief: Nearly level to very gently sloping surfaces with gradients dominantly less than 1 percent, but ranging up to 3 in small areas.
E. Drainage: Surface runoff is very slow; internal drainage is slow, mainly because a high water table is at or near the surface during the cool season.
F. Erosion hazard: Not susceptible to erosion.
G. Native vegetation: Forest, mainly of water oak, gum, and shortleaf pine with thick ground cover of shrubs, brambles, and sedges.
H. Location and extent: Small areas scattered throughout the county; total extent is 5,800 acres.
I. Utilization: Mainly forest; small areas cleared and used for pasture; 5,360 acres, or 92 percent, are under a cut-over forest cover, and 170 acres, or 3 percent, are cleared and used for pasture.

J. Suitability for agriculture: Unsuitable for cropland unless drained; best use is for forest or, if cleared, for pasture. Good pastures of lespedeza and Dallis, carpet, and Bermuda grasses can be developed.

K. Management for pasture: Phosphate disked in; weed control by mowing; regulated grazing; shallow ditching and diversion terraces.

L. Management for forest: Selective cutting and thinning; removal of undesirable species; plantings in bare areas; controlled burning.

Predictions of crop yields under different sets of management practices.—The importance of the yield predictions and the requirements for useful predictions have been outlined in the section on Yield Predictions and Soil Management Practices. This information is ordinarily presented in a table, but in some reports the yield prediction could be expressed as a part of a narrative discussion of the management of each soil, accompanying the description of that soil. The table covering yield predictions for all the soils in the county has the great advantage that the different soils can be more easily compared. In the narrative presentation, the system of management associated with each yield prediction can be more completely described.

In some reports more than one table should be used. For example, if separate tables for rotation cropland, for permanent pasture, for orchards, and for forests are used, each is fairly simple as compared to a combined table for all of them.

The details of the yield tables and the way in which the classes of soil management are defined probably vary more among reports than any other section. In the design and preparation of these tables it should be kept in mind that many of the users of the report are interested in increasing crop yields. Therefore, the predictions should include yields at optimum levels of management as indicated by recent research on the soils of the area or on similar soils in nearby areas. The sets of management practices must be defined specifically enough that the reader will be able to get an idea of the procedures and costs that are involved in obtaining higher yields through changing the management. A sample table of this kind (Sample Table C) is shown on page 424; another—the one from the Soil Survey of Tama County, Iowa— is shown in the section on Yield Predictions and Soil Management Practices.

In some areas the detail necessary for defining management classes may be too great to include in a table. If so, the management classes may be designated by letter or number in the table and defined for each soil or each group of soils in the text of the report. The requirement that the management classes be specific is not relaxed where this type of arrangement is followed.

A brief discussion of the bases for the yield table should be included, indicating the sources of information and the relative accuracy of the different values.

The management problems of each soil.—In this section the relationship between soil characteristics and management problems, and the ways in which specific practices are fitted to soil characteristics, are explained.

This information can be presented in a number of ways. In some reports the entire discussion of management appears with the descriptions of the individual mapping units. In other reports the soils are grouped according to management requirements, and discussed by groups. Tables are also useful for this purpose. For brevity, it is sometimes best to write a general discussion of the principles of good soil management as they apply to all the soils, followed by more detailed explanations of how these principles can be fitted to each soil or group of soils.

In these discussions reference should be made to the locations of important research centers where information useful in solving soil management problems in the area is being obtained, even though these centers are not within the survey area. It is sometimes helpful to call attention to similar soils outside the survey area so that users of the map may relate farm experience in other areas to problems within the survey area.

It should be emphasized that predictions rather than recommendations are given in this section on soil management. The ways in which management practices interact with soil characteristics should be the central theme. Comparisons of the effects of different management practices have more value than a "sales talk" for any one system.

Sample Table C on p. 424 shows how tables may be used to simplify presentation of information on soil management.

Practically every soil survey report contains material besides the topics already listed. Some of these additional features are as follows:

Introduction.—The best form of introduction is a brief statement of the potentialities and problems in the area, which answers the general question briefly: "What was found out about the soils in terms of their future use and development?" Unrealized potentialities of the soils should be high-lighted. Soil management problems requiring special emphasis, such as crop adjustment, needs for lime or fertilizer, runoff control, drainage, irrigation, and erosion prevention, can be high-lighted. Promising new crops or systems of farming can be mentioned. Other related problems of soil use in forestry, grazing, or combined resource development should be brought out. No one statement should deal with all of these things—only those of outstanding and general significance.

Interpretive groups for special purposes.—This feature of the report is essentially a subdivision of the section on management. The use of interpretive groupings varies even more from one area to another than the other parts of the soil management discussion.

Wherever a particular crop is of special importance to the agriculture of an area, a rating or grouping of the soils according to their suitability for that crop is useful. Corn suitability ratings have been used in some areas, for example, and suitability for tung orchards in others. Since the suitability of a soil for any crop is also dependent on soil management, the set of man-

Sample Table C

TABLE [Insert No.].—*Predicted crop and pasture yields under different systems of soil management*[1]

SOILS SUITED TO PRODUCTION OF INTERTILLED CROPS

Map Symbol	Soil	Rotation[2]	Manure, fertilizer and lime[3]	Other practices	Yields				
					Corn	Soybeans	Oats	Hay	Rotation pasture
					Bu.	*Bu.*	*Bu.*	*Tons*	*Cow-days per acre*[4]
XL	Xyz loam...	60 percent intertilled, and 20 percent meadow.	None	None	40	18	35	2: Red clover and timothy.	105: Red clover and timothy.
		30-40 percent intertilled and 30-40 percent meadow.	Lime and phosphate on new seedings; complete starter fertilizer on corn; 8 tons manure or 40-60 lb. N on second-year corn.	Tile drainage; thick planting of corn.	65	20	50	3: Alfalfa	140: Alfalfa-brome.

SOILS SUITED TO PERMANENT PASTURE

Map Symbol	Soil	Kind of pasture	Fertility practices[3]	Other management practices	Cow-days per acre[4]
VL	Vuw loam ..	Bluegrass-lespedeza	None	Deferred grazing in spring; mowing for weed control.	100
		Orchard grass-Ladino clover...	Lime plus 60 lb. P2O5 and 30 lb. K2O when seeded; annual top dressing with 0-2-1 ratio as needed.	Rotation grazing; mowing for weed control.	150

[1] In all yield predictions the use of adapted crop varieties and methods for insect, disease, and weed control is assumed.
[2] Intertilled crops refer to corn and soybeans; meadow refers to grass-legume mixtures grown in rotations and used for hay or pasture.
[3] The amounts and kind of fertilizer used should be based on test of samples submitted to the county agent at Blankville. Additional information on the fertility problems of each soil is found in the section "Soils of Blank County".
[4] Cow-days per acre refers to the number of days one acre will carry one animal unit without supplemental feed. See the pasture calendar for seasonal distribution of this grazing.

agement practices under which the rating or grouping is devised should be specified.

Other groupings according to erosion hazard, need for drainage, suitability for irrigation, and the like are necessary in certain areas. In any specific area, the users may benefit from special interpretive soil groupings according to local potentialities and problems in the area. Basically, the interpretive grouping should be regarded as a device for facilitating the use of the survey for a particular purpose. Since the purposes of such groupings vary from area to area, and even from time to time for the same area, their use in a soil survey report is based upon local needs at the time the report is written.

Interpretative soil grouping may take such forms as:

Soils well suited to alfalfa	Soils not well suited to alfalfa
Dunkirk silt loam.	Carlisle muck.
Honeoye loam.	Colwood loam.
Honeoye silt loam.	Eel silt loam.
Ontario loam, undulating phase.	Fulton silt loam.
Ontario loam, rolling phase.	Toledo silt loam.
Palmyra gravelly loam.	Poygan silty clay loam.

It is not desirable that groupings of this sort should be made for all crops or all kinds of practices, because of the space that would be required, and also because the suitability of the soils to most crops will have been brought out in the table of predicted yields, and the need for particular practices will have been shown in the table giving suitable soil management practices. Special groupings of this kind can be used to advantage, however, for (a) potentially valuable crops in the survey area with which resident farmers have had little experience; (b) crops for which quality so offsets yield that yield does not afford an adequate measure of productivity, such as most types of tobacco, for example; or (c) practices already demonstrated to be valuable on similar soils in other counties or on experiment stations, but which are not yet widely adopted by resident farmers.

It may be explained that by using the soil map in connection with soil groups or lists of this kind, special interpretive maps showing groups of soils suitable for an individual crop or practice may be prepared on uncolored copies of the soil map. Besides, it may be pointed out that single-factor maps showing groups of soils with a particular characteristic in common, such as steep slopes or slowly permeable subsoils, may be prepared from the soil map. Many users of such single-factor maps need to be cautioned against using them for purposes in which the other soil characteristics influence the interpretation of the one emphasized.

In addition to groupings for agricultural purposes, special groupings of soils for engineering purposes, especially road and airstrip construction, can be given where essential information is available. Preparation of engineering groupings require consultation with competent highway engineers who know the soil engineering problems of the survey area.

See other discussions of soil grouping, pages 391 to 395 and pages 403 to 407.

935034°—51——28

Special practices.—In some areas it may be advisable to emphasize certain groups of practices by discussing them in a separate section of the report. Practices for runoff and erosion control, drainage, irrigation, salinity control, and weed control are examples. Like the interpretive groupings, however, such material is fundamentally a subdivision of the discussion on soil management. If a separate section is used for high lighting a group of practices, such as water control, the manner in which soil characteristics influence the performance of terraces, contouring, strip cropping, drainage systems, and irrigation and water distribution systems, can be explained, with alternative solutions of the particular water-control problems indicated. In most reports it is better to handle all the practices together rather than to separate part of them for a special section. Unless the writing is carefully coordinated, the reader may get an unbalanced and incorrect impression of the whole management problem for each of the mapping units.

In forested areas, a special section on land-clearing methods may be helpful.

The morphology and genesis of the soils.—How the soils of the area were formed and how they are related to the soils of other areas are explained in this section. Ordinarily this can be done conveniently by starting with the parent materials and physiography and explaining how the soils were formed from these materials under the various soil-forming processes with time. It is important to fit this discussion to the area, rather than "forcing" the soils of the area into a predetermined pattern taken from textbooks or other survey reports. Inasmuch as soil classification is a relatively young branch of science, the criteria that are used in classifying the soils, especially into higher categories, should be explained. Other soil scientists, for example, will want to know why a soil is designated as a Chernozem or a Podzol.

Wherever possible, the mechanism by which the significant soil characteristics were formed should be explained. For example, has a claypan been formed by movement of clay, by weathering in place, or as an inheritance from stratified parent material? If such points are reasonably well established, they should be included in the report. Any laboratory data relevant to the genesis and classification of the soils may be included in this section.

Information on soil morphology and genesis is most difficult to present in a way useful to laymen. Where the report is intended primarily for other users, and the material on morphology and genesis is necessarily technical it should be placed in an appendix.

For preparing the material on morphology and genesis of the soils, the chapter on this subject in the soil survey report of Tama County, Iowa, (published 1950) presents one helpful example. The following outline is also suggested as an aid in the organization of this material.

How the soils of Blank County were formed and how they are classified (major head):

A. Introductory paragraph (without head) enumerating the forces in soil development. This will include statements concerning the influences on soil formation of parent material, climate, relief, biologic forces, and time.

B. *Factors of soil formation as related to Blank County* (second-grade head):
This subsection will tell how the environmental factors have operated to make the soils of Blank County.

C. *Classification of soils* (second-grade head):
Brief discussion of the classification of the soil series of the county into families, great soil groups, suborders, and orders, as appropriate, including mention of some of the catenary relations. Include a table showing the classification of the soil series into families, great soil groups, suborders, and orders. The table might also show for each series the environmental factors of parent material, relief, and vegetation.

D. *Morphology of soils by great soil groups and families* (second-grade head):
 1. (Great soil group name) Description.
  a. (Soil family name) Description.
   (1) Series (a detailed description is needed for one soil series in each family and for each series correlated for the first time in this county).
    (a) Setting.
    (b) Block profile description. If the genetic horizons are known, designate them consecutively from the top by letters (A, B, C, and so on), adding the appropriate numerals for subhorizons; if not known, use numbers (1, 2, 3, and so on) for the layers.
    (c) Physical and chemical data and their interpretations.
  b. (Soil family name) Description.
   (1)
    (a)
    (b)
 2. (Great soil group name) Description.
  a. (Soil family name) Description.
   (1)
    (a)
    (b)

Treat each great soil group, with its families and series, in the manner suggested above. In describing and comparing the great soil groups, families, and series, point out, as far as is known, the causal relations between the factors of soil formation and the morphology of the group.

Literature cited.—Proper credit by means of a literature citation should be given to each source of material definitely cited in the report.

At the end of the text under the major head Literature Cited arrange literature cited in the alphabetical order of authors' names. It is important that authors of soil survey reports carefully verify citations to literature, for many publications are not available to the editors at headquarters. Be sure citation is complete with name(s) of author(s), date, title of publication, publisher, number of pages, whether illustrated, and place of publication, in this order. When in doubt about abbreviations, spell out. Previously, mimeographed material and unpublished references were cited in footnotes, whereas they are now all included in Literature Cited. Indicate references to Literature Cited thus: (*12*). A footnote should be indicated thus: [6]; and footnotes are numbered consecutively from the beginning to the end of the report.

Other materials to be prepared for a soil survey report.— Wherever publication of a colored map is planned, color designations for the various soils should be submitted with the map and the manuscript. Ordinarily the number of different colors shown on the map should not exceed 15. This restriction is imposed by cost factors in color printing processes. Since practically all surveys include more than 15 separations, a grouping of soils for coloring is necessary. In the preparation of this grouping the main objective should be that of making the map easier to use.

There are two procedures that should be considered in selecting the type of color grouping. The first one is to attempt to have the greatest possible contrast in the color of adjacent soil areas. This type of grouping is of greatest value to the user interested only in a small segment of the map. It may be expected to work out well in an area where markedly different soils occur in an intricate pattern.

The second type of color grouping attempts to group similar soils under one color. This type of grouping is most useful to those interested in the entire map, since it brings out relationships between large areas at first glance. Soil characteristics that are important in determining management requirements provide the most logical basis for this type of grouping. In many reports the soils are grouped for the discussion of management practices. These groups can then become the basis of the color scheme, provided a number of important characteristics are common to all members of any group. Where dissimilar soils may happen to have the same management requirements, for example in a county where the Lithosols and Solonetz should be used only for limited grazing, they should still not be shown in the same color on the map. (See section on Soil Grouping on the Map.)

THE OUTLINE OF THE REPORT

Two suggested outlines for reports are offered to help writers include all the useful information they have about soils, to call their attention to gaps in their notes, and to help them organize the materials for the convenience of readers. It is not intended that the outlines will be followed precisely. In some areas, certain parts of the outlines require special emphasis.

The specific outline for the report should be developed by the party chief after the field work is well under way. In a real sense, the descriptive soil legend is the first tentative report. First drafts, at least, of tables, soil cards, and descriptions should be finished with the completion of field mapping. By beginning the work early, the observations and suggestions of other members of the party can be fully used. Plans can be laid for filling in gaps and for assembling data from other research groups, including especially the State agricultural experiment stations.

It is entirely possible that a good report could be prepared in which the description of the mapping unit and a discussion of its management problems and yield predictions under various defined systems of management would appear under a single major heading for each map unit. Headings for the general description of the area, plus headings for each of the mapping units, could constitute the outline of such a report. For an area with a large number of mapping units, such a report would probably be very long and repetitious. On the other extreme, if each soil characteristic and each soil management practice for all soils were discussed under a separate heading, the user would be placed to great inconvenience in locating the information about any particular mapping unit. The best outlines fall somewhere between these two extremes.

The following outlines are suggested as examples:

Outline No. I

Main topic headings:
I. Table of contents.
II. Introduction.
III. How to know the soils. (How to use the map and report.)
IV. Principles of good soil management.
V. Use and management of important soil groups. (Yield predictions are included in this section.)
VI. The soils of Blank County, their use and management. (Description and brief management discussion for each mapping unit.)
VII. Special soil groups and interpretive maps.
VIII. Geography and agriculture of Blank County.
IX. How the soils of Blank County were formed and how they are classified.
X. Literature cited.
Attachments:
1. Color grouping for map legend.
2. Table of characteristics for map supplement.

Outline No. II

I. Table of contents.
II. Introduction.
III. The soil survey report and how to use it.
IV. General character of the area.
  A. Physiography, relief, and drainage.
  B. Climate.
  C. Water supply.
  D. Vegetation.
  E. Agriculture.
V. The soils of Blank County, description and classification.
  A. Soil series and their relations.
  B. Classification of soil series into higher categories and factors that have contributed to differences in soil morphology.
  C. Soil types, phases, and miscellaneous land types (arranged alphabetically).
    1. (Soil series name) followed by description and brief discussion of management for each mapping unit.
    2. (Soil series name), etc.
VI. The soils of Blank County, interpretation and use.
  A. Use and management of soils (include basis for grouping).
    1. Soils of group 1. (This section includes a discussion of the management problems of the group, a table

of yield predictions, and the definition of the set of
management practices for each predicted yield.
  2. Soils of group 2, etc.
B. Special interpretive groupings (such as use-suitability
  groups).
  C. Soil associations.
  VII. Soil survey methods and definitions.
  VIII. Literature cited.
Attachments:
  1. Color grouping for map legend.
  2. Table of characteristics for map supplement.

SUGGESTED ORDER OF PREPARING SECTIONS OF THE REPORT

1. Prepare a card for each soil mapping unit giving the information needed in the description of the unit, the management tables, yield predictions, and tables on characteristics and classification. The use of such cards greatly simplifies and speeds up the compilation and writing, besides helping to avoid omissions and contradictions.

2. Prepare the following tables:
  a. Table—.—Average yields to be expected over a period of
     years.
  b. Table—.—General uses and management practices recommended for the soils in the area.
  c. Table—.—Some important characteristics of the soils in
     the area.
  d. Table—.—Position, parent material, and profile characteristics of the soil series in the area.
     (Some of these may be split as suggested elsewhere, and
     others may be added.)

3. Write the soil unit descriptions. The material in items 1 and 2 above will serve as sources of information and, having been arranged before, will also provide the check needed to insure completeness.

4. Prepare other sections in the outline. It may be advantageous to write outline items II and III (see p. 429) last, since by that time the pattern will be clear and examples will be in mind.

5. Prepare suggested grouping of soils for the map color legend.

6. Select illustrations, prepare titles, and enter references in the text.

7. Check references to Literature Cited closely. Accuracy is important. It is better to give too much information than not enough. The editor can then trim it down.

ILLUSTRATIONS

The value of a soil survey report can be greatly increased with good illustrations, including illustrative maps, diagrams, charts, and photographs of soil profiles, typical soil areas, and farming methods.

Work on the soil survey report, including the illustrative material to go with it, should begin as soon as the field work is well under way. Draft sketch maps and diagrams can be made and photographs obtained as the field work goes forward. These need to be planned in relation to the form of final publication, including size, proportion, and amount of reduction.

Preliminary plans or drafts of maps and diagrams should be submitted to the central office before the detailed work of preparation, so that matters of scale, size, and form may be decided upon in advance. In nearly all instances, it is most economical for the author to submit accurate drafts in pencil for final drafting by draftsmen. Few authors have the skill or facilities for preparing drawings suitable for direct reproduction. Any time spent beyond that required for an accurate draft to be followed by a skilled draftsman is wasted if the sketch must be redrawn anyway.

Yet there are instances where the author can do some drawings better than a draftsman, say pen-and-ink sketches of soil profiles for example. Then too, cooperating agencies may have facilities for preparing maps and drawings that should be used. Even in such instances, the general plan should be discussed in advance with those preparing the material for the printer to insure a useful form. The minimum of printing should be included within the drawing or sketch itself, especially of soil names or other terms that are subject to change. The printing on drafts needs to be of the size that will be clear when reductions are made. Where possible, lettering should be left in pencil until just before submission of the manuscript to the printer.

Illustrations too large for a single page may, with careful planning, be split into two parts for facing pages. Still larger ones, requiring special folding and insertion, are used, but because of cost, only when they clearly make a large and substantial contribution to the use and interpretation of the soil map. Plans for these should be made and approved well in advance of any detailed work on them. The use of funds and facilities for the preparation of illustrations cannot be allowed to delay the preparation of the basic soil map itself.

Charts should be planned for showing data only when they are much superior to tables in the text.

Preparation of drawings and maps.—As already pointed out, usually the final drawing can be done better in the central office than in the field, but the author himself or a cooperating agent may have facilities for preparing illustrations in final form that could not otherwise be included. The following suggestions may be helpful:

Line drawings reproduce best if made on clean white illustration board or bond paper of high quality.

Line drawings should be in sharp black. It is often impracticable to reproduce drawings made in color.

Maps for the text should remain uncolored. If the coloring of areas will clarify details, this should be done on a duplicate copy where needed for the guidance of the draftsman. Areas on the printed sketch map are identified with symbols or with black-

and-white printed screens (such as Zip-A-Tone). These screens can be had from dealers in artist's supplies.

Printing on maps and charts for direct reproduction needs to be done in simple standard lettering with unusual care in spelling, capitalization, word-compounding, and abbreviations. The *Style Manual* of the Government Printing Office should be followed. For example, the symbol for "percent" is not used, nor can the word be split into two or hyphenated. It must be printed as a single word, *percent*. Units of measurement should be all abbreviated or all spelled.

A map or diagram needs to be free of excessive details. A single-line border is best. Coast lines, rivers, and other lines need to be smooth enough to be clear when reduced.

Symbols for soil types and phases on special maps in the text should be identical to those used on the basic soil map; so temporary symbols in pencil should be used until the basic map legend is prepared.

If hatchings are shown on a black-and-white map, the legend with the hatched blocks and spaces for words and symbols should be placed within the border if there is room. These blocks should be large enough for clear reading with reduction, and should not contain symbols or figures besides the hatching itself.

Most drafts of diagrams, charts, and maps for the text are made about 1½ to 2 times larger than the final reproduction, with lettering to correspond.

Charts and diagrams, and most maps, should be prepared without captions. These are set in type underneath.

Photographs.—Photographs need to be kept flat and clean—free of inkstains or fingerprints. Paper clips damage them. They may be seriously damaged by typing on the back, or by writing unless it is done lightly with a pen.

Glossy prints give better results than those with a dull finish. Often commercial prints are unsatisfactory, and yet good ones can be made from a good negative. It is well to forward two prints and the negative with the manuscript.

Only good clear pictures illustrating specific parts of the discussion are included, since others detract from the publication rather than enhance it.

The taking of suitable photographs is discussed in an earlier section of this *Manual* under Examination and Description of Soils in the Field.

Size of illustrations.—Sketches, maps, diagrams, and charts should be about 1½ to 2 times larger in scale than the final illustration. The reproduction of photographs is ordinarily better if the originals are large enough to permit some reduction; but very good ones can be enlarged somewhat if necessary.

The maximum size for illustrations on the printed page in soil survey reports is about 4⅜ by 7½ inches. This includes the space for the printed lines of the legend under the cut. Observing this space requirement when handling the original copy of larger illustrations makes it possible to lay them out in proper proportion for reduction to page size, with room for the type used in the legend. Printed legends run the narrow way of the page for small cuts and also for full-page cuts with the base narrower than the height; and the long way of the page for full-page cuts with the base broader than the height. Therefore reduction to 4⅜ by not more than 7 inches will usually leave space for a legend at the bottom of the page, although a long legend may make it necessary to make the cut a little less than 7 inches. Reduction to 7½ by about 4 inches will ordinarily leave room for a legend running the long way of the page. Careful observation of these proportions saves much time and expense and makes possible effective use of the space.

Where necessary, an illustration can completely fill the page, with the legend at the foot of the facing page. This method increases the cost of printing somewhat. Since printed illustrations larger than page size need to be folded and tipped in, they are very costly. Wherever practicable, illustrations should be planned so they can be reduced to page size and still be clearly legible.

Most illustrations should come down to 4⅜ by 7 inches, with the legend at the bottom of the page; 4 by 7½ inches with the legend on the side; or 4⅜ by 3½ inches with the legend at the bottom for one-half page. Nearly all drawings may be planned with proper proportions to reduce to one of these three sizes. As guides to trimming photographs, rectangular openings of these sizes, and of proportionately larger ones, can be cut into sheets of opaque paper or cardboard. These can be laid over the print and adjusted to indicate the best part of it to use; and the margins of the print may then be trimmed away.

Labeling and assembling.—The material that goes to the printer is of two kinds: (1) The text manuscript with pages numbered 1, 2, 3, . . . and (2) the illustrations, numbered separately 1a, 2a, 3a, . . . The illustrations are numbered lightly on the back in the upper right-hand corner with a very soft pencil or crayon. The numbers are in the same order as the illustrations are mentioned in the text. The illustrations are placed in a separate large envelope, labeled with the name of the soil survey area on the outside, except for very large ones that are wrapped separately. These large ones should also be noted on the envelope.

Illustrations need to be protected and kept flat, except for large ones on paper or tracing cloth that may be rolled into mailing tubes. None should be folded.

Italic capital letters (A, B, C, . . .) are used to designate separate objects in a single numbered illustration; and small italic letters (a, b, c, . . .), abbreviations, or symbols are used to designate subparts of an object.

All lettering on illustrations in one publication should be as nearly the same type and size as possible *after* reduction. Under most conditions, authors will submit illustrations with all lettering in pencil.

Legend for illustrations.—A descriptive legend is needed for each illustration, including each photograph, clearly describing the pertinent features. The legend should be typed at the place in the text containing the reference to the illustration. A pasted carbon copy can be used.

Although a legend needs to be written compactly, it should be sufficiently self explanatory to carry the main point alone without reference back to the text.

Appropriate credit lines to individuals and organizations should be added to the legends for borrowed pictures and illustrations.

Legends on one line need to be centered. If there are two lines, make the first line page width and center the second; if there are more than two lines, indent the second and all subsequent lines at the left. This last is called "hanging indention." All three forms can be seen in almost any well-illustrated soil survey report.

Each letter for a subpart of an illustration should be explained in the legend, not simply in the text. Each illustration in a soil survey report needs to be referred to in at least one place in the text. Except for incidental reference, the order of these references in the text will determine the order of numbering the illustrations.

A list of all the legends, with the usual carbons, should accompany each manuscript in the envelope with the illustrations.

RECONNAISSANCE SOIL MAPPING

So far this *Manual* has dealt chiefly with the classification and mapping of soils in detailed basic soil surveys. The basic principles of soil description, classification, and identification are similar regardless of the scale of mapping. In broad reconnaissance mapping, the classificational units need to be grouped into soil associations. Larger inclusions of other soils are permitted within each mapping unit than in detailed surveys.

In comparatively well-known areas, the classification units that compose the associations are defined as types and phases as they are in detailed mapping. The number and kind of phases recognized depend upon the purpose for which the map is made. In new and relatively unexplored areas, the associations are defined in terms of categories higher in the classification than soil types. In many areas, these units are great soil groups or families, subdivided according to parent material, and with phases for relief and sometimes for stoniness, effects of erosion, and other features.

The mapping methods in reconnaissance surveys are somewhat different from those used in detailed surveys. In this section the major points of difference are discussed.

The kinds of soil maps have already been defined in the section on Character of Soil Maps and Reports. In this *Manual* we are concerned primarily with original field surveys rather than with generalized maps. A generalized soil map is one produced from original surveys through orderly abstraction of classificational and mapping units. Both soil boundaries and soil identification are developed in reconnaissance soil surveys by original research in the field, although parts of published reconnaissance soil maps may be generalized from detailed maps.

Any original soil survey in which only a part of the soil boundaries are actually seen by the field scientist is a reconnaissance survey, in contrast to a detailed survey in which boundaries are sketched from observations of their entire occurrence on the ground. Thus, reconnaissance surveys may be only a little less detailed than the standard detailed soil survey. These are often called semidetailed soil surveys or "detailed reconnaissance." The term "detailed reconnaissance" is objectionable, however, since it is apt to be confused with detailed-reconnaissance (with the hyphen) used for soil maps that are partly detailed and partly reconnaissance.

Beyond reconnaissance soil surveys, and even less detailed, are exploratory soil surveys, in which the boundaries are obtained mainly through compilation from existing sources as in a schematic soil map but in which the soil associations are identified mainly through original field research. The methods used in exploratory soil mapping vary so widely with objectives and conditions that they are not treated specifically in this *Manual*. Many of the same principles followed in reconnaissance soil mapping apply to exploratory soil surveys.

OBJECTIVES

Perhaps reconnaissance soil surveys may be grouped more usefully by objectives than by the physical characteristics of the maps themselves, as follows:

1. Surveys of the principal soils and soil associations in developed areas suited only to extensive uses, especially grazing and forestry: Such soil surveys are critically needed for large regions of the western part of the United States as a basis for grazing and forest management, and for estimating water intake and water yield under different conditions.

2. Surveys in developed areas to locate soils suitable for more intensive use: The soil associations of such reconnaissance surveys can be defined in terms of the same kinds of taxonomic units as those recognized in detailed soil mapping. A characteristic purpose is to locate, within regions now used for extensive cropping and grazing, areas promising for effective reclamation through irrigation or drainage. After the location of such areas, detailed soil surveys are made of them to guide the planning of the project and soil management practices. It is wasteful to make the highly detailed soil surveys needed for planning irrigation or drainage structures unless there is reasonable prospect that they will be used for that purpose. Detailed soil surveys with less categorical detail will serve fully the needs of "dry-land" farming and grazing.

3. Surveys in partially developed areas of scattered settlement or scattered villages, partly to locate new soil for expansion and development with small colonies or infiltration settlement, and partly as a basis for guiding agricultural advisory programs among existing farmers: Such surveys are usually partly generalized from sample detailed surveys in which the classification is developed and the associations defined and interpreted.[1]

4. Surveys in new or undeveloped areas to locate soils suitable for agricultural development, especially for crops, but also for grazing and forestry: The soil associations in reconnaissance and exploratory surveys of little known areas cannot be defined in terms of the narrowly defined units used in detailed soil surveys, at least not at first. Associations can be defined in terms of soil families or other subdivisions of great soil groups that differ in parent material, with phases for relief and stoniness, and perhaps for other features.

The making of such reconnaissance (or exploratory) surveys should be preceded by compiling the best possible schematic map from the available evidence on soil, relief, geology, vegeta-

---

[1] Several excellent soil surveys of this type have been made in Canada. See, for example: MITCHELL J., MOSS, H. C., and CLAYTON, J. S. SOIL SURVEY OF SOUTHERN SASKATCHEWAN (FROM TOWNSHIP 1 TO 48 INCLUSIVE). Soil Survey Report No. 12, 259 pp., illus. (maps in box). Univ. of Saskatchewan, Saskatoon. 1944.

tion, and climate. Representative sample areas are then chosen for detailed soil survey within each broad association on the schematic map. From these, taxonomic units at the family, series, or possibly type level, with appropriate phases, may be established. Then using reconnaissance methods, the boundaries of the schematic map may be redrawn from original field research.

SCALES AND BASE MATERIAL

The scales of published reconnaissance soil surveys vary widely from around 62,500 to about 1:500,000. Around 2 inches to 1 mile (1:31,680) is a common field scale. Field scales of 1:1,000,000 can be used for very broad exploratory surveys but that scale is too small for sketching boundaries from field obser-vations. The field scale depends upon the objectives of the survey, the roads available for entrance, and the base maps available for use. In sectionized areas, with established land lines around each square mile, one may use a grid or a combined grid and road map. Areas without roads can be cruised on foot with the compass, using such a map and grid.

Perhaps the best base for reconnaissance survey is the aerial mosaic at about 2 inches to the mile (1:31,680). Controlled mosaics are usually out of the question, since they are rarely made for the kinds of areas needing a reconnaissance soil map, and they are too expensive for the usual budget allowed for recon-naissance soil surveys. Photo indexes at the same scale are nearly as good. Most photo indexes have a scale of 1 inch to the mile (1:63,360), which is too small for easy reading of the patterns. But these may be enlarged for field use. Photographs at larger scales, say up to 1:20,000, give sheets of an awkward size to use or give too many to use in most reconnaissance surveys.

Where aerial photographs, vertical or oblique, are available as single pictures, they can be used to advantage as supplemental aids in sketching, even though the field mapping is done on a planimetric base of smaller scale. With the boundaries located along the lines of traverse, such pictures are a great help in sketching the course of the boundaries between located points, *provided that the scientist has an opportunity to study the soil in sample locations of each pattern that shows up in the photo-graphs.* Without such sample studies on the ground, pictures in a new kind of country can be very misleading indeed, even to the experienced scientist.

Besides a thorough search for all available base maps and aerial photographs, and a determination of their accuracy and limitations, the scientist needs to locate any geological maps, cover maps, and the like that may be useful in sketching bound-aries and in planning his work. Organization of these materials into a tentative schematic soil map in advance of field work can be most helpful.

Assuming good training in soil science, ability to visualize soil and landscape patterns, ability to recognize and interpret land forms and plant associations, and ability to travel under rough conditions without serious discomfort, perhaps the most important characteristic of a good soil mapper in reconnaissance and exploratory surveys is resourcefulness—the ability to find and use all sorts of maps and evidence that bear on his problem. Excellent soil scientists for some kinds of research, including detailed soil surveys, fail utterly in reconnaissance soil mapping. They may be unable to visualize large and complex patterns or become mentally harassed by indecision in the face of vague and apparently conflicting evidence.

SOIL CLASSIFICATION

One can scarcely be specific about soil classification for reconnaissance soil surveys in general, except to say that the principal mapping units should be defined soil associations. On this point the old reconnaissance surveys in the United States cannot be used as models. Many of these maps were valuable indeed, and still are with proper interpretation.[2] The maps did show associations, of course, but unconsciously on the part of the classifiers. For the most part each mapping unit was named according to the principal soil type in it, which was allowed to have many inclusions and many undefined phases. More appropriate boundary lines can be drawn by defining the mapping units as soil associations in the first place. Then by detailed mapping of samples in each one, the proportions of the various units can be set down with reasonable accuracy. The user of the map can then be told what units to expect in an area shown on a map, how to recognize them one from another on the ground, and their capabilities for various uses and their management requirements. In fact, the text report of reconnaissance surveys in well-developed areas should contain yield estimates and other predictions in the same form as in the detailed soil surveys for the *taxonomic units*. Naturally, for soils in areas for which only reconnaissance surveys are made, data from experimental plots and from farm or ranch experience are less abundant than for most soils in areas of detailed soil surveys. Therefore, the predictions made are less precise and depend mainly upon judgment based on known principles of relationship between soil characteristics and soil management practices and on experience with similar soils elsewhere.

In places the catenary soil association is a convenient mapping unit. The boundaries among such associations are drawn mainly on the basis of differences in land form and parent material, and the constituent units vary in characteristics related to differences in relief and drainage. But rarely can catenary associations be used conveniently throughout the whole survey area without introducing excessive detail—the very thing that must be avoided in a reconnaissance soil survey. That is, in many regions the complexity of pattern is primarily one of contrasting

---

[2] Except for the naming of several mapping units as soil series and types, rather than as soil associations, the following is a good example of a reconnaissance soil survey: CARTER, W. T., and others. SOIL SURVEY (RECONNAISSANCE) OF THE TRANS-PECOS AREA, TEXAS. U. S. Dept. Agr. Soil Survey. Series 1928. No. 35, 66 pp., illus. (maps). 1928.

parent materials—say, steep hills and alluvial valleys, contrasting interbedded sediments, or folded interbedded hills. The classifier needs to consider these complexities and not hold strictly to catenary associations.

Interpretive groups should not be used as mapping units in reconnaissance soil mapping for reasons already emphasized. Any interpretive grouping depends upon the present state of the agricultural arts and of economic conditions. As a result, any map of such groups alone soon becomes outdated and cannot be reinterpreted. By using mapping units defined on the basis of fundamental taxonomic units, many interpretations can be made for different purposes and under different conditions. Some time ago, for example, a reconnaissance soil survey was made in terms of productivity of the soils for wheat. Shortly after its completion, new varieties were introduced and new soil management practices were developed. The maps became essentially useless as a basis for prediction very soon after publication.

Nor can soils be grouped according to single factors such as slope, texture, permeability, drainage, and so on, or by some arbitrary combination of them, partly for the same reason—the combinations chosen are an interpretation based on past use experience—and partly because the significance of any one factor depends upon the others. Each individual taxonomic unit must be considered as a whole; that is why we have a soil classification in the first place. By using the names and definitions in the standard system of soil classification, an enormous number of data, collected and synthesized by these units and their close relatives, can be used for interpretation both when the survey is made and later.

In well-known areas, such as most parts of the United States, the legends for reconnaissance soil surveys can be made up of perhaps some individual soil types and phases as mapping units and of soil associations defined in terms of soil types and phases. Even here, soil families and phases of soil families, when more adequately defined, will appear as components of the soil associations and as mapping units.

In little-known areas, that is, little known in terms of soil classification, which includes large parts of the world outside of the temperate regions, it will be impossible to use taxonomic units as narrowly defined as the soil series, types, and phases of the standard system used in the United States, at least at first. The legends are made up of associations consisting of subdivisions of the great soil groups made according to parent material, with phases according to relief and stoniness and perhaps other characteristics. For many areas, the uncertainty of great soil group names and definitions, and of their adequacy, raises a serious problem of nomenclature. Thus local names are essential. The classifier should develop the definitions as nearly as he can at some one specific categorical level—great soil group, family, or series—so they may be correlated in an orderly way with one another and in a general system of soil classification.

MAPPING METHODS

The sharp distinction between detailed and reconnaissance soil surveys is in the matter of sketching boundaries. In detailed soil surveys boundaries are seen throughout their course, whereas in reconnaissance soil surveys they are sketched from estimation and secondary evidence between points of observation. Under the best conditions, roads are traversed with a car and the soils are examined to characterize specific *local* types or conditions, as is done in a detailed soil survey. That is, the classifier does not examine the profiles of an association, complex, family, or even series; rather he examines the profiles of soil types within such broader taxonomic groups or geographic associations. The classifier, then, has more definitions to remember as he interprets the results of his examinations in terms of mapping units than in a detailed soil survey. He must not be misled into the exaggeration of variants and miscellaneous land types as components of his mapping units simply because they may be more obvious as compared to the commonplace.

The examinations of soil profiles and of soil slope and other external soil features are used to recognize the components of the association. Then the mapper must decide how these fit into the defined pattern of the association around which he draws his boundary lines. Aerial pictures are useful. He observes the major changes in plants, or plant associations, the courses of streams, ridges, and escarpments, that tell him how the "country runs," and the pattern of relief and drainage, related, of course, to geological strata and land form.

In districts with few roads, it is best to traverse the roads first, with full equipment for soil examinations and mapping materials. Areas between are filled in by foot traverses, planned according to previous estimates of the conditions to be dealt with. Long trips may be made partly by boat and pack animal, with hikes from major control stations.

Along the traverses, abundant notes can be taken of value in defining the soil associations. Some of these notes can be put directly on the map and left in pencil. The degree of cartographic detail on the map should be uniform, except as clearly indicated on the map itself or in an accompanying sketch showing relative reliability.

In areas covered by reconnaissance soil maps, accessibility to the country may vary widely. Some parts may be covered in considerable detail and others only at wide intervals. These differences may be indicated on a diagram, printed beneath the legend on the published map. Certain areas may appropriately be left blank as "unexplored." The usefulness of the reconnaissance soil map having two widely different degrees of detail may be increased by using solid colors for areas mapped in the "standard detail" and by using proportional bars of color, according to the estimated proportion of each association, in large areas less completely examined.

INTERPRETATIONS

In the reconnaissance soil survey two levels or kinds of interpretations are required (1) of the soil associations as units and (2) of the individual taxonomic units that are components of the associations. For both, detailed soil maps of sample areas are exceedingly helpful.

Where possible, the same sets of predictions about yields and management practices should be given for each of the detailed taxonomic units and phases as are made in a detailed soil survey. Many uses of the reconnaissance map are concerned with small areas—fields and farms too small to show individually on the map. The reader can be given clues, especially by the use of soil keys within each association, that permit him to distinguish the local soil types within the association as he sees them on the ground. Then he can select the appropriate recommendations and interpretations for the local soil type and phases from the accompanying tables in the text.

For many uses of the reconnaissance soil survey, it is necessary to suggest potentialities of broad areas for settlement or reclamation. Problems and recommendations for flood reduction, forest potentialities, and the like, need to be explained in terms of the results disclosed by the survey. Perhaps even more than in a detailed soil survey, the soil scientist interpreting reconnaissance soil maps and classifications needs to integrate his data and judgments with those of other specialists according to the nature of the problem which the survey is to help solve.

DEVELOPMENT OF A SOIL SURVEY PROGRAM
FOR UNDEVELOPED AREAS

The results of soil classification in many undeveloped areas are desperately needed as soon as possible—long before there is time for the necessary research to establish all the taxonomic units that will be needed eventually. In such areas the following procedure, or a practical variation of it according to local conditions and problems, can be followed.

1. A schematic soil association map is compiled for the area on the basis of available data on soils, geology, relief, vegetation, and climate. The scale of such a map varies from 1:100,000 to 1:500,000, accommodated to local sources of information and soil conditions.

2. One or more representative sample areas are selected in each important soil association for detailed classification and mapping as already explained in this *Manual* for a detailed basic soil survey.[3] It is better to locate compact representative areas than to use long narrow strips chosen at random. These samples must be large enough to be representative and to disclose the pattern of the unit in the association.

As a part of the soil survey procedure, an adequate laboratory is needed for basic physical and chemical determinations on

---

[3] Soil associations made up wholly of Lithosols or other soils unsuited for use may not require detailed samples for adequate definitions.

samples of the soil horizons and for comparing any arable soils now used with virgin soils and with one another. Where possible, research plots to test crop adaptability, fertilizer needs, tillage practices, and the like, should be established in the principal contrasting taxonomic soil units.

3. For each sample area, a key to the soils *within the association* is developed for use in the assembly of all units in a system of classification for the whole area and to train agricultural advisers in local soil identification by name.

4. The best possible set of predictions and interpretations for each local soil unit is developed in terms of suitability for crops, pasture, and forestry, adapted species and varieties of crops, estimated yields, management requirements, and effects of sets of soil management practices on sustained productivity.

5. Field conferences for local agricultural advisers and other agricultural technicians can be held in each area where these people may be shown how to use the soil key, how to recognize the local soil types and phases, and how to use the tables of predictions or recommendations.

6. The map for the region is revised by reconnaissance survey methods, and an improved legend of soil associations, based upon the research in the sample area, is supplied.

7. The completed reconnaissance soil map is published with its report, which contains an assembly of the sample maps and a key to the soils of the whole region, together with predictions and interpretations for application, by local soil types and phases, to local fields and farms as well as for soil associations as a whole.

Following such a reconnaissance soil survey, detailed soil surveys can be made in the parts of the region having the greatest potentialities, considering the complementary relationships among all the resources available—soils, forests, water, and minerals— and the timing of the establishment of other services—hospitals, transport, trading centers, and the like.

This bibliography suggests books and papers for the basic reference shelf in a permanent soil survey office. To these should be added the books and bulletins dealing with the soils of the region being studied, as well as with the flora, climate, geology, geography, and agriculture. Many of the references noted in the footnotes to discussions of specific topics in this *Manual* may also be helpful. Then, too, the reference shelf should have the current scientific journals dealing with soil science, including Soils and Fertilizers, published by the Commonwealth Bureau of Soil Science, Harpenden, England, which includes abstracts of important books, bulletins, and papers that need to be added to the library. Each soil survey office should make a special effort to establish publication exchanges with other offices in the world having similar soils.

BEAMAN, W. M.
    1928. TOPOGRAPHIC MAPPING. U. S. Geol. Survey Bul. 788: 161–378, illus.
BEAR, FIRMAN E., ed.
    1945. METHODS IN CHEMICAL ANALYSES OF SOILS. Soil Sci. 59 (1): 109.

———
    1949. SOIL CLASSIFICATION. Soil Sci. 67: 77–191.
BLACK, J. D., CLAWSON, M., SAYRE, C. R., and WILCOX, W. W.
    1947. FARM MANAGEMENT. 1073 pp., illus. New York.
CLARKE, F. W.
    1924. THE DATA OF GEOCHEMISTRY. Ed. 5, U. S. Geol. Survey Bul. 770, 841 pp.
COHEN, M. R., and NAGEL, E.
    1939. AN INTRODUCTION TO LOGIC AND SCIENTIFIC METHOD. 467 pp. New York.
COTTON, C. A.
    1942. CLIMATIC ACCIDENTS IN LANDSCAPE-MAKING. 354 pp., illus. London, and Christchurch, New Zealand.

———
    1948. LANDSCAPE AS DEVELOPED BY THE PROCESSES OF NORMAL EROSION. Ed. 2, 509 pp., illus. Christchurch and New York.
FENNEMAN, N. M.
    1931. PHYSIOGRAPHY OF WESTERN UNITED STATES. 534 pp., illus. New York.

———
    1938. PHYSIOGRAPHY OF EASTERN UNITED STATES. 714 pp., illus. New York.
FLINT, R. F.
    1947. GLACIAL GEOLOGY AND THE PLEISTOCENE EPOCH. 589 pp., illus. New York.
GLINKA, K. D.
    1927. THE GREAT SOIL GROUPS OF THE WORLD AND THEIR DEVELOPMENT. [Transl. by C. F. Marbut.] 235 pp. Ann Arbor, Mich.
HITCHCOCK, A. S.
    1951. MANUAL OF THE GRASSES OF THE UNITED STATES. U. S. Dept. Agr. Misc. Pub. 200, Ed. 2. 1051 pp., illus. [Rev. by Agnes Chase.]

443

IGNATIEFF, V., ed.
1949. EFFICIENT USE OF FERTILIZERS. Food and Agr. Organ of U. N. Agr. Studies No. 9, 182 pp., illus. Washington.

INTERNATIONAL CONGRESS OF SOIL SCIENCE.
1928. PROCEEDINGS AND PAPERS. 4 v., 1st Internatl. Cong. Washington.

——— 1933. PROCEEDINGS AND PAPERS. 6 v., 2d Internatl. Cong. Moscow.

——— 1935. PROCEEDINGS. 3 v., 3d Internatl. Cong. London.

——— 1950. PROCEEDINGS. 3 v., 4th Internatl. Cong. Amsterdam.

JENNY, H.
1941. FACTORS OF SOIL FORMATION. 281 pp., illus. New York.

KEMP, J. F.
1923. A HANDBOOK OF ROCKS FOR USE WITHOUT THE MICROSCOPE. Ed. 5, 282 pp., illus. New York.

KILMER, V. J., and ALEXANDER, L. T.
1949. METHODS OF MAKING MECHANICAL ANALYSES OF SOILS. Soil Sci. 68: 15–24.

LOBECK, A. K.
1939. GEOMORPHOLOGY. 731 pp., illus. New York.

LONGWELL, C. R., KNOPF, A., FLINT, R. F., SCHUCHERT, C., and DUNBAR, C. O.
1941. OUTLINES OF GEOLOGY. Ed. 2, 381 + 291 pp., illus. New York.

LUTZ, H. F., and CHANDLER, R. F., JR.
1946. FOREST SOILS. 514 pp., illus. New York.

MARBUT, C. F.
1935. SOILS OF THE UNITED STATES. *In* U. S. Dept. Agr. Atlas of American Agriculture, pt. 3, Advance Sheets No. 8, 98 pp., illus.

MICHIGAN STATE HIGHWAY DEPARTMENT.
1946. FIELD MANUAL OF SOIL ENGINEERING. Rev. ed. 304 pp., illus. Lansing.

MILLER, E. C.
1938. PLANT PHYSIOLOGY, WITH REFERENCE TO THE GREEN PLANT. Ed. 2, 1201 pp., illus. New York and London.

NEUSTRUEV, S. S.
1927. GENESIS OF SOILS. Russ. Pedol. Invest. 3, Acad. Sci., 98 pp. Leningrad.

OLMSTEAD, F. R., HICKS, L. D., and BODMAN, G. B.
1949. ENGINEERING USE OF AGRICULTURAL SOIL MAPS. Highway Res. Bd. Bul. 22, 128 pp., illus.

PEECH, M., and others.
1947. METHODS OF SOIL ANALYSIS FOR SOIL FERTILITY INVESTIGATIONS. U. S. Dept. Agr. Cir. 757, 25 pp.

ROBINSON, G. W.
1950. SOILS, THEIR ORIGIN, CONSTITUTION, AND CLASSIFICATION; AN INTRODUCTION TO PEDOLOGY. Ed. 3, 573 pp., illus. London.

RUSSELL, SIR E. J.
1950. SOIL CONDITIONS AND PLANT GROWTH. Ed. 8, 635 pp., illus. London and New York. [Rev. by E. W. Russell.]

SMITH, GUY D.
1942. ILLINOIS LOESS—VARIATIONS IN ITS PROPERTIES AND DISTRIBUTION: A PEDOLOGIC INTERPRETATION. Ill. Agr. Expt. Sta. Bul. 490: 137–184, illus.

SMITH, H. T. U.
1943. AERIAL PHOTOGRAPHS AND THEIR APPLICATIONS. 372 pp., illus. New York.

SNEDECOR, G. W.
1946. STATISTICAL METHODS APPLIED TO EXPERIMENTS IN AGRICULTURE AND BIOLOGY. 485 pp., illus. Ames, Iowa.

SOIL SCIENCE SOCIETY OF AMERICA.
1942. LIFE AND WORK OF C. F. MARBUT. 271 pp., illus. Columbia, Mo.

UNITED STATES DEPARTMENT OF AGRICULTURE.
    1938. SOILS AND MEN. U. S. Dept. Agr. Yearbook. 1232 pp., illus.

    1941. CLIMATE AND MAN. U. S. Dept. Agr. Yearbook, 1248 pp., illus.

    1948. GRASS. U. S. Dept. Agr. Yearbook, 892 pp., illus.
UNITED STATES REGIONAL SALINITY LABORATORY.
    1947. DIAGNOSIS AND IMPROVEMENT OF SALINE AND ALKALI SOILS.
        Ed. by L. A. Richards. 157 pp., illus. [Processed.]
VON ENGELN, O. D.
    1942. GEOMORPHOLOGY. 655 pp., illus. New York.
WALLACE, T.
    1951. THE DIAGNOSIS OF MINERAL DEFICIENCIES IN PLANTS BY VISUAL
        SYMPTOMS. Ed. 2, 107 pp. + 312 pls. London.

SPECIAL BIBLIOGRAPHY OF SOIL SURVEYS

In this section is presented a bibliography of soil surveys developed in the National Cooperative Soil Survey program and published by the United States Department of Agriculture. Selections have been made to illustrate surveys, published or to be published very soon, in contrasting soil regions and various features of maps or reports. The selections are not necessarily the "best" reports and maps. In some regions, several very good reports might have been selected; in others, the one chosen may still have some serious deficiencies by present-day standards.

Progress in soil classification, mapping, and interpretation has been so rapid in recent years, since the earlier edition of this *Manual*, that few surveys made before 1940 would be made in exactly the same way today. Thus, the student will find inconsistencies between the methods used in many of the recently published surveys, including the ones listed, and those outlined in the *Manual*. This should be expected in an actively growing field of research. Many methods had to be tried out, tested in actual surveys, before a judicious selection could be made.

Some 100 or more additional soil surveys of excellent quality are under way in the field, are being prepared for publication, or are in the process of being printed. This list is offered as a general guide to reading that may be helpful to both professors and students of soil survey. Besides these surveys, many good examples can be had from other countries, as well as some special soil surveys published by State agricultural experiment stations in the United States.

Soil Survey of the Casa Grande Area, Arizona. Poulson, E. N., Wildermuth, Robert, and Harper, W. G. U. S. Dept. Agr. Soil Survey Ser. 1936, No. 7, 94 pp., illus. 1941.

The Casa Grande Area lies in the Red Desert soil region of south-central Arizona. The principal irrigated crops are cotton and alfalfa.

The map is published on a scale 1:62,500. The 129 mapping units are placed in 17 color groups based on the physical characteristics of the soil, and the legend is arranged according to the relative suitability of the soils for agriculture under irrigation. Special red boundaries and symbols on the map show the relative concentration of soluble salts and alkali.

For description in the report, the soils are grouped according to the quantity of accumulated lime and the physical character of their subsoils, but in the section on Land Uses and Management recommendations of soil management are given for each soil unit and for the groups shown on the map.

Although recent reports, like the one for Tama County, Iowa, for example, are perhaps better; at the time of its preparation this one marked a definite forward step in specifying use and management practices for individual soils.

Soil Survey of Lee County, Alabama. Wonser, C. H., Striker, M. M., Brackeen, L. G., McIntyre, C. L., and Sherard, Hoyt. U. S. Dept. Agr. Soil Survey Ser. 1938, No. 23, 80 pp., illus. 1950.

This map and report deal with Red-Yellow Podzolic soils that occur in both the Piedmont and Coastal Plain physiographic provinces in the southeastern part of the United States. The map is published on a scale of 1:48,000, and the 66 soil-mapping units are placed in 22 color groups on the basis of their principal physical characteristics, such as texture, consistence, slope, and drainage. A table giving the important physical characteristics of each mapping unit is carried as a supplement to the map.

The soil descriptions in the report are presented briefly in block form, which helps to set them apart. Estimated yields and productivity ratings under current practices and under improved practices of management are

447

given for each mapping unit. The soils are placed in eight groups, according to management requirements and responses. The photographs illustrate the shift from cotton to hay and pasture crops that is occurring in parts of the Southeast.

Although not outstanding in the treatment of any particular item, this report carries information on a considerable number of soil types common to the Piedmont and Coastal Plain.

Soil Survey of the Coalinga Area, California. Harradine, F. F., and party. U. S. Dept. Agr. Soil Survey Ser. 1944. [In press.]

The Coalinga Area lies on the western side of the San Joaquin Valley. Barley, flax, and cotton are the principal irrigated crops. The zonal soils are similar to Brown and Reddish Brown soils, but their precise identification as great soil groups is still uncertain. The map is being published at a scale of 1:63,360.

The report is good but not unusual. The descriptions of the soil units are good, and there are special sections on Alkali, Water Supply and Irrigation, and Erosion. The 86 soil-mapping units are rated according to their general productivity; tables show the relative suitability of the soils for intensive agriculture and specific crops; and the ranges in yields of the individual crops are given by the suitability classes. Sketches show the geographic distribution of the soil series according to the physiographic divisions across the valley.

Soil Survey of the Akron Area, Colorado. Knobel, E. W., and party. U. S. Dept. Agr. Soil Survey Ser. 1938, No. 14, 80 pp., illus. 1947.

The Akron Area is in a region of Brown soils and includes parts of the High Plains and Colorado Piedmont sections. The soils are used with and without irrigation.

The map is published on a scale of 1:63,360. The 61 mapping units are placed in 23 color groups, based on their physical characteristics and their physiographic position. The individual soil descriptions are good.

The discussion of cropping practices for the individual crops, based partly on research work at the Dry Land Field Station at Akron, is a strong feature of this report. Tables of estimated yields and productivity indexes are included for two levels of rainfall.

Soil Survey of the Grand Junction Area, Colorado. Knobel, E. W., Dansdill, R. K., and Richardson, M. L. U. S. Dept. Agr. Soil Survey Ser. 1940. [In press.]

The Grand Junction Area in western Colorado is an important irrigated fruit-producing area. The soils belong mainly in the Gray Desert and Alluvial great soil groups. The map is being published at 1:48,000.

This report has good discussions of the crops of the area and the crop and soil management practices. The descriptions of the individual soil series and 74 mapping units are also well done. A table of estimated yields includes only one level of management. In a special chapter, investigations on the saline soils of the area, in which the United States Regional Salinity Laboratory and the Colorado State Agricultural Experiment Station actively cooperated, are reported.

Soil Survey of the Idaho Falls Area, Idaho. Mogen, C. A., Poulson, E. N., Poulson, A. E., Van Slyke, E. J., and Colwell, W. E. U. S. Dept. Agr. Soil Survey Ser. 1939, No. 8, 69 pp., illus. 1950.

The Idaho Falls Area lies in southeastern Idaho and forms a part of the irrigated Snake River plain. The soils belong in the Brown and Sierozem great soil groups.

The map is published on a scale of 1:31,680. The 50 soil-mapping units are shown in 22 color groupings, based on physical soil characteristics and physiographic position.

This survey is representative of those dealing with irrigated soils in the Brown and Sierozem soil region. The report is not outstanding but contains the usual photographs, figures, soil descriptions, table of predicted yields at two levels of management, and discussions of soil management. The section on morphology and genesis of the soils is good.

Soil Survey of St. Joseph County, Indiana. Ulrich, H. P., and party. U. S. Dept. Agr. Soil Survey Ser. 1938, No. 27, illus. 1950.

St. Joseph County, in northern Indiana, is an area of Gray-Brown Podzolic, Prairie, and Wiesenboden (Humic-Gley) soils used in diversified agriculture.

The map is published on a scale of 1:31,680. The 112 soil-mapping units are shown in color as groups based on slope, drainage, parent materials, and physiographic position.

The generally good all-around report includes adequate descriptions of the soil units, with profile descriptions in the block form, good photographs, a good discussion of crops, a key to the soil series, a table of predicted yields at two levels of management, a discussion of soil management groups, and a good section on soil morphology and genesis. Besides, interpretive maps are included that show lime requirements and drainage, and single-factor maps of soil slope and of soil colors. This last map suggests contents of organic matter and nitrogen.

Soil Survey of Tama County, Iowa. Aandahl, A. R., and party. U. S. Dept. Agr. Soil Survey Ser. 1938, No. 22, 109 pp., illus. 1950.

Tama County, of east-central Iowa, lies in the region of Prairie soils. Some Gray-Brown Podzolic soils also exist there. Farms produce much corn and livestock.

The map is published on a scale of 1:63,360. On it, 50 kinds of soil are placed in 13 color groupings on the basis of their management requirements.

The report has excellent photographs and drawings, including diagrams of individual texture profiles. The relationships among soil series are shown in their relative position in a table that itemizes detailed soil management practices and gives predicted yields at three levels of management. An additional table outlines the management practices for the management groups shown in color on the map. Practices that control erosion and maintain soil fertility are emphasized. A glossary is added. This report is probably one of the best.

Soil Survey of Taylor County, Iowa. Leighty, Ralph G., and party.[1] U. S. Dept. Agr. Soil Survey Ser. 1947. [In press.]

Taylor County, of southwestern Iowa, is in the Prairie soil region. Corn and livestock are produced. The map is being published on a scale of 1:31,680.

A special effort has been made to point this report directly toward a farmer audience. Emphasis has been placed on simple soil descriptions and the presentation of specific combinations of management practices, for which yield predictions are given at two levels of management. Photographs and other illustrations, including block diagrams to show the relationships among soil series and the features of the landscape, are used to replace, in part, text descriptions. Although an excellent discussion of soil morphology and genesis is included, several sections appearing in other reports dealing with general agriculture are missing.

Soil Survey of Iron County, Michigan. Foster, Z. C., Veatch, J. O., and Schoenmann, L. R. U. S. Dept. Agr. Soil Survey Ser. 1930, No. 46, 29 pp., illus. 1937.

Iron County lies in the western part of the Upper Peninsula of Michigan. The soils are principally Podzols, Half Bogs, and Bogs, formerly forested but now cut over. Only a small part is suited to cultivated crops.

The map is published on a scale of 1:63,360. The 34 mapping units are shown by separate colors. Today the map would be regarded as reconnaissance rather than detailed. Any parts mapped in detail would need a larger scale for publication.

An insert map shows nine "natural land divisions" described in terms of relief, soil texture, amount of available moisture, natural fertility, and original forest growth. The discussions of soil morphology and genesis are

[1] Report prepared by W. H. Scholtes, F. F. Riecken, and Guy D. Smith.

good. Soil use is discussed generally, but the management of the individual mapping units is treated less adequately than in modern detailed soil surveys.

Soil Survey (Reconnaissance) of the Red River Valley Area, Minnesota. Nikiforoff, C. C., and party. U. S. Dept. Agr. Soil Survey Ser. 1933, No. 25, 98 pp., illus. 1939.

This report and series of maps present a broad picture of the morphology and genesis of soils developed on the lacustrine deposits of glacial Lake Agassiz in an area of transition from forest to prairie vegetation in the North Temperate region. Eight maps, printed on a scale of 1:125,000, show the schematic soil pattern of nearly 5½ million acres in eight counties. The map legend illustrates the incorrect practice of old reconnaissance maps of using the names of the dominant soil types for what are really soil associations. Thus the legend suggests far greater uniformity of soil conditions than actually exists. The report contains numerous good photographs and black-and-white sketches of soil profiles classified as Podzols,[2] Chernozems, Wiesenboden, Solonetz, and intergrades among them.

Soil Survey of Jasper County, Missouri. Shrader, W. D., Springer, M. E., Hamby, Robert, Pettijohn, W. J., and Miller, J. T. U. S. Dept. Agr. Soil Survey Ser. 1942. [In press.]

Jasper County of southwestern Missouri lies in a transitional area between the Ozark Plateau to the east and the grasslands to the west. Prairie, Planosol, and Red-Yellow Podzolic soils are represented. They are used in mixed farming. The map is being published on a scale of 1:63,360.

This survey is included mainly because of the interesting complexity of this transitional area between forest to the east and grassland to the west and between the Red-Yellow Podzolic soils to the south and the Gray-Brown Podzolic soils to the northeast. Although written concisely, with emphasis on soil management practices for the individual soil units, the report is not exceptional.

Soil Survey of Strafford County, New Hampshire. Shearin, A. E., Williams, B. H., Gladwin, F. J., Howard, Montague, Jr., and Coates, W. H. U. S. Dept. Agr. Soil Survey Ser. 1940, No. 5, 141 pp., illus. 1949.

The soils of Strafford County belong in the Brown Podzolic and Podzol great soil groups. The county lies across two physiographic provinces of New England—the Seaboard Lowland and the New England Upland. Dairy farming predominates.

The map is published in two sheets on a scale of 1:31,680; 116 mapping units are shown in 18 color groupings, based on their physical characteristics and physiographic positions. A large table enclosed with the map shows the principal characteristics of each mapping unit.

Besides detailed descriptions of the individual soil units, the report includes a list of trees, shrubs, and other plants; a key to the soil series; a generalized soil association map; and tables of predicted crop yields and productivity ratings for two levels of management. The low level of soil fertility is emphasized as the main reason for the low carrying capacity of many pastures.

Soil Survey of Jackson County, North Carolina. Goldston, E. F., Davis, W. A., and Croom, C. W.[3] U. S. Dept. Agr. Soil Survey Ser. 1938, No. 19, 87 pp., illus. 1948.

Jackson County includes a part of the Blue Ridge Mountains in western North Carolina. The normal soils belong to the Red-Yellow Podzolic and Gray-Brown Podzolic great soil groups. Somewhat less than one-half of the total area is in farms. Most are small mixed farms with a high degree of self subsistence. The rest of the county is forested.

The map is published on a scale of 1:48,000 and carries 20 color groupings

---

[2] Part of these, at least, have been identified as equivalent to the Gray-Wooded soils of Canada.

[3] Report revised by M. G. Cline, R. C. Jurney, and M. J. Edwards.

based on physical characteristics of the 78 mapping units. A descriptive legend accompanies the map.

The report gives specific recommendations of soil management practices by management groups. The soils are first grouped into five classes according to their relative suitability for use. These major groups have a total of 13 management subgroups. Crop adaptations, rotations, fertilizer and lime requirements, and practices for runoff and erosion control are given for each management group. Predicted crop yields are given for each mapping unit in another table.

The report also contains a glossary of common terms used in soil science. Soil profile descriptions are set out in block form.

Soil Survey of Morton County, North Dakota. Edwards, M. J., and party, U. S. Dept. Agr. Soil Survey Ser. 1936, No. 28, 145 pp., illus. 1951.

Morton County lies in the Chestnut soil region of the northern Great Plains. Agriculture consists of extensive grain farming, ranching, dairying, or some combination of these. Dissection and glaciation have combined to produce a detailed pattern of soils, especially of soil phases for slope, stoniness, and solonization. Unfortunately, the map is published on a scale of 1:63,360. Because of the detailed soil pattern it should have been on a larger scale.

In addition to detailed descriptions of each of the 87 mapping units, the report carries a number of useful features, including a tabular key to the soil series; a list of the grasses, shrubs, and trees; a table of productivity ratings; maps of soil associations at two levels of generalization; several photographs; and a discussion of the evolution of Solonchak, Solonetz, and solodized-Solonetz. From the field sheets of this survey, the rural lands were classified in detail for tax assessment.

Soil Survey of the Deschutes Area, Oregon. Torgerson, E. F., and party.[4] U. S. Dept. Agr. Soil Survey Ser. 1945. [In press.]

The Deschutes Area is in west-central Oregon, just east of the Cascades, and is mainly in the Brown soil region. The soils are used for livestock grazing, wheat growing, and irrigation farming. The map is being published on a scale of 1:24,000. The color groups on the map are based on soil characteristics and their use, management, and irrigation recommendations.

An outstanding feature of the report is the tabular information on soil use and management and on such irrigation practices as length of run, head of water, and frequency of watering. The text is supplemented with helpful photographs and sketches.

Soil Survey of Union County, Pennsylvania. Bacon, S. R., Taylor, David, Boileau, Alfred, and Yoder, Gerald. U. S. Dept. Agr. Soil Survey Ser. 1940, No. 2, 115 pp., illus. 1946.

Union County, of east-central Pennsylvania, lies in the Gray-Brown Podzolic soil region and within the Appalachian Valley and Ridge Section. Dairying and general farming predominate.

The map is published on a scale of 1:48,000. On it 116 soil-mapping units are placed in 18 color groupings based on drainage, parent materials, and physiographic position. The selection of colors sharply differentiate the soils of the Susquehanna Lowland from those of the mountains.

The principal characteristics of the soil series are shown in tabular form, but the report is weak on details of soil management practices for the individual soil units.

Soil Survey of Bedford County, Tennessee. Strickland, L. J., and party.[5] U. S. Dept. Agr. Soil Survey Ser. 1938, No. 12, 120 pp., illus. 1947.

Bedford County, Tennessee, in the region of Red-Yellow Podzolic soils, lies across a part of the Nashville Basin and Highland Rim escarpment. The agriculture is based largely on livestock farming, but some cotton is grown as a cash crop.

---

[4] Report prepared by W. J. Leighty.
[5] The report was revised by M. G. Cline and R. C. Jurney.

The map is published in one sheet on a scale of 1:48,000. On it, 57 soil-mapping units are placed in 8 major color groupings on the basis of physiographic or topographic position and in 18 subgroups according to drainage and steepness of slope. The color pattern gives an interesting picture of the county as a whole.

The report carries the usual features of those of this period. It includes photographs, a sketch map of the physiographic subdivisions, a tabular summary of the principal characteristics of the soil series, a description of the individual series, detailed descriptions of the individual mapping units, tables of predicted yields and productivity ratings under three levels of management, a grouping of the soils into five physical land classes based on use suitability, and a grouping of the soils according to their management requirements.

The report is generally good and is outstanding for a table showing the common use and present management of the individual soil units; a table listing the soils in management groups and giving the relative ease by which plant nutrients, soil material, and good tilth are conserved in each; a map and discussion of associations of the physical land classes; and the section on soil morphology and genesis.

Soil Survey of Benton County, Tennessee. Odom, L. E., and party. U. S. Dept. Agr. Soil Survey Ser. 1941. [In press.]

Benton County, Tennessee, is in the region of Red-Yellow Podzolic soils on the East Gulf Coastal Plain and the Highland Rim section of the Interior Low Plateaus. The map has a scale of 1:24,000. Its legend is in two parts: (1) An alphabetical list of the 95 soil units and (2) a good group legend based on physical characteristics of the soil.

The report is generally good. It has excellent photographic illustrations. The individual soil descriptions are very good, with profile descriptions set out in block form. The report has a good table of predicted yields at each level of management. Specific management requirements are well handled by soil groups. Good sections on interpretive maps and on soil morphology and genesis are included, as well as special ones on water control on the land.

This survey and the ones for Grainger, Jackson, and Bedford Counties are examples of those made as a part of the program for agricultural development in the Tennessee Valley. Many new developments of general application grew out of this intensive research, supported in part by the Tennessee Valley Authority. In the most recent surveys in progress, for example, the color groups on the soil map are based on soil management requirements.

Soil Survey of Grainger County, Tennessee. Hubbard, E. H., Matzek, B. L., and Jenkins, Clifton. U. S. Dept. Agr. Soil Survey Ser. 1940, No. 4, 203 pp., illus. 1948.

The Grainger survey covers an area, largely of Red-Yellow Podzolic soils, in the Appalachian Ridge and Valley section of northeastern Tennessee. The map is published in two sheets on a scale of 1:24,000, and the color pattern brings out the ridge-and-valley aspect of the landscape very effectively.[6] The 128 soil-mapping units are shown in 19 color groupings on the basis of broad use capability, relief, drainage, parent material, and topographic position.

The descriptions of the principal soils are given in box form, which appears to improve the readability of the text. The report includes a number of effective photographs, as well as tables of predicted crop yields, soil productivity ratings, land classes, characteristics of soil series, and acreages of land classes by the soil units. The soils are placed in 13 groups and discussed according to their use capability and management requirements. Unfortunately, the soil association map is printed at too small a scale.

---

[6] The large soil maps of Grainger County are somewhat cumbersome. Claiborne County, Tenn., has a similar map in 10 smaller and more convenient sheets. Although very good, the Claiborne County report is not quite so outstanding, perhaps, as that of Grainger County.

Soil Survey of Brown County, Texas. Templin, E. H., Mowery, I. C., Watkins, W. I., Glassey, T. W., and Beck, M. W. U. S. Dept. Agr. Soil Survey Ser. 1939, No. 4, 87 pp., illus. 1948.

Brown County lies in central Texas and includes parts of the Grand Prairie, the West Cross Timbers, and the Rolling Plains. Soils belonging in the Red-Yellow Podzolic, Reddish Prairie, Reddish Chestnut, and Rendzina great soil groups are present. Farming is varied, with ranching, cash-crop farming, and general farming as major types. Irrigation was being introduced at the time of the survey.

The map is published on a scale of 1:63,360. On it 57 soil-mapping units are grouped into 23 color patterns according to their principal physical characteristics.

The report has good photographs, a key to the soil series patterned after botanical keys, and a soil association map. The profile descriptions are set out in block form. Predicted yields and productivity ratings are given only for the most common level of management. The section on soil morphology and genesis is interesting. The report suffers from a lack of emphasis on improved soil management practices and livestock management.

Soil Survey of McLennan County, Texas. Templin, E. H., and party. U. S. Dept. Agr. Soil Survey Ser. 1942. [In press.]

McLennan County, Texas, is in the Blackland and Grand Prairies. The soils belong in the Rendzina, Reddish Prairie, and Red-Yellow Podzolic great soil groups. The map is being published on a scale of 1:48,000. Its legend is in two parts: (1) An alphabetical list of individual mapping units and (2) 14 color groups based on physical characteristics of the soils.

The discussion of the soils is very good. Soil series descriptions are integrated with the descriptions of mapping units, which have block descriptions of profiles. Soil management is discussed by soil groups, with a special section on runoff and erosion control, and a summary table. A table gives predicted yields under two levels of management. A good section on soil morphology and genesis includes a key to the mapping units.

The general descriptions of agriculture suffer from a lack of information on livestock and livestock products, farm expenses, and farm investments.

Soil Survey of the Salt Lake Area, Utah. Jennings, D. S., Youngs, F. O., and party. U. S. Dept. Agr. Soil Survey Ser. 1936, No. 22, 83 pp., illus. 1946.

The Salt Lake Area, Utah, lies at the western foot of the Wasatch Range and occupies a part of prehistoric Lake Bonneville. Probably the area belongs in the region of Brown soils. Solonchak and Solonetz soils occur extensively. A diversified irrigation agriculture is practiced.

The map is published on a scale of 1: 63,360. On its 81 soil-mapping units are shown in 5 major color groupings, based on physiographic position and drainage, and in 24 subgroups according to such additional physical factors as texture, color, permeability, and parent materials. A supplemental map, based on an intensive examination of the soils in the field and numerous readings with the Wheatstone electrolytic bridge, is used to show the distribution of the soils according to their relative content of soluble salts.

The report carries a table of predicted crop yields and a grouping of the soils according to their suitability for crop production, as based on productivity, ease of management, and water-holding capacity. A key to the soils appears in an appendix. Some of the soil series are defined somewhat more broadly than in more recent surveys; and some variants appear as phases.

Soil Survey [Detailed-Reconnaissance] of Kittitas County, Washington. Smith, L. H., Dwyer, C. H., and Schafer, George. U. S. Dept. Agr. Soil Survey Ser. 1937, No. 13, 69 pp., illus. 1945.

Kittitas County lies between the crest of the Cascades and the Columbia River to the east. Since it covers a very wide range of climatic and physiographic conditions, there are many kinds of plants and soils and types of farming.

The reconnaissance map is published on a scale of 1:125,000, and the detailed soil map at 1:63,360 as a separate sheet.

The survey was selected partly as an example of a detailed-reconnaissance survey and partly as an example of an exceedingly complex area, since it includes Podzol, Brown Podzolic, Brown, Gray Desert, Bog, and Solonchak soils. Photographs illustrate some of these conditions.

Soil Survey of Hawaii. Cline, M. G., and party. U. S. Dept. Agr. Soil Survey Ser. 1939 [In press.]

The soils are predominantly Latosols from old and recent volcanic rocks. Since rainfall, slope, elevation, and soil age vary widely, some 405 mapping units are recognized. These are placed in 45 color patterns on the map.

In the report the soils are grouped into families and great soil groups. This is the first large survey in which the family grouping has been used.

The report contains a wealth of interesting material besides descriptions of the soils. Many laboratory data are included. There are discussions of soil morphology and genesis and of the relation of the soils to climate, vegetation, and other factors of the environment.

Part of the soils are used for sugarcane and pineapples under very intensive management, including heavy fertilization, machine methods, and irrigation in places. Special chapters deal with soil management and productivity for these crops as well as for fruits, vegetables, forestry, and pasture.

Soil Survey of Puerto Rico. Roberts, R. C., and party. U. S. Dept. Agr. Soil Survey. Ser. 1936, No. 8, 503 pp., illus. 1942. [Summary in Spanish.]

Puerto Rico has a complex pattern of soils including Latosols, Red-Yellow Podzolic, Chernozem, Red Desert, Solonchak, and many others. In fact, it is an outdoor soil museum. A wide variety of crops are grown on farms varying from tiny subsistence gardens to great sugar plantations.

The soil map is published at 1:50,000. On it some 358 mapping units are placed in 46 color groups according to physical characteristics, relief, physiographic position, parent material, and climate.

The report includes excellent descriptions of the principal crops and their culture, good soil descriptions, a table of soil productivity ratings, and an interesting discussion of soil morphology and genesis.

If the survey were being made today, the mapping would be done in more detail and some mapping units would be subdivided.

APPENDIX I. MAP PREPARATION WITH THE PLANE TABLE

The use of aerial photographs in soil mapping began about 1926. Their use steadily increased until they nearly replaced other media as a base for mapping soils in the field between 1935 and 1940. Yet some soil mapping may still need to be done where aerial photographs or suitable planimetric maps are not available. In the earlier edition of this *Manual* the use of the plane table is explained in detail. Enough of that discussion is repeated here to guide the field scientist in its use where it offers the best way to proceed with the necessary soil mapping that cannot await aerial photographs.

Making of the plane-table traverse consists of plotting on paper the direction and distance of certain features of the landscape in such a way that all the objects shown occur on the map in the same relative positions that they occupy on the land. Although the system used is simple and the operation easily performed, neatness and care are required for the production of an accurate base map.

Plane table and accessories.—In soil mapping a rather simple plane table or traverse board is used (fig. 56). A tripod supports a drawing board, usually 15 by 15 inches, which is oriented by means of a compass placed in a notch at one side.[1] To the bottom of the board is screwed a brass plate by which the board is fastened to the tripod with a spring and thumbscrew. Except when in actual use, the board, together with the map on it, is kept in a leather case. The board is placed in the case with the compass at the top, and always in the same way so that the leather will not be discolored by the metallic plate, except on one side.

A high quality of special drawing paper mounted on cloth is used for the map. Such paper is cut into squares slightly smaller than the plane-table board and held in place by the four thumbscrews in the four corners. Best results are obtained by using flat paper. It should fit on the board tightly. Because the paper must be kept tight at all times, the thumbscrews should not be turned in the full distance when mounting paper during dry weather. The paper will be inclined to buckle during moist periods and then it can be tightened by turning the thumbscrews all the way down. The plane-table sheet is protected by a dull-brown cover paper, in order to confine exposure only to the parts that are actually being worked upon.

When set up for use, the plane table is made approximately level by adjusting the position of the tripod (fig. 57). The board is then oriented by the compass. Steel culverts, railroad tracks, power lines, or other sources of magnetic attraction must be avoided. Even pocket knives and similar objects must not be brought near the needle. Only brass tacks and fittings can be used in the board itself. The compass needle should be released only when in actual use in orienting the board.

For sighting, drawing lines, and measuring, a simple alidade made from flat boxwood is used. It has two beveled white celluloid edges and is fitted with folding sights and usually graduated into fiftieths of an inch (fig. 58). Of course, alidades may be made for whatever scale is most convenient.

Measurements on the ground may be made with a chain, by pacing, or with a special speedometer, called an odometer, fitted to an ordinary automobile. Such an odometer must operate directly from the front wheel and not from the drive shaft as does the speedometer on ordinary automobiles.[2]

---

[1] In areas with magnetic attraction the plane table cannot be oriented in the usual way by the magnetic compass, and the Baldwin Solar chart may be used. (See Beaman, W. M., as cited in General Bibliography.)

[2] For detailed shop suggestions for installing gears over a front-wheel brake drum, see the earlier edition of this Manual. (KELLOGG, CHARLES E. SOIL SURVEY MANUAL. U. S. Dept. of Agr. Misc. Pub. 274, 136 pp., illus. 1937.)

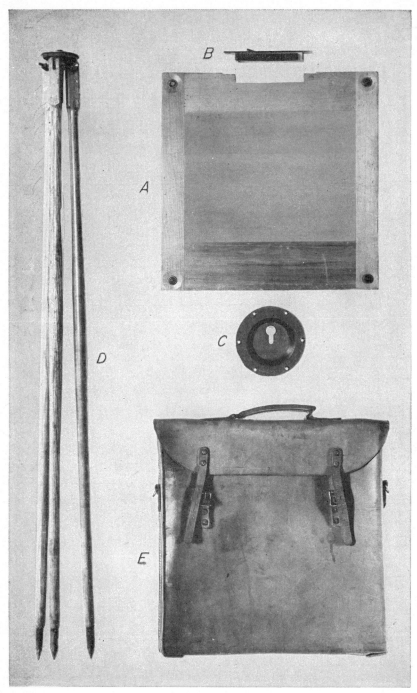

FIGURE 56.—Plane table, unassembled: *A*, Board; *B*, compass; *C*, head; *D*, tripod; and *E*, case.

Figure 57.—Plane table assembled for use.

The odometer can be adjusted roughly by the proper choice of gears. Final adjustment is made by varying the tire pressure. Along some road convenient to the survey headquarters an exact mile is laid off with a surveyor's steel tape. The tire pressure is then adjusted until the odometer gives an exact reading. It will need to be checked from time to time, since the required pressure changes with the age of the tire and with the load in the car. It also changes with temperature during the day. For example, if one is working on earth roads during the cool of the morning and later in the day drives onto a hot pavement, the tire pressure will need to be adjusted.

Where these odometers are used regularly a full set of parts should be kept on hand, for the cables and fiber gears are subject to considerable wear. By simply tilting the fiber gear, the odometer may be disengaged so that the equipment does not operate except when needed for measurements.

Measurements by use of such an odometer, even under the best conditions, are not so precise as the more time-consuming methods. Yet with care, this instrument is entirely satisfactory for surveying in all ordinary terrains that are not too hilly or where the roads are not extremely winding or crooked, especially if control points can be located accurately on the field sheets. Measurements with the odometer cannot be depended upon when roads are very slippery.

Traversing.—With the plane table set up, leveled, and oriented with the compass, a sharp-pointed needle is pressed into the paper in the exact position[3] which the plane table occupies in the area to be shown on the field sheet. To draw a line on the map between the plane table and some distant point, the margin of the alidade is placed against the needle and

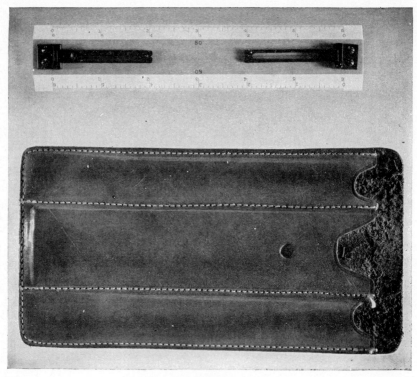

FIGURE 58.—Alidade with case.

rotated until its two sights are directly in line with the distant point.
With the alidade held firmly in place, a fine line is drawn on the paper.
The distance between the plane table and the distant point along the road
is measured with the odometer or by some other means. In the same way,
additional lines or "shots" may be drawn toward other prominent features
of the landscape.

When the work at the initial station is completed, the compass needle
is lifted from its pivot, and the surveyor proceeds in the direction of his
shot. The surveyor continues along the road until it bends, until he has
reached the distance on the ground somewhat less than one-half the length
of the compass needle on the map,[3] or until he reaches a road intersection
or some other place where a station must be made.

The surveyor may or may not need to set up the plane table at the
end of his sight. If the distance from the first station is relatively short
and if he does not need to make side "shots," he may merely record his
distance measurement and regard the point as a "turning point." Such a
turning point is the end of his last forward sight and will be the end of the
backward sight at his next station.

Let us assume that he used the end of his first sight as a turning point.
He proceeds to another bend in the road or prominent intersection as before,
noting his measurements. The plane table is set up and oriented by the
compass at the new station. The distance from the first station to the end
of the first sight—turning point—is laid out with the scale on the margin

[3] Approximate position when starting a new sheet.
[4] With such an instrument, orientation is not sufficiently accurate to proceed far on a single sight.

of the alidade and the needle pressed into the paper at that point. By placing the alidade against the needle and sighting back upon this last point, a line can be drawn to the present station. The distance from the turning point to the present station is laid out with the scale and the needle pressed into the paper at the new position of the plane table, after which a new forward sight is taken on the road and any other necessary sights are made along intersecting roads or to other features. With a mapping scale of 2 inches equals 1 mile (1:31,680) measurements can be plotted within about 15 feet.

In this system the plane table is set up at every other station, or at every other bend in the road if intermediate stations are unnecessary. This is called the system of "turning points." If errors from magnetic interference are suspected, the plane table should be set up at the intermediate point and the previous forward shot checked by a back sight. If magnetic attraction cannot be avoided, traverses can be made for a short distance by orienting the plane table by back sights rather than with the compass. This requires setting up the plane table at every station. The alidade is placed firmly on the paper parallel to the last forward shot and the board turned until the previous station is sighted. The map is then oriented, and, after determining the present position of the plane table on the map by plotting the distance, a new forward sight can be taken. The equipment described here is not sufficiently precise for use without a compass, except for short distances. When the plane table is oriented by the compass, the error is compensating; but when oriented by back sights it is accumulative.

When the plane table is set up for making sights along the primary line of traverse, houses and other features near the road may be plotted from the measured distances and by sighting with the alidade. Frequent stops to examine soils and to make side traverses should be avoided while a primary traverse is in progress. Houses and other features distant from the road may be located with reasonable accuracy by the intersection of sights made from two or three stations. The distance between these stations must be sufficiently great that the inside angle is about 90°. This technique is called "graphic triangulation." It is much simpler than the triangulation carried on with more precise instruments. Trees along a stream in open country may be located temporarily in this way and serve as guides to sketching the stream channel. Other features may be located as aids in sketching soil boundaries. It is also helpful to locate trees and other distant landmarks by intersection as aids for checking subsequent foot traverses through areas distant from the primary traverse.

All traverse work on a single sheet should be based on one starting point, preferably near the center. Ordinarily, more accurate traverses are made by starting each sheet from a separate point near the center than by traversing to the edge of one sheet and continuing from the margin of that toward the interior of another. Some distinct feature near the edge of the sheet, such as a cross road or a tree, should be selected as an end point for the traverse. This point may be located on the traverse from the center of the next sheet. It is helpful to have common roads located on each sheet by individual traverses in order to help in their final joining and adjustment.

With the completion of the primary traverse, secondary traverses are made between the primary ones for completing the base map and for plotting soils. Except in heavily wooded or brushy country, the plane table can be used conveniently. The technique is similar to that used for the primary traverse except that much of the measuring must be done by pacing. Foot traverses should be tied t⌒ control points or other points located by the primary traverse at frequent intervals. Locations on foot traverses can be checked by sights on two or more previously located points. The plane table is set up, oriented with the compass, and sights taken at the two other locations. The new station is located at the intersection of the lines drawn from these sights. In very rough country it is commonly necessary to place special flags in conspicuous places for use as control stations. In sectionized areas it is possible to identify section corners, which may be located on the map by construction from the grid of the primary traverse, supplemented by data from accurate plats, and use these points for checking secondary traverses or as control stations when locating new stations by graphic triangulation.

If it is necessary to occupy a point where the plane table cannot be oriented by the compass because of magnetic attraction, and to which measurement cannot be made, the location can be determined as follows: A forward sight is taken from a known point toward the new position. The plane table is then set up at the new station and oriented by sighting back at the previous station. A second sight is taken at some other known station, and the intersection of the two lines gives the location of the new station.

Traverse notes should be preserved until the map is finished. Measurements of distances between traverse points, turning points, streams, cross roads, houses, and soil boundaries, should be recorded in a notebook. A convenient method of recording readings is to begin at the bottom of the notebook page and proceed upwards as the work progresses. By the side of the odometer reading, the exact distance can be set down. Frequent checks of the total distance along the traverse, as shown by the odometer, with the sum of the plotted distances, serve to call attention to any possible error in plotting before a large amount of work needs to be corrected.

A line showing magnetic north is recorded on each plane-table sheet. If the magnetic declination is great, the compass may be set at an appropriate angle to the board, by means of a brass plate, so that the mapping is oriented approximately with the cardinal directions.

Control and accuracy.—When completed, the field sheets are joined and adjusted to control points by cartographers so that the completed map is geographically correct. Thus it is important that the plane-table traverse be tied to all known accurate control stations. These should be prominently marked on the field sheets. It is also helpful to locate section lines, railway stations, mileposts, and similar features that help in adjusting the traverses. The direction of the principal traverses should be shown with small arrows in red ink. The closure error—overlaps or gaps of plotted lines at the point of closure—are indicated by looped lines in red ink.

The date of survey is shown on each map, and the accuracy of the cultural features is considered as of that date.

Errors may arise in several ways. They may be caused by incorrect measurements or inaccurate plotting of the distances, by incorrect measurement of angles, or by mistakes in field computations. An error in sketching may result from the misinterpretation of the shape of a distant or otherwise veiled feature seen in perspective. Sometimes one error is followed by another error in the opposite direction. Such errors are called "compensating," since one tends to offset the other. If compensating errors are nearly equal, results under some conditions may give the false appearance of accuracy, since the traverse will close, and yet the traverse may be in error in two or more places. Small compensating errors may be disregarded, but large errors must be found and corrected.

In order to guard against errors, traverse lines should be run in circuits closing on themselves, or run from one located point to another located point, insofar as possible. Even if no mistakes are made, a traverse rarely closes exactly, because of the normal error due to the instruments. These "closure errors" should not be adjusted in the field but should be left for adjustment by cartographers. If the closure error is greater than the allowable error for the survey, however, and the error is not revealed by replotting the field data, the traverse should be run again.

Mounting partial maps on the plane table.—Topographic maps, planimetric maps, or aerial photographs may be placed on the board and held with brass thumbtacks. The plane-table is oriented by the compass in some known position shown on the map from which a distant known point, also shown on the map, is clearly visible. A faint line is drawn between the two points and the alidade kept carefully parallel with this line. The map to be mounted is placed in approximate position and lightly fastened by one tack and then rotated until the alidade is sighted directly on the distant object. The map or photograph can then be fastened firmly by additional thumbtacks.

APPENDIX II. MAP PREPARATION WITH COMPASS TRAVERSE

In heavily wooded country the compass may be preferable to the plane table, especially for secondary traverses. Since it is less convenient and less accurate than the plane table, it should not be substituted for it unless there is already an adequate planimetric base or grid of land lines that can be followed. Traverse with an ordinary compass requires more time than one with the plane table, since each reading must be plotted on the map with a protractor.

Under ordinary circumstances in wooded country it is best to follow a straight line with the compass and avoid the need for plotting frequent changes in direction. In sectionized country it is best to follow the land lines, since the mapper has an opportunity to locate section corners for control. If the going gets especially difficult, time may be saved by plotting the traverse on a path or foot trail, but ordinarily these trails are so crooked that their ease of travel does not compensate for the time required in plotting their meanderings. As with the plane table, a record of the compass readings and of the distances measured by paces or chain should be preserved for any necessary recalculations to locate errors. Compass readings are noted as so many degrees east or west of true north or of true south, whichever is more convenient.

The most convenient compass for traversing under these conditions is the forester's or geologist's compass shown in figure 59,A. For short secondary traverses this compass is held in the hand, but for more accurate work a Jacob's staff is used as a support. This is a staff about 4 or 5 feet long, fitted with a steel point at the lower end for thrusting into the soil and with an adjustable universal joint at the upper end for fastening onto the compass.

The forester's compass should be adjusted for the magnetic declinations, so that readings can be taken directly in respect to true north, thus avoiding the need for making individual corrections with each reading. Compasses brought into a new area are frequently out of adjustment. The sliding weight on the needle must be moved if the needle is so out of balance that one end touches the glass cover of the box when leveled.

In areas with magnetic attraction a sundial compass must be used. One is shown in figure 59,B that is similar to the forester's compass, except that a string extends from the top of the rear sight to the opposite side of the box and a sundial is marked on the margin. This compass cannot be used in the hand but must be well supported by a Jacob's staff. The compass is fitted with a needle similar to that of the ordinary forester's compass, so that it can be used like any ordinary compass in nonmagnetic areas.

Each sundial compass must be individually standardized for the particular area where it is to be used and from time to time within that area. First, a true north-and-south line is established. If the attraction is only local, this can be done with a magnetic compass in a nonmagnetic part of the survey area. Generally a line of known direction can be found even in a magnetic country. After the compass has been oriented in a true north-and-south line, beginning early in the morning and continuing throughout the day, readings are taken on the sundial at intervals of 5 minutes as determined with an unusually accurate watch. A watch varying more than a few seconds within 24 hours is unsatisfactory. After the readings have been obtained, they are plotted on regular coordinate paper, using the time by the watch as one axis and that of the sundial as the other. A curve showing the relationship between the two is then drawn by connecting the points. Curves are individual for each compass and have small but irregular and significant variations from a true straight line of 45°. This curve is carried by the mapper in the field.

To establish direction in the field with a sundial compass, the instrument

FIGURE 59.—A, Forester's or geologist's compass; B, sundial compass.

is first set up firmly with a Jacob's staff and leveled. A point on the curve about 1 minute in advance of the time by the watch is chosen, and the equivalent time on the sundial noted from the curve. The compass is moved so that the instant the chosen time on the watch is reached, the equivalent time is indicated on the sundial. The compass is now oriented in a true north-and-south line. By releasing the needle and noting the variation, the direction of lines in respect to true north can be obtained. Orientation by this method is more dependable in the middle of the day than in early morning or late afternoon when the shadows move more rapidly.

No compass less precise than the ordinary geologist's or forester's compass should be used for traverse work. The common pocket, or box, compass, although convenient for picking one's way, is not suitable in survey work. With a good instrument and experience in the woods, a mapper can run satisfactory lines for considerable distances; yet, where measurements are made by pacing, frequent checks on section corners or other control points established by a primary traverse are essential.

Pacing.—Many short distances plotted on soil maps are measured by pacing. Each surveyor's pace, like the Roman pace, consists of two full steps, and the paces are counted by counting alternate steps. Where much pacing is necessary, a surveyor should use a tally register and not attempt to carry the count in his mind. Each individual needs to determine the length of his natural stride. Then he will need to train himself to keep this natural stride, regardless of the slope, ground cover or fatigue. His paces must be exactly the same on the open highway as they are in the brush or in the field. An individual can standardize his pacing against a known distance and prepare a table showing the number of paces for each division on the mapping scale. Many men have about 1,000 paces for a mile.

Although an experienced man becomes very skilled at pacing, he may make errors because of fatigue or minor illnesses of which he is unaware. Either plane table or compass traverses, where measurements are made by pacing, need to have frequent control even with good terrain. Experience has shown that about 3 miles between control points is the extreme outside limit for pacing by the most experienced men.

Saddle horses need to be used in extremely rough and broken country where walking is too difficult and too slow. Occasionally saddle horses may be found that pace with some uniformity; but ordinarily locations must be established by graphic triangulation, intersection from section corners, or by following some base map, land grid, or air photo.

APPENDIX III. NOTES ON MAP COMPILATION AND REPRODUCTION

Soil maps can be constructed or compiled by several different methods. Techniques and methods depend mainly on the material used as a base for the soil survey. With some techniques, highly accurate maps are made at low cost. Other techniques, made necessary because of the type of base material used, lead to far less accurate maps, increased cost, or both.

Each job should be planned prior to commencing the field work. Before starting the map compilation careful study and analysis should be made of the field material, existing control, other map data, and lithographic requirements in order to select the most economical methods for producing a satisfactory map.

Such work is handled by cartographers familiar with mapping and surveying and able to judge the control needed for various methods of base construction and the degree of accuracy that may be expected. Understanding of the various types of aerial photographs and skill in photogrammetric methods are especially needed by those compiling modern soil maps. Besides methods in cartographic assembly, lithographic processing must be understood in order to prepare the kind of copy necessary for economical and accurate reproduction.

One of three major methods of preparation are usually used with soil maps, although some techniques are common to two or more methods: (1) The construction of base maps and soil surveys from aerial photographs; (2) the assembly of base maps from existing published maps on which the soil data are plotted; and (3) the assembly of bases and soil surveys from original plane-table surveys. Although some are more adaptable than others, any one of these methods generally can be adapted to permit reasonable standardization of techniques and procedures. Combinations of two or more of the methods increase the difficulties of map construction.

METHODS OF MAP CONSTRUCTION FROM AERIAL PHOTOGRAPHS

Methods of map construction from aerial photographs are varied. So are the instruments used and the kinds of maps produced. The largest producer of topographic maps in the United States, the United States Geological Survey, has found through many years of research that such stereoscopic plotting instruments as the Multiplex, Aerocartograph, Twinplex Plotter, and Kelsh Plotter are necessary in their photogrammetric work if their published maps are to meet the modern requirements of standard map accuracy. Several other mapping agencies use either these or similar types of stereoscopic plotting instruments. The United States Army Engineers maintain an experimental station where all types of plotting instruments are tested and evaluated.

Planimetric maps of a uniformly high degree of accuracy may be made from aerial photographs without the use of the stereoscopic plotting instruments. In areas with considerable relief however, the work can be performed more accurately and economically with a plotting instrument.

For the proper orientation and location of planimetric detail from aerial photographs the Cartographic Section of the Division of Soil Survey uses the "slotted-templet" method.[1] This method is adapted to the needs of the Soil Survey because it provides reasonable accuracy of radial triangulation, or establishment of secondary control points, with a minimum of labor and material. It enables the cartographer to utilize widely spaced ground-control points. This is especially important since few soil survey parties can be equipped and staffed to establish control.

---

[1] For details of the method, see KELSH, H. T. THE SLOTTED-TEMPLET METHOD FOR CONTROLLING MAPS MADE FROM AERIAL PHOTOGRAPHS. U. S. Dept. Agr. Misc. Pub. 404, 30 pp., illus. 1940.

465

Briefly, the slotted-templet method is based on the principle that lines radiating from the center of each aerial photograph, and drawn through common points identified in the overlap of the photographs, will intersect and give the proper location of each point when correctly assembled. First the ground-control points are pricked on the photograph. Besides these, nine points are normally identified and pricked on each photograph. A point very near the geometric center of the photograph is selected and is transferred stereoscopically to the overlap portion of the photographs above and below it in line of flight. Then three points are pricked parallel with the center points, one in each corner and one in the middle, on both sides of the photograph and in the common sidelap with photographs in the adjoining flights.

After these radial points have been identified and pricked on all photographs to be used in the assembly (the ground-control points having been previously pricked) the photographs are placed over bristolboard that has been cut to the size of the photographs, and all points are pricked through the photographs and into the bristolboard, which becomes the templet. The templets are then facsimiles of the photographs in the sense that all radial and ground-control points maintain their same geometric relations to one another. The center point of the templet is punched out, leaving a small hole. The templet is then placed on the slot cutter, and elongated slots of the same width as the diameter of the center hole are cut, radially, from the center through all other points pricked through from the photograph to the templet. These slots are centered on the radial points. The center of each overlapping photograph is replaced with a slot, and the other six points, three on each side, are replaced with slots. Occasionally, where considerable differences of relief exist in an area, additional points are pricked and slotted to afford the compiler less adjustment when the photographic detail is being transferred to the map base. Basic map assemblies may be made at scales other than that of the photographs by simply reducing or lengthening the distance of the center of the slots from the central point of the templet in ratio to the known scale of the photographs and the desired map scale.

The templets are then ready for assembling on a projection, usually polyconic, which is constructed at the desired scale of the map base and at the same scale as the templets (fig. 60). The projection used for the templet assembly is constructed on rigidly mounted masonite sheets, on the surface of which has been painted two or more coats of enamel. This surface is buffed, and the projection constructed and inked on with fine lines. All ground-control points that have been identified and pricked on the photographs and slotted on the templets have then been plotted carefully on the projection by their geographic positions. A round flat-base metal stud, with a shaft pierced for insertion of a needle, is fastened securely and precisely over each plotted ground-control point. The templets are then assembled by flights, with the slots of the ground-control stations fitting with very close tolerance over the control-station studs. Additional studs are placed in all radial-point slots and center holes. These latter studs are placed beneath the bottom templet so that their base is against the projection and they are free to move longitudinally along the slot. In this manner the center of each stud finds its true position mechanically when the slots of all overlapping templets are placed over the stud and force it into position. The hole in each stud now represents the original photographic centers and radial points identified and pricked on the photographs; but now the points are located in their true positions on the projections as they were on the surface of the ground.

When the templet assembly has been completed a needle is inserted through the hole in each radial-point stud and a small point pricked on the projection base. The templets are removed, the pricked points recovered, and a small inked circle inscribed around each. This completes the work of the slot-templet assembly.

The projection, ground-control points, and radial points are then transferred to sheets of vinylite transparent plastic used as a compilation base for the map. The photographs are placed in overhead projectors, adjusted

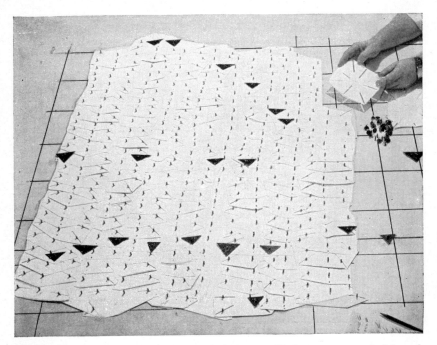

FIGURE 60.—View showing templets being assembled on an enameled board, with projection lines inked.

by enlargement or reduction to fit the scale of the compilation bases, and all basic map features are traced on the vinylite in pencil. The radial triangulation points here play their important part by enabling the compiler to adjust the reflected image of the photograph and compilation base to the same relative scale between the radial points, which are visible on each. Additional adjustments are necessary within the areas bounded by three or four radial points, and these are accomplished visually by the compiler with the slight scale differences of the points as arguments. After all needed features have been delineated on the bases from the photographs they are inked by the compiler. This serves as a manuscript map for the additional phases of map preparation.

No expensive stereoscopic plotting instruments are required in the slotted-templet assembly work. Actually the only major instruments needed are stereoscopes, accurate scales, center-point and slot cutters, projectors, and light tables. The photographs and bristolboard are the only items expended. The other instruments are small and usually found in every well-equipped mapping office. Even the photographs used are of the least expensive type—unrectified contact prints.

Dependable soil maps are constructed with extreme care, patience, and accuracy. The photogrammetric construction requires people well trained in surveying, photogrammetry, and photo interpretation and with some appreciation of soil patterns and their relation to the other physical features.

METHODS OF MAP ASSEMBLY FROM EXISTING MAPS

Soil maps can also be compiled on published base maps of high quality, if ones of recent issue are available. Techniques vary with the kind of map, the form of the field sheets, and other factors.

One such method employs the negatives from the color separation plates of the original map. From the negatives, black-line impressions of the culture and drainage are reproduced on a dimensionally stable plastic. A nonphotographic composite of the base map is also reproduced for transfer, adjustment, and correlation of the soil data. After the soil data have been adjusted to the nonphotographic composite they are transferred, through photographic processes, to the black-line impression of the culture plate. This method of compilation produces copy suitable for reproduction by lithography without the need for reinking the culture and drainage of the original map. It does, however, require the normal finishing techniques for the soil data, the necessary changes in cultural and drainage features, and the addition or shifting of place names and marginal data.

In other methods of compilation the existing published maps are used simply as manuscripts. A set of the base maps bearing the soil data are assembled and adjusted to fit a master grid for the sheet sizes desired. The assembled maps are copied and reproduced in nonphotographic images on dimensionally stable materials. The nonphotographic images are then used as a manuscript for finishing the various color separations for the lithographic copy.

The assembly of soil maps from plane-table sheets employs techniques similar to those used in compiling the map from published quadrangles. The adjustment of the plane-table sheets is usually more complicated and frequently requires the optical projection of the data in order to assemble the manuscript. Once the manuscript map is completed the finishing of the color separations follows the same techniques as used in other methods.

MAP FINISHING

Map finishing requires the preparation of color separations suitable for direct copy for lithography. This operation involves the finishing of the line work to prescribed standards, the blocking of soil areas for the tint screens, the layouts for placement of lettering, and the arrangement of place names, marginal notes, borders, and legends.

To reproduce the soil map in color it is necessary to prepare a separate plate for each group of various features to be reproduced in one color or tint. One plate is used for all features to be printed in black, another for those in blue, and another for each of the separate tints of the three primary colors, blue, red, and yellow, used for the soil areas. Screen rulings used with the latter three colors make possible a total of 63 tints on the published map. With two color plates and screen rulings, 15 color tints can be had. While a much greater number of tints can be obtained by additional plates, the cost is greatly increased, because of the extra press runs and the cost of the additional separation negatives. Since the use of many colors on the map is costly, their number should be held to a minimum.

To obtain these color plates the manuscript map is reproduced in a nonphotographic image on metal-mounted map paper or glass. A separate plate is made for each proposed color or tint. The symbols and areas to be reproduced in a given color are then inked on one specific plate.

It is standard practice in map finishing to ink on paper mounted on aluminum sheets, so that a minimum amount of dimensional change takes place. The manuscript map is reproduced in nonphotographic blue on a set of these plates. The culture, soil symbols and boundaries, and lettering are finished in black, using the nonphotographic image of the manuscript as a guide. The drainage is inked in black on another set of plates. Since these inked plates are for direct reproduction, the ink work must meet rigid specifications for symboling, spacing, and density of line work. The color plates are made by making the areas to be tinted opaque on an acetate overlay placed over the soil plate or on an additional set of the blue-line plates.

In another common method of finishing maps, the manuscript map is reproduced on glass plates, which have been coated with an opaque solution and sensitized. Drafting is done on this glass, which serves either as a negative for a press plate or for reproducing a black-line plastic print, which may be used as copy by the lithographer. The plastic print is necessary if the final map scale is to be different from the compilation scale. Color tints are prepared from blue-line plastic prints.

The glass-drafting technique may be used when the soil mapping is done on aerial mosaics and the map is to be reproduced with a photographic background. The mosaics bearing the soil data are reproduced with a half-tone screen and printed on a coated glass plate. The survey data are then drafted on a separate glass plate, which serves as a negative, drafting one for each color. The press plates are made from the half-tone negative and from the separate glass negatives for culture, drainage, and soils. The engraving needs to be done to highly precise standards, with special drafting tools for cutting roads, drainage, houses, soil boundaries, and other features.

All lettering used on soil maps is prepared by letter-press printing with standard types and sizes. The type is set and printed on thin transparent acetate sheets. Small sheets with the appropriate lettering are coated with a wax adhesive and applied to the finished map.

MAP EDITING AND PROOFING

Normally a thorough edit is given the manuscript map. Control, projections, culture, drainage, soil boundaries, soil symbols, and other items affecting the accuracy of the map are carefully reviewed and inspected. As the manuscript map is not in finished form, the final appearance of the map and its quality for reproduction cannot be checked at this stage. By thoroughly checking all items affecting the accuracy of the map, however, most corrections can be made before the map is prepared in finished form.

After the color separations have been inked or drafted on glass the plates are reviewed for appearance and quality of line work. Symbols used, spacing and weight of lines, density of ink work, placement and spelling of lettering, arrangement of legend, marginal notes, and other items affecting the final appearance of the map are checked.

Upon completion of this edit it is necessary to proof the various color separations for register. A composite copy of the different color separations is reproduced in color. Various photographic and direct printing processes are used to make the color copy. The colored print is then reviewed to insure that all tints for the soils appear in the proper areas, are of the proper screen patterns, and that the combinations of the various tints produce the required patterns. Registration of the separate features is checked and careful inspection given to the legibility of the map as a whole.

MAP REPRODUCTION AND LITHOGRAPHY

Adequate facilities for map reproduction are essential throughout the preparation of a soil map. First, field workers are supplied with contact prints or enlargements of aerial photographs, copies of various forms of base maps, or controlled mosaics. As the preparation of the map is undertaken, field sheets are copied and reproduced; manuscript maps are reproduced on metal-mounted papers and glass; prints of the various color separation plates are reproduced for lettering layouts and editing work; black-and-white composites are made for area determination and editing; and color proofs are used for final checking. Special maps, line drawings, and the like are used in the soil survey report. Workers with a wide range of skills are required.

All final soil map reproduction of the Division of Soil Survey is done by commercial lithographers under contract. The Cartographic Section prepares the specifications for the lithography, estimates costs, and inspects and checks the work prior to acceptance.

Lithographers prepare lithographic plates from the finished color separations supplied. These are done either by photographic copy or direct printing, depending on the material supplied and whether scale changes are necessary. The lithographic plates are attached to the press-plate holder, the rollers inked, and the map sheets fed through the press to obtain an impression of one color. The plate for the next color is then put on the press, rollers inked, and the second color run on the same map sheets. This process is continued until all colors have been run and the final composite-colored map is produced.

During the process the lithographer supplies lithographic proofs. The first proof shows the culture, drainage, and soil boundaries, and the second one shows the color tints. The last combined proof is usually sent to the chief of the party and to others who may have cooperated in the survey. Since the field sheets are retained in the Cartographic Section, this proof is checked only for titles, credit lines, and similar items. Where practicable, the party chief is given an opportunity to inspect the map after the edit of the color separations and before it goes to the lithographer. Necessary corrections can be made at this stage at minimum cost. Corrections made after receipt of the final lithographic proof are very expensive and should be avoided unless absolutely necessary. Proof copies requiring no changes need only to be acknowledged by letter as correct.

APPENDIX IV.   SAMPLE DESCRIPTIONS OF SOIL SERIES

As general guides, a few descriptions of soil series follow. Since these are intended as official standards, they are abstracted from a great many individual soil descriptions. An actual soil profile must, of course, represent some one type in the series. As research continues, these need to be revised from time to time.

Barnes series

The Barnes soils are Chernozems developed on highly calcareous glacial till of Late Wisconsin age. Moderately low precipitation (16–22 inches), an abundance of tall-grass vegetation, and good drainage combine to furnish ideal conditions for the development of maximum blackness in these soils. The Barnes differ from the Clarion soils of the Prairie soil region in having slightly less thick but darker surface horizons and stronger prismatic structure in their B horizons. They may be distinguished from Williams soils of the Chestnut soil region by their darker surface layers and the less well marked prismatic structure of their B horizons. They have deeper profiles and better development than the Buse soils developing on the same materials but on steep slopes and hilltops. Barnes soils have thinner surface soils and subsoils of stronger color than the associated Aastad soils. The Barnes catena includes the Barnes, Aastad, Flom, and Parnell soils.

Soil profile (Barnes loam—virgin) :

A_{11} 0 to 1½ inches, very dark grayish-brown (10YR 3/1, dry) to black (10YR 2/1, moist) very friable loam of imperfect granular or fine crumb structure, filled with grass roots that form a sod; neutral in reaction. 1 to 2 inches thick.

A_{12} 1½ to 10½ inches, dark-brown (10YR 3/2, dry) to black (10YR 2/1, moist) friable loam of weak or moderate prismatic structure; neutral to slightly acid. 8 to 11 inches thick.

B   10½ to 14 inches, transition horizon that changes color downward from dark-brown (black when wet) to brown (10YR 4/2, when dry) or dark-brown (10YR 3/2, when moist) firm clay loam. Weak prismatic structure; neutral in reaction. 3 to 5 inches thick.

C_{ca} 14 to 24 inches, horizon of lime carbonate accumulation. Light grayish-brown (2.5Y 6/2, dry) to yellowish-brown (2.5Y 5/4, moist) firm massive clay loam with white spots and streaks of calcium carbonate; mildly alkaline in reaction. 8 to 14 inches thick.

C   24 inches +, pale-yellow (2.5Y 7/4, dry) to yellowish-brown (2.5Y 5/4, moist) clay loam till. Occasional iron stains are present. Free lime carbonate is present, but in lesser amount than in the horizon above. Fragments of partly decomposed rock, mainly granites, gneisses, and limestone transported by glaciers, make up a considerable part of this material.

     Pebbles and stones are scattered over the surface and through the soil.

Range in characteristics.—These soils vary considerably in stoniness. The surface layer varies in thickness with relief. Locally, a thin layer of loess, up to 20 inches thick, caps the glacial till. The C horizon ranges from firm plastic clay loam to friable loam.

Relief.—Undulating to knobby.

Drainage.—These soils are well drained, both externally and internally.

Vegetation.—A good cover of tall grasses.

Use.—Spring wheat and other small grains are grown over most of the Barnes soil areas. Corn is grown in the southern part of their distribution.

471

Tame hay crops, including alfalfa, are widely grown. The soil is highly productive in years of good rainfall, but a deficiency of rainfall reduces yields in some years. Stony phases are used for pasture land.

Distribution.—Eastern parts of North Dakota and South Dakota, western Minnesota.

Type location: Grant County, South Dakota.

Series established: Lamoure County, North Dakota, 1914.

Canaseraga series

The Canaseraga soils are well-drained Brown Podzolic soils developed on recessional and lateral moraines in the Allegheny Plateau section of southwestern New York. Their parent materials are a mixture of glacial outwash, glacial-lake clay, and glacial till deposited by a fluctuating ice front; outwash, lacustrine, and till materials were mixed and deposited as morainic dumps during long stands of the ice in valleys. They commonly occur at divides in some through valleys and at the heads of north-flowing valleys. They occur well within the region of acid soils, but enough calcareous till is present to make the parent material weakly calcareous or neutral at depths of 8 or 10 feet. The Canaseraga soils are the well-drained associates of the moderately well drained Dalton soils. They commonly occur just south of and at slightly higher elevations than Caneadea soils, which are derived from unmixed lacustrine materials.

Soil profile (Canaseraga very fine sandy loam—virgin):

A_o Matted mor humus ,ayer; pH 4.0–4.5. 2 to 4 inches thick.

A_1 0 to 1 inch, dark grayish-brown (10YR 4/2) very fine sandy loam with weak fine crumb structure; very friable; white flecks of an incipient bleicherde may occur; pH 4.5–5.2. ½ to 2 inches thick.

B_{21} 1 to 8 inches, yellowish-brown (10YR 5/6) very fine sandy loam with weak fine crumb structure; very friable; some stone fragments; pH 5.0–5.4. 5 to 10 inches thick.

B_{22} 8 to 18 inches, yellowish-brown (10YR 5/4) very fine sandy loam with weak medium crumb structure; friable; some stone fragments; pH 5.0–5.4. 8 to 12 inches thick.

B_3 18 to 26 inches, light yellowish-brown (10YR 6/4) fine sandy loam or loam with weak coarse crumb structure; friable; some stone fragments; pH 5.2–5.6. 7 to 12 inches thick.

C_1 26 to 80 inches, pale-brown (10YR 6/3) to light brownish-gray (10YR 6/2) silt loam or loam with moderate numbers of gravel and stone fragments; weakly coarse platy; firm to very firm and moderately compact in place; large roots penetrate this horizon; pH increases from 5.5 at the top to about 6.5 at the bottom. 40 to 80 inches thick.

C_2 80 inches +, material similar to horizon C_1 but near neutrality; pH increases slightly with depth and weakly calcareous material may occur at depths greater than 12 feet. Commonly some stratification is apparent.

Range in characteristics.—Texture of the surface layer varies from fine sandy loam to silt loam. Textures below 3 feet range from fine sandy loam to silty clay. Where textures of the substratum are heavier than a silt loam, the underlying material is apparently unconformable with the solum. Textures of the substratum range widely within short distances. Where these soils lie adjacent to the Caneadea soil a Canaseraga solum, only 18 inches thick, may rest unconformably on the silty clay Caneadea soil material. A few such areas are included in the unit in mapping. In those places where the substratum is heavier textured than normal, the pH approaches neutrality at depths of 4 feet. The soils generally carry some gravel but commonly not sufficient to be classed as a gravelly type.

Relief.—Gently sloping to rolling or hilly morainic landscape with dominant slopes ranging from 3 to 25 percent in gradient.

Drainage.—Good. Runoff is medium to rapid; internal drainage is medium. Where the compaction of the substratum is sufficient to restrict internal drainage greatly, the soils fall into the moderately well drained Dalton series.

Vegetation.—The mixed hardwood and coniferous forest, consisting mainly of sugar maple, beech, red oak, white pine, and some hemlock and hickory species, includes mainly the medium- and low-calcium species.

Use.—A high proportion of the area is cleared and used for general farm crops, including hay, corn for silage, wheat, oats, buckwheat, and, in some places, potatoes. Pastures occupy a moderate proportion of the area. Yields are moderate.

Distribution.—Southwestern New York near divides in through valleys and near valley heads in north-flowing stream valleys.

Type location: Allegany County, New York.

Series established: Allegany County, New York, 1946.

Source of name: Village of Canaseraga, Allegany County, New York.

Remarks.—Colors apply to the moist soil.

Cecil series

The Cecil series includes red members of the Red-Yellow Podzolic soils derived from materials weathered from metamorphic and igneous rocks, chiefly in the southern and central parts of the Piedmont Plateau region. The soils have been formed from weathered gneisses, gneissoid schists, mica schists, and occasional granites. They are associated with or related to the Appling, Durham, Madison, Georgeville, Lloyd, Louisburg, Lockhart, and Cataula series. The Cecil soils have redder B horizons than the Appling soils, which in turn have redder B horizons than the Durham soils. Furthermore, the Appling series has been formed primarily from granites and gneisses and the Durham soils mainly from granites. Cecil soils have deeper sola and a much higher degree of horizon differentiation than do Louisburg soils, the associated Lithosol. They lack the large numbers of feldspar crystals that characterize the Lockhart soils. They are lighter colored and more friable in the B horizon than are the Cataula soils, in addition to having been formed from slightly less basic rocks. Cecil soils lack the brown A horizons and are lighter colored in the B horizons than the Lloyd soils, which have been formed from a mixture of acidic and basic rocks. In color they are like the Georgeville soils derived from slates, but the Cecil soils contain more and coarser sand and less silt in all horizons. They are less micaceous throughout the profile, especially in the upper C horizon, than are the Madison soils. The Cecil series is widely distributed and extensive. It is one of the most important soils for agriculture among those of the Piedmont Plateau.

Soil profile (Cecil sandy loam):

A$_{00}$	A thin layer of leaves and pine needles.
A$_1$	0 to 2 inches, brownish-gray very friable sandy loam with fine weak crumb structure; strongly acid. 1 to 4 inches thick.
A$_2$	2 to 8 inches, weak-yellow to light yellowish-brown nearly loose or very friable sandy loam; strongly acid. 4 to 10 inches thick.
B$_1$	8 to 10 inches, weak reddish-brown to strong-brown friable heavy sandy loam or light sandy clay loam with medium granular structure; strongly acid. 2 to 4 inches thick.
B$_2$	10 to 38 inches, moderate to strong reddish-brown clay that is plastic when wet, very firm when moist, and very hard when dry. The clay has a medium moderately blocky structure and contains some white sand grains and small mica flakes; strongly acid. 20 to 36 inches thick.
B$_3$	38 to 60 inches, light to moderate reddish-brown clay loam with mottles or splotches of yellow; firm to friable when moist. The soil contains enough small mica flakes to make it feel slick when rubbed between the fingers; it has a weak coarse blocky structure and is strongly acid. 10 to 30 inches thick.
C	60 inches +, mottled or splotched light reddish-brown, yellowish-brown, light-gray, and black friable disintegrated rock material in which there is usually much mica; strongly acid. 20 to 60 inches thick.

Range in characteristics.—The principal types are coarse sandy loam, sandy loam, very fine sandy loam, and clay loam. This last is mapped where the original A horizon has been removed by accelerated erosion. The A_1 is commonly mixed with A_2 and loses its identity under cultivation. In eroded fields, the B_1 and part of the B_2 are often mixed in the furrow slice to make the soil weak reddish brown to moderate brown in color. Thickness of the solum ranges from about 30 inches in a few places to as much as 80 inches, although it commonly falls near 60 inches as described. The depth to solid rock may range from 2 to 80 feet, or even greater, but it commonly is less than 8 feet. In places the mapping unit includes similar soils lying on materials washed into old gullies of a previous erosion cycle, rather than on material weathered in place. Gravelly and stony types are mapped where there are enough fragments of quartz, gneiss, or granite in the soil to interfere with cultivation. Over the geographic range from Alabama to Virginia, there are some differences in the color of the B horizon. Soils in the southern Piedmont have redder B horizons than those in the northern Piedmont.

Relief.—Undulating to nearly level on broad interstream divides and rolling to hilly in more dissected areas. Slopes commonly range from 5 to 15 percent but may range from 2 to 30 percent.

Drainage.—Well drained with medium to rapid runoff and medium internal drainage.

Vegetation.—White, red, post, Spanish, and blackjack oaks and hickory, with some dogwood, sourwood, blackgum, black locust, sweetgum, poplar, cedar, and shortleaf pine. Formerly cultivated and abandoned areas are covered by shortleaf, loblolly, or Virginia pine.

Use.—Approximately one-half of the total acreage is in cultivation, with the other one-half divided about equally between pasture and forest. The most common crops are corn, cotton, wheat, oats, tobacco, cowpeas, lespedeza, forage crops, and sweetpotatoes. Less common crops are soybeans, apples, peaches, other fruits, and vegetables.

Distribution.—Virginia, North Carolina, South Carolina, Georgia, and eastern Alabama; little in Arkansas.

Type location: Forsythe County, North Carolina.

Series established: Cecil County, Maryland, 1899.

Remarks.—The series was redefined in the Raleigh to New Bern Area, North Carolina, in 1900 and is no longer mapped in Maryland.

Charlton series

The Charlton series includes deep well-drained Brown Podzolic soils, developed on firm Late Wisconsin till derived dominantly from gray mica schist, but containing a small amount of granitic material in most places. The Charlton soils are members of the catena that includes the shallow-to-bedrock Hollis, the loose, well-drained Grafton, the moderately well-drained Sutton, the poorly drained Leicester, and the very poorly drained Whitman soils. The Charlton soils in most places are in intimate association with the other members of the catena and adjoin areas of the Brookfield, Paxton, Woodbridge, Gloucester, and Hollis soils. They differ from the Brookfield in that the parent material does not contain and has not been derived from limonitic mica schist; from the Gloucester in that the parent material is largely derived from gray mica schist rather than from granite; and from the Hollis in greater depth to bedrock. The Grafton soils are similar to the Charlton soils except that the parent material is loose instead of firm. The Paxton and Woodbridge soils have developed on till similar in lithological composition to that of the Charlton but on very compact rather than firm till. The Paxton soils are well drained; the Woodbridge soils are moderately well drained.

Soil profile (Charlton loam—virgin):

A_0 Loose leaves or needles underlain by a thin layer of dark brown (when moist) partly disintegrated leaves and twigs. 1 to 3 inches thick.

A_1 0 to 2 inches, grayish-brown loam[1] when moist; brown or yellowish

---

[1] The soil contains 5 to 10 percent of small schist fragments throughout the solum and in the C.

brown when dry; loose; weak medium or fine crumb structure; strongly acid. 1 to 4 inches thick.

B21   2 to 6 inches, yellowish-brown or brown loam when moist; coherent in place; very friable when removed; weak very fine crumb structure; strongly acid. 3 to 5 inches thick.

B22   6 to 15 inches, like the above except light yellowish brown to yellowish brown in color. 6 to 10 inches thick.

B.3   15 to 24 inches, light yellowish-brown loam when moist; firm in place, friable when removed; weak very fine crumb structure; strongly acid. 10 to 12 inches thick.

B3   24 to 30 inches, olive or light yellowish-brown loam when moist; firm in place, friable when removed; weak very fine crumb structure that may grade into weak medium platy in the lower part; strongly acid. 6 to 12 inches thick.

C   30 inches +, olive loam when moist; both crushed and uncrushed aggregates have the same color, very seldom with any surface skin on the aggregates; compact in place, friable when removed; medium platy; strongly acid. (Water seldom runs horizontally above this horizon as it does in the Paxton and Woodbridge soils.)

Range in characteristics.—These soils are stony both internally and externally, but not so much so as the Gloucester soils. The thickness of solum is about 30 to 36 inches in southern New England and about 24 to 30 inches in northern New England. At the boundary of the Podzol region these soils grade into the Berkshire soils—their Podzol analogs—and a nearly arbitrary line of demarcation needs to be established in detailed surveys.

Relief.—The soils are on nearly level to steep uplands including drumloidal hills. Soil slopes vary from 5 to 20 percent.

Drainage.—Well drained; runoff is rapid, and internal drainage is medium.

Vegetation.—Red and white oaks, sugar and red maples, gray birch, white pine. Pastures contain sweetfern, sumac, blueberry, and hardhack.

Use.—Approximately 50 to 60 percent of the soil is cleared and used for hay, mainly timothy and clover. Other crops are silage corn, oats, rye, potatoes, and apples. Yields are good with adequate fertilization. The unimproved stony areas are in forest and pasture.

Distribution.—Central Connecticut, central Massachusetts, southeastern Vermont, southern New Hampshire, southern Maine, and eastern New York. Series established: Worcester County, Massachusetts, 1922.

Type location: Worcester County, Massachusetts.

Source of name: Charlton Township, Worcester County, Massachusetts.

Remarks.—The Charlton soils as now defined were previously classified with the Gloucester soils. The Charlton soils included both loose and moderately compact till up until about 1940, when the soils on the loose till were recognized separately as Grafton series. The soils of Providence County, Rhode Island, correlated as Charlton, appear to be developed on this loose till. Considerable experimental work has been done on the Charlton soils. Experimental pasture plots have been established on this soil at Storrs by the Connecticut Agricultural Experiment Station and at Highmoor Farm in eastern Maine by the Maine Agricultural Experiment Station. Bulletin 139 (1926), Connecticut Agricultural Experiment Station, compares farm management on Charlton and Gloucester soils.

Cookeville series

The Cookeville series includes Red-Yellow Podzolic soils in the transitional belt between the Red-Yellow Podzolic and Gray-Brown Podzolic regions. These soils are developed from slightly cherty moderately high grade Mississippian limestones and occur chiefly in association with Baxter, Bewleyville, Montview, and Dickson soils. They contain less chert than the Baxter soils to a depth of 4 to 6 feet. In contrast to the Bewleyville soils, B horizons of the Cookeville are red and the solum is derived chiefly from limestone residuum, whereas the solum of the Bewleyville is brownish and developed chiefly in thin loess. The Cookeville soils are fairly extensive and important agriculturally. The silt loam is the most important type.

Soil profile (Cookeville silt loam):

A$_p$ 0 to 8 inches, brown (10YR 5/3 or 4/3) to yellowish-brown (10YR 5/4) very friable silt loam with a moderate medium crumb structure. 6 to 10 inches thick.

B$_1$ 8 to 20 inches, yellowish-red (5YR 5/8) to reddish-yellow (5YR 6/6) friable moderate medium blocky silty clay loam that becomes redder, heavier, and more distinct in structure in the lower part. 10 to 14 inches thick.

B$_2$ 20 to 40 inches, dark-red (2.5YR 3/6) or red (2.5YR 5/8) firm heavy silty clay loam or silty clay with a strong medium blocky structure; the crushed material is distinctly yellow as compared with the red color of the aggregates; contains much very finely divided chert and some fine angular chert pieces. 16 to 24 inches thick.

C   40 inches +, dark-red (2.5YR 3/6) or red (2.5YR 5/8) very firm silty clay splotched and streaked with yellow, yellowish brown, and strong brown; contains much finely divided chert and some angular chert pieces; extends to bedrock, usually at depths of 6 to 10 feet or more.

Range in characteristics.—Cookeville soils are medium to strongly acid throughout the profile. The combined thickness of the A and B$_1$ horizons ranges between 16 and 30 inches. The B$_2$ horizon may be chert-free but characteristically has a considerable amount of very finely divided chert throughout. The C horizon may vary considerably in color and chert content within short distances. A thin discontinuous layer of loesslike silt is a component of the upper solum in places. Moderately eroded areas have a characteristic three-color pattern of pale brown, yellowish red, and dark red.

Relief.—Undulating to rolling (and karst).

Drainage.—Well drained; medium to rapid runoff and medium internal drainage.

Vegetation.—Originally hardwood trees consisting chiefly of red, black, post, and white oaks, with some hickory, elm, dogwood, and some maples, especially near the northern limits of its occurrence.

Use.—Practically all the soil is cleared and used for the production of general farm crops, including corn, alfalfa, lespedeza, clovers, and cotton. Strawberries and other truck crops are grown locally.

Distribution.—Mississippian Plateau of Kentucky, Tennessee, and Alabama. Type location: Central Putnam County, Tennessee.

Series established: Limestone County, Alabama, 1946.

Dalhart series

The Dalhart series includes brown to dark-brown noncalcareous well-drained Reddish Chestnut soils having brown, friable, granular, permeable B horizons. These soils occur in extreme northwestern Texas and adjacent areas, mainly on the High Plains, in association with Pullman, Richfield, and Mansker soils. Generally, the parent materials are strongly calcareous, moderately sandy aeolian mantles deposited relatively late in the Pleistocene. The Dalhart series is less reddish than Amarillo, generally is calcareous at somewhat shallower depths, occurs in the more northerly or somewhat cooler areas, and appears to be developed mainly from more recently deposited parent materials. The B horizons of Dalhart soils are more sandy than those of Pullman and Richfield and less sandy than those of Springer and Pratt.

Soil profile (Dalhart fine sandy loam):

A$_1$ 0 to 8 inches, brown (10YR 5/3; 4/2.5, moist) fine sandy loam; moderate medium granular; very friable when moist, slightly hard when dry; grades abruptly into the B horizon; neutral. 6 to 11 inches thick.

B$_2$ 8 to 21 inches, brown (10YR 5/3; 4/3, moist) sandy clay loam; mixed strong very coarse prismatic and moderate medium granular structure; friable when moist, and very hard when dry; neutral to mildly alkaline but noncalcareous. 10 to 20 inches thick.

B₃ 21 to 33 inches, light-brown (7.5YR 6/4; 5/4, moist) sandy clay loam; friable when moist, very hard when dry; weak coarse to medium granular structure; mildly alkaline. 0 to 15 inches thick.

C_ca 33 to 54 inches, very pale brown (10YR 7/4) strongly calcareous sandy clay loam or sandy clay intermixed with 5 to 40 percent of soft white concretions of $CaCO_3$; changes gradually to less calcareous material below. 10 to 30 inches thick.

Range in characteristics.—Types range from loamy fine sand to clay loam. The color of the surface soil darkens slightly with decreasing sandiness. The color of A₁ horizon ranges from brown to dark brown and dark grayish brown and includes hues 7.5YR to 10YR, values 4 to 5.5, and chroma 2 to 3. The color of the B₂ horizon ranges from brown to grayish brown, and its texture from sandy clay loam to sandy clay or light clay. The color of the B₃ horizon ranges from grayish brown to light brown. It is calcareous or absent where the carbonate horizon occurs within 2 feet. The depth to the C_ca horizon ranges from about 15 to 45 inches. In many places there are buried soils below 3 feet.

Relief.—Nearly level to gently sloping upland. May have subdued stabilized dunes several hundred feet wide and only a few feet high.

Drainage.—Good; slow to medium runoff. Naturally the substrata are permanently dry.

Vegetation.—Short grasses (mainly buffalo and gramas) on the clay loam, short grasses and mid-grasses on the sandy loams, and little bluestem and sand sage on the loamy sands.

Use.—Besides native pasture, the moderately fine textured types are used mainly for winter wheat, the sandy loam for winter wheat and sorghums, and the loamy fine sand for sorghums.

Distribution.—Panhandle of Texas and adjacent parts of Oklahoma, New Mexico, and Kansas; mostly on the High Plains north of the Canadian River; very extensive.

Type location: Dallam County, Texas.

Series established: Union County, New Mexico, 1938

Drummer series

The Drummer series includes Humic-Gley soils (Wiesenboden) of the Prairie soil region developed on water-worked glacial sediments of the uplands, or mixed loess, till, and glacial sediments of the outwash plains under poor or very poor natural drainage. The soils are coextensive with the nearly level to depressional areas and are mapped in association with the Proctor and Brenton soils of the outwash plains as well as with the soils of the Saybrook and Flanagan catenas. The solum is about neutral in reaction.

Soil profile (Drummer clay loam):

A₁₁ 0 to 10 inches, black (10YR 2/1, moist) silt loam to clay loam with moderate medium granular structure; neutral to slightly acid. 8 to 20 inches thick.

A₁₂ 10 to 17 inches, very dark-gray (10YR 3/1, moist) clay loam or silty clay loam; moderate medium granular structure; neutral to slightly acid. 6 to 8 inches thick.

B_g 17 to 27 inches, dark-gray (5Y 4/1, moist) to gray (10YR 5/1, moist) clay loam or silty clay loam with some sand; some mottling of brownish yellow and splotches of very dark gray where organic matter has come down from above; moderate medium blocky structure; neutral to slightly alkaline. 8 to 15 inches thick.

C 27 inches +, gray (10YR 5/1 to 6/1, moist) heavy loam to clay loam with brownish-yellow mottles, resting on silty, sandy, or gravelly material at 40 to 50 inches; neutral to calcareous.

Range in characteristics.—The texture of the surface soil layers ranges from silty clay loam to clay loam or silty clay. The color, texture, and mottlings of the B horizon vary. The depth to the loose sand and gravel substratum varies but is usually more than 36 inches. Small areas with sandy B horizons may be included.

Relief.—Nearly level to depressional; slopes are usually less than ½ percent.

Drainage.—Developed under high water table; natural drainage poor to very poor; runoff, very slow or none. Adapted to tile drainage.

Vegetation.—Water-loving grasses and sedges.

Use.—General farming, principally corn and soybeans.

Distribution.—Central, north-central, northeastern, and east-central parts of Illinois and adjoining States where parent materials and soil-forming forces are similar.

Type location: Iroquois County, Illinois.

Series established: Ford County, Illinois, 1929.

Source of name: Township in Ford County, Illinois.

Fargo series

The Fargo soils are Humic-Gley soils, or chernozemic Wiesenboden, of the northern Chernozem region from clayey sediments deposited in old glacial lakes and in valleys formerly blocked by till or ice. Drainage outlets have been established for most of the areas. The characteristic features of the Fargo soils are a dark, granular clayey surface soil; gray, or mottled light and dark gray, clayey subsoil; and a fairly well-defined layer of lime accumulation (C_{ca}). These soils differ from the associated Bearden series in being composed of clayey materials throughout. They resemble Parnell soils but are a little better developed, are on older sediments, and are commonly better drained.

Soil profile (Fargo clay):

A₁   0 to 16 inches, very dark-gray (N 3/, dry) to black (N 2/, moist) heavy clay, finely granular in structure. 12 to 20 inches thick.

B_g 16 to 21 inches, dark-gray (N 4/, dry) to dark olive-gray (5Y 4/2, moist) fine subangular blocky clay. 5 to 8 inches thick.

C_{ca} 21 to 33 inches, gray (N/5, dry) to dark olive-gray (5Y 4/1, moist) massive clay containing large amounts of fine lime carbonate, either uniformly disseminated or in the form of nodules and concretions. 6 to 18 inches thick.

C   33 inches +, pale-yellow (2.5Y 7/4, dry) to yellowish-brown (2.5Y 5/4, moist) calcareous lacustrine clay, showing prominent varves in some localities.

Range in characteristics.—The thickness of the dark surface horizon and the depth to free carbonates vary considerably. In a few places the soil is calcareous from the surface down. Some profiles have a C_{cs} layer. Buried soils are not uncommon.

Relief.—Level or very gently undulating.

Drainage.—Natural drainage is imperfect to poor; internal drainage is slow. The greater part of the extensive areas of Fargo soils has been improved by artificial drainage.

Vegetation.—Originally covered by a dense stand of tall prairie grasses.

Use.—Nearly all the Fargo is cultivated, especially in the Red River Valley. Wheat and other small grains are the principal crops, but alfalfa, flax, corn, and sweetclover are also grown. Uncultivated areas are used for pasture and hay.

Distribution.—North Dakota, South Dakota, and Minnesota. The largest area is in the Red River Valley.

Type location: Cass County, North Dakota.

Series established: Grand Forks area, North Dakota, 1902.

Fruita series

The Fruita soils are developed in the Gray Desert soil region from highly calcareous alluvial materials washed mainly from sandstones and sandy shales of the Cretaceous, Jurassic, and Tertiary ages. In places there is an appreciable admixture of quartzite. These zonal soils are related to the Moffat, Mesa, and Hinman series. They have weakly developed texture profiles, moderately developed horizons of lime accumulation, and substrata of fine earthy alluvium deposited, usually, over shale and sandstone bedrock. Although otherwise generally similar, their profiles are less red than those of the Moffat soils and more red than those of the Hinman. The B horizons of the Fruita soils are coarser in texture than those of the Hinman and their profiles lack the gravelly substrata of the Hinman. The Fruita soils are younger and have less segregated lime than the Mesa soils and lack their gravelly substrata. In stage of development, they resemble the Meeteetse series but appear to have developed from a more highly calcareous alluvium, to have more segregated lime, and to be less red in color.

Soil profile (Fruita very fine sandy loam) :

A_p 0 to 8 inches, light-brown (7.5YR 6/4) to brown (7.5YR 4/4, moist) calcareous very fine sandy loam; slightly hard and weakly cloddy. (Under virgin cover the surface ¼ to ½ inch is a soft to slightly hard vesicular crust of fine sandy loam over loose moderate very fine granular fine sandy loam to 1 or 2 inches. These horizons are very pale brown (10YR 7/3) to pink (7.5YR 8/4). Below this the light-brown very fine sandy loam to loam has a slightly hard weak coarse horizontal blocky structure. These peds readily crumble into medium granules.) 6 to 10 inches thick.

B_{21} 8 to 15 inches, light-brown (7.5YR 6/4) calcareous loam; slightly hard to hard weak very coarse blocky to prismatic and weak medium and fine granular structure; when moist, the soil is brown (7.5YR 5/4) and very friable. 4 to 10 inches thick. This layer grades into:

B_{22} 15 to 20 inches, very pale-brown (10YR 7/4) strongly calcareous loam; slight amount of segregated lime occurs in thin veins or in small white (10YR 8/2) mottles comprising less than 5 percent of the soil mass. Dry soil is slightly hard to hard and is weakly granular. The brown (7.5YR 5/4) moist soil is very friable. 3 to 8 inches thick.

B_{3ca} 20 to 30 inches, very pale-brown (10YR 7/4) with 20- to 70-percent white (10YR 8/2) mottles, strongly and very strongly calcareous loam to light clay loam; hard weak subangular blocky structure; segregated lime occurs in seams and as lime flour in 2- to 10-inch mottlings and splotches; the moist soil is friable and brown (7.5YR 5/4), mottled with pinkish white (7.5YR 8/2). 8 to 20 inches thick. This layer grades into:

C_{ca} 30 to 40 inches, very pale-brown (10YR 7/4), with mottles of white (10YR 8/2) comprising 10 to 30 percent of soil mass and decreasing in the lower part of the horizon, strongly and very strongly calcareous fine sandy loam to light clay loam; hard but friable to weak granular structure; segregated lime occurs as lime flour throughout the soil-mass and is concentrated in large and small mottles and splotches; the very friable moist soil is reddish yellow (7.5YR 6/6) mottled with pinkish white (7.5YR 8/2). 5 to 15 inches thick.

C   40 to 72 inches, very pale-brown (10YR 7/4) to pale-yellow (5Y 8/3) strongly calcareous fine sandy loam to light clay loam; massive, slightly hard to hard. The moist soil is friable. 10 to 32 inches thick.

D   Bedrock of shale or sandstone at varying depths below 72 inches.

Range in characteristics.—Light brown (7.5YR 6/4) is the dominant color of the A_p and B_2. Mapping units include soils with horizons having the browner limits of the Moffat series (i.e., light reddish brown (5YR 6/4, dry) and reddish brown (5YR 4/4, moist) as well as very pale brown (10YR 7/3). The degree of lime segregation is generally moderate but varies from slight in a horizon with 5 percent lime mottlings to strong in a horizon where 90 percent of the soil color is dominated by very strongly calcareous material. Although generally not gravelly, some mapping units include soils with varying quantities of sandstone gravel distributed throughout the profile. The depth of the alluvium over bedrock shale and sandstone is typically more than 6 feet, but a few shallower areas occur.

Relief.—Generally smooth nearly level to gently sloping alluvial fans and alluvial fan benches. Sloping and steep phases occur on deeply trenched fans.

Drainage.—Runoff is slow to medium on nearly level and gentle slopes. Internal drainage is medium. Soils are generally free of harmful concentrations of salts except where they are shallow over saline shale and are affected by seepage from irrigation.

Vegetation.—Shadscale, small sagebrush, rabbitbrush, and a few thorny desert shrubs, with 5- to 20-percent cover of galleta, black grama, bunchgrasses, and annual weeds and herbs.

Use.—These soils are productive and yields are high with good management under irrigation. They are used principally for truck crops, fruits, alfalfa, hay, and cereal grains.

Distribution.—Arid valleys in western Colorado, eastern Utah, and Wyoming.

Type location: Alluvial fan benches north of Fruita in Mesa County, Colorado. Series established: Grand Junction Area, Colorado, 1905.

Remarks.—In the soil survey of the Grand Junction Area in 1905 the Fruita series included soils occupying the low, young alluvial fans and river flood plains. The Fruita series has been redefined, and in the resurvey of the Grand Junction Area in 1947 the soils formerly called Fruita have been classified as types of the Billings, Ravola, and Green River series.

Lyons series

The Lyons series includes very poorly drained Humic-Gley (Wiesenboden) soils on calcareous glacial till from limestone with varying proportions of shale and sandstone as major constituents. Its modal profile is that of the very poorly drained member of a catena that includes the well-drained Gray-Brown Podzolic soil, Honeoye, the moderately well-drained Lima, and the poorly drained Kendaia, but its range includes the Humic-Gley associates of several Gray-Brown Podzolic and Brown Forest soils in New York developed from medium-textured materials of high to medium lime content. These include catenas of which the well-drained members are Fenner, Grenville, Nellis, Dover, and Pittsfield among Brown Forest soils; Honeoye, Ontario, and Wassaic among modal Gray-Brown Podzolic soils; and Lansing, Madrid, Lowville, and Stockbridge among intergrades between Brown Forest or Gray-Brown Podzolic soils and Brown Podzolic soils. The series is used only tentatively in some of these catenas, but in most of them the hydromorphic character of the soil overshadows differences of parent material that give rise to significant differences among zonal soils.

Soil profile (Lyons silt loam—virgin):

A₀   1 to 0 inch, forest litter, usually without a humus mat. 0 to 2 inches thick.

A₁   0 to 6 inches, very dark-gray to black (10YR 3/1-2/1) silt loam high in organic matter; moderate medium crumb structure; friable; neutral to slightly acid; filled with small roots. 5 to 8 inches thick.

G₁   6 to 12 inches, gray (10YR 5/1) silt loam with weak medium blocky structure when dry; nearly massive when wet; brown streaks along old root channels; neutral to slightly alkaline, locally, slightly acid; few small roots present; an intensely reduced horizon. 5 to 8 inches thick.

G₂   12 to 24 inches, mottled-gray (10YR 5/1) and yellowish-brown heavy silt loam with weak coarse blocky structure when dry but nearly massive when wet; firm, slightly plastic; slightly alkaline, may be calcareous; only a few large roots present. 8 to 18 inches thick.

CG   24 to 40 inches, gray calcareous silt loam from glacial till, mottled with varying shades of brown; moderately compact; firm, slightly plastic; weak coarse platy structure; mottling decreases with depth. 10 to 20 inches thick.

C   40 inches +, gray highly calcareous firm laminated glacial till with loam or silt loam texture.

Range in characteristics.—The thickness of the A₁ horizon ranges widely, especially in cultivated areas where material has been washed from adjacent fields and deposited on these low-lying areas. The degree of mottling is variable. The depth to carbonates ranges from 12 to 30 inches. Surface textures range from loam to silty clay loam.

Relief.—Nearly level; commonly in depressions, locally seepage spots on slopes.

Drainage.—Very poor; runoff, very slow; internal drainage is very slow or slow, although permeability is moderate to considerable depths.

Vegetation.—Red maple, elm, ash, willow, alder.

Use.—Forested mainly or used for pasture. When adequately drained, a productive soil for hay, pasture, corn, and vegetables.

Distribution.—Ontario Plain and Mohawk, Black River, and Hudson valleys of New York, western Massachusetts, and southwestern Vermont. Tentatively recognized in northern New York.

Type location: Wayne County, New York.

Series established: Wayne County, New York, 1919.

Source of name: Lyons, Wayne County, New York.

Mesa series

The Mesa soils are Gray Desert soils developed on old alluvial valley fillings. They occupy flat-topped mesas and piedmont plains, which are remnants of old terraces. These soils occur in many of the intermountain valleys west of the Continental Divide, where they have developed under a desert-shrub vegetation. The mean annual precipitation ranges from 7 to about 10 inches. The summers are very dry, and the winters are cold but sunny. These are mature zonal soils that have very pale-brown to light reddish-brown calcareous upper horizons over a thick, nearly white layer of accumulated lime. They are underlain by very gravelly, cobbly, or stony alluvium. Soils in the Orchard series have similar profile characteristics but have developed from alluvium of basic igneous origin. The Mesa soils are less red in color than those of the associated Bennett series; they lack the cementation of the lime horizon that occurs in the Neola soils; and they have a deeper profile over the high-lime horizon and gravel strata than the Naturita soils. The associated younger Hinman and Moffat soils have moderately developed horizons of lime accumulation. The very gravelly, cobbly, and stony alluvium occurs at much greater depths in the Hinman than in the Mesa series.

Soil profile (Mesa clay loam):

A₁₁   0 to ¼ inch, light-brown (7.5YR 6/4) or very pale-brown (10YR 7/4) loam in a soft vesicular crust; generally calcareous. ⅛ to ¼ inch thick.

A₁₂   ¼ to 4 inches, light-brown (7.5YR 6/4) to very pale-brown (10YR 7/4) loam with soft weak platy structure that breaks to moderate fine granules; generally calcareous; structural aggregation less distinct in very friable brown (7.5YR 4/4 to 10YR 4/3) moist soil. 2 to 6 inches thick.

B₂   4 to 15 inches, reddish-yellow (7.5YR 6/6) to light reddish-brown (5YR 6/4) calcareous clay loam containing an increasing amount of mottles of pinkish white (7.5YR 8/2) or white (10YR 8/2); large splotches of soft segregated lime, especially in the lower part; slightly hard to hard, medium to coarse blocky to prismatic structure that easily breaks down to weak medium and coarse granules. The strong-brown (7.5YR 5/8) to reddish-brown (5YR 4/4) moist soil is very friable and has a weak blocky structure. 4 to 18 inches thick.

Cca   15 to 32 inches, white (10YR 8/2) to pinkish-white (7.5YR 8/2) very strongly calcareous clay loam. Lime occurs mostly as lime flour well disseminated in the soil mass. Large irregular mottles of light brown (7.5YR 6/4) or pink (7.5YR 8/4) of less calcareous soil appear in the upper part. The dry soil is hard and massive. The pinkish-white (7.5YR 8/2) to pink (7.5YR 8/4) moist soil is friable. 10 to 40 inches thick.

D_{ca}   32 to 50 inches +, white (10YR 8/2) to pink (7.5YR 7/4) very strongly calcareous very gravelly to very stony loam; hard and massive but not cemented; friable when moist.

D   50 inches +, loose porous strata of pebbles, cobbles, and stones in a matrix of sand to loam; undersides of fragments are lime-coated, especially in the upper part.

Range in characteristics.—The 8- or 10-inch plowed depth of these soils is a light-brown, pale-brown, or light reddish-brown heavy loam or light clay loam. Varying quantities of water-worn gravel occur over the soil surface and throughout the profile. The very gravelly, cobbly, or stony stratum is usually present at some depth within the 5-foot profile, although there are exceptions. The fine soil material ranges in texture from sand to light clay loam. The texture and firmness of the B₂ horizon varies from a slightly hard light clay loam to a hard heavy clay loam. The degree of mottling of segregated lime in the B₂ horizon is variable. The amount of segregated lime occurring in the C_{ca} and D_{ca} horizons is generally very great, but soils having only moderately developed horizons of lime accumulation occur in mapping units.

Relief.—Nearly level to gently sloping or undulating terraces and on mesas and piedmont plains that are remnants of old terraces and fluviatile plains.

Drainage.—These soils are well drained. Their permeable profiles and dominantly gentle slopes lead to medium runoff.

Vegetation.—Shadscale, small sagebrush, and a few thorny desert shrubs, with a 5 to 20 percent cover of galleta, black grama, and bunchgrasses, and annual weeds and herbs.

Use.—The Mesa soils are productive under irrigation. Large areas of these soils are under irrigation in western Colorado where yields of grains and root and truck crops are high because of the responsiveness of these soils to good management practices. They are used extensively and success-fully for growing peaches in the Grand Junction area of Colorado. The carrying capacity of the native desert range is very low.

Distribution.—Intermountain Valleys in Colorado, Utah, and northern New Mexico.

Type location: Uncompahgre Valley Area, Colorado.

Series established: Grand Junction Area, Colorado, 1905.

Miami series

The Miami series consists of Gray-Brown Podzolic soils developed on highly calcareous glacial till of Late Wisconsin age. The Miami soils are the well-drained members of the soil catena that also includes the moderately well drained Celina, imperfectly drained Crosby, poorly drained Bethel (a Planosol), poorly drained dark-colored Brookston, and the very poorly drained very dark-colored Kokomo series. The Russell soils are distinguished from the Miami soils by the greater degree of weathering and the greater depth to calcareous till in tills of equivalent textures. The Russell soils are south of the belt of Miami and associated soils. The Miami soils have a smaller proportion of clay and dark shale fragments in the parent material and the solum than the St. Clair soils and somewhat deeper sola.

Soil profile (Miami silt loam):

A₀   Partly decomposed forest litter from deciduous trees. ¼ to 2 inches thick.

A₁   0 to 3 inches, very dark-gray to dark grayish-brown (10YR 3/1 to 4/2, moist) silt loam; moderate fine crumb structure; friable when moist, soft when dry, and nonsticky when wet; organic content relatively high; gradual and wavy horizon boundary; slightly acid. 2 to 4 inches thick.

A₂   3 to 12 inches, light yellowish-brown to brown (10YR 6/4 to 5/3, moist) silt loam; weak thin platy structure; friable when moist; slightly hard when dry, and slightly sticky when wet; gradual lower horizon boundary; slightly to medium acid. 7 to 11 inches thick.

B₁ 12 to 16 inches, light yellowish-brown to yellowish-brown (10YR 6/4 to 5/4, moist) heavy silt loam to light silty clay loam; moderate fine subangular blocky structure; friable to slightly firm when moist, slightly hard when dry, and slightly sticky-when wet; medium to strongly acid; irregular lower horizon boundary. 3 to 5 inches thick.

B₂₁ 16 to 24 inches, brown (7.5YR 5/4, moist) to yellowish-brown (10YR 5/4, moist) silty clay loam; strong medium to coarse subangular blocky structure; firm when moist, hard when dry, and sticky when wet; variable quantities of small partly weathered rock fragments; wavy lower horizon boundary; strongly to medium acid. 6 to 14 inches thick.

B₂₂ 24 to 28 inches, dark-brown (7.5YR 3/2 to 10YR 4/3, moist) silty clay loam; strong coarse to very coarse subangular blocky structure; firm when moist, hard when dry, and sticky when wet; variable quantity of partly weathered rock fragments; wavy lower horizon boundary; neutral to slightly acid. 2 to 6 inches thick.

C 28 inches +, light yellowish-brown (2.5Y 6/4 to 10YR 6/4, moist) mixed clay loam till with coarse fragments and stones; massive to weak very coarse subangular blocky structure; varying mineralogical composition with sufficient lime to produce general effervescence with dilute acid; usually has a high percentage of limestone rock fragments.

Range in characteristics.—The color of the cultivated surface soil is grayish brown to yellowish brown when moist. The reaction of the A and B horizons in local areas is slightly acid. Silt loam, loam, sandy loam, and fine sandy loam types have been mapped. The sandier types usually have correspondingly sandier B and C horizons.

Relief.—The soil occurs on till plains or moraines; usually it occupies the high well-drained areas on an undulating terrain. Typical profiles are developed on slopes of 2 to about 7 percent, although slopes range up to 25 percent or more, especially next to low lying terraces, or drainageways.

Drainage.—Good; runoff is medium on the milder slopes, and rapid on the steeper ones; internal drainage is medium.

Vegetation.—The native vegetation included deciduous trees, principally white and red oaks, maple, ash, elm, and hickory.

Use.—Most of the Miami soils have been cleared and are used for general farming. The principal crops are corn, oats, wheat, clover, soybeans, and alfalfa, and, to a lesser extent, vegetables. Dairying is a specialty in some districts. These soils require rotations that include a considerable proportion of legumes and the liberal use of barnyard or green manures and commercial fertilizers to increase productivity. A large part of the strongly sloping phase is in permanent bluegrass pasture, and a smaller part is in forest.

Distribution.—South-central Michigan; central-western and western Ohio; central, northern, and eastern Indiana; southeastern Wisconsin; and northeastern Illinois.

Type location: SW¼ sec. 8, T. 15 N., R. 14 E. (Lewis Woods), Wayne County, Indiana.

Series established: Montgomery County, Ohio, 1900.

Source of name: Named for Miami River in western Ohio.

Ontario series

The Ontario series includes well-developed, well-drained Gray-Brown Podzolic soils on strongly calcareous firm glacial till. The till consists mainly of limestone, sandstone, and some shale, with enough reddish sandstone or shale to make the till pinkish gray when dry. The textural profile is strongly expressed. Ontario soils are commonly, but not necessarily, associated with drumlins. The Ontario series is the well-drained member of a catena that includes the imperfectly drained Hilton, the poorly drained Kendaia, and the very poorly drained Lyons soils. It differs from the Honeoye soils mainly in content of reddish materials of the parent material, which is reflected in brown or slightly reddish colors of the till and solum. Although

Honeoye soils are commonly more nearly neutral in the solum, pH as well as depth to carbonates cover approximately the same range throughout the total extent of both soils.

Soil profile (Ontario loam—virgin):

A_{00} 1 to 0 inch, litter of deciduous trees, nearly all decomposed and mixed with mineral soil by midsummer. 0 to 3 inches thick.

A_1 0 to 4 inches, very dark-brown (10YR 2/2) loam having moderate medium crumb structure; very friable; neutral; high in organic matter; numerous worm casts; very numerous roots. 3 to 5 inches thick.

A_{21} 4 to 9 inches, light yellowish-brown (10YR 6/4) loam with weak fine crumb structure; very friable; medium acid; organic matter present in worm casts; roots are numerous. 2 to 10 inches thick.

A_{22} 9 to 13 inches, pale-brown (10YR 6/3) loam with weak coarse crumb to medium subangular blocky structure; friable; medium to slightly acid; a few worm casts are present; roots are numerous. 3 to 6 inches thick.

B_1 13 to 18 inches, brown (7.5YR 5/4) heavy loam with moderate medium subangular blocky structure; the aggregates coated with thin films of pale-brown silty material; friable; slightly acid; roots present. 3 to 6 inches thick.

B_{21} 18 to 25 inches, brown (7.5YR 5/4) clay loam with strong medium subangular blocky structure; moderately sticky and plastic when moist; slightly acid or neutral; a few worm casts present, and large roots penetrate the horizons. 6 to 8 inches thick.

B_{22} 25 to 33 inches, brown (7.5YR 5/2) clay loam with moderate coarse angular blocky structure; sticky and plastic when wet, friable when moist; neutral or mildly alkaline; a few worm casts; large roots penetrate the horizon. 7 to 8 inches thick.

B_{23} 33 to 38 inches, brown (7.5YR 5/2) loam or light clay loam with weak coarse blocky structure; friable; weakly calcareous; large roots present. 4 to 6 inches thick.

C   38 inches +, brown (6YR 5/3) gravelly loam with medium to coarse platy structure; firm in place but friable; strongly calcareous; large roots extend into this horizon; pinkish gray (7.5YR 6/2) when dry.

Range in characteristics.—At the least acid extreme of the range, the entire solum is above pH 6.0 and the A_{21} horizon is very weakly expressed; at the most acid extreme, the pH of the A_{22} and B_1 horizons is near 5.5 or slightly below, and the A_{21} horizon is very strongly expressed and is 8 or 10 inches thick. Organic-matter content decreases with increasing acidity. Depths to carbonates range from 30 to 42 inches. Loam is the dominant type but silt loam, gravelly loam, and fine sandy loam types are included.

Relief.—Gently sloping to hilly. Part of the soils are on drumlins.

Drainage.—Good; runoff is medium to rapid, and internal drainage is medium.

Vegetation.—Sugar maple, basswood, black cherry, ash, tulip-poplar, beech, hophornbeam, shagbark hickory.

Use.—Crops include alfalfa, timothy and clover, small grains, corn for both silage and grain, cabbage, vegetables for canning, apples, cherries, pears, small fruits, and pasture. Where gently sloping this is a very productive soil, but strong soil slope limits the use of many areas.

Distribution.—Ontario Plain to the Mohawk Valley in western and central New York.

Type location: 4 miles north of Port Byron, Cayuga County, New York.

Series established: Monroe County, New York, 1910.

Source of name: Ontario County, New York.

Remarks.—The color names are for moist soil. When first established the series included nearly all soils of central and western New York in which limestone was an important constituent of the till. In 1913 the Honeoye series was redefined to include those soils not influenced by red materials. In 1945 the Sodus series was proposed to segregate those soils on reddish materials which are intergrades to Brown Podzolic soils.

Parsons series

The Parsons series includes relatively light-colored Planosols associated with Prairie and Reddish-Prairie soils, developed in silty and clayey materials weathered from noncalcareous gray and brown shales, chiefly of Carboniferous age. The associated Cherokee soils are nearly level, more strongly developed Planosols with still lighter colored A horizons and more strongly developed claypans. Woodson soils are darker colored throughout. Parsons soils grade into Dennis soils, which have well-developed clayey B horizons but are not Planosols.

Soil profile (Parsons silt loam):

A₁ 0 to 5 inches, grayish-brown (10YR 5/1.5, dry) to dark grayish-brown (10YR 4/1.5, moist) weak thin platy friable silt loam; medium to strongly acid. 3 to 7 inches thick.

A₂ 5 to 12 inches, light grayish-brown or light-gray (10YR 6/1.5 or 6/0.5, dry) silt loam; weak crumb or thin platy structure; medium to strongly acid. 5 to 12 inches thick.

B₂₁ 12 to 18 inches, grayish-brown (10YR 5/1.5, dry) clay mottled with brown (10YR 4/3) and light gray (10YR 6/0.5) and, in places, with light reddish brown; coarse blocky structure; this claypan hard and tough when dry and very plastic when wet; colors one step darker in the moist soil; medium acid. 4 to 8 inches thick.

B₂₂ 18 to 36 inches, light olive-gray (5.0Y 6/2, dry) to yellowish-brown (2.5Y 5/3, dry) or olive-gray (5.0Y 4.5/2, moist) clay, mottled with brown and gray, with structure and consistence about like horizon above; medium to slightly acid. 14 to 24 inches thick.

C 36 to 60 inches, light olive-gray, pale-yellow, and dark-brown mottled massive clay or silty clay, grading into gray or brown clayey, silty, or slightly sandy shale. 6 to 30 inches thick.

D 60 inches +, shale.

Range in characteristics.—Textures of the surface soil range from very fine sandy loam to silty clay loam, and the total thickness of A₁ and A₂ horizons ranges from about 10 to 20 inches. Where this thickness consistently exceeds about 12 inches, phases are recognized. Total thickness of solum above bedrock ranges from about 30 inches on moderate slopes to about 6 feet on some nearly level soil areas.

Relief.—Nearly level to moderately sloping uplands with slope gradients from about 1 to about 4 percent.

Drainage.—Imperfect; runoff, medium to slow; permeability, slow to very slow; crops are subject to drought on these soils.

Vegetation.—Prairie grasses, chiefly bluestems.

Use.—Oats, wheat, flax, and sorghums are the principal crops. Yields are fair. Corn is also grown, but because of the droughtiness of the soil, yields are uncertain. Some of the land is in native meadow.

Distribution.—Eastern Oklahoma, southeastern Kansas, and southwestern Missouri.

Type location: Crawford County, Kansas.

Series established: Labette County, Kansas, 1926.

Williams series

The Williams series includes modal Chestnut soils developed from calcareous glacial drift. The surface horizons are slightly thinner and lighter in color than those of the Barnes soils of the Chernozem region and slightly thicker and darker than those of the Scobey soils of the Brown soil region. Their profiles are thicker and better developed than those of the Zahl series, developed in the same region on steeper slopes. Boulders are common on the surface and throughout the profile, and many of the hilltops and slopes are stony and gravelly.

Soil profile (Williams loam):

A₁₁   0 to 1 inch, brown (10YR 5/2, dry) to very dark-brown (10YR 2/2, moist) loam with soft crumb structure; neutral or mildly alkaline. 1 to 2 inches thick.

A₁₂   1 to 4 inches, brown (10YR 4/2, dry) to very dark-brown (10YR 2/2, moist) loam; weak platy structure readily crushed to a medium crumb; neutral or mildly alkaline. 2 to 4 inches thick.

A₃   4 to 10 inches, brown (10YR 4/2, dry) to dark-brown (10YR 3/2, moist) heavy loam or silt loam; moderate prismatic structure; neutral to slightly acid. 5 to 7 inches thick.

B₂   10 to 20 inches, grayish-brown (2.5Y 5/2, dry) to dark grayish-brown (2.5Y 4/2, moist) heavy loam; strong prismatic structure in the upper part and strong very coarse blocky below; slightly calcareous. 8 to 12 inches thick.

C_ca   20 to 26 inches, light grayish-brown (2.5Y 6/2, dry) to yellowish-brown (2.5Y 5/4, moist) friable massive or weak coarse subangular blocky loam or silt loam; highly calcareous. 5 to 7 inches thick.

C   26 inches +, light-gray (2.5Y 7/2, dry) to yellowish-brown (2.5Y 5/4, moist) sandy clay or clay loam till.

Range in characteristics.—The solum varies in thickness, especially with degree of slope. The depth to the horizon of maximum free carbonate varies between about 15 and 24 inches. Phases for stoniness and for solonization are needed in detailed mapping.

Relief.—Nearly level or undulating to strongly rolling.

Drainage.—Good; runoff and internal drainage are medium.

Vegetation.—Short grasses, mainly blue grama, western wheatgrass, and associated species.

Use.—The soils are used chiefly for spring wheat but oats, barley, corn, rye, and flax are also grown. Areas of stony and strongly sloping phases are grazed.

Distribution.—Western parts of North Dakota and South Dakota and northeastern Montana.

Type location: Williams County, North Dakota.

Series established: Williston Area, Williams County, North Dakota, 1906.

APPENDIX V. GUIDE TO MAP SCALES

SCALE	FEET PER INCH	INCHES PER 1 000 FEET	INCHES PER MILE	MILES PER INCH	METERS PER INCH	ACRES PER SQUARE INCH	SQUARE INCHES PER ACRE	SQUARE MILES PER SQUARE INCH
1:500	41.67	24.00	126.72	0.008	12.70	0.040	25.091	0.00006
1:600	50.00	20.00	105.60	0.009	15.24	0.057	17.424	0.00009
1:1 000	83.33	12.00	63.36	0.016	25.40	0.159	6.273	0.00025
1:1 200	100.00	10.00	52.80	0.019	30.48	0.230	4.356	0.00036
1:1 500	125.00	8.00	42.24	0.024	38.10	0.359	2.788	0.00056
1:2 000	166.67	6.00	31.68	0.032	50.80	0.638	1.568	0.00100
1:2 400	200.00	5.00	26.40	0.038	60.96	0.918	1.089	0.0014
1:2 500	208.33	4.80	25.34	0.039	63.50	0.996	1.004	0.0016
1:3 000	250.00	4.00	21.12	0.047	76.20	1.435	0.697	0.0022
1:4 000	333.33	3.00	15.84	0.063	101.60	2.551	0.392	0.0040
1:5 000	416.67	2.40	12.67	0.079	127.00	3.986	0.251	0.0062
1:6 000	500.00	2.00	10.56	0.095	152.40	5.739	0.174	0.0090
1:7 920	660.00	1.515	8.00	0.125	201.17	10.000	0.100	0.0156
1:8 000	666.67	1.500	7.92	0.126	203.20	10.203	0.098	0.0159
1:9 600	800.00	1.250	6.60	0.152	243.84	14.692	0.068	0.0230
1:10 000	833.33	1.200	6.336	0.158	254.00	15.942	0.063	0.0249
1:12 000	1000.00	1.000	5.280	0.189	304.80	22.957	0.044	0.0359
1:15 000	1250.00	0.800	4.224	0.237	381.00	35.870	0.028	0.0560
1:15 840	1320.00	0.758	4.000	0.250	402.34	40.000	0.025	0.0625
1:19 200	1600.00	0.625	3.300	0.303	487.68	58.770	0.017	0.0918
1:20 000	1666.67	0.600	3.168	0.316	508.00	63.769	0.016	0.0996
1:21 120	1760.00	0.568	3.000	0.333	536.45	71.111	0.014	0.1111
1:24 000	2000.00	0.500	2.640	0.379	609.60	91.827	0.011	0.1435
1:25 000	2083.33	0.480	2.534	0.395	635.00	99.639	0.010	0.1557
1:31 680	2640.00	0.379	2.000	0.500	804.67	160.000	0.006	0.2500
1:48 000	4000.00	0.250	1.320	0.758	1219.20	367.309	0.003	0.5739
1:62 500	5208.33	0.192	1.014	0.986	1587.50	622.744	0.0016	0.9730
1:63 360	5280.00	0.189	1.000	1.000	1609.35	640.000	0.0016	1.00
1:100 000	8333.33	0.120	0.634	1.578	2540.00	1594.225	0.0006	2.49
1:125 000	10416.67	0.096	0.507	1.973	3175.01	2490.980	0.0004	3.89
1:126 720	10560.00	0.095	0.500	2.000	3218.69	2560.000	0.0004	4.00
1:250 000	20833.33	0.048	0.253	3.946	6350.01	9963.907	0.0001	15.57
1:253 440	21120.00	0.047	0.250	4.000	6437.39	10244.202	0.0001	16.00
1:500 000	41666.67	0.024	0.127	7.891	12700.02	39855.627	$0.^425$	62.27
1:750 000	62500.00	0.016	0.084	11.837	19050.04	89675.161	$0.^411$	140.12
1:1 000 000	83333.33	0.012	0.063	15.783	25400.05	159422.507	$0.^562$	249.10
FORMULAE	$\dfrac{SCALE}{12}$	$\dfrac{12000}{SCALE}$	$\dfrac{63360}{SCALE}$	$\dfrac{SCALE}{63360}$	FEET PER INCH x 0.3048006	$\dfrac{(SCALE)^2}{43560 \times 144}$	$\dfrac{43560 \times 144}{(SCALE)^2}$	$\dfrac{(FEET\ PER\ INCH)^2}{(5280)^2}$

487

INDEX

[Numbers in **bold type** indicate references to principal definitions or explanations]

U. S. GOVERNMENT PRINTING OFFICE: 1951—935034